PRACTICAL
SPECTROSCOPY

PRENTICE-HALL PHYSICS SERIES

Donald H. Menzel, *Editor*

PRACTICAL

SPECTROSCOPY

By

GEORGE R. HARRISON, Ph.D., Sc.D.

Professor of Physics

RICHARD C. LORD, Ph.D.

Professor of Chemistry

JOHN R. LOOFBOUROW, Sc.D.

Professor of Biophysics

OF THE
SPECTROSCOPY LABORATORY
MASSACHUSETTS INSTITUTE OF TECHNOLOGY

PRENTICE-HALL, INC.
Englewood Cliffs, N. J.

First Printing ....October, 1948
Second Printing ....October, 1949
Third Printing ....June, 1954
Fourth Printing ....October, 1955
Fifth Printing ....July, 1957
Sixth Printing ....March, 1959
Seventh Printing ....January, 1962
Eighth Printing .... June, 1963
Ninth Printing ....August, 1965

ONULP.

Preface

In operating the Spectroscopy Laboratory of the Massachusetts Institute of Technology, the authors have for some years felt the need of a text and reference book that would help the worker in any branch of science to evaluate the aid which the techniques of spectroscopy might lend to the solution of his own problems. In our attempt to fill this need, we, as a physicist, a chemist, and a biophysicist, respectively, have tried to synthesize our three viewpoints in a way that would be helpful to all who use or might use the techniques of experimental spectroscopy.

Since other texts are available which present effectively the history of spectroscopy, we have avoided the historical method of approach and have attempted rather to give a comprehensive view of the status and possibilities of experimental spectroscopy as it exists today. Because the subject matter to be covered is so extensive, we have had to choose between comprehensive and exhaustive coverage and have selected the former alternative.

In Chapter 1 we view the field as from a great altitude, to enable the reader who is unacquainted with the methods and accomplishments of spectroscopy to judge for himself which parts, if any, may be of importance to him. In the remainder of the book we reconsider the various topics in considerably greater detail. We have endeavoured to include a sufficient number of appropriate specific references to the literature to enable the reader to investigate still more closely subjects which may directly concern him.

References to specific points are given as footnotes; at the ends of most chapters appropriate general references are also given. While the bibliography is not intended to be exhaustive, we have attempted in specific references to cite both the original and the most up-to-date treatment of the topic involved, and in the general references to cover the subject broadly. Since we discuss many topics from several viewpoints, we have made liberal use of cross-references.

A book covering spectroscopy from several aspects is likely to contain a certain amount of inconsistency in terminology. Resolution of such inconsistencies is not made simpler by the fact that the symbology of spectroscopy is far from stabilized.

We gratefully acknowledge the courtesy of the Technology Press, John Wiley and Sons, the McGraw-Hill Book Co., Inc., Prentice-Hall, Inc., and others as specified later, for permission to reproduce figures and tables, and appreciate deeply the willing cooperation of the various manufacturers of spectroscopic equipment who have furnished illustrations of apparatus, as credited in each instance. We are especially grateful for the suggestions of Messrs. W. R. Brode, R. S. McDonald, W. F. Meggers, K. W. Meissner, R. A. Sawyer, A. L. Schoen, and Van Zandt Williams, each of whom has read and criticized one or more chapters dealing with his own specialty. We also thank Professor Donald H. Menzel, editor of the series of which the book forms a part, for his suggestions regarding the manuscript.

George R. Harrison
Richard C. Lord
John R. Loofbourow

Cambridge, Massachusetts

Contents

PRACTICAL
SPECTROSCOPY

CHAPTER 1

Spectroscopy as a Scientific Tool

THE ACCOMPLISHMENTS ACHIEVED BY SCIENTISTS through use of the spectroscope form a list so imposing as to leave no doubt that this instrument is one of the most powerful now available for investigating the natural universe. But spectroscopy is valuable not only to the research scientist; it finds everyday and increasing use in technological laboratories. Today directors of such varied enterprises as factories, assay offices, arsenals, mines, crime detection bureaus, public health departments, hospitals, museums, and technical research institutes consider access to spectroscopic equipment essential to the proper functioning of their laboratories.

THE SPECTRUM

A *spectrum* has been defined as the ordered arrangement of radiation according to wavelength. Electromagnetic radiations have been discovered that have wavelengths of every value in the range from thousands of kilometers to trillionths of a millimeter. A complete electromagnetic spectrum would comprise all these radiations arranged in order from the longest to the shortest wavelengths. Since no single instrument exists that will separate radiation containing all these wavelengths into a spectrum, the electromagnetic spectrum has been divided into various "regions" in accordance with the types of instruments available to produce and detect the waves of various lengths.

Long electromagnetic waves, upwards of a meter in length, can be separated from each other by means of ordinary tuned radio circuits. Shorter waves, down to a few millimeters long, can be analyzed by microwave equipment. When absorbed by matter, all electromagnetic waves produce heat. Since waves shorter than a few millimeters and longer than about 3×10^{-3} mm can be detected by

1

this effect more readily than by any other, they are often called *heat waves*. The range of waves from a few millimeters to 2.5×10^{-2} mm in length is known as the *far infrared* region; that from 2.5×10^{-2} to 7.5×10^{-4} mm is known as the *near infrared*. Waves that can be seen by the eye range in length from 7.5×10^{-4} mm in the red to 4×10^{-4} mm in the violet; this range is called the *visible region*. Waves slightly too short to see, 4×10^{-4} to 3×10^{-4} mm, lie in the *near ultraviolet;* then come the *far ultraviolet* and the *extreme ultraviolet* regions, which extend from 3×10^{-4} to 2×10^{-4} mm and from there to 2×10^{-6} mm, respectively. Since air is opaque to these shorter waves, they are studied in vacuum, and the range from 2×10^{-4} to 2×10^{-6} mm is also known as the *vacuum ultraviolet*. We then come to the region of *soft Xrays*, and below 10^{-7} mm to the *hard Xray* and *gamma-ray* regions, to which air is again transparent. The names, ranges, and properties of these spectral regions are summarized in Table 1.1.

1.1. Spectroscopy. The term *spectroscopy* as used in this book is restricted to the study of those radiations which lie in the infrared, visible, ultraviolet, and vacuum ultraviolet regions. The techniques discussed are quite distinct from those used in such fields as microwave spectroscopy, X-ray spectroscopy, gamma-ray spectroscopy, and mass spectroscopy. We are concerned here only with those electromagnetic waves which can readily be separated into a spectrum by means of prisms, optical gratings, and optical interferometers.

1.2. Origins of Spectroscopy. The best-known early investigator of the spectrum was Sir Isaac Newton, who in 1666 inserted a prism in a beam of sunlight shining into a dark room and saw a band of colors on the wall. By using a lens in conjunction with the prism he was able to spread the colors out into a fairly pure spectrum 10 in. long. He fell short of producing a spectroscope of the modern type only because he let the light shine through a round hole instead of a narrow slit. It was not until 1802 that W. H. Wollaston, and in 1814 Joseph Fraunhofer, independently observed *spectrum lines*, that is, images of a narrow slit each containing only light of one color. The first practical spectroscope was developed by G. R. Kirchhoff and R. Bunsen in 1859.

Newton is responsible for the practical application of the prism and Fraunhofer for that of the diffraction grating; these are the basic components used in spectroscopes today to separate the wavelengths of light. Kirchhoff and Bunsen showed that the spectroscope could

TABLE 1.1

<small>THE SPECTROSCOPIC PART OF THE ELECTROMAGNETIC SPECTRUM</small>

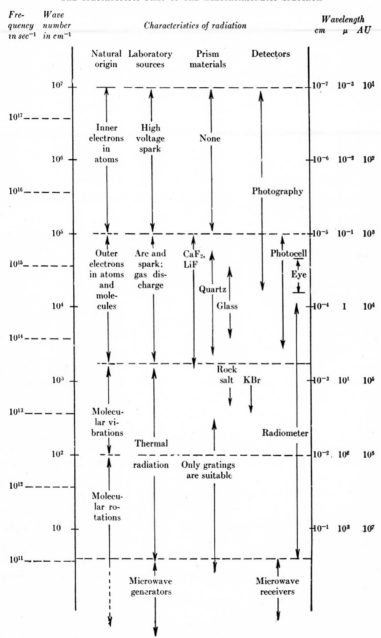

be used as a new means of qualitative chemical analysis; with it they discovered several new elements and were able to demonstrate the presence of many known elements in the sun.   They are in a very real sense the founders of modern spectroscopy.

1.3.   Measurement of the Spectrum.   The waves with which we are here concerned have lengths lying between 1 mm and 10^{-6} mm, which can be measured with a precision varying from one part in ten thousand to one part in sixty million, depending on the spectral region involved.   Various systems of units have been developed in which to record wavelengths conveniently; of these the following are the most common:

$$1 \ \mu \ (\text{micron}) \ = \ 10^{-4} \ \text{cm} \ = \ 10^{-3} \ \text{mm}$$
$$1 \ \text{m}\mu \ (\text{millimicron}) \ = \ 10^{-7} \ \text{cm} \ = \ 10^{-6} \ \text{mm}$$
$$1 \ \text{A} \ (\text{angstrom*}) \ = \ 10^{-8} \ \text{cm} \ = \ 10^{-7} \ \text{mm}$$
$$1 \ \mu \ = \ 10,000 \ \text{A} \ = \ 1000 \ \text{m}\mu$$

In the infrared region wavelengths are commonly measured in microns, and in the range shorter than 1 μ in angstroms.   Chemists and biologists frequently use the millimicron.   The mean wavelength of the strong yellow light emitted by sodium atoms is, in the three systems, 0.5893 μ, 589.3 mμ, and 5893 A.

Spectroscopes analyze radiation in accordance with its wavelengths, but atoms and molecules emit radiation of characteristic frequencies. In a sense frequency is more fundamental than wavelength, for the frequency of monochromatic light remains constant no matter in what medium it may be traveling, whereas the wavelength varies inversely with the velocity of light in the medium.   Therefore, in addition to the wavelength λ of a beam of light, it is often useful to specify the frequency of oscillation ν.   This is related to λ by the formula $\lambda\nu = c_{(m)}$, where $c_{(m)}$ is the velocity of light in the medium.   Frequencies in the optical range are, however, very large numbers (4 to 7.5 $\times$ 10^{14}), and it is more convenient to use a smaller number, the wave number σ, which is the number of waves per centimeter of path in vacuum. λ and σ are related by the formula $\lambda\sigma = 10^8$ when λ is expressed in angstroms. σ is then expressed in reciprocal centimeters, written cm^{-1}.

1.4.   The Infrared Spectrum.   Sir William Herschel in 1800 used a simple thermometer to measure the heating power of the various

---

* For a more exact definition of the angstrom see § 9.8.

colors in the spectrum of sunlight. He found the greatest heating effect entirely outside the visible portion, just beyond the red edge of the spectrum. Thus he discovered the *infrared region*. His son, Sir John Herschel, in 1840 moistened a piece of blackened paper with alcohol and found that the alcohol evaporated faster in certain places than in others when the infrared part of the solar spectrum was allowed to fall on it, revealing in this way the presence of infrared bands of absorption and transmission.

Infrared radiation can be dispersed into a spectrum by means of coarse diffraction gratings or prisms of special material such as rock salt, which is transparent to much longer waves than is glass, and the rays can then be detected with a device sensitive to small heating effects. Bolometers, thermocouples, and various other radiometers can be used for this purpose. Globar heaters and other incandescent sources emit infrared radiation profusely. The methods and apparatus used for infrared spectroscopy are discussed in detail in Chapter 17.

The infrared region, as has been indicated, is conveniently divided into the near infrared, which extends from the edge of the visible up to about 25 μ (250,000 A) and the far infrared, which extends from the near infrared to 1 mm (1000 μ or 10 million angstroms). The distinction between regions is usually made on the basis of the type of spectrograph used, since prisms have not been available which transmit much beyond 25 μ. However, the two spectral regions also correspond roughly to those which contain the vibrational frequencies of light molecules (near infrared) and their rotational frequencies (far infrared). A further subdivision of the near infrared is sometimes made when spectroscopists distinguish a region called the *photographic* or *photoelectric* infrared, because radiation of wavelengths up to the neighborhood of 2 μ can be detected photographically and photoelectrically. Radiation in this region penetrates atmospheric haze better than do the shorter waves of visible light, and so infrared photography is useful when long distances are involved in camera work. The invisibility of these waves also makes them of importance in military signaling. Contrary to a widespread impression, however, infrared radiation in the photographic and photoelectric region will not penetrate fog or mist to a significantly greater extent than will visible radiation.

The near infrared spectrum has assumed great importance in chemical and biological research because of the highly specific absorption of chemical compounds at these wavelengths. The near infrared absorption spectrum of a molecule has aptly been called the molecule's fingerprint. Recent development of good commercial infrared prism spectrometers has done much to make the fingerprinting process more widely usable.

1.5. The Visible Spectrum. The spectral sensitivity of the eye of a typical observer is shown in Fig. 1.1. The actual limits of sensitivity at the two ends differ somewhat from observer to observer,

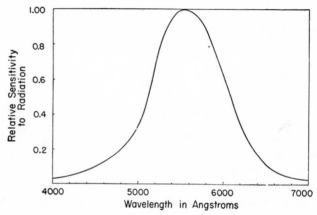

Fig. 1.1. Spectral sensitivity of the human eye.

some people being able to see slightly farther into the infrared and others farther into the ultraviolet. The visible region is usually arbitrarily set between the limits 4000 A and 7500 A. The fact that rays in this band can be seen makes possible visual spectroscopy and the entire science of colorimetry. The eye is an excellent detector of visible radiation and is a moderately satisfactory comparison device, but it is not a good quantitative measuring instrument. Its use in spectroscopy is discussed in Chapters 12 and 14.

In addition to affecting the optic nerve, waves in the visible part of the spectrum are characterized by their ability to pass through glasses of various types that are readily obtainable, which can be fashioned into prisms and lenses for the production of optical equipment. Visible radiation can be photographed, though special sensitization of the photographic emulsion is required for waves longer than about 5000 A, in the blue-green.

1.6. The Ultraviolet. The *ultraviolet region*, which begins at ap-

call # A-M —> 3rd T

N-Z —> 4th T

DNA Repair – QH467 D185 2006

UV visible reflectron – QC454 R4 R38
2004

UV reflectron – QC879. N55
1996 EXIN

If ordering a book that crw ii... order) "0" course id, Professor's na...

> **If the order is for additional co**
> name, loan period and call numbe...

> **If the order is for additional Edi...**
> name, loan period and call numbe...

> **If more than one copy** is needed...
> request and highlight it

3. **(Submit this order)** request to our acquisitio...

4. **(When the order sheet has been returned...**
   this sheet alphabetically by course, and prof...
   Order".

5. **(If not owned by any U of T library)**, searc...
   Global Books in Print for a bibliographic rec...

proximately 4000 A, was discovered in 1801 by J. W. Ritter. In his studies of the relative efficacies of rays in different portions of the spectrum in blackening silver chloride, he found that the most active rays lie beyond the violet.

Many minerals and organic materials fluoresce strongly in ultra-violet light, converting the invisible radiation into visible light. Ultraviolet light also causes numerous photochemical reactions, and in the range of waves shorter than 2900 A it is markedly bactericidal. Photoelectric effects are particularly pronounced in the ultraviolet.

Since ordinary glass is not sufficiently transparent to ultraviolet radiation, optical parts of quartz, fluorite, rock salt, or special modern glasses are used. Water is highly transparent to ultraviolet waves longer than 1900 A. The region is of great importance in absorption spectrophotometry and in the analysis of materials by the emission spectrum, and forms one of the richest and most productive regions of the entire spectrum.

The frequently used division into *near* and *far* ultraviolet is some-what artificial. It arises from the fact that the solar spectrum is cut off below 2900 A as a result of absorption by the ozone layer in the atmosphere. Beyond the far ultraviolet, that is, below 2000 A, lies the extreme or vacuum ultraviolet, which is the region of radiation absorbed markedly by the oxygen and water vapor in the air. Hy-drogen and helium, and to a much lesser degree nitrogen, are trans-parent to these shorter waves. Victor Schumann in 1893 used optical parts of fluorite, pumped the air out of his spectrograph, and eliminated most of the gelatin from the photographic emulsions he used. By these three measures he was able to extend the spectrum from 2000 down to 1250 A. Lithium fluoride has since been found to be somewhat transparent down to nearly 1000 A, but below this wavelength no solid material has been discovered from which prisms and lenses can be constructed. Diffraction gratings mounted in a vacuum can be used to study the spectrum at shorter wavelengths. In the hands of Lyman, of Millikan and his collaborators, and of Siegbahn and his associates the spectrum has been studied with gratings to 10 A, where the methods of X-ray spectroscopy become more effective. Hence the *extreme ultraviolet*, discussed in Chapter 19, covers the range between 2000 and 10 A.

1.7. **Spectroscopes and Spectrographs.** Any instrument that can be used to produce a spectrum, visible or invisible, is called a *spectro-scope*. Under this general heading instruments are classified acoording to the means by which the spectrum is observed. A *spectrograph* produces a photographic record of the spectrum called a *spectrogram*. The word *spectroscope* is sometimes used in a restricted sense to designate an instrument arranged so that the spectrum can be viewed by eye. It will be used in this book only in the broad sense; the term *visual spectroscope* will be used to designate instruments arranged for direct eye observation of the spectrum. *Spectrometers* are so built that an observer can determine wavelengths by reading a scale, which may or may not be calibrated to read directly in microns, millimicrons, or angstroms.

Most spectroscopes contain three main elements: a slit; a dispersing device such as a prism or a diffraction grating to separate radiation

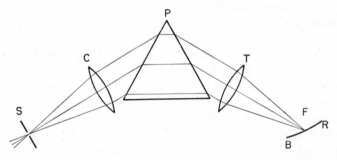

Fig. 1.2. Optical system of a simple spectroscope. *S*, slit; *C*, collimator lens; *P*, prism; *T*, telescope lens; *F*, curve along which the various parts of the spectrum are in focus; *B*, blue or short wavelength part; *R*, red or long wavelength part.

according to wavelength; and a suitable optical system to produce the spectrum lines, which are monochromatic images of the slit. A simple spectroscope optical system is shown in Fig. 1.2. The spectrum lines are arrayed along a focal curve where they may be photographed, observed with an eyepiece if visible, or isolated from their neighbors by a second slit. The first method is used in spectrographs, the second in visual spectroscopes, and the third in monochromators.

Spectrum lines are detected or recorded by various means. Infrared spectroscopes are usually equipped with radiometers, which produce variations in current through a galvanometer and hence vary its deflection. These variations of deflection may be recorded in curves of the type shown in Fig. 1.3. The spectrum can be recorded by this means at any wavelength, but more sensitive methods are used in

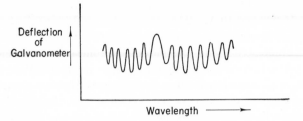

Fig 1.3.   Record of galvanometer deflections produced by an infrared spectrometer.   See also Fig. 11.7.

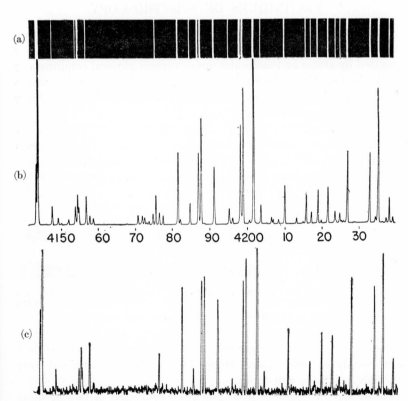

Fig. 1.4.   Photographic and photoelectric records of the same spectrum. (a) Photograph of the spectrum of iron in the violet region; (b) photoelectric record of the same spectrum; (c) densitometer record of the spectrogram shown in (a).   (Courtesy Prof. G. H. Dieke.)

spectral regions where they are available.   Photography is feasible
between 15,000 and 10 A.   Though sensitive and convenient, photography requires careful control if quantitative results are to be obtained.   Fluorescence and phosphorescence methods, combined with
visual observation or photography, can also be used between 15,000
and 10 A, with some loss in sharpness of narrow lines.   Photoelectric
recording has been used between 33,000 A and the short vacuum
ultraviolet.   In all these cases the 10 A limit is purely arbitrary, since
the sensitivity extends on into the region of X-ray spectroscopy.
Records obtained by means of the two principal detection and recording methods are shown in Fig. 1.4.

TECHNIQUES OF SPECTROSCOPY

In using the techniques of spectroscopy, one is concerned either
with studying the wavelengths and intensities of the radiations
emitted by atoms and molecules under various physical conditions or
with the radiations absorbed on passing through matter in various
forms.   Thus it is useful to distinguish between *emission spectroscopy*
and *absorption spectroscopy*.

1.8.   Emission Spectroscopy.   Three kinds of emission spectra can
be distinguished, known respectively as line, band, and continuous
spectra.   Typical examples of each of these are shown in Fig. 1.5.

Line spectra originate from atoms or atomic ions which are separated

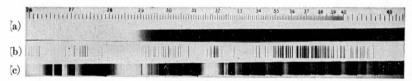

Fig. 1.5.   Typical emission spectra taken with a low-dispersion spectrograph.
(a) Continuous spectrum of an incandescent filament; (b) line spectrum of the
iron arc; (c) band spectrum of molecular nitrogen (N_2).

by such distances from their neighbors that between collisions they
can radiate as individuals.   Hence line spectra are obtained from
incandescent gases and vapors.

Band spectra originate from molecules composed of two or more
atoms, either ionized or un-ionized, when these molecules are sufficiently separated to be fairly independent of their neighbors.   Band
spectra are emitted from polyatomic incandescent gases and vapors

which are cool enough that not all the molecules are dissociated into atoms and ions. Many band spectra, such as those emitted by the hydrogen molecule H_2, have the appearance of line spectra, because the individual lines in the bands are of wide separation, and the intermingling of neighboring band lines is extensive.

Continuous spectra result when light is radiated from incandescent solids or liquids, or under certain special circumstances from individual atoms or molecules. A continuous spectrum may be regarded as the equivalent of an infinite number of spectrum lines forming a dense array of overlapping monochromatic images of the slit.

When the light from an electric arc is sent through a spectroscope, all three types of spectra—line, band, and continuous—are likely to be observed together, since the arc stream contains atoms, ions, molecules, and gross incandescent particles.

1.9. Qualitative Spectroscopic Analysis of Materials. Each type of atom or molecule can be made to produce a characteristic set of spectrum lines or bands which serve to indicate the presence of that atom or molecule as a radiating center, whether in a sample of metal in the laboratory or in a star or nebula. More than half a million different atomic spectrum lines and countless bands have been observed. Most of the more intense atomic lines have been assigned to their atom or ion of origin. Since it is possible to measure their wavelengths to a precision of 1 part in several million if necessary, most spectrum lines can be identified as to parent atom without possibility of error; and since each atom emits many characteristic spectrum lines, the presence or absence of a particular type of atom can be determined quite readily by spectroscopic means.

The spectroscope provides one of the most highly specific of all methods of qualitative analysis; it is in addition direct, rapid, and simple. A small piece of the material to be analyzed can be burned in an electric arc or spark and its spectrum recorded within a few seconds. A simple inspection of the resulting pattern of spectrum lines serves to identify the presence or absence of some 70 of the chemical elements. All metallic elements present are revealed in a single operation without requiring a guess on the part of the operator as to which will be found.

The emission method is not directly applicable to the detection of molecules except in certain special instances, because most molecules are dissociated in the electric arc or spark. Nor does the method detect negative radicals. Such elements as sulfur, selenium, the halogens, and the gases require special spectroscopic techniques, which are frequently more complicated than alternative methods of chemical detection. Analytical techniques based on emission spectra are discussed in Chapters 15 and 16.

1.10. Quantitative Spectroscopic Analysis. At very low concentrations of an element in a sample, the amount of light emitted by that element is directly proportional to the number of its atoms present, if all other factors are kept constant. This linearity provides a very convenient basis for quantitative analysis by the emission spectrum. The number of factors other than concentration that affect intensity is great, however, so that only a null method of analysis is satisfactory. A sample can be analyzed if one duplicates it fairly closely with a mixture of known content, which when burned in the arc emits lines of similar relative intensities. This procedure is not difficult when concentrations of 1 per cent or less of each important element are involved, because then no constituent in a sample influences the light emission of the others, and it is possible to determine simultaneously the concentration of a large number of impurities in a given sample.

The spectrographic method can be applied quantitatively to the determination of any element that can be detected qualitatively. As a result more than 70 elements of the periodic table are susceptible to a method that is much more rapid than chemical wet methods and can be carried out on much smaller samples, 10 mg usually being sufficient for a determination. The method is also extremely sensitive, being effective in some cases down to concentrations of 1 part in 100 million.

Spectrographic quantitative analysis provides fairly uniform precision at all concentrations. Thus it is as easy to measure the difference between 0.0010 and 0.0011 per cent content of an impurity as that between 1.00 and 1.10 per cent. At low concentrations the precision of the spectrographic method is superior to that of chemical wet methods, but it becomes inferior at concentrations of about 5 per cent and over. At concentrations below 5 per cent it is possible to reduce the average deviation among successive determinations on the same sample to less than 2 per cent.

Analysis by emission spectra, commonly called *spectrochemical analysis*, is now widely used in industry, especially for the analysis of impurities in metals, for the determination of constituents in alloys, and for the examination and testing of biological, medical, and food products.

1.11. Absorption Spectroscopy. When a beam of light passes through a piece of colored glass, certain wavelengths are reduced in intensity by absorption. Even glass that appears colorless will show absorption in the infrared and ultraviolet regions. Pure liquids and solids in solution exhibit similar absorption. Each band of wavelengths removed by a solid or liquid is usually fairly wide and may extend over many hundreds of angstroms, as shown in Fig. 1.6.

The spectroscopic study of the absorption of radiation has three broad objectives: to learn *which* wavelengths of radiation are absorbed; to learn *how much* radiation is absorbed under specific conditions; and to learn *why* the radiation is absorbed. The first of these objectives is of value because it furnishes information that serves as a basis for the qualitative analysis of the absorbing material, as in the "fingerprinting" of chemical substances by their infrared absorption

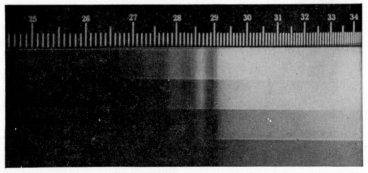

Fig. 1.6. Absorption spectrum of the cytosine molecule in the solid state at liquid-hydrogen temperature.

spectra. Such information is also useful for the production of radiation filters required for the removal of certain waves from a beam of light, for example in the removal of infrared rays by a heat filter from the beam in a motion-picture projector. The second objective permits extending chemical analysis, by means of absorption, from the qualitative to the quantitative. The use of ultraviolet absorption spectra, for instance, is widespread in the quantitative analysis of vitamins and of many other important substances that are difficult to analyze by other means. In the achievement of the third objective, one seeks to understand the absorption of radiation in terms of the atoms and molecules responsible for it. No feature of the absorption spectrum can be overlooked in this process, and in the course of understanding details of the spectrum one can obtain detailed knowledge of how atoms are held together in molecules. This knowledge is of great value to the physicist and the chemist.

1.12. Absorption Spectrophotometry. Absorption spectrophotometry is quantitative absorption spectroscopy. It can be used for the quantitative determination of organic molecules, for example in the estimation of dye concentrations and in the analysis of vitamins, hormones, and other complex organic molecules. By means of an absorption photograph of the type shown in Fig. 1.6, a curve may be determined as shown in Fig. 1.7, which gives the relative absorption of light at various wavelengths through a given thickness of the sample. Absorption can be measured by means of a spectrophotometer. Once the specific absorption at all wavelengths is known for a material, the resulting curve enables one to determine the actual amounts of absorbing material present. Thus, though the absorption method is not highly specific for qualitative analysis, it is extremely precise in a quantitative sense and can be made even more sensitive than emission analysis in certain cases. Absorption spectrophotometry forms the subject of Chapter 14.

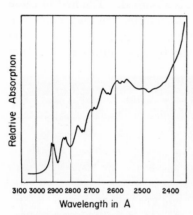

Fig. 1.7. Absorption curve determined from the spectrogram shown in Fig. 1.6, with wavelength scale reversed.

1.13. Fluorescence Spectroscopy. A branch of spectroscopy capable of much further development is that involving the use of fluorescence. Fluorescence spectroscopy is widely applied in mineralogy, biochemistry, biology, medicine, and the food industries.

When one uses fluorescence spectroscopy, the object to be studied, for example a mineral specimen, is shielded from extraneous light and is then illuminated with ultraviolet light, usually from a quartz mercury lamp covered with a filter that removes visible radiation. The specimen is likely to glow brightly; if it does, its type can often be determined from the color of its fluorescence.

Many organic materials fluoresce. Certain species of bacteria have characteristic fluorescence, and different strains of the same species may show different shades of color. Molds and bacterial growth on meat samples can be detected, and in some cases identified, by means of their fluorescence. Various parts of plant or animal cells often fluoresce with different colors, so details that cannot be seen in ordinary light are sometimes revealed by a fluorescence microscope. Mineral oil has a characteristic blue fluorescence not found in most organic oils, and it is thus possible to detect contamination or dilution of organic oils by mineral oil. Oleomargarine can be detected in butter by means of fluorescence; as little as 5 per cent of artificial fat in butter can be shown up in the same way.   Flour of one type may show a bluish fluorescence, whereas another glows white and a third exhibits a pinkish glow.   Many other food products can be tested for quality by fluorescence analysis.   Real and artificial gems can also be distinguished by this means.   The spectroscope makes fluorescence analysis more specific than does visual observation of fluorescence.

USES OF SPECTROSCOPY

A complete catalogue of the uses of spectroscopy would be too lengthy for the present chapter, but we may list (a) the study of the absorption and emission of light by matter in all forms; (b) the analysis of the atomic and molecular varieties present in a given sample of matter and determination of their relative numbers; (c) the investigation of the structures of atoms and molecules, and (d) the determination of the size, mass, temperature, speed of motion, and many other characteristics of the heavenly bodies.   Spectroscopy has thus contributed materially to all the natural sciences, particularly to astronomy, physics, chemistry, and biology.

1.14. The Spectroscope in Chemistry. When the spectroscope was first developed in practical form (1859), it was used immediately by chemists as a powerful tool for qualitative analysis. As a byproduct of this use came the discovery of many chemical elements, among them cesium and rubidium by Bunsen and Kirchhoff, and later helium, gallium, indium, and thallium by various other chemists. In addition, spectroscopic analysis was such a powerful aid in the separation of the various rare-earth elements that the discovery of many of these may properly be credited to the spectroscope.   The spectroscopically discovered elements are listed in Table 1.2.   In later years the same application of spectroscopic methods, grown more powerful with the passage of time, led to the discovery of rare

TABLE 1.2

LIST OF CHEMICAL ELEMENTS DISCOVERED SPECTROSCOPICALLY

Element	Discoverer	Date
Cesium	Bunsen and Kirchhoff	1860
Rubidium	Bunsen and Kirchhoff	1861
Thallium	Crookes	1861
Indium	Reich and Richter	1863
Helium	Lockyer	1868
Gallium	de Boisbaudran	1875
Thulium	Cleve	1879
Praseodymium	von Welsbach	1885
Neodymium	von Welsbach	1885
Samarium	de Boisbaudran	1886
Holmium	de Boisbaudran	1886
Ytterbium	Urbain; von Welsbach	1907
Lutecium	Urbain; von Welsbach	1907

isotopes of the common elements hydrogen (Urey, 1932), carbon, nitrogen, and oxygen. Improvements in techniques of measuring emission and absorption intensities also permitted the extension of these methods to quantitative chemical analysis, as has been mentioned above. Thus the spectroscope, in one form or another, has

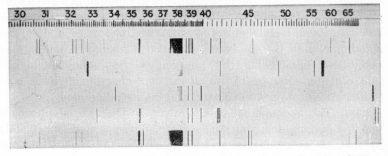

Fig. 1.8. Emission spectra of the alkali metals. Top to bottom: lithium, sodium, potassium, rubidium, cesium.

become a foremost instrument in all branches of chemistry because of its analytical power.

The contributions of spectroscopy to chemistry are by no means limited to the field of analysis, however, because no chemical substance can emit or absorb radiation without revealing much about its fundamental nature. By study of the emission of radiation from isolated atoms and ions, enough information about the electronic structure of atoms has been obtained to explain completely the arrangement of the chemical elements in the periodic table (see Chapter 10).   Similarly, the structures of many molecules, including some of great complexity, have been revealed by their spectra.   The chemist has profited both in the determination of the actual geometry of molecules whose structural formulas were previously known and in the elucidation of unknown structural formulas.   The structures of such molecules as penicillin and vitamin K, for example, were worked out with extensive help from the spectroscope.

The chemist is somewhat more interested in the reactions that molecules undergo than in their structures while at rest between reactions. Since both the speed of a reaction and the extent to which it takes place are dependent on the forces between atoms, that is, the chemical bond forces, any information about these is of chemical importance. The contribution of spectroscopy here has been a double one.   The actual strengths of the chemical bonds (dissociation energies) have been measured spectroscopically for many diatomic molecules, frequently with an accuracy that could not be attained by other means. In addition, spectroscopic data have been used to make highly precise calculations of chemical equilibrium constants, which determine how far reactions proceed.   For example, the equilibrium of the reaction of hydrogen and chlorine to form hydrogen chloride gas at any temperature up to 5000°C can be calculated entirely from spectroscopic data, with precision far greater than that with which it can be determined otherwise.

One branch of chemistry that should be expected to make extensive use of spectroscopy is the highly complex field of photochemistry. The existence and nature of molecular fragments which cannot be chemically isolated but which are important links in a chain of steps making up photochemical reactions have been demonstrated spectroscopically.   As examples of such fragmentary molecules one can cite scores of diatomic hydrides, such as the OH radical, which have only a fleeting existence in an arc or flame or in the high-temperature areas of a reaction vessel, but whose properties, such as interatomic distances, vibration and rotation frequencies, and electronic states, have been determined spectroscopically in minute detail.   At present, photosynthesis, the great problem of photochemistry, is being attacked in many ways, but the spectroscope is never absent from the laboratories of those concerned with the problem.

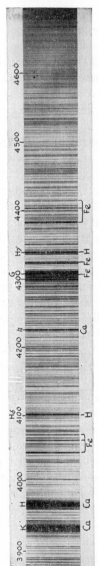

Fig. 1.9a. A portion of the solar spectrum. (Courtesy Mount Wilson Observatory.)

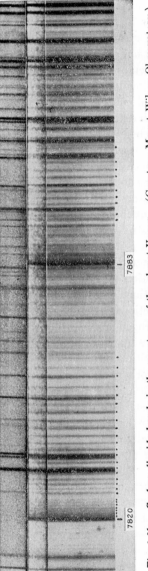

Fig. 1.9b. Carbon dioxide bands in the spectrum of the planet Venus. (Courtesy Mount Wilson Observatory.)

The kinds of spectroscopy in which chemists are most interested at present are qualitative and quantitative emission spectroscopy, ultraviolet and infrared absorption spectrophotometry, and Raman spectroscopy. These subjects and some chemical problems to which they can be applied are discussed in Chapters 14 through 19.

1.15. Spectroscopy in Astronomy. Modern astronomers have completely refuted the dictum of Auguste Comte, "There are some things of which the human race must remain forever in ignorance, for example, the chemical constitution of the heavenly bodies." By using the spectroscope, astronomers have been able to make qualitative analyses of many of the stars and also a quantitative analysis of

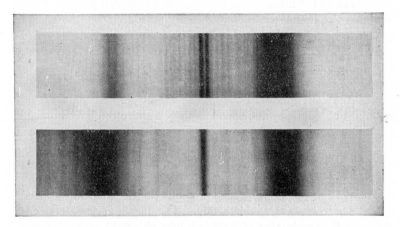

Fig. 1.9c.   Spectrum of the star β Aurigae, showing Doppler effect.
(Courtesy Harvard Observatory.)

the surface of the sun that is perhaps more complete than any yet made of the earth. Astrophysicists have thus been able to demonstrate that many of the same chemical elements which we find on earth compose the sun, stars, and the most distant nebulae. Sixty-six elements have been found spectroscopically in the sun. A number of spectrum lines, which were for many years unidentified, are found in the spectra of the solar corona and of various nebulae; these were once thought to arise from atoms not found on earth. It has since been proved that every one of these lines originates from a familiar atom found in the stars in some special state of excitation not ordinarily produced in the laboratory.

A large proportion of the information that the astronomer possesses regarding the constitution of the heavenly bodies has come via spectroscopy. Spectra obtained when astronomers collect light from a star with a large telescope and then separate it by means of an attached spectroscope serve for the detection and estimation of molecules in the stars. The Doppler effect of spectral lines can be used to measure the approach and recession velocities of stars and nebulae (see Fig. 1.9c) and the rotation of the sun; a spectral line from a calcium atom, for example, is shifted toward shorter wavelengths when emitted by a star that is approaching and toward longer wavelengths if from one that is receding.

The spectroscope has been used to measure the sun's motion among the stars and the distances of hundreds of individual stars, and it has revealed the double character of many stars that are too close together to be resolved as double by the telescope.

1.16. Spectroscopy in Physics. In physics the trail of spectroscopic discoveries is longer than in any other science. Spectroscopic data give the most precise standards of length, and it has been suggested that the standard meter bar might well be replaced as a standard of length by the wavelength of a sharp red line emitted by cadmium atoms, or of a sharp green line emitted by mercury atoms of the isotope 198. The lengths of such waves may well be expected to remain more constant over the passing ages than that of any man-made standard.

Most of our precise information about the electronic structures of atoms has come via spectroscopy. The physicist is interested in studying the production of light in a magnetic field, and through the Zeeman and related effects he has been able to determine the quantum numbers and the locations of the electrons in the various kinds of atoms. Many apparently sharp lines can be resolved into a number of still sharper monochromatic lines packed close together. This so-called hyperfine structure reveals information regarding the spin of the nucleus of the emitting atom. Magnetic susceptibilities and the electronic configurations of some atoms in the solid state can also be determined by spectroscopic means.

Much of the attention of the spectroscopist has been given to determining electronic energy levels in atoms. It has been found possible to remove electrons one by one from atoms and to study the new array of spectrum lines that results each time another electron is removed. Thus normal uranium atoms, with 92 electrons around the nucleus of each, emit many thousands of spectrum lines when excited. When an electron is removed from such an atom, an entirely new array of thousands of spectrum lines will result on excitation. When two electrons are removed, still another new spectrum can be produced. Thus it is theoretically possible to have 92 different characteristic spectra of uranium. Analogous series of ionization spectra may be obtained with the other chemical elements, so that more than 4000 different kinds of atoms and atomic ions can be expected to emit independent spectra, and many millions of atomic spectrum lines will thus be produced. To date only some 350,000 of these spectrum lines have been assigned to their parent atoms, and a much smaller number have been classified in terms of the energy levels and the state of ionization of the atom from which they originate.

1.17. Spectroscopy in Biology and Medicine. Qualitative and quantitative analyses made by means of the emission spectrum have been employed extensively for determining the presence of metallic elements in biochemical substances, cells, and tissues. Such studies provide the biologist with a means of determining the various trace elements needed by cells for life and growth. In medicine, their greatest application has been to the investigation of toxicological problems, as for example, in determining the accumulation of lead, copper, and so on, in the blood and tissues of persons exposed to such substances in the course of their daily work. Attempts have also been made to apply emission spectroscopy to diagnostic procedures in certain pathological conditions characterized by changes in the heavy-metal content of the body fluids.

Biochemists and biologists are confronted by unusually difficult problems of molecular structure, in which the molecules involved are large, complex, and often ill-defined entities. Infrared and Raman spectroscopy, and visible and ultraviolet absorption spectrophotometry, have been invaluable in the study of such problems. Such spectroscopic methods have, for example, contributed to the elucidation of the structures of many of the known vitamins, enzymes, and coenzymes.

Absorption spectrophotometry, in particular, is useful in controlling the preliminary isolation of biochemical substances and in their later characterization and qualitative or quantitative assay after they have been isolated and identified. The characteristic absorption band of vitamin A, with a maximum at 3280 A, is used, for example, in the quantitative determination of this substance and in tests of the purity of vitamin A preparations. The kinetics of enzyme activity are readily studied by absorption spectrophotometric methods, both in the visible and ultraviolet regions.

Fluorescence spectroscopy is similarly useful in the isolation and identification of those biochemical substances which exhibit characteristic fluorescence. One of the most striking examples of the application of this technique has been the identification of a coal-tar constituent that is responsible for causing "coal-tar cancer," as a complex polycyclic hydrocarbon, 3:4-benzpyrene. Fluorescence is employed routinely in the quantitative analysis of various biochemical substances, such as vitamins B_1 and B_2.

Microabsorption spectrophotometry in the ultraviolet is finding increasing application in the study of the distribution of substances like nucleic acids in cells and tissues in relation to fundamental biological and medical problems, such as those of cell division, growth, differentiation, normal physiology, and pathology. The use of this technique in the visible region (in connection with specific color reactions) and in the infrared promises to lead to the solution of many hitherto abstruse biological and medical problems. Microfluorescence spectroscopy, though not yet used on a wide scale, has similar applications.

Spectroscopy of the extreme ultraviolet has thus far been used but little in the study of biochemical substances. It may be expected to receive increasing application to the study of biochemical structure problems involving saturated organic compounds.

1.18. Spectroscopy in Food Research. Spectroscopic methods are being used increasingly in testing and controlling the production of foods and their containers as advances in knowledge indicate the importance of substances that may be beneficial or injurious in very minute quantities. The great sensitivity of spectroscopic methods and the smallness of the samples required for analysis are of considerable importance in food technology.

An example of the use of the spectrograph for determining small but important concentrations of metals in foods is given by the measurement of copper in cranberries. The cranberry bogs in the Cape Cod district had for many years been sprayed with copper sulfate solution as an aid in pest control, and there was some fear that copper salts might be accumulating in the soil to a degree that would result in undesirably large quantities of copper in the cranberries. Spectrographic analysis was used to determine the concentration of copper in soil samples, in various parts of the cranberry plant, and in the berries themselves, with the result that it was found that the danger level had not been remotely approached.

Lead determinations in condensed milk are another example of control procedures. By means of the spectroscope, comparison runs of different brands can easily be made whenever desired. The lead content is usually found to lie between 3 and 20 parts per ten million. Chocolate manufacturers who wish to know the metallic content of

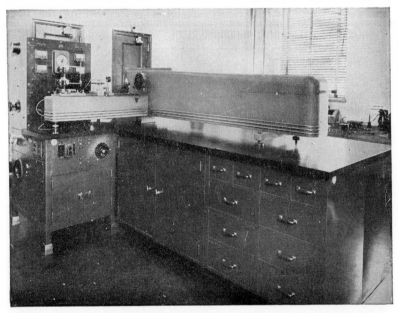

Fig. 1.10. Corner of an industrial spectroscopy laboratory. (Courtesy Aluminum Company of America.)

their product find the spectrograph indispensable. The metallic content of beer kept in cans and in bottles is determined in a routine manner with the spectrograph.

Absorption spectrophotometry is useful in testing comestible oils, liquors, and other liquids. Absorption and fluorescence methods are widely used in the food industries in the assay of foods for their vitamin content.

1.19. Spectroscopy in Metallurgy and Mineralogy. For many years archeologists were unable to solve the secret of the origin of the purple color of the gold sequins found on mummies in Egyptian tombs. An eminent spectroscopist was called to their aid, and found that the color was due to certain impurities present naturally in some samples of gold. By identifying these impurities he made it possible to fix definitely the place where the gold had been mined and to duplicate the purple color. Since only a minute amount of material was available for analysis, the spectrograph was particularly useful; not a single sequin had to be destroyed in order to give the answer.

In metallurgy the spectrograph is especially valuable because of the speed with which analyses can be made. Two hundred tons of copper

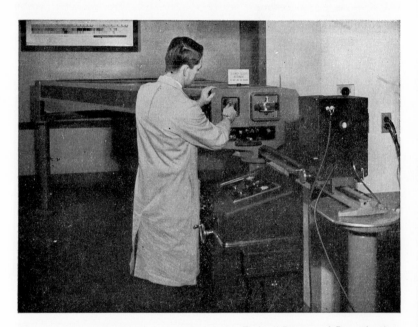

Fig. 1.11. A spectroscopy laboratory of the Federal Bureau of Investigation. (Courtesy F. B. I.)

ore may be smelted at one time in a furnace, and it is of great importance to stop the smelting process at the exact instant when the concentrations of various impurities are at the optimum. A spectroscope can be used to give the desired result within five minutes or less. For this reason, spectroscopy has come into wide application in the various metals industries, particularly in iron and steel foundries, in copper smelting, and in the production of the more valuable metals.

Much steel is made by the addition of industrial scrap to new material obtained from iron ore. Over the years the percentage of impurities introduced with scrap into American steel had slowly been rising, until in the 1930's a level had been reached at which the tin content was becoming so high as to affect the rolling properties of the steel. The tin concentration was still low enough, however, so that it could be determined readily only by means of spectrographic analysis.

Minerals can be identified with the aid of the spectrograph, and the more than 2700 recognized varieties have been analyzed for their constituent elements at least partially by this means. The important role that fluorescence spectroscopy plays in mineralogy has already been mentioned.

1.20. Forensic Spectroscopy. Most up-to-date police laboratories use the spectrograph as an aid in criminal investigations. An expert of the Massachusetts State Police has given the following as an example of the nature of the problems that a police laboratory may be called upon to solve: "In the course of a typical day one may receive a half dozen quart jars filled with human organs to be analyzed for small traces of poison, from another case a chisel having on its surface an almost invisible amount of a foreign metal, while again one may receive a pair of old trousers with traces of dust on the knees, or paint from a car involved in a hit-and-run accident, or blood stains on a knife, or a pellet of shot removed from a body, or ashes and debris from an incendiary fire, or broken pieces of a burglar's tool, or residues from the scene of an explosion. Unusual and varied subject matter requires versatile methods and instruments. In many of these cases spectrographic analysis can be advantageously applied and in a few it is essential."

The principal advantages of using spectrographic techniques in police work appear to result from the rapidity with which the results of an analysis can be obtained, and from the fact that the samples to be studied are often very small. In one case the lead pellets available from a shotgun homicide case weighed but 65 mg, yet 10 mg sufficed for spectrographic analyses adequate for identification.

From the above examples, which have been selected at random, it is apparent that spectroscopic methods may be applied to the solution of many diverse problems. The chapters that follow contain detailed information designed to aid in selection of the most suitable spectroscopic equipment for solving any specific problem, and in its effective use.

GENERAL REFERENCES

1.1. R. A. Sawyer, *Experimental Spectroscopy.* New York: Prentice-Hall, Inc., 1944.

1.2. W. R. Brode, *Chemical Spectroscopy.* New York: John Wiley & Sons, Inc., 1943.

1.3. G. R. Harrison (Ed.), *Proceedings of the M.I.T. Conferences on Spectroscopy and Its Applications.* New York: John Wiley & Sons, Inc., 5th, 6th, and 7th Conferences, 1938, 1939, 1940.

1.4. T. R. P. Gibb, Jr., *Optical Methods of Chemical Analysis.* New York: McGraw-Hill Book Company, Inc., 1942.

1.5. S. Judd Lewis, *Spectroscopy in Science and Industry.* London: Adam Hilger, Ltd., 1933.

1.6. F. Twyman, *Spectrochemical Analysis of Metals and Alloys.* London: Adam Hilger, Ltd., 1941.

1.7. Walter Gerlach and Werner Gerlach, *Clinical and Pathological Applications of Spectrum Analysis.* London: Adam Hilger, Ltd., 1934.

1.8. R. A. Morton, *The Application of Absorption Spectrophotometry to the Study of Vitamins, Hormones, and Enzymes.* London: Adam Hilger, Ltd., 1942.

1.9. L. Heilmeyer, *Spectrophotometry in Medicine.* London: Adam Hilger, Ltd., 1943.

1.10. R. B. Barnes, R. C. Gore, U. Liddel, and V. Z. Williams, *Infrared Spectroscopy.* New York: Reinhold Publishing Corporation, 1944.

1.11. George Glockler, "The Raman Effect." *Rev. Mod. Phys.,* **15,** 111 (1943).

CHAPTER 2

Selection of Spectroscopic Instruments

SPECTROSCOPES ARE AVAILABLE IN MANY DIFFERENT TYPES, and selection of even an all-purpose instrument allows of a certain degree of choice. To be considered in making such a choice are (a) the range of wavelengths over which the spectroscope can be used, (b) the extent to which it disperses light, (c) the variation of this dispersion with wavelength, (d) the resolving power of the instrument, and (e) the brightness of the spectrum that it produces. Important secondary considerations are freedom from scattered light and false lines, suitable shape and size of the spectrum lines produced, and ease of adjustment. The relative bulkiness and portability, as well as the availability of different instruments, will often influence the final choice. The relative importance of the factors enumerated may well determine whether a prism or a grating spectroscope will be chosen.

2.1. **Dispersion.** The dispersion of a spectroscope is a measure of the way it distributes light in space according to wavelength. This property can be expressed as angular or as linear dispersion. *Angular dispersion* ($d\theta/d\lambda$ in Fig. 2.1) is fundamental. It depends on the dispersing element used, and measures the variation with wavelength λ

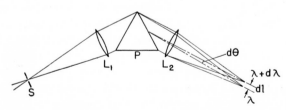

Fig. 2.1. Angular dispersion, $d\theta/d\lambda$, and linear dispersion, $dl/d\lambda$.

of the angle of deviation θ of the emergent light beam. Of more frequent practical use is the *linear dispersion* $dl/d\lambda$, which gives the actual distance dl of separation in the spectrum of two close lines differing in wavelength by $d\lambda$. The reciprocal of this ratio, called the *plate factor* or sometimes the *reciprocal dispersion*, is almost always used in common practice to measure the dispersion; thus 30 A/mm indicates a low dispersion, whereas 1 A/mm corresponds to a relatively high value. The linear dispersion obtained with most dispersing elements can be controlled, since it depends not only on the angular dispersion but also on the distance between the dispersing element P and the focal curve. The inclination of this curve to the optic axis of the output side of the spectroscope also affects the linear dispersion (Fig. 2.1).

2.2. Resolving Power. The *resolving power* P_r of a spectroscope is defined as $\lambda/d\lambda$, $d\lambda$ being the wavelength interval between two close lines of similar intensity that can just be resolved with the instrument at wavelength λ. Each spectrum line is an image of the slit. Even if the slit is extremely narrow, its image is of appreciable width, in the form of a diffraction pattern consisting of a bright central maximum on each side of which are lesser maxima. Two spectrum lines of equal intensity are considered as being just resolved when the diffraction maximum of one falls on the first minimum of the other.[1] The resolving powers of most spectroscopes lie between 5000 and 200,000.

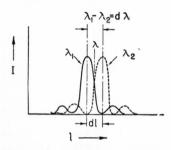

Fig. 2.2. Intensity distribution of the diffraction patterns of two spectrum lines of wavelengths λ_1 and λ_2, that are just resolved, plotted as a function of linear position, l in the spectrum. The resolving power is $\lambda/d\lambda$, and the linear dispersion is $dl/d\lambda$.

Dispersion and resolving power are often confused. Figure 2.2 illustrates their difference. Dispersion determines the approximate position in the spectrum at which light of a given wavelength will fall; resolving power determines how well that light can be separated from light of other wavelengths falling near by. Resolving power and dispersion are closely related, since the resolving power of any optically perfect spectroscopic device is equal to its dispersing power multiplied by its effective linear aperture A. In a prism spectroscope, A is as shown in Fig. 2.3. Resolving power thus depends fundamentally on the material, shape, and quality of the dispersing element. However, the actual power of an instrument

---

[1] Lord Rayleigh, "Wave Theory," *Encyc. Britt.*, 9th ed., XXIV, (1888).

to resolve two close spectrum lines may be reduced by its auxiliary parts. In a visual spectroscope an inferior telescope lens or eyepiece may reduce the resolution to a value below that to be expected from the resolving power of the prism or grating used. In a spectrograph the same loss may result from attempting to photograph the spectrum on a plate whose graininess is too coarse to separate the lines definitely.

   2.3. The Dispersing Element. In general, prism instruments are more readily portable and somewhat more rugged than grating instruments. They suffer from the disadvantage that their dispersion changes markedly with wavelength; as a consequence, any particular instrument is useful over only a comparatively limited band of wavelengths. Their principal uses are for measuring simple emission and absorption spectra, for special purposes involving relatively high light-gathering power, and as small portable instruments.

   Diffraction-grating spectroscopes give more uniform dispersion than prism instruments, and a single grating can be used to

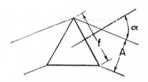

Fig. 2.3. Effective linear aperture, A, of a prism for a beam of radiation emerging from the exit face at an angle α to the perpendicular. If f is the length of the exit face, $A = f \cos \alpha$.

cover a very wide spectral range. A good grating gives, in general, greater dispersion and resolving power than a prism of similar aperture or cost. For that reason grating spectrographs are widely used in research laboratories, especially for emission spectroscopy. The principal disadvantage of most diffraction-grating instruments is that they suffer from astigmatism; this defect can, however, be eliminated by methods discussed below. The shortcomings sometimes noted in the past, that gratings are fragile, wasteful of light, and produce so many false lines as to be useless for analytical purposes, have been eliminated. Overlapping of different orders of grating spectra in certain regions need cause little difficulty.

   2.4. Dispersing Prisms. The dispersive action of a prism arises from the variation with wavelength of the refractive index of the material of which it is composed and from the angle between its entrance and exit faces. In regions of normal dispersion, rays of short wavelength are bent more in passing through a prism than are those of longer wavelength. The variation with wavelength of the refractive index of a suitable prism material, and hence the dispersion of a prism formed from it, tends to increase rapidly as an absorption band is approached from either side. The usefulness of the material therefore becomes greater from the standpoint of dispersion as it becomes less from the standpoint of light transmission. This relation is illustrated in Fig. 2.4, where curves showing the variation of refrac-

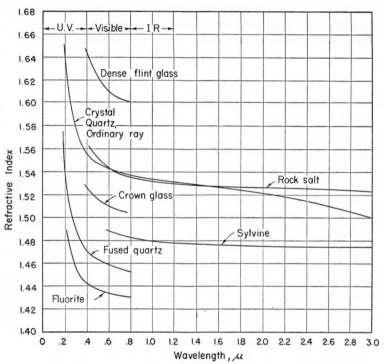

Fig. 2.4.   Refractive index as a function of wavelength for several prism materials.

tive index and absorption with wavelength are given for several of the materials most commonly used in prisms. The dispersion at any wavelength is measured by the slope of the refractive index curve, and is greater as this is steeper.

The dispersive power of a prism is often 20 times as great at one end of its useful spectral range as at the other, with a resultant equivalent variation in resolving power. Quartz prisms, though transparent at wavelengths longer than 4500 A, have diminished usefulness there because of their low dispersion, and at wavelengths shorter than 2000 A their transparency is low. Most glass prisms are effective only in the spectral range 10,000 to 3500 A.

Modern dispersing prisms are usually cut with 60-deg refracting angles. This choice is a compromise between smaller angles, which give less dispersion, and larger angles, which require more material, produce a greater loss of light, and result in decreased aperture. With material of low average refractive index, it would be advantageous to use a prism of larger refracting angle than 60 deg, but the 60-deg compromise is close enough to the optimum in most cases to make special angles unnecessary.

The angular dispersion $d\theta/d\lambda$ of a prism is given approximately by the formula

$$\frac{d\theta}{d\lambda} = \frac{dn}{d\lambda} \cdot \frac{2 \tan i}{n}$$

where θ (the angle of deviation) is the angle between the rays incident upon and emergent from the prism, n is the refractive index of the prism material, and i is the angle of incidence of the ray on the prism, as shown in Fig. 2.5. This formula is strictly true only for the case of minimum deviation, in which the rays pass through the prism symmetrically, the incident and emergent rays making equal angles with the normals to the prism faces at which the rays enter and emerge.

The resolving power P_r, defined as $\lambda/d\lambda$, is given for a prism by the formula

$$P_r = T \frac{dn}{d\lambda} \cdot \frac{1.22}{n}$$

where T is the thickness of the prism base. It can be shown that this value is equal to the dispersion, as given above, times the linear width A of the beam entering the prism.

A prism is ordinarily shaped so that it will accept a beam of circular cross section falling on its front face at approximately the angle

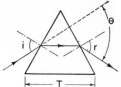

Fig. 2.5. Ray passing through a prism at minimum deviation, under which conditions $\angle i = \angle r$; θ is the angle of deviation; T, prism thickness.

of minimum deviation. This condition leads to a standard set of dimension ratios for any material, the length of face of a 60-deg prism being for most substances roughly 1.6 times its height. For good definition the prism height should be at least three times as great as the maximum length of slit that is to be used with it, and preferably the ratio should be even greater. Spectrum lines produced with prisms are curved, and definition may be lost when the prism-slit height ratio is too small.

Both dispersion and resolving power can be increased if a number of prisms are used in train, or if a beam of light is sent through the

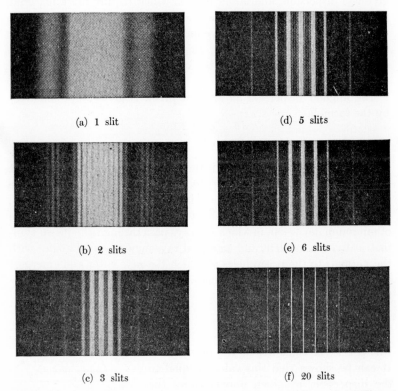

(a) 1 slit

(b) 2 slits

(c) 3 slits

(d) 5 slits

(e) 6 slits

(f) 20 slits

Fig. 2.6.   Diffraction patterns produced by various numbers of equidistant slits illuminated by parallel Monochromatic light.   (From F. A. Jenkins and H. E. White, *Fundamentals of Physical Optics*, McGraw-Hill Book Company, Inc., New York (1937), page 147.   Courtesy authors and publisher.)

same prism several times.   Attempts to bring about a large increase in these quantities by either means usually result in difficulties due to scattered light or to undue loss of light by reflection and absorption, long before resolving powers are reached that are equivalent to those obtainable with diffraction gratings.

2.5.   **Diffraction Gratings.**   The diffraction grating has been in use for more than a hundred years, but its full potentialities have not yet been realized on account of the difficulty of ruling and reproducing in quantity gratings of high quality.   Even so, many modern gratings are superior in a variety of ways to modern prisms. A diffraction grating consists essentially of a large number of close equidistant slits or diffracting lines. The greater the number N of these slits, the greater the theoretical resolving power of the grating. The more closely the lines are packed together, the greater the dispersion of the grating.

Figure 2.6 illustrates the diffraction patterns that result when a collimated beam of monochromatic light from a slit falls on various numbers of equidistant slits and is then brought to focus by a telescope lens. The grating space, or distance between the slits, has been assumed to remain constant in the various diagrams. The successive maxima, which correspond to the different orders of a diffraction grating, are seen to become sharper and more definite as the number of slits (grating rulings) is increased. Multiple patterns are produced by a grating when a beam of light containing several wavelengths

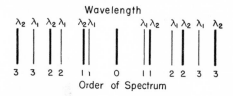

Fig. 2.7.   Distribution of various orders of spectra produced by a diffraction grating for radiation of two wavelengths, λ_1 and λ_2.

falls on it, each pattern to a scale proportional to the wavelength of light involved in its production. The resulting composite pattern forms a group of spectra in various orders. This condition is illustrated in Fig. 2.7, drawn for a beam containing waves of two lengths.

In small grating spectrometers and spectroscopes, transmission gratings are commonly used. These consist of transparent plates on which there are thousands of diffracting lines. The lines may be as few as 500 per inch in a very coarse grating or as many as 30,000 per inch in a fine high-dispersion grating.

Large spectrographs generally employ reflection gratings. Original gratings of this type are ruled on highly polished mirrors, of aluminum-coated glass or of other materials, and may be either plane or concave. Concave mirrors up to seven inches in diameter have been successfully ruled with as many as 180,000 lines, and even larger plane gratings have been ruled. The ruling of a large diffraction grating presents considerable difficulty, since the lines, engraved on the polished surface by a sharp diamond, must be straight, parallel, and equally spaced. Standard ruling spacings are approximately 5000, 7500, 10,000, 15,000, 25,000, and 30,000 lines to the inch. Ruling a large grating may require two weeks or more, during which time the ruling engine must be kept operating uniformly and at constant temperature.

A reflection grating has the great advantage that the light does not traverse material which will inevitably vary in transparency in different regions of the spectrum. If necessary, a single grating can be used to cover the range 100 to 10,000 A. When a grating is ruled on a concave mirror, a *concave grating* is obtained, which requires no lenses for collimating or focusing. The concave reflection grating, developed by H. A. Rowland in 1882,[2] is one of the most powerful dispersing devices available.

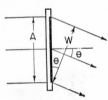

Fig. 2.8. Linear aperture A of a diffraction grating. The width W of a beam of radiation diffracted at an angle θ is related to the linear aperture A by the expression $W = A \cos \theta$.

The angular dispersion of a diffraction grating with fixed slit is given by the formula

$$\frac{d\theta}{d\lambda} = \frac{Nm}{A \cos \theta}$$

where N is the number of rulings on the grating, m is the order used, and A is the linear aperture of the grating, in this case the distance from the first ruled line to the last, as shown in Fig. 2.8. The direction θ in which any particular wavelength λ will be thrown by the grating is given by the formula

$$m\lambda = \frac{A}{N} (\sin i \pm \sin \theta)$$

where i is the angle of incidence of the light on the grating and θ is the angle of emergence, both measured from the normal. Differentiating this formula gives the dispersion formula previously cited.

Near the normal to the grating, the dispersion is almost uniform, and a so-called *normal spectrum* is obtained. This spectrum is most convenient for the identification of spectrum lines. By varying i, any desired range of wavelengths can be thrown to the vicinity of the normal.

The resolving power P_r of a grating is given by the formula

$$P_r = \frac{\lambda}{d\lambda} = Nm$$

[2] H. A. Rowland, *Phil. Mag.*, **13**, 469 (1882).

where N, as before, is the total number of rulings and m the order used, λ is the average wavelength of the lines, and $d\lambda$ is their separation in wavelength. Two spectrum lines that are just distinguishable in a given order of a grating containing, say, 10,000 rulings, will appear as a single line if a grating with a smaller number of rulings is used, owing to the decrease in sharpness of the diffraction patterns produced and the resulting lower resolution.

As an example of the use of the above formulas, we may consider the case of the first-order spectrum of a 30,000 line/in. grating with 6 in. of ruled width, for which $m = 1$ and $N = 180,000$. Changing all units of length into angstroms, $A = 6$ in. $\times$ 25.4 mm/in. $\times$ 10^7 A/mm $= 152 \times 10^7$ A; $\cos \theta = 1$; $d\theta/d\lambda = 0.000118$ radian per A for the dispersion on the normal in the first order. If this grating were used in a spectrograph that focused the spectrum at a distance r of 21 ft (6300 mm) from the grating, the linear dispersion $dl/d\lambda$ would be $r \cdot d\theta/d\lambda$ or 0.743 mm/A. Inverting this to get the plate factor, we obtain 1.35 A/mm. The theoretical resolving power of this grating $P_r = Nm = \lambda/d\lambda$ would be 180,000 in the first order, 360,000 in the second order, 540,000 in the third order, and so on. A perfect grating of this type could then be expected to separate, at 6000 A, two lines of equal intensity not closer than 0.033 A in the first order, 0.0167 A in the second, and 0.011 A in the third. A grating capable of such performance has not yet been ruled. Although in a good grating the first order is likely to give nearly the theoretical resolving power, the second will perhaps give only half again as much as the first, and the third perhaps only double the first. In any actual grating some orders come much closer to perfection than others, for reasons discussed in Chapter 4.

The ruled area on a grating is rectangular in shape, the length of a ruling usually not exceeding 2 in. on a concave grating and 4 in. on a plane grating. Factors having to do with astigmatism make short rulings desirable in the case of a concave grating.

Most of the diffraction gratings used in small spectroscopes up to 1947 were not original gratings but were replicas made by a process devised by Thorp[3] and perfected by Wallace,[4] in which a thin film is formed when dissolved collodion or gelatin is poured on the surface of a grating. When this film hardens, it forms a cast of the rulings.

[3] T. Thorp, *Manchester Lit. and Phil. Soc. Mem.*, **44**, 1 (1900).
[4] R. J. Wallace, *Astrophys. Jour.*, **22**, 123 (1905).

The film is stripped off and is then carefully mounted on a plate of optical glass. Such a grating cannot be expected to show the full resolution of its parent but may give slightly greater dispersion as a result of shrinkage of the grating space. Its use is of course limited to the transmission region of glass.

In 1947 White and Frazer[5] of the Perkin-Elmer Corporation developed a process of making fairly good concave grating reflection replicas by casting a thin plastic model, fronted with an evaporated aluminum coating and backed with flexible plate glass, of a convex master grating ruled by R. W. Wood at Johns Hopkins. Although the replicas duplicated the master grating closely, the thinness of the flexible backing appeared to limit the resolution obtainable. It seems probable that improved replica gratings will soon become widely available.

The distribution of light among a number of grating orders naturally results in a loss of light in any one order. This loss can be reduced considerably by shaping the point of the ruling diamond so that more light will be thrown in one direction than in another. It is desirable, in any case, to have most of the light thrown into the orders on one side of the central image. When very high resolving power is desired, a grating can sometimes be found in which most of the energy is thrown into the higher orders. In general, if a grating shows high intensity in one order in a given direction, lines of all other orders lying in that same direction will tend to be strong. Thus a grating that is found to give high intensity on one side in the second-order green (5500 A) may be expected to be bright also in the infrared near 11,000 A in the first order and in the ultraviolet near 3660 A in the third order. This effect cannot always be counted on, however, since target pattern may change the distribution of light, as discussed in Chapter 4.

Before proceeding to the detailed comparison of prism and grating spectroscopes, it is convenient to consider other parts of the instruments that are essentially identical in the two cases.

2.6. The Slit. Since a spectrum line is merely a monochromatic image of the slit, the slit is one of the most important parts of a spectroscope. The accuracy with which it is made and can be adjusted governs the character of the spectrum lines produced. Therefore the slit may have an important effect on resolution.

---

[5] See R. W. Wood, *Jour. Opt. Soc. Am.*, **36**, 715 (1946).

The slit width should be variable and in fine instruments should be capable of adjustment between 1 mm and 0.005 mm.   The slit jaws are usually separated by a calibrated screw acting in opposition to a spring that tends to move them together.   A typical spectrograph slit is shown in Fig. 2.9.

Fig. 2.9.   Typical small-spectograph slit.   (Courtesy Jarrell-Ash Company, Boston.)

In order that the space between the jaws shall form a suitable line, it is necessary that the edges of the jaws be accurately ground to straightness and mounted truly parallel, and that the front faces of the jaws lie in the same plane.   The jaw edges are ordinarily beveled so that light reflected from them will not enter the spectroscope, and the beveled side is turned away from the entering beam.

Slits in which only one jaw is movable, the so-called unilateral type, are cheaper than the symmetrically opening type but have the disadvantage that the centers of spectrum lines produced with them move when the slit width is changed.   Although the bilateral slit is necessarily more complicated to construct, a number of very satisfactory forms have been devised.   A slit of this type is desirable on any good spectroscope. The best adjustable slits are made to close at the ends only, so that their sharp jaw edges will not be marred by careless closure. The jaws should be made of some hard and durable material, such as stellite or stainless steel, which can be ground to a sharp edge and polished.

A simple slit can be made by coating a plate of quartz or other transparent material with a thin opaque coating of metal or lacquer and by engraving lines of the desired width in this. Slits of several widths may thus be provided, the proper one being set into the slit holder as needed. For certain purposes such slits are more useful than the adjustable type, since a definite slit width can be reproduced more accurately than by setting a screw for which backlash and zero position may change.

The slit is usually mounted in a drawtube in such a way that it can be moved into or out of the spectroscope for focusing purposes and rotated about a horizontal axis so as to be brought accurately parallel to the edges of the dispersing element. Diaphragms should be provided with which the effective length of the slit or the portions of it through which light passes can be varied.

A slit that is almost closed may cause horizontal streaks to appear in the spectrum, because of dust particles which close the slit entirely

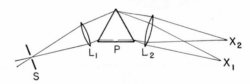

Fig. 2.10.   Simple spectroscope system. S, slit; L_1, collimator lens; P, prism; L_2, telescope lens; $X_1 - X_2$, spectrum.

at the spots where they occur. Any adjustable slit should occasionally be cleaned by opening it and carefully stroking its edges in one direction with a freshly sharpened stick of soft wood.

2.7. The Collimating and Focusing Systems. To give the greatest resolution, dispersing devices must be illuminated with a collimated beam of light, usually one in which the rays are parallel. The light that has passed through a slit is divergent. It may be made parallel by a positive lens called the collimating lens, shown as L_1 in Fig. 2.10. After passing through the dispersing system (prism P in Fig. 2.10) the beam must be brought to a focus to give sharply defined images of the slit. The lens that fulfills this function is called the *telescope lens*, *camera lens*, or *focusing lens*, depending on whether a visual spectroscope or spectrometer, a spectrograph, or a monochromator is involved. The functions of these lenses can, of course, be carried out by mirrors, which are sometimes used, especially in the infrared region. Lenses have the advantages over mirrors of giving greater light transmissivity at most wavelengths except the infrared, of fitting somewhat better into the geometry of the spectroscope, and of being easier to correct for certain aberrations.

In a good spectroscope, all lenses or mirrors are corrected for spherical aberration, and so as to focus the spectrum on a fairly flat focal surface. This surface is often curved to some extent, but the curvature is made as small and as even as possible. The focal surface in a prism spectrograph is sometimes sharply inclined to the light rays that strike it, being closer to the prism at short wavelengths, owing to the higher index of refraction of the lens material for these waves. This condition is not undesirable, since the increased apparent linear dispersion produced may in some cases be an advantage; spectrograph lenses are therefore usually left uncorrected for chromatic aberration.

2.8. Observing and Recording Systems. When the spectrum is to be examined by eye, an eyepiece is provided that magnifies by from 3 to 10 times the spectrum imaged by the telescope lens. This eyepiece, together with the telescope lens, forms a telescope for observing the beams of monochromatic light that leave the dispersing element. This telescope may be arranged to swing on an arm about the prism so that it can be pointed at the prism from different angles to observe the various parts of the spectrum. Alternatively, the telescope may be fixed in position and a special prism may be used which, when rotated, sends successive spectral regions into the eyepiece. The eyepiece is usually provided with a fine cross hair, or with an illuminated scale or pointer, to serve as a reference mark.

The collimating and telescope lenses of good visual spectroscopes are always corrected for chromatic aberration, to avoid the necessity of changing the focus of the eyepiece with wavelength.

In a spectrograph, no eyepiece is needed. Instead, provision is made for holding a photographic plate or film so that the spectrum is in focus on it throughout the range to be recorded at one time. One criterion by which a good spectrograph may be distinguished from a poor one is the ability to focus sharply, at one time, all the lines within the spectral range incident on the plate. The plateholder (see the following paragraph) should be such as to bend the plate to fit the focal curve exactly. It is desirable to keep this curvature as small as possible to avoid the necessity of using films or very thin glass plates. In some instruments there is so little curvature of the focal surface that the entire spectrum can be focused sharply on a flat plate.

The plate or film is held in a *plateholder* or *cassette*, which, if necessary, is provided with templates to bend the plate to the proper curvature. The plateholder is often provided with a dark slide that can be opened after the plateholder is in place, and closed when the plate is to be carried to the darkroom for development. The plateholder mounting usually has provision for moving the plateholder vertically, so that a number of different spectra can be photographed on the same plate.

Prism instruments are sometimes provided with wavelength scales, which can be impressed on the spectrogram by swinging the engraved transparent scale into position before the plate and making a brief exposure to a small incandescent lamp. These scales are apt to shift with use and can be relied on to a few angstroms only.

2.9. Comparison of Prism and Grating Spectrographs. Discussion of detailed designs of prism and grating spectrographs will be reserved for Chapters 3 and 4, but it is convenient now to compare the general characteristics of instruments of the two types. Most important, perhaps, is the range of spectrum covered. As mentioned previously, when a concave diffraction grating is used, only one spectrograph is required for working in the ultraviolet, visible, and near infrared regions of the spectrum. With a prism spectrograph, however, at least two sets of optical parts are required to cover these regions satisfactorily. Quartz prisms and lenses are ordinarily used for the ultraviolet region, glass for the visible, and rock salt, fluorite, lithium fluoride, or potassium bromide for the near infrared. Some prism spectroscopes are provided with interchangeable optical trains.

To compare the relative dispersions of prism and grating instruments, it is convenient to express the angular dispersion of a prism in terms of the number of lines per inch required on a grating of equivalent dispersion (and if of the same linear aperture, a grating having equivalent theoretical resolving power). Such data are given in Table 2.1, where the first column lists the types of prisms considered, the second column gives the wavelengths to which the data apply, and the third column shows the number of lines per inch in a grating having the same angular dispersion as the prism referred to. It is evident that a grating can be ruled which will give dispersion in any spectral region as great as that given by a standard prism. Since most gratings are ruled with from 15,000 to 30,000 lines per inch, Table 2.1 shows that practical gratings produce dispersions superior to those of single prisms for all wavelengths longer than about 2000 A, even in the first order.

TABLE 2.1

APPROXIMATE NUMBERS OF LINES PER INCH ON A CONCAVE GRATING
NEEDED TO MATCH DISPERSIONS OF 60-DEGREE PRISMS

Prism type	Wavelength, in angstroms	Angular dispersion	Linear dispersion with maximum plate tilt
Glass	8000	500	1500
	6000	1250	3500
	4000	5000	14,000
Quartz	4000	2000	6000
	3000	5000	15,000
	2000	30,000	90,000

It is much easier to obtain a diffraction grating having a ruled surface 6 in. wide than it is to obtain a transparent prism of equivalent aperture. Commonly used gratings have three times the linear aperture of the most commonly used prisms, so that the grating has, in general, a considerable advantage in resolving power.

In prism spectrographs, the plate is often tilted because of variation of the focal length of the camera lens with wavelength, and the linear dispersion along the plate is greater than the value obtained by multiplying the angular dispersion by the focal distance. With standard quartz spectrographs, the apparent magnification of dispersion which results may be as great as threefold, as shown in column 4 of Table 2.1. Even when this additional apparent dispersion of the prism spectrograph is taken into account, practical gratings give dispersions exceeding those of single prisms at all wavelengths longer than about 2500 A.

If we compare spectrographs having the same linear aperture and focal length, a 30,000-line-per-inch grating instrument will excel a glass-prism instrument in dispersion and resolving power at all wavelengths, and a quartz-prism instrument at all wavelengths longer than 2500 A, even in the first order. The second order of the grating is also available for the short wavelengths, giving double the dispersion and increased resolution.

That the various orders of a grating overlap is sometimes cited as a disadvantage of the grating spectrograph. Undesired orders can usually be removed, however, by filters or by crossing with another spectroscope, which may be one of low dispersion.

Figure 2.11 shows the distribution of wavelengths in typical spectrograms taken with prism and grating spectrographs that give

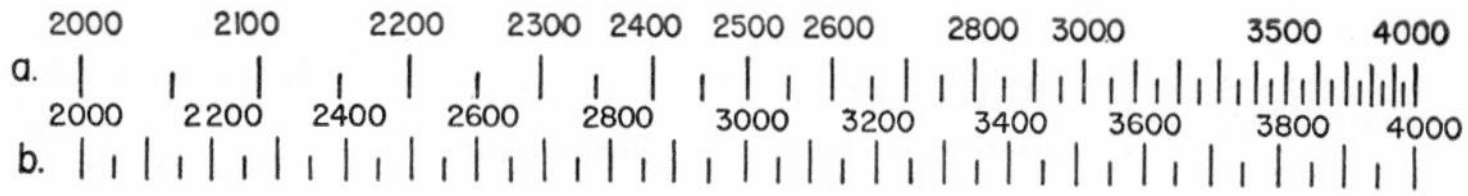

Fig. 2.11. Comparison of a prism scale, a, for a quartz prism, and a grating scale, b, for normal dispersion, in the case of two spectra of equal length from 2000 to 4000 A.

spectra of the same over-all length from 2000 to 4000 A. The crowding of the prism spectrum at long wavelengths is obvious. It should be emphasized, however, that this crowding is of importance only where wavelengths are being considered. In terms of frequencies or wave numbers, the prism scale is more uniform than that of the grating.

2.10. Speed and Efficiency. The principal purpose of a spectroscope is to separate light in accordance with its wavelengths. The greater the resolution of the instrument used, the greater the purity of the spectrum produced, other factors remaining constant. However, the purity of the spectrum depends also on the width of the slit used, the focal lengths of the collimating and camera lenses, and the freedom from scattered light and false lines.

The spectral purity of light that can be isolated by a slit of given width can be increased by increasing the focal length of the camera lens. This procedure will cut down the intensity of the spectrum, however. For a given prism or grating the intensity of light at a given position in the spectrum and the purity of the spectrum at that point can each be altered only at the expense of the other. The *efficiency* of a spectroscope is defined as the product of intensity times purity. A small prism instrument of high light-gathering power and low dispersion may be as efficient as a large concave-grating spectrograph of low light-gathering power and high dispersion.

The *speed* of a spectrograph is a measure of the intensity of the light it transmits at any wavelength. The speed at each wavelength varies directly with the transmission factor of the instrument and inversely with its aperture ratio, which is the ratio of the focal length of the spectrograph to its linear aperture. The aperture ratio is equivalent to the f number as used with ordinary camera lenses. Aperture ratios of prism spectrographs usually lie between 7 and 15, whereas large quartz Littrow instruments usually have an aperture ratio of about 23. A standard 21-ft concave-grating spectrograph ordinarily has an aperture ratio of 42 horizontally and 120 vertically.

Concave gratings are ordinarily not used at high-aperture ratios because the greater the curvature of a grating blank, the more difficult is it to rule, since the ruling diamond will cut on different portions of its edge at different stages of the stroke. The aperture ratio of a given grating can be doubled by using the stigmatic mounting discussed in § 4.7, which cuts the effective focal distance of the grating in half, making readily available a horizontal aperture ratio of 21.

The diffraction grating has a fundamental advantage over the prism in separating energy in accordance with wavelength. This advantage was at one time offset more often than not by the low transmission factor resulting from the low reflecting power of grating-mirror materials, which resulted in greater loss of light than that caused by the absorption and reflections in prism instruments. Since the introduction of gratings ruled on aluminum-covered glass surfaces, grating spectrographs have been made with transmission factors larger than those of prism instruments equivalent in size and in purity of spectrum. Grating spectrographs have the reputation of low light transmission because in the past they were ruled on speculum metal, which has a reflecting power of 10 per cent or less for wavelengths in the far ultraviolet. Aluminum-on-glass gratings having reflection factors of 65 per cent even in the ultraviolet are not uncommon today.

Formerly, another limitation of the grating was its waste of light, since as much as 50 per cent of the light sometimes went into the undispersed central image and 60 per cent of the remainder into orders not being used. This effect has been overcome by selection of diamond points so shaped that they engrave rulings which throw much of the light in one general direction. An aluminum-on-glass grating ruled by R. W. Wood [6] has been found by measurement to throw 80 per cent of its reflected green light into one first order. This directional effect, coupled with an 80 per cent reflection coefficient for the grating material, results in the appearance in one first order of more than half of the green light sent into the instrument. Such a transmission factor is somewhat greater than that of most prism spectrographs, where the presence of from 6 to 14 quartz-to-air or glass-to-air surfaces results in large losses by reflection and scattering. Prism spectroscopes have seldom been found to transmit more than 30 per cent of the light sent into them when their transmission factors have been measured precisely.

2.11. Scattered Light and False Lines. Most concave-grating spectrographs using original ruled gratings, as opposed to replicas, show less scattered light than prism instruments, because of the smaller number of optical surfaces they contain. Usually the light scattered from a grating ruled on an aluminum surface is far less than that from a speculum metal grating, because of the grainy character of the latter. Coating a speculum-metal grating with aluminum will increase its reflecting power and hence its speed, but this is of little aid in reducing scattered light, since the latter is increased in intensity proportionately to the increase in intensity of the spectrum.

All gratings show false lines of a type known as *ghosts*.[7] Rowland ghosts are produced by periodic errors in the screw that moves the diamond forward a definite amount between strokes while the grating is being ruled. These ghosts, though annoying if intense, cause much less trouble than the so-called Lyman ghosts, which are produced by a different type of irregularity in the drive of the ruling engine. Lyman ghosts are usually widely separated from their parent lines. Thus a line of wavelength λ may be found to have Lyman ghosts at positions corresponding to λ/a, $2\lambda/a$, $3\lambda/a$, ... $n\lambda/a$, where a is an integer. Although these ghosts have the color of the parent line and so can often be distinguished visually, in spectrographs they may cause great confusion and have led to many errors in the past. Fortunately, Lyman ghosts are seldom strongly present in gratings ruled on modern engines. A grating that shows them in intensity greater than about 0.01 per cent of that of the parent line should be considered

---

[6] R. W. Wood, *Jour. Opt. Soc. Am.*, **34**, 509 (1944).

[7] See W. F. Meggers, C. C. Kiess, C. Runge, and J. A. Anderson, *Jour. Opt. Soc. Am.*, **6**, 417 (1922).

as unsuitable for ordinary work.   The presence of Lyman ghosts can readily be detected by methods described in § 5.3 and in Reference 7.

Rowland ghosts, if present, are easy to detect.   Usually two or more pairs of equally intense ghosts will be found symmetrically placed about every very strong line, as shown in Fig. 2.12.   The user, once familiar with a given grating, has no difficulty in identifying Rowland ghosts or in knowing when their presence can be neglected.   In a good grating such ghosts will have intensity less than 0.1 per cent of the parent line and can usually be neglected entirely.

2.12.   Shapes of Spectrum Lines.   The lines produced in a prism spectrograph are not straight but are curved as a result of the increased deviation of rays that pass through the prism obliquely.   This curvature sets a limit to the length of slit that can be used with a given collimator lens.

Fig. 2.12. Photo-graph of Rowland ghosts of a diffraction grating (mercury line at 5461 A).

Gratings produce very straight spectrum lines and give fairly uniform magnification of the slit images, an important consideration in many types of photographic photometry, including those using logarithmic spiral disks or step sectors.

The contour of a spectrum line is likely to be of the form shown in Fig. 2.13a.   A prism spectrogram or one from a good grating will usually show smooth and symmetrical line contours, but in imperfect gratings the lines are apt to appear irregular or asymmetrical, as shown in Fig. 2.13b.   This effect is usually apparent only in gratings of high dispersion and resolving power.   It will be discussed further in §§ 9.12 and 20.4.

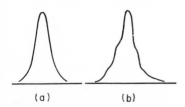

(a)   (b)

Fig. 2.13.   Contours of spectrum lines.   (a) Regular contour, as produced by a good grating or prism; (b) irregular contour, as produced by a defective grating.

2.13.   Astigmatism.   A lens or mirror, unless anastigmatically designed, produces a true image of an object only when both lie close to the optic axis.   As the angle of a beam of light departs from the optic axis more and more, greater amounts of astigmatism are introduced, the rays being brought to a line focus at one distance and to a second line focus perpendicular to the first at a greater distance, as shown in Fig. 2.14.   In ordinary prism spectrographs, most of the rays passing through the camera lens deviate very little from the optic axis, and the astigmatism can usually be neglected, since extremely fine focus is needed only in the horizontal direction to resolve close spectrum lines, and a

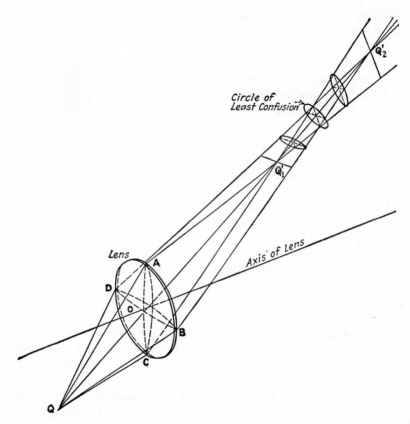

Fig. 2.14. **Astigmatism produced by a lens.** Off-axis rays from the point Q come to focus in two line images, Q_1' and Q_2'. The position of minimum beam cross section is called the *circle of least confusion*. (From A. C. Hardy and F. H. Perrin, *Principles of Optics*, McGraw-Hill Book Company, Inc., New York (1932), page 100. Courtesy authors and publishers.)

focus only one-tenth as sharp will serve in the vertical direction. Also, the camera lens can be figured so as to reduce astigmatism.

The spectrum lines produced by a concave diffraction grating, as ordinarily used, are astigmatic images of the slit, each illuminated point on the slit being imaged as a vertical line in the spectrum rather than as a point. No decrease in the purity of the spectrum results so long as the slit is accurately parallel to the rulings of the grating and neither the slit nor the astigmatic images are curved. With most gratings a very slight line curvature does exist, and it is advisable to keep the illuminated portion of the slit or grating as short as possible in the vertical plane when high resolving power is required.

Since each astigmatic line image is longer than the slit that produced it, astigmatism may result in a decrease of speed, which becomes very serious at large angles of incidence and reflection. In the high orders of a grating, astigmatism may produce a twentyfold decrease in intensity when a short slit is used, as discussed in § 4.9.

A more important disadvantage of astigmatism is that the long, even spectrum lines produced by an astigmatic spectrograph mask the variation of illumination along the slit, which might otherwise reveal important information about the source of light being studied. A prism or a diaphragm for producing comparison spectra cannot be placed at the slit of such an instrument, nor can rotating photometric disks be used at the slit, as they can with a stigmatic instrument, unless special compensation is introduced.

Astigmatism is occasionally useful, as with certain types of intensity measurements, and for producing spectrograms that are neat in appearance. The astigmatism of concave gratings and methods for overcoming this, some of which are applicable to all astigmatic spectrographs, are further discussed in § 4.9.

2.14. Space Requirements. A grating spectrograph requires no more space than an equivalent prism spectrograph. Many grating installations are large because bulk can be tolerated and much can be accomplished with the increased dispersion and range thus made available. Prism instruments are not made large principally because large prisms are very expensive and are apt to absorb much light at short wavelengths, and because of optical limitations on the lenses used. The standard 6-in. grating usually has a 21-ft focal length. This focal distance results in a large spectrograph. If the size must be held to that of a standard Littrow prism spectrograph, a smaller grating can be used and the instrument will then occupy no more space than the equivalent prism instrument. Various designs of prism instruments are discussed in Chapter 3, and in Chapter 4 the different mountings in which concave gratings have been used are described in detail.

A diffraction grating can be arranged to give at high dispersion with a single setting that part of the spectrum most commonly photographed, from 2000 to 5000 A. When one uses the stigmatic mounting discussed in Chapter 4, it is often convenient to cover 2500 to 5000 A in the first order, with 2000 to 2500 A overlapping in the second order. This overlapping ordinarily causes little inconvenience when line emission spectra are involved. Three 10-in. plates placed end to end can be used to cover this range with a dispersion corresponding to 3.3 A/mm, which is sufficient for much routine work. Photographing 30 in. of spectrum at one time requires that the spectrograph be somewhat wider than the standard prism instrument. In the prism spectrograph these three ranges would be photographed separately, one after the other, adjustments of the prism, plate, and optical system being required between exposures. When space is more important than time, a narrow mounting can be used for the grating spectrograph, enabling a single plate to be used with adjustments similar to those required by the prism instrument.

2.15. Summary of Comparison. The results of the foregoing discussion are summed up in Table 2.2 where + indicates that the device so marked is superior to the other in the quality indicated.

TABLE 2.2

SUMMARY OF COMPARISON BETWEEN PRISM AND GRATING SPECTROGRAPHS

Characteristics	Prism instruments	Grating instruments
Spectral range		+
Linear aperture		+
Resolving power		+
Relative dispersion		·+
Uniformity of dispersion:		
By wavelength		+
By frequency	+	
Speed	+	
Freedom from:		
Astigmatism	+	
Stray light		+
Spurious lines	+	
Line curvature		+

In the past, grating spectrographs have been used less often than prism spectrographs for a very simple reason: the difficulty of constructing and operating satisfactory ruling engines. A second problem to be solved has been a metallurgical one : to obtain a metal hard enough to be figured accurately and polished like glass and soft enough to avoid wearing out the ruling diamond too rapidly. A practical solution has been to figure a glass mirror and to evaporate on this a coating of chromium, and then on this a coating of aluminum. The ruling is then done on the soft aluminum surface, which gradually protects itself with a thin transparent film of oxide, leaving a surface that reflects quite well all wavelengths between 1000 and 10,000 A. Such gratings are not so sturdy as prisms but last well under proper care.

Original diffraction gratings cost from $200 to $1500 apiece, although the price varies greatly with the source of supply, and the size; replicas are somewhat cheaper. A quartz prism costs about the same per unit area of aperture, and a glass prism somewhat, though not much, less. Since both quartz and glass prisms must be provided to give the desirable spectrum coverage, to say nothing of the auxiliary lenses and prisms that are required, it is justifiable to conclude that a grating spectrograph is fundamentally a less expensive piece of apparatus to build than a prism spectrograph. A concave grating costing $800 can be made to do the work of a quartz prism costing $10,000, if mere size is a criterion. Gratings seem destined to come into much wider use as their availability increases.

A partial list of manufacturers of spectroscopic equipment is given at the end of this chapter. Most of the firms listed are glad to furnish material giving detailed descriptions of their apparatus, and are usually willing to supply sample spectrograms. The most widely used types of prism spectrographs are described in the next chapter, and grating instruments are discussed in Chapter 4.

2.16. Monochromatic Illuminators. Isolation of a comparatively narrow band of spectral wavelengths can be produced by means of absorption filters, refraction filters, interference filters, or especially adapted spectroscopes called *monochromators*. The various types of filters are described in Chapter 14. Monochromators may be of special design, to give convenience in changing the wavelength of the isolated beam or extreme freedom from scattered light, or may consist merely of spectroscopes in which an exit slit has been provided in place of a viewing eyepiece. The most satisfactory monochromators are those designed with fixed entrance and exit slits, so that the emergent beam has a fixed direction no matter what its wavelength. Prism monochromators are described in Chapter 3 and those using gratings in Chapter 4. Almost all spectrometers for use in the infrared region are monochromators of types described in detail in Chapter 17.

REPRESENTATIVE MANUFACTURERS OF SPECTROSCOPIC EQUIPMENT

The specialties listed for each manufacturer are intended to be indicative only, and do not imply that products are limited to those mentioned.

Applied Research Laboratories, Glendale, Calif. (grating spectrographs and equipment).

Applied Physics Corporation, Pasadena, Calif. (automatic recording spectrophotometers).

Baird Associates, Cambridge, Mass. (grating spectrographs, infrared equipment).

Bausch & Lomb Optical Company, Rochester, N. Y. (prism apparatus).

Ch. Beaudoin, Paris (prism apparatus).

R. and J. Beck, Ltd., London (small prism apparatus). Agents in U.S.A.: Jarrell-Ash Company, Boston, and Pfaltz and Bauer, Inc., New York.

Bellingham and Stanley, Ltd., London (prism apparatus).

Central Scientific Company, Chicago (small grating and prism apparatus).

Gaertner Scientific Corporation, Chicago (prism spectroscopic instruments).

General Electric Company, Schenectady, N. Y. (recording spectrophotometers for the visible region).

Hilger and Watts, Ltd. (formerly Adam Hilger, Ltd.), London (spectroscopic equipment of all types). Agents in U.S.A.: Jarrell-Ash Company, Boston.

Huet (Société Générale d'Optique), Paris (prism apparatus).

Jarrell-Ash Company, Boston (grating spectrographs, dealers in and importers of spectroscopic equipment of all types).

Kipp and Zonen, Delft, Holland (prism apparatus and equipment). Agents in U.S.A.: James G. Biddle Co., Philadelphia.

Lane-Wells Company, Pasadena, Calif. (Prism Spectrographs for Raman effect).

National Technical Laboratories, South Pasadena, Calif. (spectrophotometers, infrared equipment, flame photometers).

Perkin-Elmer Corporation, Glenbrook, Conn. (infrared equipment, flame photometers).

CHAPTER 3

Prism Spectroscopes and Spectrographs

Representative models of prism spectroscopes will be described
in this chapter, to illustrate the forms commonly used. Where apparatus of a particular maker is depicted, the basis of selection is to
some extent arbitrary, since equally good instruments of a similar type
are often obtainable from other manufacturers.

3.1. **Materials for Dispersive Prisms.** The chart in Fig. 3.1
shows the relative dispersive powers and ranges of transmission of

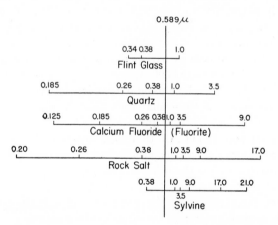

Fig. 3.1. Useful regions of transmission and relative spectral dispersions of
several materials employed for prisms, on wavelength scales centered on
λ5896 A.

several optical materials found useful in the various regions of the
spectrum commonly studied. Optical glasses, on account of their
narrow transmission ranges, can be used for prisms only in the visible
region, the near infrared, and the near ultraviolet. Since most glasses
produce greater dispersion in these regions than do other optical
materials, glasses are commonly used in visual spectroscopes. The

51

various kinds of optical glass differ greatly in dispersion, in refractive index in a given wavelength region, and in permanence of surface. Flint glasses are likely to be transparent at longer wavelengths than are crown glasses. Special glasses such as Uviol and Corex transmit somewhat farther into the ultraviolet than do ordinary glasses.

Quartz in the crystalline form found in nature, as distinct from so-called fused quartz, is doubly refracting. If a prism is cut from a quartz crystal, its optic axis should be made to coincide with the optic axis of the crystal, to avoid doubling of the spectrum. Even when this condition is fulfilled, a slight doubling of the spectrum lines results from the circular polarization produced by the quartz. This defect can be eliminated by a method devised by Cornu, in which half of the prism is cut from a crystal producing right-handed rotation and half from a crystal producing left-handed rotation. Fused or vitreous quartz does not produce birefringence or circular polarization, but it has less dispersive power than crystalline quartz, absorbs wavelengths shorter than 2800 A more strongly, and is seldom produced in sufficient homogeneity to give high optical quality. Even natural quartz crystals vary somewhat in transmission from sample to sample, especially for wavelengths shorter than 2500 A. Manufacturers will, on occasion, furnish optical parts especially selected for high transparency in the region near 2000 A.

Because rock salt and potassium bromide are very hygroscopic, optical parts made of these materials must be carefully protected from moisture. Despite this limitation, rock salt is so transparent between 1800 and 160,000 A that it is occasionally used in commercial spectrographs for the visible and ultraviolet. It is widely used in instruments for the infrared and will be discussed further in this connection in Chapter 17. Sylvine (KCl) and potassium bromide extend even farther into the infrared than rock salt (to 230,000 and 270,000 A, respectively), and are often used for prisms.

Fluorite (calcium fluoride) held for many years the unique position of being the only material suitable for optical parts transparent to wavelengths as short as 1250 A, but pieces larger than an inch in diameter were prohibitive in cost. During World War II, considerable progress was made in growing large crystals of this material [1] and of lithium fluoride, which is transparent to about 1050 A.[2] The latter material has the disadvantage of being brittle and difficult to work

---

[1] D. C. Stockbarger, *O.S.R.D. Report No.* 4690.
[2] D. C. Stockbarger, *Rev. Sci. Inst.*, **7**, 133 (1936).

without cleaving, and it is fortunate that synthetic calcium fluoride crystals[3] have become obtainable in diameters as large as may be desired for spectroscopic equipment.

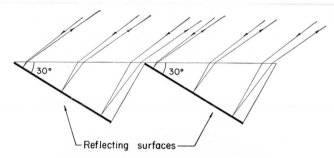

Fig. 3.2.   Multiple prism of the Littrow type.

Prisms of extreme size are sometimes needed, not so much for the increased resolving power given by greater base thickness as for the larger prism aperture, which will transmit more radiant flux.   In very large prisms this advantage may be offset by increased transmission

Fig. 3.3.   Divided-circle spectrometer with prism removed.   (Courtesy Gaertner Scientific Corp., Chicago.)

losses through absorption and scattering in the thicker material.   It may then be desirable to use instead a multiple prism of lower resolving power, as shown in Fig. 3.2.

[3] From the Harshaw Chemical Co., East 97th Street, Cleveland 6, Ohio.

Numerous special types of dispersing prisms have been designed. Most of these are not in common use; certain especially useful forms are described below in connection with spectroscopes designed around them.

3.2. The Simple Spectrometer. A type of prism spectrometer extensively used in teaching and research laboratories is illustrated in Fig. 3.3. The slit is affixed to the collimator tube in such a manner as to slide in and out for focusing adjustment, and the glass collimator' lens is rigidly mounted at the end of this tube. The prism is mounted on a table that rotates about a vertical axis, and the telescope tube

Fig. 3.4. Spekker Steeloscope, a two-prism spectroscope for analysis of ferrous alloys by visual observation of spectra. (Courtesy Adam Hilger, Ltd., London.)

rotates about the same axis, carrying an objective lens and an eye-piece. Graduated circles with vernier scales are provided to read the angles through which the prism and the telescope arm are turned. Such spectrometers are used extensively for instructional purposes, for measuring the indices of refraction of various solid materials in prism form, for testing prisms, and for observing simple spectra.

A small transmission grating can be used in place of the prism in such a spectrometer. It is then desirable that ample swing be provided for the telescope tube, to permit observation of orders on both sides of the normal.

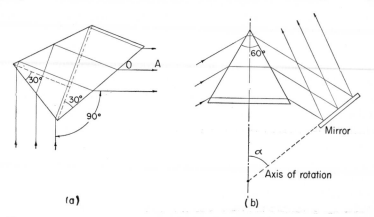

Fig. 3.5. Arrangements to obtain constant deviation for rays traversing the prism at minimum deviation. (a) Pellin-Broca prism for 90-deg. deviation. (b) Wadsworth mounting, with which the over-all deviation depends upon the angle α.

For routine examination of selected spectra, prism spectrometers can be obtained in which collimator tube, prism, and telescope tube are all fixed in position, as in Fig. 3.4, where the Hilger Spekker Steeloscope is depicted. These spectrometers are usually provided with scales on which the positions of important lines are marked. If the prism and the lenses of such an instrument are made of quartz, a

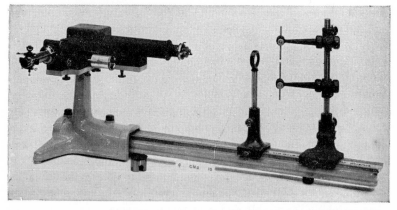

Fig. 3.6. Constant-deviation wavelength spectrometer mounted with source on optical bench. (Courtesy Adam Hilger, Ltd., London.)

fluorescent eyepiece can be used which may make possible observation of ultraviolet lines as far down as 1850 A.

3.3. Modern Wavelength Spectrometers. A very convenient type of spectrometer is one using the constant-deviation prism of Abbe[4] as modified by Pellin-Broca.[5]   As shown by the dotted lines in Fig. 3.5a, the single prism of peculiar shape is equivalent to two 30-deg dispersing prisms connected by a 45-deg total reflecting prism. When one wishes to scan the spectrum, the prism is rotated, and various wavelengths are sent successively in the direction OA at right angles to the incoming rays of light.   All lenses are corrected for chromatic aberration, to avoid the necessity of refocusing for each wavelength.   A calibrated drum is provided from which wavelengths can be read directly to within a few angstroms (Fig. 3.6).

The resolving power of this type of constant-deviation spectroscope as manufactured by Gaertner, Hilger, and others is usually less than

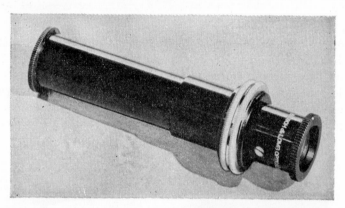

Fig. 3.7. Direct-vision spectroscope employing an Amici prism (two prisms of crown glass and one of flint glass). (Courtesy Bausch & Lomb Optical Company, Rochester, N. Y.)

5000.   An eyepiece provided with a pointer can be obtained.   By means of a small mirror this pointer can be illuminated from the source through screens of various colors, so that a color that contrasts with any part of the spectrum can be chosen.   Small cameras can also be obtained which, when fastened in place after removal of the observing telescope, transform the instrument into a spectrograph for photographing the visible region at low dispersion.

[4] E. Abbe, *Jena Zeitschr. f. Med. u. Naturwiss.*, **5**, 459 (1870).

[5] P. Pellin and A. Broca, *Jour. de Phys.*, **8**, 314 (1899).

3.4. Direct-Vision Spectroscopes. The simplest type of spectroscope, and one that can be made small enough to carry in the pocket, is a small replica diffraction grating, mounted in a flat container that has a hole passing through it. If a source of small extent is looked at through this device, spectra in various orders will be visible; and if the source is very small, monochromatic images will be seen.

A somewhat more elegant device is the direct-vision spectroscope which makes use of a nondeviating prism. A Bausch & Lomb model of this instrument is illustrated in Fig. 3.7. The dispersing system

Fig. 3.8.   Zeiss three-prism spectrograph, with cover removed.

consists of several prisms alternately of dense flint and crown glass, so arranged that the mean deviation of the light beam by one set of prisms is neutralized by that of the other set, while a certain amount of dispersion remains. This prism is mounted in a convenient tube with an adjustable slit and a magnifying eyepiece. A well-constructed instrument of this type will resolve many of the Fraunhofer lines in the solar spectrum.

3.5. Portable Spectrographs. A spectrograph is a spectroscope provided with a camera. This camera usually consists of a pair of ways on which slides a cassette or plateholder. The latter holds the photographic plate or film and can be moved up and down in order to photograph a number of spectra on the same spectrogram.

In a small spectrograph the entire transmitted spectrum can usually be photographed at a single setting, so that no motion of the prism or varying focusing adjustment is necessary. In larger instruments, where the spectrum cannot be recorded on a plate of reasonable size, some provision must be made for turning the prism and changing the focal distance of the lenses and the tilt of the plate when various regions of the spectrum are to be photographed.

Fig. 3.9.   Small quartz spectrograph with source mounted on optical bench.
(Courtesy Adam Hilger, Ltd., London.)

3.6.   Special Glass-Prism Spectrographs. For many years Zeiss manufactured a three-prism spectrograph having the optical system illustrated in Fig. 3.8. The prism train is that designed by Försterling, which gives constant deviation with dispersion equivalent to that of three 60-deg prisms. All three prisms are arranged on a mounting that turns about an axis, above which the central constant-deviation prism is placed. The other prisms are kept at minimum deviation by steel bands which communicate to their mountings the proper rotations as the wavelength drum is turned.

The instrument covers the range 3700 to 10,000 A and is provided with three interchangeable cameras having 6-cm-diameter lenses of 85, 27, and 11 cm focus, respectively.   A collimating lens of 30 cm focus and 6 cm diameter is used.   With the long camera the plate factors are 58, 27, and 6 A/mm at 8000, 6000, and 4000 A, respectively. The cameras of shorter focal length give proportionately smaller dispersions but concentrate the same amount of light into smaller and hence brighter spectra.   Four sets of adjustments of the optical parts are needed to photograph the whole visible spectrum with the long camera, whereas with the others single settings suffice.   The long camera takes plates of 4.5 × 12 cm; those of the shorter cameras are 6 × 9 cm.

Fig. 3.10.   Medium quartz spectrograph.   (Courtesy Bausch & Lomb Optical Company, Rochester, N. Y.)

Hilger manufactures a large-aperture glass spectrograph in which two dense 55-deg prisms are used.   The camera objective is 3.5 in. in diameter and is used at $f/5.7$.   The spectrum from 8000 to 3500 A is 4 in. long and is photographed on a $3\frac{1}{4}$- × $4\frac{1}{2}$-in. plate.

3.7. Quartz-Prism Spectrographs.   Spectrographs containing quartz optical parts are widely used.   These can be obtained in three standard sizes, the small and medium models covering the entire spectral range with a single setting of the focusing adjustments.

A small spectrograph covering the range 8000 to 1850 A, with a spectrum length of about 85 mm, as manufactured by Hilger, Stein-heil, Gaertner, and others, is illustrated in Fig. 3.9, where the Hilger model is depicted. This type finds its greatest usefulness at wavelengths shorter than 2500 A, where its relatively high light transmission aids in photography of a region somewhat difficult to record, since prism absorption and lack of plate sensitivity in this region conspire to reduce the density of spectrograms. The spectrograph can be obtained fitted with a transparent wavelength scale. A fluorescent screen can be used to make the ultraviolet spectrum visible and thus aid in the preliminary focusing adjustments.

Probably the most commonly used of all spectrographs are the medium-sized quartz instruments, types of which are manufactured by several firms. The Bausch & Lomb instrument is shown in

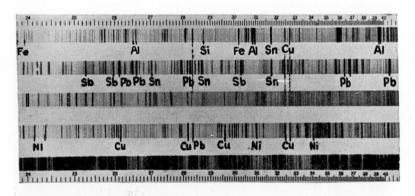

Fig. 3.11.   Spectra and wavelength scale taken with medium quartz spectrograph of the type illustrated in Fig. 3.10.   (Courtesy Bausch & Lomb Optical Company, Rochester, N. Y.)

Fig. 3.10.   Lenses of 600 mm focus and 51 mm diameter are used, giving a spectrum extending from 2100 to 8000 A which is about 200 mm long. The prism, of the Cornu type, is 41 mm high by 65 mm length of face. A standard 4- × 10-in. photographic plate is used. This is the largest standard size of quartz instrument that will give the entire ultraviolet region in air at a single setting of the prism and camera.

The medium quartz spectrograph can be obtained with or without a transparent scale of wavelengths or frequencies. The variation of dispersion with wavelength is illustrated by the scale shown in Fig. 3.11. When such a scale is purchased, care should be taken to see that each division is properly spaced, because some manufacturers have used a uniform and hence incorrect spacing between correctly spaced 100-A divisions.

Hilger also manufactures a spectrograph of this type which extends to 1850 A the range of the spectrum covered. In this case the quartz optical system gives the range 3700 to 1850 A in a spectrum 225 mm long, whereas when the spectrum is photographed with a corresponding glass system it extends from beyond the red end of the visible to 3650 A. The quartz instrument is rather unusual in that the camera lens produces an image field in which the residual curvature is reduced to a fraction of a millimeter, so that ordinary thick and rigid photographic plates can be used if desired.

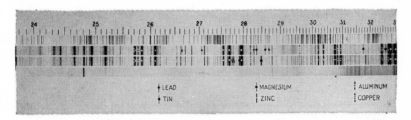

Fig. 3.12.   Spectrograms of two die-casting alloys taken with the quartz spectrograph illustrated in Fig. 3.10.   (Courtesy Bausch & Lomb Optical Company, Rochester, N. Y.)

Typical spectrograms taken with the instrument depicted in Fig. 3.10 are shown in Figs. 3.11 and 3.12. The aperture of the spectrograph is $f/12$, which is sufficient to give satisfactory exposures in a few seconds with most ordinary arc and spark sources. The resolution and dispersion in the ultraviolet are ample for use with simple emission spectra and for absorption spectroscopy of solutions.

In purchasing any single-setting instrument, care should be taken to see that the manufacturer has mounted prisms and lenses with such rigidity that they will not readily get out of focus when once adjusted, and that the plateholder, if of wood, is constructed so that it will not warp. The slit should be of high quality, since very fine lines can be obtained with the resolving power available. It is of advantage to use 4- × 10-in. plates when possible, since this size is readily obtainable in almost all emulsions. Manufacturers should be asked to submit sample spectrograms taken on the instrument to be purchased.

In cases where higher dispersion is needed than is available from the medium quartz instrument, recourse is usually had to the Littrow type of mounting, in order to save space and improve rigidity.

Some types of quartz spectrographs can be obtained with auxiliary glass optical parts, which render them more suitable for use in the visible. Though quartz is also transparent in this region, its dispersion is so low that quartz spectrographs are not especially useful at wavelengths longer than about 5200 A, where the ordinary photographic plate becomes insensitive, and special plates must be used in any case.

3.8. The Littrow Mounting. The device of autocollimation developed by Littrow is widely used with both prisms and plane gratings in spectrographs designed to give high linear dispersion with a camera lens of long focus. The principle of the method is illustrated in

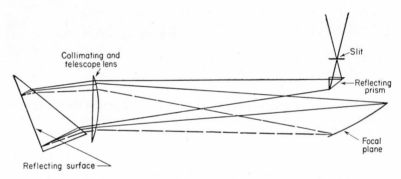

Fig. 3.13. **Diagram of the optical system of a Littrow spectrograph.**
The lens has been reversed to reduce scattered light.

Fig. 3.13. The beam of radiation diverging from the slit is made parallel by the collimator lens and enters the dispersing system, which in this case is a 30-deg prism mirror-coated on its back face. The radiation is reflected from this, passes back through the prism, and retraverses the collimator, which behaves now as a camera lens and brings the spectrum to a focus. Special advantages accrue when quartz is used, for the passage through the 30-deg prism in the reverse direction compensates for any optical rotation produced in the initial passage, and crystalline quartz of a single type will suffice.

Two inherent defects keep the Littrow mounting from replacing other types of prism mounting to the extent that its simplicity and rigidity would lead one to expect. The proximity of slit and plateholder requires the introduction of a reflecting prism or other device to separate the incoming and outgoing beams, and the reflection and scattering of light from the front face of the collimator directly back to the photographic plate is liable to cause objectionable fogging that is hard to eliminate. This false light can often be thrown off the plate by tipping the lens slightly, thus introducing a certain amount of astigmatism, or much of it can be trapped by introducing stops and diaphragms at strategic points. In any event the inside of the case surrounding a Littrow mount should be thoroughly blackened, and numerous baffles should be used to cut down stray light.

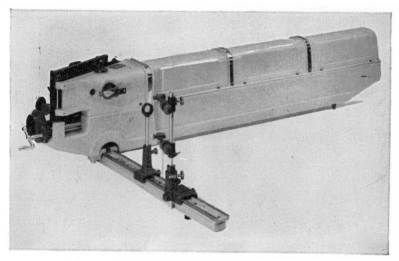

Fig. 3.14.   Large quartz spectrograph of the Littrow type.
(Courtesy Adam Hilger, Ltd., London.)

A widely used type of Littrow instrument having quartz optical parts, made by several manufacturers, is shown in Fig. 3.14, where the Hilger E492 model is illustrated. The lens and prism system of a corresponding model by Bausch & Lomb is shown in Fig. 3.15. The length of the case is slightly more than 6 ft, but since the optical system may be considered as having been folded together in the middle by use of the autocollimation principle, the dispersion is equivalent to that of an instrument of the ordinary type almost twice as long.

The quartz prism and lens are mounted on a carriage that moves along a slide, their position on this being determined by means of a scale and index.   The prism can be rotated to throw various regions of the spectrum on the 4- × 10-in. plate.   The plateholder can be rotated to bring it into coincidence with the focal curve for any spectral region between 2000 and 8000 A.   In the model illustrated, all necessary adjustments for any spectral region can be carried out from the operator's position at the slit end of the instrument.

Spectrographs of this type are found highly satisfactory in analytical work for which the dispersion of the medium-size quartz spectrograph is not sufficiently great.   In the region 2500 to 2000 A, the linear

Fig. 3.15.   Lens and prism system of large Littrow quartz spectrograph.
(Courtesy Bausch & Lomb Optical Company, Rochester, N. Y.)

dispersion given by a large Littrow instrument is as great as that of a large concave-grating spectrograph (see Table 2.1).

Glass optical parts can be obtained to fit the standard large Littrow spectrographs.   With glass parts in the Hilger model the spectrum from 9000 to 4000 A is about 34 cm long, and can be photographed in two settings on 4- × 10-in. plates.

Hilger manufactures a very large glass-prism Littrow spectrograph, working at aperture $f/7$, which contains one 60-deg and one 30-deg prism.   These prisms are 6 in. on a side and 4.6 in. high.   A 5-in.-diameter camera objective is used, the spectrum from 3850 to 8000 A being 9 in. long so that it can be photographed in one exposure on a 4- × 10-in. plate.   The lens has been figured to reduce astigmatism to a negligible amount over a 10-in. region. In order to retain the advantages of glass and yet to extend to shorter wavelengths the range of the spectrum covered, ultraviolet transmitting glass is sometimes used in this model, extending its transparency to 2900 A. This type of glass is especially useful in astronomical work, where the atmosphere absorbs wavelengths shorter than 2900 A. A glass that will transmit down to this limit is as satisfactory as the more expensive quartz and is more dispersive in this region.

A small Littrow spectrograph has been developed by Bausch & Lomb to obtain moderate dispersion in the ultraviolet at relatively low cost. This instrument has an optical system of crystalline quartz and covers the range 2100 to 7000 A, giving a 150-mm spectrum on a 5- × 7-in. plate.   Four standard fixed slits are provided, ranging from 0.002 to 0.02 mm width, each cut on a protected metallic coating deposited on a single quartz slide. The manufacturers point out

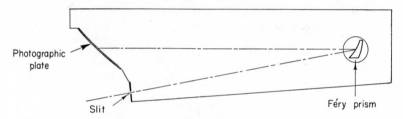

Fig. 3.16.   Diagram of Féry spectrograph.

that this type of slit, though inexpensive, has the advantage of mechanical stability, parallelism of edges, and ease of cleaning, since the exposed quartz side can be readily wiped with a cloth.

Other applications of the Littrow mounting are described in § 3.11, where certain instruments having interchangeable optical parts are discussed.

3.9. The Féry Spectrograph. An ingenious application of the autocollimation principle was made by Féry, who designed a single quartz optical unit that combines the properties of prism, mirror, and lenses. The front face of the prism is usually a cylindrical surface with axis vertical, so figured that diverging rays from the slit all strike it at the proper angle for minimum deviation. The rear surface, also a vertical cylinder, is backed by a metallic coating chosen to give high reflection in the ultraviolet. The spectrum is brought into horizontal focus on a surface of fairly great curvature, as shown in Fig. 3.16.

The Féry spectrograph presents its greatest advantage in the far ultraviolet, where loss of light is minimized by the small number of air-quartz surfaces and the small thickness of optical material used. These virtues are to some extent offset by the high degree of astigmatism involved, since the light is not focused at all in the vertical direction. Each point on the slit is spread out in the spectrum into a line 2 in. or more in height. No provision need be made for moving the plateholder up and down, since various spectrograms can be taken

Fig. 3.17.   Large two-lens quartz spectrograph.   (Courtesy Gaertner Scientific Corp., Chicago.)

by means of a diaphragm that moves vertically in front of the plate, covering all of each spectrum line except a region of the desired height. The astigmatism produces very straight and even lines, so that Féry spectrograms are usually of excellent appearance. The instrument is compact and readily portable.

3.10.   The Gaertner Large Quartz Spectrograph.   Gaertner has introduced a large quartz-prism spectrograph designed to eliminate the disadvantages of the Littrow mounting while retaining its compactness. In this instrument no attempt is made to use a single lens for both collimating and camera lenses, but the length of the instrument is cut in half by the introduction of a large first-surface mirror. In addition, the right-angle prism just behind the slit has been eliminated. In this way it has been found possible to reduce greatly the scattered and stray light customarily found with the Littrow mounting.

A view of the instrument is shown in Fig. 3.17, and Fig. 3.18 shows its optical system. The light entering the slit falls directly on a collimator lens and passes through a quartz prism, after which it is focused by a camera lens in the usual manner. After leaving this lens

Fig. 3.18. Optical arrangement of spectrograph illustrated in Fig. 3.17.
(Courtesy Gaertner Scientific Corp., Chicago.)

the light path is reversed by a plane first-surface mirror so that the camera can be placed immediately beside the slit. This arrangement gives the advantage possessed by the Littrow mounting of bringing all adjustment controls to one end of the spectrograph.

The plateholder will take a 14-in. plate which at the dispersion used will cover the spectrum from 2500 to 5900 A with a single exposure. A handwheel control adjusts the wavelength region, and brings the lenses to the proper positions and the plateholder to the proper tilt, giving accurate focus of any part of the spectrum from 2000 to 8000 A. An arrangement is provided whereby the wavelength at the center of the plate and the wavelengths at each end are projected on a large ground-glass screen on top of the spectrograph, where they can readily be observed.

3.11. Spectrographs with Interchangeable Optical Systems. Some of the prism spectrographs described above can be obtained with interchangeable optical parts. The autocollimation principle (§ 3.8) lends itself particularly to interchangeability, since the focusing-dispersing unit may consist of a lens and one or more prisms, a lens

Fig. 3.19.   Quartz monochromator employing a Cornu prism in a Wadsworth mounting.   (Courtesy Gaertner Scientific Corp., Chicago.)

and a plane grating (§ 4.1), a Féry prism (§ 3.9), or a concave grating (§ 4.6).

Hilger manufactures an interchangeable mounting of the Littrow type that can be obtained fitted with glass or quartz lenses of 100, 150, or 300 cm focal length. Behind the lens can be placed a single 30-deg reflecting prism, a combination of one of these with a single 60-deg prism, or a plane grating. Alternatively, a concave grating can be used without the lens, forming an Eagle mounting of the type discussed in § 4.6. The design of this line of instruments has been standardized to ensure interchangeability of the optical systems. Plates 4 × 10 in. in size are used, and two models are made—one in which all parts are adjusted by hand, the other in which automatic adjustments are provided.   The Bausch & Lomb large Littrow instrument with interchangeable optical parts is also provided with automatic focusing for predetermined regions of the spectrum.

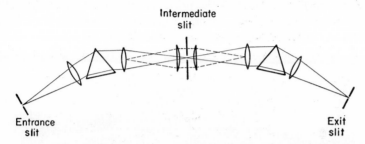

Fig. 3.20.   The optical system of the van Cittert zero dispersion monochromator. The position and width of the intermediate slit determine the spectral range transmitted by the instrument.   The dash lines show that the first camera lens is imaged on the second collimator lens.

3.12.   Prism Monochromators.   For use in the visible region, almost any constant-deviation spectroscope can be converted into a monochromator, if an exit slit is substituted for the eyepiece.   For the ultraviolet region a constant-deviation method due to Wadsworth[6] is frequently used, in which a Cornu prism and reflecting mirror are

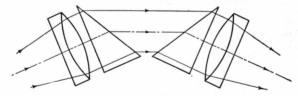

Fig. 3.21.   Young-Thollon arrangement of two 30-deg dispersing prisms with lenses.

rotated to vary the spectral band emerging through the exit slit.   The optical system of this device is shown in Fig. 3.5b, and a quartz monochromator employing the principle is illustrated in Fig. 3.19.

Since uncorrected quartz lenses have strong chromatic aberration, it is necessary in ultraviolet instruments to refocus the collimating and focusing lenses for each new wavelength region, as well as to turn

---

[6] F. L. O. Wadsworth, *Astrophys. Jour.*, **1**, 232 (1895).

the prism table.   Infrared monochromators (Chapter 17) use mirrors instead of lenses and thus eliminate the need for refocusing.   A monochromator principle which is very effective for use in that region involves a single mirror which serves as both collimator and focusing element.   Parallel light from the collimator traverses the prism in one direction, and then is reflected by a plane mirror (or a backed 30-deg prism) again through the prism to be focused on the exit slit by the original collimating mirror.   Improved surfaces for ultraviolet reflection are making possible the utilization of this simple system in the visible and ultraviolet regions, but scattered light must be

Fig. 3.22.   Monochromator employing Young-Thollon prism arrangement and achromatic collimator and telescope lenses.   (Courtesy Farrand Optical Company, New York.)

reduced by other means when this mirror analogue of the Littrow mounting is used.

On account of the frequent importance of reducing scattered light to a minimum, double monochromators of various types have been designed, of which outstanding models are those of van Cittert,[7] manufactured by Kipp and Zonen, and of Müller, manufactured by Hilger.   A diagram of the optical system of the former is shown in Fig. 3.20.   Several sizes of ultraviolet monochromators that use quartz-lithium fluoride achromatic lenses and double prisms of the Young-Thollon type (Fig. 3.21) are manufactured by the Farrand Optical Company.   These instruments, one of which is illustrated in Fig. 3.22, may also be obtained with glass optics for the visible region.

Grating monochromators are discussed in § 4.11.

[7] P. H. van Cittert, *Rev. d'Optique*, **5**, 393 (1926); *Physica*, **3**, 181 (1923).

CHAPTER 4

Diffraction-Grating Spectrographs

A GENERAL COMPARISON OF PRISM AND GRATING SPECTROGRAPHS was made in Chapter 2. The present chapter deals with the methods of mounting diffraction gratings that have been found most useful and with descriptions of commercial grating spectrographs.

The advantages of the diffraction-grating spectrograph over the prism instrument may again be summarized as follows: broader spectral coverage, greater available dispersion and resolving power per unit cost, greater uniformity of dispersion, greater light transmission in certain cases, and the possibility of greater freedom from scattered light. The relative disadvantages are greater astigmatism (except as discussed below); more rapid deterioration with age; and until the late 1940's, comparative scarcity. Costs of the two types of instruments are not greatly dissimilar.

Large gratings of long focal distance are used mainly in physics research laboratories. Such gratings involve mountings that may be from 20 to 35 ft long, filling an entire room, and under these circumstances the various parts of the spectrograph are usually mounted separately. Most commercial grating spectrographs, on the other hand, are small or medium-sized instruments ranging in length from 3 to 17 ft, which are built to be handled as a single unit.

Small diffraction gratings are tested and guaranteed by the spectrograph manufacturer, but large gratings must usually be obtained directly from laboratories that operate ruling engines. Although gratings are commonly sold on a guarantee basis, the user should be prepared to test them. Methods for the selection and testing of diffraction gratings are discussed in § 5.3.

4.1. Plane-Grating Spectrographs. Transmission gratings, as discussed in § 2.5, are seldom used in any but small spectrometers and in instruments for student use. Most instruments in which plane gratings are used for the general purposes of spectroscopy contain

71

gratings of the reflection type and are ordinarily used in a Littrow mounting similar to that of the autocollimation prism spectrograph (§ 3.8). A typical mounting of a plane diffraction grating is shown in Fig. 4.1.

Several large plane-grating installations are in existence, the largest being probably an autocollimating instrument at Mount Wilson Observatory, which has a focal length of 75 ft. Plane gratings having 8 in. of ruling and giving nearly theoretical resolving power in the second or third orders have been produced occasionally.

A grating so mounted is somewhat similar in its behavior to a concave grating in the Eagle mounting (§ 4.6). It has the advantage over the latter that it gives stigmatic images over the narrow spectral range ordinarily used at any one setting, with a resulting gain in brightness and resolution in the higher orders. To change from one

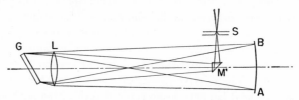

Fig. 4.1.   Diagram of a Littrow mounting of a plane diffraction grating.   S, slit; M, reflecting mirror or prism;   L, collimator and telescope lens;   G, grating; A B, spectrum.

spectral region to another with such a spectrograph, it is necessary to rotate the grating, refocus the lens, L of Fig. 4.1, and rotate the plateholder so that it will lie in the focal curve determined by the color correction of the lens. A lens carefully corrected for chromatic aberration is required if the plane grating is to be used in orders higher than the first; otherwise, lines of overlapping orders will not be brought to a focus on the same curve.

The lens used should have the same aperture as the grating. Since chromatically corrected lenses of large sizes have in the past been obtainable only of glass, plane-grating spectrographs have ordinarily been used only for the visible region and the near ultraviolet and infrared. If a large quartz lens is available, even without color correction, the ultraviolet first order can be used, but special arrangements must be made to throw out the overlapping second order at wavelengths longer than 4000 A. A right-angle prism must be used behind the slit to separate slit from plateholder, except in instruments of very long focal length, where the two can be separated without introducing a large angle of incidence that would increase astigmatism and coma.

A mirror can be used for collimating the light on a plane grating, and this type of mounting is found especially effective with monochromators. It is discussed further in § 4.11, and for the infrared in Chapter 17.

4.2.   The Rowland Concave Grating.   One of the most important advances in the history of spectroscopy occurred in 1882, when Rowland [1] showed that a spherical concave mirror, ruled with parallel lines equally spaced along the chord of its arc, will produce spectrum lines in sharp focus on a circle whose diameter is equal to the radius of curvature of the mirror. This "Rowland circle" is shown in Fig. 4.2. Eliminating the need for any transparent materials as it does, the concave grating has become one of the most powerful tools of spectroscopy. It can be made to provide greater dispersion and resolution than are obtainable with prisms and can be used at any wavelengths for which its rulings are properly spaced. A single grating has been used to cover the range from 100 to 11,000 A.

In the ruling of concave gratings, spacings of approximately 7500, 10,000, 15,000, 25,000, or 30,000 lines per inch are commonly used. Certain of the largest concave gratings thus far successfully ruled, the so-called

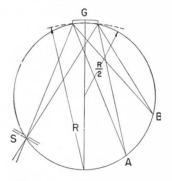

Fig. 4.2.   Diagram of the Rowland circle. *S*, slit; *G*, grating; *AB*, spectrum; *R*/2, radius of Rowland circle; *R*, radius of curvature of grating.

"seven-inch" gratings, contain about 180,000 lines on a ruled area about 15×5 cm. In the higher orders, resolving powers of 400,000 have been attained on occasion. The maximum useful radius of curvature of a "seven-inch" grating for photographic purposes is about 10 meters, as may be demonstrated by calculating the plate factor required to match the resolving power of a grating to that of the photographic emulsions commonly used with it. Emulsions of suitable speed for large grating spectrographs are capable of resolving about 30 lines/mm (§ 7.5). The resolving power of an

[1] H. A. Rowland, *Phil. Mag.*, **13**, 469 (1882); **16**, 197, 210 (1883).

excellent grating with 6 in. of ruling is not likely to be greater than 300,000 (§ 2.5). At wavelength 5000 A, substituting in the formula $P_r = \lambda/d\lambda$, we obtain $d\lambda = 0.016$ A. If this spectral range is to cover not more than 0.033 mm of emulsion, a plate factor of 0.5 A/mm is required. This would be obtained in the third order of a 15,000-line-per-inch grating of 10-meter radius (§ 2.5).

A concave grating is somewhat more difficult to rule than a plane grating of equal size and spacing, and in general the longer the radius of curvature, the easier it is to produce a good grating. Standard radii of curvature are approximately 1, 2, and 3 meters, 10, 15, and 21 ft, and 10 meters. The actual radius obtained may vary as much as ±5 per cent from the value ordered; hence it is usually wise to build a spectrograph with ample flexibility of adjustment.

Up to about 1932, most concave gratings designed for use in the visible and ultraviolet regions were ruled on speculum metal, which has moderately high reflecting power in the visible region but much less at shorter wavelengths, reaching a low of 10 per cent or less at normal incidence in the extreme ultraviolet. R. W. Wood has ruled concave gratings on glass for the vacuum region, and many experiments have been made on coating these with evaporated or sputtered metals to increase their reflecting power.[2] The most satisfactory gratings at present are those ruled on an aluminum surface that has been evaporated on glass. The only question in regard to these is that of permanence—any damage to the aluminum surface may damage the rulings irreparably. For this reason, experiments have been conducted with a new technique of ruling the grating on a gold-on-chromium surface evaporated on glass, which is then coated with evaporated aluminum.[3]

Concave gratings can sometimes be obtained from university and other laboratories which operate ruling engines. The physics department of the Johns Hopkins University has in the past supplied many gratings. Gratings are being increasingly supplied mounted in spectrographs by the firms listed on page 50 as dealing in grating equipment.

In mounting a concave grating the slit may be placed anywhere on the Rowland circle. The location chosen will depend on the type of work to be done. The resulting positions of the various orders and wavelengths can be quickly determined by drawing a diagram like

[2] J. Strong, *Astrophys. Jour.*, **83,** 401 (1936).
[3] J. Strong, unpublished communication.

Fig. 4.3, after Beutler,[4] which shows the distribution of wavelengths for various positions of the slit as calculated from the formula of § 2.5,

$$\lambda = \frac{A}{mN} \,(\sin i \pm \sin \theta)$$

where the symbols have the meanings given there.

The five mountings of concave gratings most commonly used are described in succeeding sections. In selecting a mounting, one should

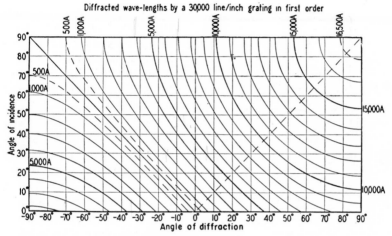

Fig. 4.3. Angles of incidence and diffraction for various wavelengths for a 30,000-line-per-inch diffraction grating. (From H. G. Beutler[4], by permission Jour. Opt. Soc. Am.)

consider the grating orders to be used, the wavelength range to be covered, the degree of astigmatism that can be tolerated,[5] the brightness of the resulting spectra, the freedom from spurious lines (which may depend on angle), and the departure from uniform dispersion (smallest on the normal). In general, the most satisfactory spectra are obtained in the direction of the normal to the grating.

A large concave grating should be mounted only in a room that can be kept clean and dry. The inside of the room is itself the camera and must be kept dark during an exposure. The former custom was to paint the inside of a grating-room black, but modern

---

[4] H. G. Beutler, *Jour. Opt. Soc. Am.*, **35**, 318 (1945).
[5] G. H. Dieke, *Jour. Opt. Soc. Am.*, **23**, 274 (1933).

practice inclines toward light colors for the ceiling and walls, with a black strip extending up perhaps 5 ft from the floor. All developing work should be carried out in a separate room from that in which the grating is mounted. Excessive vibration of a large-grating mounting will of course make it impossible to obtain sharp spectrum lines even with short exposures, and with long exposures it is also necessary to guard against temperature changes of the grating itself. As the grating expands, the distance between its rulings increases and the dispersion correspondingly decreases, so the relative positions of the lines in the spectrum are shifted. For this reason most rooms containing large gratings are thermostated, and the temperature is held constant to 0.1°F or better. To test whether the constancy of temperature is sufficient in any given case, three brief superposed exposures may be taken at 10-hour intervals; if the resulting spectrum lines are as sharp as those taken in a single equivalent exposure, no loss of resolution from this cause is to be expected in a 20-hour exposure to weak light.

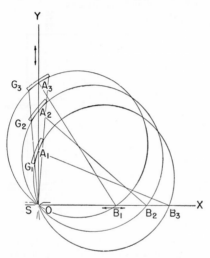

Fig. 4.4. Rowland mounting. S, slit; G_1, G_2, G_3, various positions of grating along bar OY; $AB = R$ where R = radius of grating; B_1, B_2, B_3, various intercepts of grating-normal bar with bar OX.

A convenient height above the floor should be chosen for the plane containing the slit, grating, and focal curve. Forty-six inches is a standard value that gives suitable clearances for mounting optical benches and similar parts on ordinary tables. Slit, grating, and plate carriers should all be based on heavy concrete or brick piers resting on a solid foundation. Wherever any part passes through a wall, sufficient clearance should be provided around it to ensure against vibrations being communicated to any member involved in the optical system.

Beutler[6] has given a very thorough discussion of the theory of the

[6] H. G. Beutler, *Jour. Opt. Soc. Am.*, **35**, 311 (1945).

concave grating and has prepared many charts that show at a glance its properties in various mountings.   His paper should be consulted by anyone contemplating the construction of a grating spectrograph.

4.3. The Rowland Mounting. The classical mounting for the concave grating, used less nowadays than formerly, is that originally described by Rowland [7] and illustrated in Fig. 4.4.   The plateholder and grating are rigidly mounted at opposite ends of a stiff beam whose ends are held on carriages that run on tracks placed at right angles to one another.   The slit is placed at the junction of these two tracks, and the light passing through it falls on the grating and is spread by this around the Rowland circle.   Only that portion of the spectrum is used which falls on a plateholder placed at the normal to the grating.   This arrangement gives a spectrum of almost uniform dispersion, a property of great advantage when wavelength meas-urements are to be made in terms of only a few standard lines.   Nowa-days, however, so many standards of wavelength are accurately known that wavelength interpolations need be made over only short distances, and a normal spectrum is not so necessary as it once was.

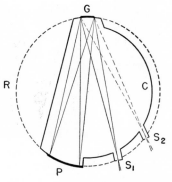

Fig. 4.5.   Optical system of mod-ified Abney mounting illustrated in Fig. 4.6. R, Rowland circle; S_1 and S_2, fixed slits so placed that either of two different regions of the spectrum may be photographed by illuminating the appropriate slit; P, plateholder; C, light-tight case.

The disadvantages of the Row-land mounting are that only a limited region of the spectrum can be photographed at one setting; that it has a high degree of astigma-tism, so that much intensity may be lost, especially in the higher orders; and that the highest orders of the grating cannot be reached.   Also, the mounting is somewhat cumbersome, and the fact that the grating and plateholder both move is a disadvantage.   The Rowland mounting can be used most satis-factorily with gratings relatively free from error of run; if this is present, the focal curve tends to depart from the expected circle.

In order to secure good temperature control, necessary for research

[7] H. A. Rowland, *Phil. Mag.*, **16**, 197, 210 (1883).

purposes, the Rowland mounting is sometimes arranged vertically, the grating being placed at the bottom of a pit, and the end of the arm that carries the plateholder moving on a horizontal track at the floor level.   This mounting results in saving of space but has disadvantages, such as a horizontal slit and a vertical illuminating beam; also, the grating, lying face up near the bottom of the pit, is liable to injury from falling objects and to coating with dust, and is rather inaccessible.   The chief advantage lies in the constancy of temperature obtainable at the bottom of a deep pit.

4.4.   The Abney Mounting.   This mounting,[8] shown in Fig. 4.5, is

Fig. 4.6.   Commercial spectrograph employing a 1.5-meter concave grating in a modified Abney mounting.   (Courtesy Applied Research Laboratories, Pasadena, Calif.)

a variant of the Rowland mounting but has the property that both grating and plateholder are kept stationary while the slit is moved when different regions of the spectrum are to be photographed.   The Abney mounting has never come into wide use with large gratings because of the difficulty of moving the source, condensing lenses, and other external equipment to keep pace with the slit whenever the slit is moved, so that a different spectrum region will be thrown onto the plate.   It is more convenient to have a number of slits for one instrument, from two to ten sometimes being provided.   This is practicable because the same fairly long plateholder, capable of photographing several feet of spectrum at one time, can be used for all slits.

[8] W. de W. Abney, *Phil. Trans.*, **177**, 11, 457 (1886).

A commercial form of the Abney mounting, widely used for spectrographic analysis of materials, is the instrument manufactured by the Applied Research Laboratories and shown in Fig. 4.6. This mounting uses a small grating having a ruled width of about 2 in. and height of about 1 in., with 150 cm radius of curvature and 24,000 lines per inch. This combination results in a plate factor in the first order of about 6 A/mm. Two slit positions are provided, each covering a spectral range of about 2200 A in the first order, so that the spectrum from 2130 to 6570 A can be photographed in two exposures.

Because of the high degree of curvature of so small a Rowland circle, film is used instead of plates for photographing the spectrum. A convenient holder is provided so that motion-picture film of standard 35-mm width can be used. Special equipment is furnished for use with the instrument to simplify the procedures of handling, developing, and drying film.

The Abney mounting suffers from the same limitations of bulk and astigmatism as the Rowland mounting.

4.5. The Paschen-Runge Mounting. The mounting most commonly used at present for large concave gratings of the research type is that originally described by Paschen and Runge.[9] It has the

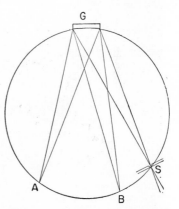

Fig. 4.7. Diagram of Paschen-Runge mounting of the concave grating. *S*, slit; *G*, grating; *A B*, spectrum.

great advantage that slit, grating, and plateholder are all fixed, so that all parts of the spectrum are in focus at all times and its entire extent can be photographed with a single exposure on many plates. The mounting can be arranged so that almost the complete Rowland circle is available, or the entire spectrum can be covered by using one or more orders on only one side. A diagram of a typical arrangement of the Paschen-Runge mounting is shown in Fig. 4.7. Figure 4.8 reproduces a photograph of a portion of a 10-meter Paschen-Runge mounting in the Spectroscopy Laboratory of the Massachusetts Institute of Technology.

[9] C. R. Runge and F. Paschen, *Abh. d. K. Akad. d. Wiss. z. Berlin*, Anhang 1 (1902)

One of the first problems in setting up a grating in the Paschen-Runge mounting is the angle of incidence to be chosen for its illumination.   Although the whole circle may be available, the region at the normal to the grating is the most valuable because there are found

Fig. 4.8.   Paschen-Runge mounting in the M.I.T. Spectroscopy Laboratory.

the most uniform dispersion, the least astigmatism (for a chosen angle of incidence, but not the least attainable—see Fig. 4.18, page 91), and in some cases the highest resolving power.   The slit is placed on the normal only when it is necessary to obtain the low orders on both sides of the grating, as for certain types of intensity measurements. Where higher orders are to be used, illumination at 12- to 60-deg incidence is common.

It is not unusual to provide Paschen-Runge mountings with two slits, one placed for illumination at about 13 deg and the other at 40 deg. The small angle of incidence is used when low orders are to be studied, and the large angle for higher orders. The two slits give the added advantage of providing space for two complete source setups; thus cumbersome apparatus for the Zeeman effect, for example, can be left in place at one slit while the other is available for general use.

Where the main use of a Paschen-Runge mounting is to be in making wavelength measurements, a fixed track is usually provided

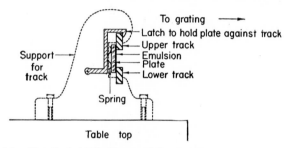

Fig. 4.9. Detail of plateholder track for Paschen-Runge mounting in the M.I.T. Spectroscopy Laboratory.

to hold a series of plates bent to the Rowland circle. One method of holding plates on such a track is shown in Fig. 4.9, the long (2- × 20-in.) plates being clipped with their emulsion side against the *back* of the track, to avoid any displacement due to varying glass thickness. The posts holding the track are usually bolted to heavy slabs of Alberene stone or slate mounted on concrete piers to give great rigidity and are arranged so as to permit a certain amount of adjustment for focusing before being finally bolted in place.

For routine photography of selected spectral regions, and for intensity work where a number of spectra are to be photographed on the same plate, it is desirable to provide cassettes (Fig. 4.10) that slide along a horizontal track following the Rowland circle and carry plateholders taking 4- × 10-in. or similar plates. Both types of track are visible in Fig. 4.8. Each has the spectrum brought into proper

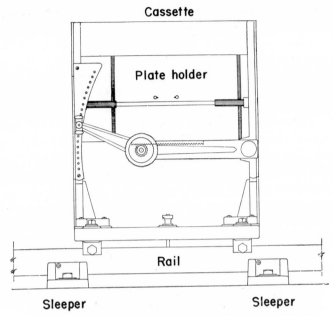

Fig. 4.10. Detail of cassette for Paschen-Runge mounting in the M.I.T. Spectroscopy Laboratory.

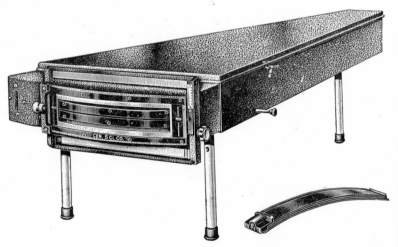

Fig. 4.11. Small Paschen-Runge spectrograph employing a concave grating replica. (Courtesy Central Scientific Company, Chicago.)

focus on it when its own slit is used.   Calculations indicate that by properly displacing the slit the focal curve of a 10-meter grating may be caused to depart as much as a foot from the Rowland circle without introducing objectionable aberrations.

A small model of the Paschen-Runge mounting appears in commercial form in the Cenco grating spectrograph produced by the

Fig. 4.12.   Spectrogram of a copper arc in the region 5400–4400 A, taken with the Cenco grating spectrograph.

Central Scientific Company (Fig. 4.11).   A replica grating having a ruled surface about 1 in. square with a radius of curvature of about 1 meter produces a spectrum covering the range 2300 to 8000 A in one setting.   The entire spectrum is covered with a plate factor of 16 A/mm on a film 10 in. long, so the instrument can be kept in permanent adjustment.   A section of a spectrogram taken with this spectrograph is shown in Fig. 4.12.

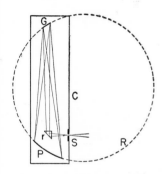

Fig. 4.13.   Eagle mounting of the concave grating.   R, Rowland circle;   S, slit;   r, reflecting prism;   G, concave grating;   P, plate;   C, light-tight case.

4.6.   The Eagle Mounting.   A mounting described in detail by Eagle[10] but used long before in vacuum spectrographs[11] is not only economical of space but also keeps astigmatism as low as is possible without increasing the complexity of the optical system, and simplifies the control of the grating temperature.   The Eagle mounting is illustrated in Fig. 4.13.   This mounting occupies a long narrow space, a characteristic that led to its extensive use in vacuum spectrographs of the normal-incidence type in the manner originated by Lyman.   Higher orders can be reached than in the Rowland Mounting and the astigmatism is less.   In changing from one wavelength range to

[10] A. Eagle, *Astrophys. Jour.*, **31**, 120 (1910).
[11] T. Lyman, *Spectroscopy of the Extreme Ultraviolet*.   New York: Longmans, Green and Company, 1928.

another, it is necessary to turn the grating, change its distance from the plate, and rotate the plateholder. The Eagle mounting of the concave grating is similar to the Littrow mounting of the plane grating, but it is superior in that no lens is needed, so that it can be used in all spectral regions. It does not suffer greatly from the Littrow's defect of scattering light directly back onto the photo-

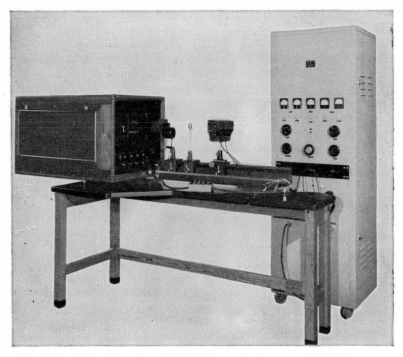

Fig. 4.14. Optical bench and plateholder end of commercial Eagle spectrograph, showing power unit for arc and spark sources. (Courtesy Baird Associates, Cambridge, Mass.)

graphic plate. It has the disadvantage of not being as stigmatic as the Littrow.

The Eagle mounting is used in a commercial instrument manufactured by the Baird Associates, shown in Fig. 4.14. In the standard model a grating with 4 in. of ruling, having 15,000 lines to the inch and a 3-meter radius of curvature, is used, which gives 5.2 A/mm plate factor in the first order. The spectrum from 2000 to 10,000 A can be covered in several orders in a series of exposures, with a range

of 1200 A recorded at one exposure in the first order. The three necessary focusing adjustments are controlled by electric motors operated
by push buttons, and it is a matter of but a few moments to bring
the spectrograph to focus in a new spectral region. One motor drives
the screw that moves the grating forward or backward on stainless
steel ways, a second motor turns the grating to the proper angle, and
a third racks the plateholder. All adjustments are controlled from
the front panel, and automatic end stops are provided. Each motion
is controlled by two switches, one of which provides high-speed
adjustment forward and reverse, and the other a one-tenth-speed
motion for accurate setting. Revolution counters are connected
through flexible cable to the part controlled so that accurate setting
is easy. Sufficient travel is provided to allow the red of the fourth
order to be covered, in which order the plate factor is 0.4 A/mm.
The gratings used have a high concentration of visible light in the
first order and are sometimes even faster than prism instruments.
Four- by ten-inch plates or films can be used, but the plateholder
is arranged to hold any plate 10 in. long and narrower than 4 in.
Models of shorter focus, having correspondingly greater compactness
and less dispersion, are also manufactured by the Baird Associates.

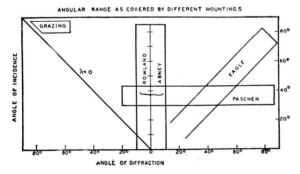

Fig. 4.15.   Angular ranges of various grating mountings.   (From H. G.
Beutler,[12] by permission Jour. Opt. Soc. Am.)

Figure 4.15, after Beutler,[12] shows the angular range covered by the
various grating mountings.

4.7. The Wadsworth Stigmatic Mounting. A disadvantage for
many purposes of all mountings of the concave grating previously
discussed is that they are astigmatic to a greater or less degree (see

[12] H. G. Beutler, *Jour. Opt. Soc. Am.*, **35**, 318 (1935).

§ 4.9). Wadsworth[13] noted that this astigmatism might be eliminated, at least over any desired short region of the spectrum, by making use of the fact that if a grating is illuminated with a beam of parallel light, a normal stigmatic spectrum is produced at the normal

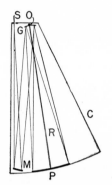

to the grating. The dispersion is then cut in half, however, since at the normal the new focal curve lies halfway out to the Rowland circle. Various workers used a large convex lens to make parallel the light on the grating, and Meggers and Burns[14] originated a mounting of this type in which a concave mirror is used. The loss in light from the extra reflection is more than compensated by the increased angular aperture of the system and by the elimination of astigmatism.

Fig. 4.16. Wadsworth mounting of the concave grating. S, slit; M, concave mirror; G, concave grating; P, plateholder; R, bar along which plateholder slides; O, axis of rotation of grating and of bar R; C, light-tight case.

A Wadsworth mounting of the Meggers-Burns type is illustrated in Fig. 4.16. Grating and plateholder are connected by a rigid bar, but provision must be made for adjustment of their distance apart, since the focal curve is a parabola. The grating turns with the bar so that the plateholder is always on its normal, whereas the slit and concave mirror remain fixed. The curvature of the plate must be changed slightly from one region of the spectrum to another. Though truly stigmatic images are obtained only on the normal, for practical purposes a range of many hundred angstroms can be arranged for use at one setting. In general, a length of spectrum equal to about one-sixth of the distance from plateholder to grating will be found in sufficiently stigmatic focus to permit use of a rotating-sector disk or other photometric device at the slit.

When designing a Wadsworth mounting one should select a grating that does not have more than 15,000 or 20,000 lines per inch. In the formula for wavelength position,

$$m\lambda = \frac{A}{N} (\sin i \pm \sin \theta)$$

[13] F. L. O. Wadsworth, *Astrophys. Jour.*, **3**, 54 (1896).
[14] W. F. Meggers and K. Burns, *Bur. Standards Sci. Paper* 411, **18**, 185 (1922).

θ is always close to 0 deg for the Wadsworth mounting, so the formula reduces to

$$m\lambda = \frac{A}{N} \sin i$$

Thus it will be seen that with a 30,000-line-per-inch grating the longest wavelength that can be reached at any reasonable angle of incidence i (not over 45 deg) is about 8000 A. The wavelengths that will appear on the normal for a 15,000-line-per-inch grating at any given angle for a stigmatic mounting are given in Table 4.1.

TABLE 4.1

WAVELENGTHS AND FOCAL DISTANCES ON THE NORMAL IN THE WADSWORTH MOUNTING FOR VARIOUS ANGLES OF INCIDENCE

Angle of incidence	Wavelength on normal	Focal distance (fraction of R)
8°	2359 A	0.5024
10°	2943	0.5038
12°	3524	0.5055
14°	4100	0.5075
16°	4672	0.5099
18°	5238	0.5126
20°	5797	0.5156
24°	6894	0.5226
28°	7958	0.5311
32°	8981	0.5411
36°	9963	0.5523

The figures in Table 4.1 hold for a 15,000-line-per-inch grating in the first order. If other orders are used, the wavelengths are to be divided by the order number. The wavelengths for a 30,000-line-per-inch grating are obtained by dividing those in the table by 2. The focal distance in any unit is given by R, the radius of curvature of the grating in that unit, multiplied by the fraction in column 3.

A very satisfactory Wadsworth stigmatic mounting in operation at the Massachusetts Institute of Technology, where two instruments of this type have been in frequent use for many years, consists of a 35-ft concave grating used in conjunction with a 7-in. aluminized glass mirror of equal radius of curvature. A plateholder 30 in. long is provided that will hold one, two, or three 4- × 10-in. spectrum plates, or one centered 2- × 20-in. plate, at one time. Arrangement is made for moving this plateholder up and down so that as many as 40 spectra can be photographed on a single plate. The fixed bar on which rod R in Fig. 4.16 slides is calibrated with a wavelength scale. In changing from one spectral range to another, the movable rod R is first put in the desired position, so that the proper spectral region will be centered on the plateholder P, and then the plateholder is moved along the rod to the position given by a numerical table of focal positions. The only other adjustment required is a slight change in curvature of the plateholder. This can be made flexible, or separate plateholders can be provided for the various regions. The curvature adjustment can be made by means of calibrated screws at each end of the plateholder. In one instrument, all other adjustments are made with electric motors; and the racking adjustment,

Fig. 4.17. Commercial 21-ft concave-grating spectrograph of the Wadsworth type. (Courtesy Jarrell-Ash Company, Boston.)

which is also done electrically, can be controlled from outside the room in which the grating is mounted.

The plate factor obtained with the Massachusetts Institute of Technology instruments is 3.3 A/mm in the first order and 1.65 A/mm in the second order. Any spectral region from 2000 to 10,000 A is readily available, and in the first order a region 2500 A long can be photographed at one time on three 10-in. plates placed end to end. Each instrument occupies a space about 18 ft long by 12 ft wide. One of these spectrographs, having a grating that throws most of its light into one first order, is very fast, a 3-second exposure being sufficient to give a strong spectrogram of an iron arc throughout most of the visible and ultraviolet regions.

The Jarrell-Ash Company manufactures a spectrograph of the Wadsworth type,[15] shown in Fig. 4.17.

[15] R. F. Jarrell, *Jour. Opt. Soc. Am.*, **32**, 666 (1942).

For many routine purposes, such as qualitative and quantitative spectrographic analysis of materials, it is convenient to have a Wadsworth mounting in fixed and permanent focus. For analyzing ferrous materials and other spectra rich in lines, it is desirable to have a plate factor of 5 A/mm or less. Most routine analyses can be made using lines lying in the region 2400 to 4400 A. To meet the requirement that this 2000-A range should be photographed on a single plate with a plate factor of 5 A/mm, a plate 400 mm, or about 16 in. long, is needed. Or one can photograph the entire range from 2000 to 5000 A on a plate only 20 in. long, covering 2500 to 5000 A in the first order and 2000 to 2500 A in the second. Such overlapping is much less objectionable in emission analysis than is often supposed, because of the high dispersion available with such gratings.

The criterion that the stigmatic range in a Wadsworth mounting is about one-sixth of the grating-plate distance indicates that we should make this distance at least 10 ft in designing a fixed-focus spectrograph. A plate factor of 5 A/mm will be obtained at a focal distance of 10 ft with a grating having about 15,000 lines per inch. Thus a 6-in. concave grating with 15,000 lines per inch and having a 21-ft radius of curvature could serve as the heart of such an instrument.

4.8. The Choice of a Grating Mounting. Small commercial concave-grating instruments, which are of necessity portable, usually are made with the Eagle mounting, or in some cases with the Abney. When one is faced with the necessity of choosing the most suitable mounting for a large grating, the first consideration must be that of space. Where only a long narrow corridor or vertical shaft can be used, the Eagle mounting is suitable. The cross section of its containing box is determined only by the length of spectrum to be photographed at one setting and by the baffles needed to cut down stray light.

If a room of medium size (say 12 × 15 ft) is available, a 21-ft grating in the Wadsworth mounting will probably be found more useful than a shorter-focus grating in any other mounting. The grating of longer radius will cost no more than a shorter one for the same area of ruling, and the advantages of a stigmatic mounting are obtained; moreover, the grating can also be used at its full dispersion later if a larger space becomes available. When space is available and astigmatism is unobjectionable, the Paschen-Runge mounting is so much more flexible than the others that its use is advantageous.

As to the choice of grating spacing and number of lines, much depends on the type of problem to be attacked. In general it is advantageous to have a large number of lines and a close line spacing, provided ghost intensity is not thereby increased and high orders need not be reached. No instrument has ever suffered from too much resolving power, and dispersion can always be decreased if necessary by using auxiliary mirrors as in the Wadsworth mounting. For constant angular aperture and slit width, increased dispersion decreases the intensity of continuous spectra but not of mono_ chromatic line spectra. Increasing the dispersion, of course, decreases the range of spectrum that can be photographed on a plate of given length.

Modern mirror coatings having high reflecting power in the ultra-violet region as well as in the visible make practicable a number of modifications of the standard mountings. Thus by use of a single plane mirror and a slit that can be rotated about a vertical axis, the grating can be illuminated from any angle in a Paschen mounting, which can then be used also as an Abney mounting. Two movable mirrors and a fixed slit can also be used. One of the systems described in § 4.9 for eliminating astigmatism with the help of a cylindrical quartz lens can sometimes be introduced to impart to any mounting some of the stigmatic advantages of the Wadsworth mounting.

4.9. Astigmatism of the Concave Grating and Its Reduction. The astigmatism of a concave-grating spectrograph can be measured in terms of the length of the line into which a point on the slit is focused on the Rowland circle. This length depends on the grating and how it is illuminated, and is proportional to the length of the rulings. Calculations of astigmatism are usually given in terms of the quantity ζ, which measures the astigmatism per unit length of ruling:

$$\zeta = \sin^2 \theta + \frac{\sin^2 i \cos \theta}{\cos i}$$

Figure 4.18, from a chart due to Beutler,[17] shows the astigmatism to be expected when various angles of incidence and diffraction are used. The Eagle mounting has much less astigmatism than the Rowland and is somewhat superior in this respect to the Paschen. In general, the least astigmatism is found at the normal to the grating and when the angle of incidence of the light on the grating is kept small. However, to get minimum astigmatism at a given wavelength, i should be set equal to θ, as in the Eagle mounting.

Astigmatism reduces the intensity of a line if light is sent through only a short portion of the slit, because the lengthening of the image spreads the light over a longer line. The intensity of a line produced in an astigmatic spectrograph can, therefore, be increased by illuminating a longer portion of the slit. If a sufficient length of the slit is illuminated, the intensity in the middle of the line will be as great as that in a stigmatic image. The source used must of course be of sufficient extent that the cone of light from it will completely fill the grating.

Astigmatism reduces resolution slightly, since the astigmatic line images are slightly curved. This effect is very small, however, and is of importance only when extremely high resolution is required.

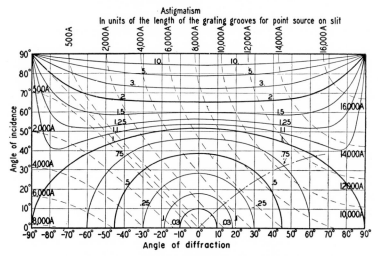

Fig. 4.18. Astigmatism in units of the length of grating grooves for a point source at the slit for various angles of incidence and diffraction. (From H. G. Beutler[17], by permission Jour. Opt. Soc. Am.)

The principal drawback of astigmatism in a concave-grating spectrograph is that it prevents use of several of the more effective methods of photographic photometry that are valuable in quantitative spectrographic analysis. Astigmatism has been discussed in some detail by Dieke[16] and by Beutler.[17] Oldenberg[18] has critically dis-

[16] G. H. Dieke, *Jour. Opt. Soc. Am.*, **23**, 274 (1933).

[17] H. G. Beutler, *Jour. Opt. Soc. Am.*, **35**, 324 (1945).

[18] O. Oldenberg, *Jour. Opt. Soc. Am.*, **22**, 441 (1932); also G. H. Dieke, *Proc. Sixth Summer Conf. on Spectrography*, p. 71. New York: John Wiley & Sons, Inc., 1939.

cussed several methods that have been suggested for eliminating the effects of astigmatism in the concave grating. A method due to Sirks[19] is widely used, and is here reproduced.

The Rowland circle represents the horizontal focus of a grating, but somewhere outside of this circle the light from the slit passes through a vertical focus, where each point on the slit is imaged as a horizontal line. Any point on the Rowland circle marks also the vertical focus of some point outside of the slit. This positioning is easier to visualize if one thinks of a point source of light placed at the position of a spectrum line, which

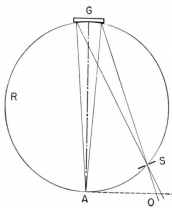

will be brought to a horizontal focus (vertical line) on the slit and to a vertical focus beyond this. Thus in Fig. 4.19 an object placed at the outer focus O will be brought to a vertical focus on the circle at the grating normal, provided no lenses intervene, and a diaphragm. step weakener, or logarithmic sector (§ 13.3) can be placed there. The point O is located in the general case by extending the straight line which connects the position of the plateholder on the Rowland circle with the intersection of the normal to the grating and the circle, until it intersects the line connecting slit and grating. Its distance d from the slit is given for the Eagle mounting by the formula

Fig. 4.19. Sirks' construction, for the special case in which a grating is used on the normal, to find the position, O, at which horizontal stops may be placed so as to be imaged as points along the spectrum lines. R, Rowland circle; G, grating; S, slit; AO, tangent to Rowland circle at intersection of grating normal with the circle; O, position at which horizontal stops should be placed.

$$d = R \sin i \tan 2i$$

where R is the radius of curvature of the grating. Obviously, only a relatively short region of the spectrum can be covered in this way at one setting of O.

Runge and Mannkopf[20] have devised a means of producing a stigmatic image of the *source* on the plate by using a combination of a spherical lens and a cylindrical lens, or a concave mirror, to form

[19] J. L. Sirks, *Astron. and Astrophys.*, **13**, 763 (1894).
[20] C. R. Runge and R. Mannkopf, *Z. f. Phys.*, **45**, 13 (1927).

an astigmatic bundle of rays that has its horizontal focus at the slit. Using uncorrected quartz lenses, they were able to produce stigmatic images of the source over as much as 1000 A with a single setting of the lenses, the natural dispersion of the quartz serving to extend the normal range.

We may obtain a stigmatic spectrum without sacrificing dispersion by placing a small cylindrical quartz lens with its axis horizontal between slit and grating.[21]   In this position the lens throws a virtual vertical image of the slit back to the outer focus of the grating; and stigmatic, though enlarged, images of the slit are produced on some part of the Rowland circle, the exact position of the lens being chosen to fit the particular region of the spectrum being studied.   It is usually possible to bring two regions of the spectrum into stigmatic focus simultaneously, and the natural dispersion of the quartz may again be used to extend the range.   A 5- × 5-cm plano-convex cylindrical lens of 150 cm focal length in the vertical plane will be found suitable for a 21-ft or 10-meter grating.

In all the above arrangements, the gain in light intensity is only that incidental to the production of a stigmatic image, and in some cases there may be loss of light if care is not taken to see that the full length of the slit and the full aperture of the grating are filled with light.   We may, however, obtain a very great increase in line brightness, as shown by Humphreys and by Gehrcke,[22] by placing a short-focus cylindrical lens in front of the plate.   All of the light that formerly covered a line say 5 cm long is now focused down into a length of perhaps 5 mm, with a resulting tenfold increase in intensity. For general work an accurate 5- × 5-cm cylindrical quartz lens with a focal length of about 20 cm is recommended.   This should not be placed parallel to the plate but normal to the beam incident on the lens; to avoid a decrease in resolution, great care must be taken to see that its axis is truly horizontal.   Only a short portion of the spectrum at a time can be covered with a small lens, of course, and the arrangement finds its greatest use in studying hyperfine structure patterns or very faint band heads.

4.10. The Testing of Diffraction Gratings.   When a spectrograph is purchased from a manufacturer, he is of course responsible for the satisfactory performance of its optical parts.   Probably as many imperfect prisms as imperfect gratings have been produced in the past,

[21] See O. Oldenberg, *Jour. Opt. Soc. Am.*, **22**, 447 (1932).
[22] W. J. Humphreys, *Astrophys. Jour.*, **18**, 324 (1903); E. Gehrcke, *Z. f. Instr. Kde.*, **31**, 87, 217 (1911).

but the former have been weeded out by the manufacturers so that the user seldom sees one. Gratings, on the other hand, are in many cases purchased directly from those who rule them, and since a perfect diffraction grating has never been ruled, it is desirable that the user should be familiar with tests that indicate the merit of any grating that may come into his hands. These tests should cover spectrum intensity, Lyman ghost intensity, Rowland ghost intensity, line shape, target pattern, resolving power, scattered light intensity, satellite intensity, and the variation of these with angle of illumination and with wavelength. The details of such tests are discussed in §§ 5.3–5.5.

4.11. Grating Monochromators. In the past, most commercial monochromators (§§ 2.16, 3.12, 17.2) have been constructed with prisms as dispersing agents, but the introduction of the aluminum-coated grating, with its increase in intensity, decrease in scattered light, and simple optical system, has made possible design of excellent grating monochromators. Harrison[23] has described a simple mono-chromator using a 3-meter concave grating that makes beams of high radiant flux and great purity available. As discussed in Chapter 6, the larger a given type of monochromator, the greater the radiant flux of a given degree of purity that can be isolated by it. For certain applications great gains result, when numerical aperture can no longer be increased, by merely increasing the actual sizes of the source, slit, monochromator, and receiver. Other things being equal, a hundred times as much monochromatic flux can be obtained with an instrument built around a 10-ft concave grating as with one of ordinary type having a 12-in. collimator. The transmission of a good grating instrument is fully as great as that of an equivalent prism type.

Plane gratings lend themselves to use in monochromators, with an off-axis parabolic mirror for both collimating and focusing, as described in § 17.2 for infrared prism instruments. The improved reflecting powers in the ultraviolet now available for mirrors make possible the design of new types of monochromators that cover the entire range 2000 to 10,000 A at fairly uniform dispersion. Since no refocusing of chromatically uncorrected lenses is needed, a simple wavelength control with a direct-reading dial can be provided.

Speculum-metal gratings scatter more light than is desirable for use in monochromators, even when coated with aluminum. A grating

---

[23] G. R. Harrison, *Proc. Sixth Conf. on Spec.*, p. 91, New York: John Wiley & Sons, Inc., 1934; also G. R. Harrison and E. P. Bentley, *Jour. Opt. Soc. Am.*, 30, 290 (1940).

ruled directly on an evaporated metal surface is likely to give such freedom from scattered light that a monochromator constructed with it will be intermediate in spectral purity between an ordinary single-prism and a double-prism monochromator. A very simple pre-dispersion instrument then suffices for use with it to make scattering effects negligible.

CHAPTER 5

The Testing, Adjustment, and Care of Spectroscopic Equipment

THE ADJUSTMENT OF GENERAL TYPES OF SPECTROSCOPIC EQUIPMENT is discussed in this chapter. Details of adjustment of apparatus for special applications, such as infrared spectroscopy, absorption spectrophotometry, Raman spectroscopy, and spectroscopy of the vacuum ultraviolet, will be found in the chapters dealing specifically with those techniques.

THE TESTING OF SPECTROSCOPIC COMPONENTS

5.1. The Testing of Slits. The jaws of an adjustable slit should be polished to almost mirror smoothness, and should be closely parallel to each other and in the same plane. To determine whether these requirements are fulfilled satisfactorily, a demounted slit having adjustable jaws may be tested by laying it on an illuminated opal or ground glass, or supporting it so that a sheet of white paper may be viewed through it. The slit opening may be examined with a low-power magnifier, while the slit is closed slowly. At the instant of complete closure, if the jaws are straight and parallel to each other, the light will be extinguished simultaneously at all points along the slit; and if the jaws are in the same plane, this simultaneity will be observed no matter at what angle the slit is viewed. If the width of the slit appears to vary with the aspect from which it is viewed, the two jaws are not accurately in the same plane. Adjustments are usually provided whereby the jaws may be made parallel if they are found to be improperly aligned. Jaws of a slit in which the beveled edges do not lie in the same plane should be reground for thickness.

Another method of testing is to photograph an image of the slit under actual working conditions, with the slit mounted as it is to be used. If the slit belongs to a visual spectroscope with a viewing eyepiece or to a monochromator with an exit aperture, the eyepiece or exit aperture should be removed so that the spectral image can be photographed in the position at which it is most sharply in focus. A source comparatively rich in fine lines, such as an iron arc or a copper or tungsten spark, may be used. With a slit opening of 0.01 to 0.02 mm, the spectrum should be focused carefully until sharp images of the slit are obtained in the portion of the spectrum to be used for testing. The slit should then be opened to a width of about 1 mm and its edges cleaned carefully by stroking them with a sharpened stick of clean wood in one direction. A series of test spectra should then be photographed with slit openings varying from about 0.04 mm to full closure. During these exposures the full length of the slit should be illuminated, any diaphragms or apertures that might shield portions of it from illumination being removed. If the photographed spectrum lines appear wedge-shaped, lack of parallelism of the jaws is indicated. If the spectrum lines appear ragged or uneven (Fig. 5.1) the cause is probably dirt on the jaws, imperfections in their edges, or bluntness of the jaws.

The second method of testing slits is applicable only to spectroscopic systems in which stigmatic images of the slit are formed in the focal plane. In astigmatic spectroscopes, the slit can usually be demounted and tested by the first method described above. Figure 5.1 shows spectra taken with dirty and defective slits.

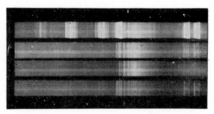

Fig. 5.1. Out-of-focus spectra photographed with a dirty and defective spectrograph slit.

5.2. **The Testing of Prisms and Lenses.** The spectroscopist has little occasion to test prisms or lenses except in instances in which he is concerned with the design and construction of special equipment. Inspection of such components for striae, bubbles, surfaces scratches, and other gross imperfections can be accomplished easily with the aid of a low-power magnifier. There is usually no need to go beyond such cursory examination, since components are tested for performance in the optical shops where they are fabricated. Instructions regarding the measurement of indices of refraction, dispersion, prism angles, focal lengths of lenses and mirrors, and the various aberrations of lenses and mirrors are given in standard treatises on optics. Information regarding the testing of mirrors, lenses, and prisms in combination is given in §§ 5.4 and 5.5.

5.3.   The Testing of Gratings.   No two diffraction gratings are precisely alike.   The performance of most gratings can be improved by masking areas in which the rulings are imperfect, especially at the edges.   Increasing commercial production of grating spectrographs is helping to relieve the individual spectroscopist of the necessity of subjecting new gratings to test, but it is still often important to be able to determine the performance of a grating in the laboratory.

a. The Foucault Knife-edge Test.   This test is useful in locating imperfect areas in concave gratings (Fig. 5.2).   A knife-edge (for example, a razor blade) is mounted on a carriage in such a manner that it can be moved along the focal plane, through the image of an intense, isolated spectrum line such as one emitted by a mercury arc.

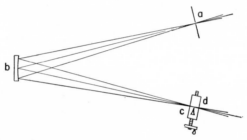

Fig. 5.2.   Foucault knife-edge test as used with a concave grating.   *a*, Slit; *b*, grating; *c*, knife-edge on carriage movable by a transverse screw; *d*, position of observer's eye.

When viewed from close behind the image, the grating will appear to be filled with light, since light from all parts of the grating passes through the image into the eye pupil.   If each part contributes its proportionate share of light to the image, and if the image is sharp and free from effects of aberrations, moving the knife-edge into the image will cause the light to be cut off uniformly and simultaneously from all parts of the grating.   If, however, large bright areas are observed on the grating when the knife-edge is moved into the image, these areas are usually due to imperfect rulings, which should be masked.   The effect of masking such areas on the quality of the spectra produced by the grating should then be tried.

b. Target-Pattern Test.   Another method of determining defective areas of concave gratings is to view target patterns of strong mercury

lines (or other distinct, intense spectrum lines) on screens placed
about one-third the distance from the image plane to the grating,[1]
with the grating otherwise set up as for normal use.   Typical target
patterns are shown in Fig. 5.3.   The images so obtained are broad
areas corresponding to bundles of rays converging toward each
spectrum line.   If the various portions of the grating all contribute

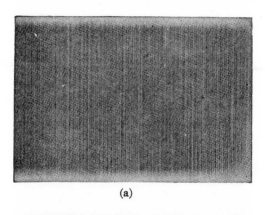

(a)

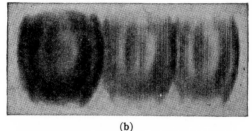

(b)

Figs. 5.3 a, b.   Typical target patterns.   (a) Pattern of a single wavelength
from a good grating.   (b) Patterns of three wavelengths from an inferior grating.
Reproduced from *Proceedings of the Seventh Summer Conference on Spectroscopy
and Its Applications,* by permission of the publishers (the Technology Press and
John Wiley & Sons, Inc., New York.)

their proportionate share of light to the formation of a sharp image,
the target pattern will have a uniform or a channeled structure.
Otherwise, the pattern will show irregular patches.   If the pattern
is irregular, the effects of masking can be tried, the optimum masking
being determined by trial and error.

<hr />

[1] G. R. Harrison, *Proceedings of the Seventh Summer Conference on Spectroscopy
and Its Applications.* New York: John Wiley & Sons, Inc., 1940.

c. Determination of Defects That Give Rise to Satellites. A third method, originated by R. W. Wood,[2] is applicable to determining defective areas in plane or concave gratings which give rise to prominent satellites. A slit is placed in the focal plane in such a position as to pass the light from a satellite but to obscure the principal line and other lines. The light that passes through the slit is sent through a lens onto a photographic plate in such a manner as to form an image of the grating on the plate. If only certain portions of the grating contribute to formation of the satellite, these portions will appear most prominent in the photograph of the grating. Once their position has been determined by this means, they may be masked. It is sometimes found that the position of a satellite varies with reference to the principal line as the spectrum is traversed, the satellite coinciding with the line at the grating normal.

d. Observation of Ghosts. Although Rowland and Lyman ghosts cannot be eliminated by masking, since all portions of the ruled surfaces contribute to them, it is of importance to determine their prominence. To observe Lyman ghosts, the grating should be set up as for normal use. If the slit is illuminated with a source having only a few strong lines in the visible, such as a mercury arc, the Lyman ghosts will be observed most easily as visible lines in the region between the violet end of the first-order visible spectrum and the central image. Visible Lyman ghosts have the same colors and appearance as their parent lines. Hence if one employs a source having doublets or triplets in the visible spectrum, the corresponding Lyman ghosts will be doublets or triplets of the same color. Almost any grating will show Lyman ghosts if a wide slit and intense source are used in the search for them. A grating having Lyman ghosts more intense than 1/10,000 of their parent lines should be viewed with suspicion for all but a few spectroscopic purposes. In case of doubt, the relative intensities of ghosts and lines should be determined photographically.

Rowland ghosts may be observed by using a narrow entrance slit and viewing the first- or second-order visible spectrum lines with an eyepiece. The ghosts appear as additional weak lines regularly spaced on either side of all strong lines, as shown in Fig. 2.12. By taking a series of photographs of the spectrum with different times of exposure and determining the time ratios for which the ghosts produce the same blackening in one photograph as the parent lines in another,

---

[2] R. W. Wood, *Physical Optics.* New York: The Macmillan Company, 1934.

one may determine the approximate relative intensities of the ghosts. Alternatively, a rotating logarithmic sector may be used. In the first-order spectrum of a good grating, the intensities of Rowland ghosts should be less than 1/1000 of those of their parent lines. The relative intensity of ghost to line can be expected to increase approximately as the square of the order; ghosts in the second order will be about four times as strong relative to their parent lines as in the first. This rule is only approximate, because some orders may show inordinately strong ghosts. In general, Rowland ghosts produce less confusion in the spectrum than Lyman ghosts.

5.4. The Testing of Prism Spectrographs. An easy qualitative test is to photograph the spectrum of a source rich in sharp lines, such as an iron arc, and then to compare this spectrogram with one made on an instrument known to perform satisfactorily. Prints of iron-arc spectra and other spectrograms made with good instruments of high dispersion may be obtained from spectrograph manufacturers. A narrow slit should be used, and the focus of the spectrograph should be adjusted carefully before the test is made (see § 5.9). The test spectrograms should be taken on plates of moderate contrast, developed to give average tonal gradations. This procedure is essential in order that relatively weak imperfections will not be obliterated when the exposure and development are such as to result in appropriate blackening of the stronger lines.

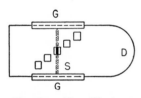

Fig. 5.4. The Hartmann Diaphragm. The diaphragm *D* contains several small openings, any one of which can be brought into juxtaposition with the slit *S* by sliding the diaphragm sideways in the grooves *G*.

Spectrograms taken with the full slit illuminated should be compared with those taken with various portions of the slit covered by means of a Hartmann diaphragm (Fig. 5.4). The line sharpness should be essentially the same whether the total slit length or only portions of it are used. If this is not the case, either the focus is not properly adjusted or defects in the components are indicated. If, with the spectrograph in proper adjustment, the lines are abnormally fuzzy or irregular or are found to be accompanied by satellites when compared with standard spectrograms, defects in the components may be suspected.

5.5. The Hartmann Test. If component defects are indicated by

the above procedure, a simple test method devised by Hartmann[3] may
be used to locate the defects.   In this test a small light source,
such as a condensed spark between tungsten-steel electrodes or a
Western Union concentrated arc lamp, is used.   The source is
mounted at a distance of about 25 cm from the slit, on a carriage that
will permit it to be moved laterally in a plane parallel to the plane
of the slit and along a line perpendicular to the slit (Fig. 5.5).   With
the source placed approximately on the optic axis of the collimator
lens, the slit is narrowed until its central diffraction maximum covers
only a small portion of the collimator lens.   By moving the source
laterally, it is then possible to direct light in the horizontal plane
through different portions of the spectrograph optics.   By using
different openings in a Hartmann diaphragm over the slit, it is further
possible to send light through different portions of the optics in the
vertical plane.

For each setting of the Hartmann diaphragm, a series of five or

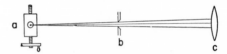

Fig. 5.5.   The Hartmann Test. a, Point source mounted on carriage with transverse screw motion; b, slit of spectrograph; c, collimator lens.

more spectrograms is taken with the source positioned so as to
illuminate different portions of the optics.   If there are no appreciable
aberrations or other defects in the system and if the spectrograph is
in proper adjustment, the spectrum lines in all these test spectra
should be in good alignment with each other.   If the plate is in front
of or behind the true focal plane, there will be a progressive shifting
of the lines with change in position of the source or of the diaphragm
openings.   The focus should then be readjusted until the shifting of
the lines is reduced to a minimum.   If there are serious lens aberrations or inhomogeneities in the prism or lens materials, irregular
shifting of the lines will be observed even after the best focus has been
attained.   When such defects occur, their effect may often be reduced
materially, or eliminated, by masking portions of the prism or lenses.
This masking may be accomplished by trial and error, those portions

[3] J. Hartmann, *Zeits. f. Instrumentenkunde*, **20**, 47 (1900).   See also *U. S. Bureau of
Standards Scientific Papers*, numbers 311 and 494.

of the optics which the test spectrograms show to be the worst offenders being masked first.

The above test shows only whether light beams suffer irregular deviations in traveling through particular portions of the lens and prism optics. For any particular beam, the test does not indicate whether the collimator lens, the prism, or the telescope lens is the offending component. For Littrow-type spectrographs, the lens may be tested separately by the Hartmann method if the prism is removed and a mirror substituted in such a manner as to reflect the rays back through the lens along their ordinary path. In this test, the radiation is not spread into a spectrum; hence chromatic aberration, ordinarily compensated by tilting of the spectrum plate, may cause appreciable broadening of the slit image. This difficulty may be overcome by using a source with widely spaced lines, such as a mercury arc, and isolating one line by a suitable filter so that the slit is illuminated with approximately monochromatic radiation. In general, the best focus under such conditions will not correspond to the position of sharp focus with the prism in place, since a different light path is followed by the rays in traveling from the mirror to the plate when no prism is interposed. Accordingly, the focus must be adjusted before a final test plate is made.

If defects are found by the Hartmann test, it may be advisable to remove the lenses and to test them individually, either by the knife-edge test,* as described for gratings in § 5.3, or by other standard methods (see General References 5.1–5.3). It is well to look for defects in the prism first. This search is made most simply by substituting another prism and repeating the Hartmann test for the complete system.

ADJUSTMENT OF PRISM AND GRATING SPECTROGRAPHS

5.6. Adjustments Required for Various Types of Instruments. Spectroscopic equipment is of many different types, each of which involves particular adjustments for best performance. In general, such adjustments involve (a) setting the slit to an appropriate opening, and to parallelism with respect to a prism apex or to the ruled lines of a grating, (b) optically aligning the component parts of the

---

* A pinhole source is used, mounted on the optic axis in the case of a lens and as near the optic axis as feasible in the case of a mirror.

system, and (c) focusing the components. These operations should be carried out in the order given to achieve approximate adjustment, after which it may be necessary to repeat the various procedures until the best adjustment has been reached as a result of successive approximations.

Commercial spectrographs, spectrophotometers, and monochromators are usually designed so that the necessary adjustments are few in number. The optical components are sometimes permanently aligned and fixed in position by the manufacturer, with no provision for further adjustment. In almost all instruments, however, adjustment of slits and focusing are required.

5.7. Adjustment of Slit Width and Length. Methods of testing and adjusting slits for parallelism of the jaws were described in § 5.1. Some slits are made without provision for adjusting the jaws for parallelism. If they are found to be seriously nonparallel, a more perfect slit must be substituted.

Slits should be kept free from dust particles or dirt, which may interfere with the uniformity of the slit aperture. A method of cleaning the edges of open slits was described in § 5.1. Some adjustable slits and most fixed slits are covered by plates of quartz or glass on the side toward the light source. Cover plates should be cleaned by wiping them with lint-free cloth or lens tissues, moistened with ether or alcohol. Special care should be taken to avoid finger marks on quartz cover plates. Any fingerprints present should be removed carefully with a grease solvent before exposure to ultraviolet radiation, because if such radiation falls on fats or other organic substances, it may cause permanent etching of quartz.

When open arcs or sparks are used, danger of pitting or fouling of the slit edges by material from the source may be reduced by placing a transparent protecting plate between the source and the slit, or by using a condensing lens so that the source can be moved farther away.

Protecting plates, or plates used for the mounting of fixed slits, may, as the result of interference arising from multiple reflections, give rise to variations in the intensity of the radiation transmitted through different portions of the slit. The errors that such effects may introduce in quantitative emission analysis, and their elimination, have been discussed by Stern.[4]

The width of an adjustable spectroscope slit is usually set at be-

[4] Joshua Stern, *J. Opt. Soc. Am.*, **36**, 654 (1946).

tween 0.01 and 0.06 mm. The optimum opening depends on the instrument and its application. Details of the calculation of optimum widths are given in Chapter 6.

A diaphragm with V-shaped opening is usually provided for adjusting the length of slit to be illuminated. Ordinarily only a portion of the total length is used. In stigmatic instruments, increasing the slit length usually merely increases the length of the spectrum lines produced; in astigmatic instruments it may greatly increase intensity.

Lenses of short focal length may be used in lieu of slits. A pseudo slit of this type has been described by King.[5]

5.8. **Adjustment of Slit Perpendicular to the Direction of Dispersion.** The slit should be parallel to the apex of the prism or to the rulings of the grating used. This adjustment is accomplished by rotating the slit in its own plane, after the prism or the grating and the other optical components of the system are in proper alignment.

Often it is sufficient to set the slit so that the spectrum lines from a source such as a mercury arc or neon discharge tube appear perpendicular to the line along which the various wavelengths are dispersed, as viewed on a ground-glass screen. Reference lines marked on the screen, or a piece of translucent coordinate paper, may be used for checking perpendicularity. In stigmatic instruments the slit length may be closed down almost to a point, so that the resulting spectrum, if continuous, appears as a line; if discontinuous, as a series of points along a line. One of the coordinates of the screen or graph paper may then be set parallel to this line, after which the entire slit length may be exposed to light from a line source, the slit being rotated until the spectrum lines are properly aligned with respect to the perpendicular coordinates.

For the most precise adjustment, the foregoing method may be used merely for preliminary alignment. Then a series of trial spectrograms, taken with the instrument properly focused and with slight changes in the rotation of the slit for each new exposure, may be used to determine the slit angle that gives the sharpest spectrum lines perpendicular to the line of dispersion.

In the case of prism instruments, the spectrum lines are appreciably curved. Therefore only a short middle portion of each line will appear strictly perpendicular to the spectrum, but it is usually possible to judge fairly well when the curved lines are symmetrically

[5] C. M. King, *J. Opt. Soc. Am.*, **36**, 164 (1946).

disposed with reference to the perpendicular coordinates. Lines from gratings are only slightly curved. This curvature, and any inclination of the slit, decreases resolution in astigmatic instruments.

5.9. Focusing the Spectrum: Commercial Prism Spectrographs. It will be assumed in this section that the slit has been adjusted properly and that the optical components are suitably aligned. Procedures for aligning various components are given in subsequent sections.

Procedures for focusing vary considerably for different types of instruments. In the simplest instruments, such as the usual hand spectroscopes or spectrographs, only one focusing adjustment is pro-

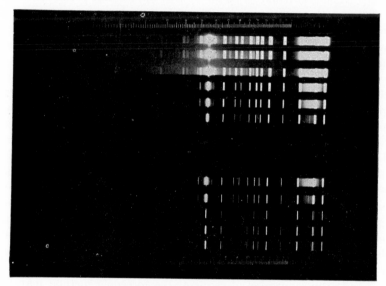

Fig. 5.6.   Trial spectra photographed with different focus
settings of the spectrograph collimator.

vided, and there is no provision for change of plate tilt. The focusing adjustment may move either the slit or the collimator lens, so as to change the distance between these components. Alternatively, the adjustment may move the telescope lens toward or away from the eyepiece or plateholder. In visual instruments equipped with fixed cross hairs or a fixed aperture viewed by an eyepiece, the focus should be adjusted so that the spectrum is sharply imaged in the plane of the cross hairs or aperture. When the adjustment has been made properly, no parallax should be observed as the eye is moved from side to side. If movable, the eyepiece lens should first be focused so that the cross hairs or aperture appear sharp and clear.

In photographic instruments, preliminary focusing may be accomplished by observing on a ground-glass screen the images of widely spaced spectrum lines, such as those from a neon tube or mercury arc. Several spectrograms should then be taken, corresponding to slight differences in focus (Fig. 5.6). The final setting to be chosen is the one that yields the sharpest lines in the portion of the spectrum to be observed. In small or medium quartz spectrographs, for example, the best setting for lines in the visible and near ultraviolet may be somewhat different from that for lines in the far ultraviolet.

A second case is that of spectrographs on which there is only one focusing adjustment but on which the tilt of the plate may also be changed. Preliminary focusing and plate-tilt adjustments may be accomplished by observation of visible lines on a ground-glass screen. A test plate is then taken in the manner described above, and that position of focus is selected which gives the sharpest line images near the center of rotation of the plate. In large spectrographs other than those of the Littrow type (discussed below) it may be necessary as a preliminary measure to shift the plate holder along the spectrum to a position corresponding to the spectral range to be photographed. After the spectrum has been focused sharply for the center of rotation of the plate, a second test plate is taken on which is photographed a series of spectrograms corresponding to different plate tilts. The tilt finally chosen should be that which gives the sharpest line images throughout the range of the spectrum to be observed. If a line drawn on the spectrogram connecting the positions of best focus in successive, uniformly spaced exposures is straight but inclined, only a change in angle is required. If it is curved, the plate must be bent to achieve the best focus.

5.10. **Focusing the Spectrum: Commercial Littrow and Eagle-Mounting Spectrographs.** Spectrographs of the Littrow type require successive adjustment of the angle of the prism or grating, the focus of the lens, and the angle of the plateholder. Commercial instruments of this type are usually supplied with calibration tables showing the proper settings of these three adjustments for various wavelength regions. Often two or more of the adjustments are geared together so as to be accomplished automatically when the setting is shifted from one spectral region to another.

If automatic coupled adjustments are not used, it is first necessary to set the dispersing element to cause the desired spectral region to fall on the plate.   If calibration data are lacking, this is accomplished easily for the visible region by visual inspection, using a ground-glass screen and a source providing widely spaced, easily identified spectrum lines.   In the ultraviolet region a fluorescent screen may be substituted for the ground glass, or a series of test spectrograms may be taken with approximately correct plate angle and focusing adjustments, and with different prism inclinations.   After the angle that gives the proper spectral range has been chosen, precise focusing and plate-angle adjustments are accomplished as outlined in § 5.9.   When all the procedures have been carried out and the proper settings determined, these should be recorded to facilitate the making of future adjustments.

In concave-grating instruments using the Eagle mounting, the adjustments are analogous to those described and are carried out in a similar manner.   The concave grating corresponds to the Littrow prism and lens system combined.

Precise focusing in all the above cases may be facilitated by use of the Hartmann test method (§ 5.5) or by a simple modification thereof in which aperture stops are placed on the collimator lens.

5.11.   Adjustment of Spectrometers.   Collimators and telescopes with multiple movements and adjustments are provided on many spectrometers.   The following adjustments must, in general, be made : (a) The eyepiece of the telescope must be set so that the cross hairs appear sharp to the observer;   (b) the telescope must be focused so that parallel light is brought to a sharp image in the plane of the cross hairs;   (c) the collimator must be focused so that the light from each portion of the slit is sent into a parallel beam;   (d) both the telescope and collimator must be adjusted so that their optic axes are perpendicular to the axis about which the prism or grating rotates; (e) the prism or grating must be leveled so that the prism apex or grating rulings lie parallel to the axis of rotation of the prism table; (f) the collimator and telescope must be set for an angle of deviation approximately correct for the wavelength region to be observed; (g) the slit must be adjusted for proper width and for parallelism to the prism apex or grating rulings;   and (h) the prism must be adjusted for approximately minimum deviation at the wavelength to be observed.   Thus the use of a spectrometer often involves a complicated series of adjustments.   Nevertheless, these adjustments are not difficult to make if undertaken systematically in the sequence indicated.

5.12. Adjustment of Concave Gratings.   The testing of gratings is described in § 5.3. Methods of adjusting commercial grating instruments are discussed in § 5.10 for Littrow and Eagle spectrographs, and in § 5.11 for spectrometers. Here we will consider certain more general problems that arise when the spectroscopist is not using a commercial spectrograph previously assembled by a manufacturer, but is confronted with the necessity of installing a grating and of undertaking all the adjustments himself. Such situations arise particularly in the use of concave gratings of long focal length. One or more grating holders may be set up in a room that can be darkened, in which there is a permanently installed Paschen-Runge or Wadsworth mounting, or both. The slits to be used are usually mounted in openings in a wall of the room, so that the light sources to be studied may be placed outside the room. When the original gratings are set up or when different ones are substituted or added, a series of careful adjustments must be made if full advantage is to be taken of available resolving power.

The adjustments will be described here only qualitatively. Discussions of the quantitative effects of each of the several adjustments are given in various publications,[6] including General Reference 5.3.

Five principal types of mountings, described in Chapter 4, are used with concave gratings: Rowland, Paschen, Abney, Eagle, and Wadsworth. In all of these except the Wadsworth, the grating and plateholder are mounted on the Rowland circle. In the first three mountings the slit is also on the Rowland circle; this would be true also of the Eagle mounting were it not for the fact that light is introduced from a slit at the side and reflected toward the grating by a prism or mirror. Accordingly, grating adjustments will be discussed first with particular reference to the Rowland circle, and the special problems that arise with respect to the Wadsworth mounting will be considered separately.

a. The Grating Holder. It is essential that the grating holder be rigidly constructed and mounted. Adjustments should be provided for rotating by accurately controlled amounts around each of three mutually perpendicular axes (Fig. 5.7). One of these axes, x, lies in the plane of the Rowland circle and is perpendicular to the grating at the center of the ruled space. A second, y, also lies in the plane of the Rowland circle, is perpendicular to x, and passes through x at its point of intersection with the grating. The third, z, is perpendicular

---

[6] H. G. Beutler, *J. Opt. Soc. Am.*, **35**, 311 (1945).

to the plane of the Rowland circle and passes through the point of intersection of x and y. Thus, for the usual setup, x and y are approximately horizontal and z is approximately vertical.

Motion about x rotates the grating in its own plane. Motion about y tilts the plane of the grating with respect to the plane of the Rowland circle. Motion about z rolls the grating plane about a vertical axis.

Limited motions about the x and y axes may be accomplished quite simply by mounting the grating on a leveling table. If a leveling table is used, there should also be provision for rotating the grating in its own plane (about the x axis) for rough adjustment, and for rotating in this plane precisely through 180 deg from any starting position. The leveling table may be set on another table that can be rotated about a vertical axis (the z axis), care being taken to align the center of the grating with this axis.

Other designs of grating holders that provide the required adjustments may, of course, be used. In addition to the provisions for rotation of the grating, there should be means of moving the holder along a line normal to the grating, to permit accurate adjustment of the distance from the grating to those parts of the mechanical mount which must coincide with the Rowland circle.

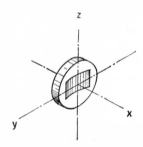

Fig. 5.7. The three axes about which motion of a concave grating should be provided.

A grating must be free from strain when mounted, so that the curvature of its surface will not be altered by pressure from screws or springs; yet it must be held firmly so that when once adjusted it will not move. Various holders for gratings are described in the literature, among the best being those which press lightly with leaf springs against the front face at three points on its unruled surface, while three screws press from behind directly opposite the points of contact of the springs. In such a mounting the orientation of the grating can be adjusted slightly with the screws, and its weight is carried loosely on its base. That a grating when mounted is free from strain and has a good optical figure can be determined by illuminating the grating through a narrow slit and viewing the central image or any strong line at its focal point with an eyepiece; or the Foucault test described in § 5.3 can be used.

When not in use, gratings should be protected from dust, fumes, and other deleterious substances. This objective can be conveniently accomplished by designing the holder so that closure of a cover shuts the grating into a tightly enclosed compartment. It should be possible to open and close this cover without disturbing the grating adjustment, and provision should be made for mounting occulting masks in front of the grating, to shield portions of the ruled surface from illumination if necessary.

b. Approximate Adjustments. After the grating has been mounted in its holder, approximate adjustments should be made. These may be accomplished by observations, measurements, and tests with light beams as in the setting up and alignment of any optical system.

Since most gratings throw the light unequally into equivalent orders of the two sides of the central image, the more desirable side should first be found. Ordinarily one chooses the first or second order that is most intense in the visible region. This choice can often be made by holding the grating in the hand in a darkened room, illuminating it with the full light of a mercury lamp, and observing the spectra thrown on walls or ceiling. The eye is not a particularly good judge of relative intensities, however, so if this test does not show one order to be much more intense than its counterpart, photographic tests should be made.

The combination of direct-intensity tests and target-pattern tests will ordinarily settle the question of which orders are most useful in a given grating for a given spectral region. Gratings tend to throw their light in a given direction rather than into a given order, so if the first order on one side is particularly bright at say 5500 A, the second order at 2750 A can be expected to be bright on that side. Target-pattern changes or decreased reflecting power of the grating in the ultraviolet may intervene to alter this tendency.

Once the side of the grating to be used has been chosen, the face of the grating should be set so that it lies approximately in a vertical plane tangent to the Rowland circle and at such a height that the xy plane is coincident with that of the Rowland circle. The grating should be rotated so that its rulings are approximately vertical. The slit should be set on the Rowland circle, with its aperture approximately vertical, and at a height such that the xy plane normal to the grating (that is, the plane of the Rowland circle) bisects the slit length.*

---

* An exception occurs in mountings of the Eagle type, in which the slit is sometimes placed slightly above or below the plane of the Rowland circle.

It is assumed that the disposition of the grating with respect to the slit along the circumference of the Rowland circle has been determined by the type of mounting to be used. The approximate position in which spectra will be formed should be known from this choice and from the constants of the grating (see Chapter 4).

c. Rotation About the y Axis. The central portion of the widened slit should be illuminated with light from a mercury arc, and the visible spectra should be observed on white screens or the walls of the darkened room. If the spectra are thrown above or below the Rowland circle, the grating should be rotated about its y axis until the spectra are coincident with the Rowland circle. After this adjustment has been made, rotation of the grating about the z axis should not raise or lower the spectra with respect to the Rowland circle if the center of the slit is accurately in the plane of the Rowland circle. If raising or lowering occurs, the slit height and rotation of the grating about the y axis should be adjusted until rotation of the grating about the z axis no longer causes such motion.

While this adjustment is being undertaken, it may be necessary to rotate the grating slightly in its own plane (about the x axis) in order to bring the line of dispersion of the spectrum into parallelism with the plane of the Rowland circle, since the grating lines must be perpendicular to this plane if the spectra are to be parallel to it.

d. Focusing the Grating. The grating is next focused approximately for the portion of the spectrum to be photographed. This focusing is accomplished by motion of the holder along a line normal to the grating. For the visible region, preliminary adjustment may be made by visual observation of the spectrum lines on a viewing screen in the plateholder or with an eyepiece held in the hand, but a series of test spectra should always be photographed to determine the best setting.

Often it will be found that it is not possible to focus sharply all lines within the desired range along the curve of the plate (Rowland circle curve), because errors of run usually cause gratings to focus their spectrum lines along a curve slightly different from that of the true Rowland circle. This effect can be overcome to a considerable extent by rotating the grating slightly about its z axis, so that the plane of the grating is no longer strictly tangent to the Rowland circle. This adjustment is known as *rolling* the grating, or as setting the grating *in aberration*, since a perfect grating so rotated away from the true tangential position would exhibit considerable aberration.

Many gratings have a false focus that is easy to confuse with the real focus.   As the target pattern narrows down to form the spectrum line, it splits into a constantly decreasing number of fairly sharp fringes of varying intensity, and in some gratings a strong fringe and a weak fringe pass through each other to form the spectrum line.   If too faint an exposure is made, the strong fringe may be mistaken for the spectrum line itself, and for this reason typical lines should always be exposed up to high densities.   Such exposure is also necessary to show the presence of satellites.

e. Setting the Grating in Aberration.   Before one starts the rolling adjustment (rotation about the z axis), an approximate determination should be made of the effect of rotating the grating through 180 deg in its own plane (about the x axis) on the position of the focal plane of the spectrum.   The grating holder should be moved along the normal of the grating until such 180-deg x-axis rotation throws the spectrum equal distances behind and in front of the Rowland circle. The grating may then be rolled on its z axis until trial indicates that rotation through 180 deg on the x axis causes no appreciable motion of the spectrum and until the spectrum is sharp along the entire length of the Rowland circle encompassed by the plateholder.

f. Setting the Slit Aperture Parallel to the Grating Rulings.   Finally, to obtain lines of the greatest sharpness, it is necessary to adjust the slit so that it is strictly parallel to the grating rulings.   For this purpose it is desirable that the slit be provided with a tangential adjusting screw whereby small angles of rotation may be accomplished accurately and reproducibly.

The effect of lack of parallelism of the slit and the rulings is to broaden out the spectrum lines.   By using a source that yields many fine spectrum lines, and a narrow slit, and then photographing a series of test spectra with the slit set at slightly different angles, one may readily determine the optimum adjustment.

g. Final Tests.   The resolving power $\lambda/d\lambda$ of a large grating can readily be estimated by observing the hyperfine structure of the green line at 5461 A as emitted by a cool mercury arc (see § 20.1), or by photographing close and fine lines from an arc containing rare-earth salts, a source giving nitrogen bands in emission, or an iodine absorption tube.   Great care should be taken to see that the slit is accurately parallel to the rulings on the grating when resolving power is being tested.

A point that has been insufficiently emphasized in the past is that the effective resolving power obtainable in practice is definitely a function of the density of the lines produced, and that line shape may change markedly with density. Almost all gratings are tested by the makers for resolution. A common procedure is to photograph some line that shows hyperfine structure, such as mercury 5461 A, with enough exposure so that this line is brought to low or medium density. If close-lying components of the line are resolved, the grating is said to be good. However, almost all gratings produce lines not of simple shapes, but with many satellites grouped fairly close together. Owing to the nonlinearity of the curve that connects light intensity with plate density, the apparent shape of the line is altered as the density increases, and its center of gravity may be shifted. For this reason a grating should be tested for resolving power at all useful densities, some lines being overexposed. At extreme overexposures, of course, any grating will show false lines.

5.13. Adjustments of Wadsworth Grating Mountings. In the case of the Wadsworth mounting, it is necessary first to adjust the distance from the mirror to the slit, so that light is rendered parallel by the mirror. This adjustment may be accomplished approximately by inspection of the reflected light beam and somewhat more accurately by an autocollimating method. In the latter method, a plane mirror is set up so as to return the reflected light to the collimating mirror. The latter is turned on a vertical axis until it forms an image of the slit directly to one side of the slit. The collimating mirror is then focused until the slit image is sharp.

After having been focused, the collimating mirror should be rotated about its x, y, and z axes until the parallel beam of light from it is centered on the aperture of the grating.

The grating adjustments are accomplished as described in the preceding sections. Strict coincidence of the plate with the focal plane of the spectrum is obtained by the use of specially curved plateholders. The rotation of the grating with respect to its z axis is usually governed by the fact that it is desirable to photograph the spectrum as near to the normal of the grating as is feasible. Since the focal curve of the Wadsworth mounting is not a circle, it is necessary to change adjustments of plate curvature and plate angle when moving from one region of the spectrum to another.

5.14. Adjustment of Plane Gratings. The foregoing discussion applies to concave gratings. In the case of a plane grating, an auxiliary lens system is used, which has a single combined collimator and telescope lens in Littrow mountings, and separate collimator and telescope lenses in other mountings. The characteristics of the lenses (chromatic aberration, flatness of field, and so on) and their positions with respect to the grating, as well as the constants of the grating, determine the position and shape of the focal plane of the spectrum.

The choice of grating and lenses, and of their mechanical disposition with respect to one another, depends on the intended application of the system, as discussed in Chapter 4. For any given system, all adjustments of the grating except with respect to rotation about the y axis are analogous to those described for concave gratings. The y-axis setting must be such as to obtain the desired angle of incident illumination on the grating, and to send the appropriate spectral region through the telescope lens.

THE CARE OF SPECTROSCOPIC EQUIPMENT

5.15. General. Instruments should be protected from dirt and corrosive vapors or fumes. The spectroscopic laboratory should be clean and dust-free, and preferably air-conditioned. Plateholders and other parts that are subject to wear and possible damage during use should be inspected periodically. Oiling or greasing of sliding or rolling surfaces may occasionally be necessary. When lubricants are used, the surfaces should be cleaned and a small amount of oil or vaseline of good quality should be applied.

Enclosures designed to be light-tight may require testing for light leaks. Visual inspection in conjunction with a bright source of light is usually the most satisfactory, but photographic tests may be helpful when small leaks are involved.

5.16. Care of Mirrors, Prisms, and Lenses. The best way to keep mirrors, prisms, and lenses clean is to protect them from accumulations of dust and dirt by housing them in tight enclosures that are opened to the outside air only during use. Such components should be cleaned when necessary, but this operation must be performed with care, especially with first-surface mirrors and gratings. Dust may be removed from glass and quartz surfaces by wiping with lens paper, or with soft, lint-free cloth. Fingerprints should be removed with a grease solvent such as pure ethyl alcohol. Rock-salt lenses and prisms must be protected from moisture by keeping them in a dry atmosphere. Their surfaces should be cleaned only with dry lens paper or lint-free cloth.

The greatest care should be used in cleaning first-surface mirrors in order to avoid abrading or scratching the surface. Dust particles may be removed by careful stroking with a clean camel's-hair brush. Light polishing with chamois or lens paper may sometimes be accomplished without damage to the surface, but considerable risk is involved. Fingerprints on aluminized surfaces may sometimes be removed satisfactorily with a very weak ammonia solution, followed quickly by rinsing with distilled water. Caustic solutions dissolve aluminum rapidly and offer the greatest danger to aluminized surfaces.

5.17. Cleaning and Care of Gratings. The surfaces of gratings are so easily damaged by cleaning that every precaution should be taken to protect them from dust, dirt, corrosive fumes, and especially from fingerprints. The ruled surface of a grating should never be touched with the fingers under any circumstances. If a grating is used exposed in a room, it is desirable that the air supply to the room be filtered to free it from dust. In any event, the grating should be covered by a tight enclosure when not in use.

A properly housed and protected grating should not have to be cleaned more than once in every two or three years. When cleaning is necessary, the collodion or gelatin stripping technique is very effective for speculum gratings, but it must be used with great caution on gratings ruled on aluminum or other metal films deposited on glass. A thin film of dissolved collodion or gelatin is poured over the rulings and the surrounding area and allowed to harden. The film is then carefully lifted at one edge and pulled off. Speculum or steel gratings may be immersed in distilled water to facilitate removal of the collodion film. Dirt particles remain embedded in the film and are removed with it. Before applying this method to metal-on-glass gratings, the stripping technique should be tested on a small portion of the unruled area to make sure that the metal film will not be stripped from the glass. This method should not be used to clean replicas.

Dust particles are sometimes removed from gratings by stroking the grating gently in the direction of the rulings with a clean camel's-hair brush or tuft of cotton. This procedure should be applied with caution, especially in the case of metal-on-glass rulings or first-surface replicas.

Metal-on-glass gratings may be swabbed lightly with distilled water in the direction of the rulings. Alternatively, a very dilute solution of ammonia may be used to remove stains, grease, and other accretions, followed quickly by thorough rinsing with distilled water to remove the ammonia solution. Wet swabbing should not be applied to metal-on-glass gratings or first-surface reflection replicas unless trial on an unruled portion has indicated that the procedure is safe.

Second-surface replicas, in which a collodion cast of the master is mounted with rulings adjacent to the supporting surface, may be cleaned by wiping them carefully with cotton or lens paper. Since the rulings are protected, the principal reason for caution is to avoid scratching the collodion surface.

The reflecting power of metal-surfaced reflection gratings deteriorates with age. In the case of speculum-metal gratings, this deterioration is due to the formation of copper oxide coatings, which may be removed rather effectively by dilute ammonia, as described above. After the first year, deterioration of the reflecting power of metal-surfaced gratings is not marked over a period of 10 to 15 years, provided the gratings are properly protected and cleaned periodically. The greatest change is usually found to be a decrease in ultraviolet reflection.

GENERAL REFERENCES

5.1. A. C. Hardy and F. H. Perrin, *The Principles of Optics.* New York: McGraw-Hill Book Company, Inc., 1932.
5.2. G. F. C. Searle, *Experimental Optics.* London: Cambridge University Press, 1925.
5.3. R. A. Sawyer, *Experimental Spectroscopy.* New York: Prentice-Hall, Inc., 1944.

CHAPTER 6

Illumination of the Spectroscope

WHEN ONE ARRANGES THE ILLUMINATION of a spectroscopic system, it is important to remember the following points:

1. To take advantage of the theoretical resolving power of the system, the full width of the prism, ruled grating surface, or other dispersing device should be filled with light (except insofar as optical defects in the system need to be masked out).

2. To achieve minimum times of exposure in using spectrographs or to obtain maximum radiant power in the spectra formed by spectroscopic instruments, it is essential (a) that the full aperture of the system be filled with light and (b) that the source employed have the highest practicable radiance (radiant power output per unit solid angle per unit area of emitting surface) within the desired spectral range.

3. To achieve accuracy in spectrophotometric procedures, quantitative emission analysis, and various other spectroscopic applications, it is frequently necessary that the slit of the spectroscopic system be illuminated uniformly throughout its length.

In particular situations, it is sometimes necessary to effect a compromise in which one or more of these conditions are not fulfilled as completely as might be desired.

6.1. **Coherent and Noncoherent Radiation.** When one considers the illumination of spectroscopic systems, it is convenient to distinguish between coherent and noncoherent radiation. In coherent radiation, there are definite phase relationships between radiation at different positions in a cross section of the radiant energy beam, whereas in noncoherent radiation these relationships are random. For example, a slit is filled with approximately coherent radiation when it receives light from a small distant source, because every portion of the slit is then illuminated by the light from each radiating atom or molecule of the source. On the other hand, a slit which has an image of the source formed on it is filled with approximately noncoherent radiation, since each point of the slit is then illuminated essentially by a single point of the source.

In practice, the illumination of any surface or aperture is never completely coherent or noncoherent, but the approximation to one of these two extremes may be very close. The importance of distinguishing between the extremes arises from the fact that radiation from coherently illuminated apertures or surfaces may give rise to interference phenomena, whereas such phenomena do not occur if the illumination is noncoherent.

The computation of the theoretical resolving power of dispersing components, for example, prisms and lenses, is usually based on the assumption that they are illuminated with radiation that is coherent throughout the entire width of their dispersing surfaces (see Chapters 3 and 4). This assumption is strictly true only if the dispersing component is illuminated by radiation originating from a point source or an infinitely narrow slit. In practice, the slit always has finite size. If the illumination of the slit itself is noncoherent, the illumination of the dispersing component will be nearly coherent if the optical paths from the two edges of the slit to the dispersing component do not differ by more than about one-fourth the wavelength of the radiation used. If the illumination of the slit is coherent, the same approximation to coherence at the dispersing component is achieved with path-length differences from the two edges of the slit of about one-half wavelength. Thus a coherently illuminated slit may be made approximately twice as wide as a noncoherently illuminated one for equally effective achievement of the maximum resolving power of a dispersing system illuminated by the slit.

6.2. Spectral Line Shape and the Rayleigh Criterion for Resolution. The expressions for the theoretical resolving power of spectroscopic systems given in Chapters 3 and 4 were based on the assumption that the entrance slit is equivalent to an infinitely narrow light source and that the broadening of the slit images in the spectrum, which limits the resolving power $\lambda/d\lambda$, is due entirely to diffraction effects. In addition, aberrations and imperfections in optical components may cause diffuseness, broadening, or irregularity in the slit images and may thereby reduce the realizable resolving power. Moreover, since the slit is never infinitely narrow, it is necessary to take into account the effect of slit width on effective resolving power and spectral purity.

The intensity distribution of a spectrum line, as produced by a spectrograph of high resolving power, is somewhat like that shown in Fig. 6.1. No definite width can be set for such a line, so it is customary to use instead the half-intensity breadth b, or breadth at the intensity which is half that at the maximum. The observed intensity distribution of the line is governed by two factors: the distribution of energy in the line as a function of wavelength, which is determined by the emitter, and the distribution of monochromatic radiation along the spectrum, which is determined by the spectroscopic apparatus. Each approximately monochromatic section of the true line shape is subject to the "apparatus broadening," and the resulting spectrum line is the sum of all these sections taken together. Of considerable effect on this line shape are the width of the slit being used and the mode by which it is illuminated.

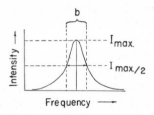

Fig. 6.1. Intensity distribution of a typical spectrum line at high resolution; b, half-intensity breadth.

Any definition of what constitutes the limit of resolution between partially overlapping spectrum lines is arbitrary. The Rayleigh criterion, previously referred to, states that two images of infinitely narrow line sources, or point sources, are to be considered resolvable when they are separated by such an amount that the central diffraction maximum of one falls on the first diffraction minimum of the other (Fig. 6.2). If the maxima are of equal intensity and if the intensity curves as a function of distance from the central maxima are of such shape as would be expected from elementary diffraction theory, the intensity midway between the maxima is about 82 per cent of that at either maximum.

The Rayleigh criterion provides a good working rule as to what may be expected in the ability of the eye or of the photographic plate to separate two neighboring diffraction maxima. The actual separation of the maxima required in order that they may be distinguished as separate depends upon a variety of factors, including (a) the response of the light receptor, such as the eye, a photographic plate, or a photoelectric device, to variations in intensity; (b) the shapes of the intensity curves in the diffraction patterns; (c) the relative intensities of the diffraction maxima; (d) the effects of imperfections in optical-image formation as a result of mechanical vibrations, optical aberrations, and defects in the optical system; and (e) the effects of grain size or other resolution-limiting characteristics of the receptor.

The general problem of criteria of resolving power has been considered in detail by several workers.[1] For our purposes it will be sufficient to use the Rayleigh criterion as one that is convenient and closely in agreement with average practical experience.

6.3. Selection of Optimum Slit Width. Suppose the slit to be illuminated by light from a source that yields two monochromatic spectrum lines of equal intensity and of just sufficient difference in wavelength, $d\lambda$, to be resolvable by the spectroscopic system, according to the Rayleigh criterion. Suppose the slit to be opened very slightly, say to a width such that its optical image in the plane of the spectrum (as determined by geometrical optics) is one-twentieth the width of its observable pattern.

Two diffraction patterns, corresponding to the two spectrum lines, will appear side by side in the spectrum, each with an intensity-distribution curve approximately that shown in Fig. 6.2. The central diffraction maximum of each pattern will lie over the first minimum of the other pattern, as in Fig. 6.2, since it has been assumed that the separation of the patterns is just such as to satisfy the Rayleigh criterion of resolution.

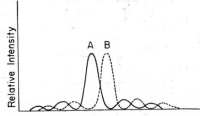

Fig. 6.2. **Rayleigh criterion for the resolution of spectrum lines.** The central diffraction maximum of line A falls upon the first diffraction minimum of line B at the limit of resolution as defined by the Rayleigh criterion.

Let us now consider one of these diffraction patterns only (say A in Fig. 6.2) and examine the effect on it of increasing the slit width. Suppose the slit is opened symmetrically to three times its original width—that is, to a width such that its optical image is three-twentieths the width of the original diffraction pattern. If the slit is illuminated with noncoherent radiation—that is, if there are no definite and continuing phase relationships between radiation coming from different portions of the slit—the effect will be as though a new slit were placed on each side of the original slit, all being of equal width. We can consider each of these new slits as contributing its own diffraction pattern but displaced to the right and to the left of the original pattern by one-twentieth the distance between the

---

[1] The following papers include references to earlier work: B. P. Ramsey, E. L. Cleveland, and W. A. Bowen, Jr., *Jour. Opt. Soc. Am.*, **32**, 288 (1942); B. P. Ramsey, O. T. Koppius, and E. L. Cleveland, *Jour. Opt. Soc. Am.*, **31**, 202 (1941).

minima. The new intensity distribution may be obtained by summing up the three distribution curves. If this is done it will be found that the effect of increasing the slit width by three times has been primarily to increase the intensity of the central maximum by approximately three times without broadening the intensity distribution curve materially and, therefore, without substantially influencing the separation required for resolution.

As the slit is widened further, the central maximum continues to increase in intensity but at a proportionately lesser rate. Finally, when the slit is sufficiently wide to give a geometrical image of about half the width of the original diffraction pattern, as measured between the two minima lying at either side of the central maximum, further increase in slit width contributes negligibly to the intensity of the central maximum. The principal effect of further opening of the slit is to increase the effective width of the diffraction pattern and thus to increase the wavelength difference necessary in order that two neighboring spectrum lines may be separated.

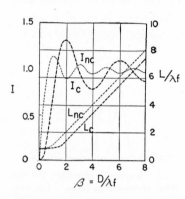

Fig. 6.3. Variation of intensity, *I,* of the central diffraction maximum, and of the half-intensity line width, *L,* as a function of the slit-width factor β. $\beta = D/\lambda f$, where *D* is the slit width, λ is the wavelength and *f* is the aperture ratio of the collimator lens. The subscripts *c* and *nc* refer respectively to coherent and noncoherent illumination of the slit, values for which are from van Cittert[2].

Figure 6.3 shows the variation of the intensity of the central maximum and of the line breadth with slit width, in accordance with the theoretical results of van Cittert.[2]

Curves are given for cases in which the slit is illuminated by noncoherent and coherent radiation, and results for any actual case will usually lie somewhere between the two sets of curves.

In particular, one should note that for any spectrograph there is a critical slit width, corresponding to an optical image about one-fourth to one-half the width of the central diffraction maximum, beyond

---

[2] P. H. van Cittert, *Zeitschr. f. Phys.*, **65**, 547 (1930); **69**, 298 (1931).

which the peak intensity of a spectrum line is influenced but little as the slit is widened, whereas its breadth increases greatly. Under circumstances where maximum resolution is desired without undue increase in time of exposure, one should use this critical slit width. This width can be calculated from the formula $D = \beta f \lambda$, where D is the width of the slit, λ is the wavelength considered, and f is the numerical aperture of the system, usually taken as the focal length of the collimator lens divided by its diameter. The factor β lies between 1 and 2, being approximately 2 for coherent radiation and 1 for noncoherent (see Fig. 6.3). Thus, for a prism spectrograph having a collimator lens of 5 cm diameter and of 40 cm focal length ($f = 40/5 = 8$), the critical slit width for λ 5000 A is 40,000 A or 0.004 mm for noncoherent radiation and 0.008 mm for coherent. Because a wide range of wavelengths is usually involved and the radiation is likely to be a mixture of coherent and noncoherent, in any actual case it is best to calculate the approximate critical slit width, set the slit at some value less than this, and then gradually widen the slit while observing the illumination behind the slit on a white card. As the critical slit width is reached, a considerable increase in brightness is observed, beyond which the brightness increases very slowly.

Another procedure makes use of the diffraction pattern produced by the slit itself upon illumination with coherent light. The central maximum of this pattern just fills the collimator with light when the slit is sufficiently narrow to produce a geometrical image half as wide as the half breadth b of the spectral diffraction patterns.* The slit is illuminated by an approximately point source placed on the optic axis at a distance of 25 cm or more. Starting with a slit width too great to fill the collimator with light by diffraction, the observer narrows the slit until, on looking through the system from the position of the spectrum, he sees the central diffraction maximum fill about two-thirds of the collimator.

The above adjustments must be made with visible light. Since the appropriate slit width for the condition desired depends upon the wavelength, this factor should be taken into account in making proportionate adjustments for the wavelength region to be employed.

When maximum resolution is desired, it is customary to try first a slit width corresponding to an optical image about one-fourth to

---

* This statement is true only when the collimator and the dispersing element have the same effective aperture, which is usually the case.

one-half the width of the diffraction pattern. Theoretically, this width should give a good compromise between maximum line intensity and best possible resolution. One then experiments with slightly different slit widths until the best results are obtained.

The effects of slit width on spectral purity for the noncoherent and coherent modes of illumination have been considered theoretically and experimentally by several workers, including Schuster,[3] van Cittert,[2] Münster,[4] and Stockbarger and Burns.[5] Precise analyses from the standpoint of diffraction theory are of limited applicability to practical cases, both because the illumination of the slit is in practice never completely coherent or incoherent and because effects other than diffraction, such as aberrations, influence the practical results.

6.4. Filling the Aperture of the Spectroscope with Light. When the slit is wide enough so that diffraction effects may be neglected (slit width $> 2\beta f\lambda$), light may be considered as traveling in straight lines through the slit to the collimator, and the conditions for filling the aperture of the spectroscope with light may be determined by simple geometrical considerations. It will be assumed (a) that the entire effective width of the collimator must be filled with radiation to achieve maximum resolution, and (b) that the entire apertures of both slit and collimator must be filled to achieve maximum transmission of radiant power into the spectrum. Sometimes the design of the system is such that some component other than the collimator, such as a prism or telescope lens, acts as a limiting aperture stop, thereby reducing the area of the collimator aperture that can contribute effective radiation to the system. In such cases it is the *effective* aperture of the collimator, as limited by the smallest aperture stop or dispersing element in the system, that must be illuminated. If both slit and collimator are filled with light, no additional system of lenses or mirrors will increase the total radiant flux through the system.

The entire spectroscope aperture will be filled with radiation when lines drawn from any position within the effective area of the collimating component through any portion of the slit intersect an emitting area of the source. The angle that must be filled with

---

[3] A. Schuster, *Theory of Optics*. London: Edward Arnold, 1909. Also *Astrophys. Jour.*, **21**, 197 (1905).

[4] C. Münster, *Ann. d. Physik*, **15**, 619 (1932).

[5] D. C. Stockbarger and L. Burns, *Jour. Opt. Soc. Am.*, **23**, 379 (1933).

radiation in any plane passing through the optic axis of the collimator is defined by the most oblique rays that can be drawn from the edges of the effective aperture of the collimator past edges of the slit (for example the solid lines in Fig. 6.4).

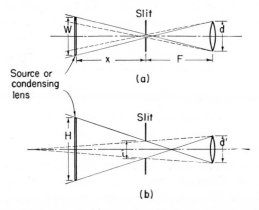

Fig. 6.4. Geometrical condition for filling the spectroscope aperture with light. (a) Section of collimating system in plane perpendicular to slit. (b) Section of collimating system in plane parallel to slit.

Many sources are too small to fill the limiting angles with radiation even when placed close to the slit, or they cannot be placed close enough to the slit to fill the collimator. Condensing lenses of sufficient aperture (Fig. 6.5) are then used.

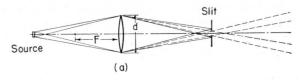

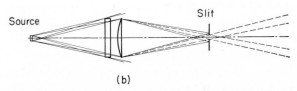

Fig. 6.5. Use of condensing lenses to fill the spectroscope aperture with light when the source is too small to accomplish this purpose.   (a) Spherical condensing lens. (b) Two cylindrical condensing lenses.

6.5. **Use of a Condensing Lens or Mirror.** In many uses of the spectroscope, an image of the source is formed on the slit with a condensing lens. If the lens is to be used throughout the visible and ultraviolet, it may conveniently be an achromatic triplet with two outer components of quartz and an inner component of fluorite. A simple quartz lens, which has small chromatic aberration in the visible, or a glass achromatic lens, will serve for the visible. The problem of chromatic aberration is eliminated if a spherical concave mirror is used (preferably one coated with aluminum for the visible and ultraviolet), but the geometry of the condensing system is not so convenient as with a lens.

When an image of the source is formed on the slit of a stigmatic spectroscope, the spectrum lines will not be of uniform intensity throughout, since different parts of the source will contribute to different parts of each line. An astigmatic spectroscope will tend to diminish these differences and produce more uniform and better appearing lines. These do not, however, reveal so much information regarding variation in radiation from different parts of the source.

The approximate linear dimensions of the source or condensing lens required to fill the effective aperture of the collimator may be computed as follows. Let the focal length of the collimating component be F and its aperture ratio $f = F/d$, where d is the width of this component. Let the length of the slit be l and the distance from the source—or from the condensing lens if one is used—to the slit be x. The width of the slit may be neglected in this computation. If the required dimension of the source or condensing lens in the direction parallel to the slit is called the height H, then, to a first approximation,

$$H = x\frac{d}{F} + l\left(\frac{x}{F} + 1\right) \tag{6.1}$$

If x is small in proportion to F, the second term in this equation is approximately equal to the slit length, l. If the required dimension of the source or condensing lens in the direction perpendicular to the slit is called W, then

$$W = x\frac{d}{F} \tag{6.2}$$

Thus for a collimator lens of aperture ratio $f/10$ and of 25 cm focal length, a slit length of 0.4 cm, and a source-to-slit distance of 10 cm, $H = 2.72$ cm and $W = 2.0$ cm.

If maximum resolution is the primary consideration, coherent radiation should fill the aperture of the dispersing element in the plane perpendicular to the slit. Filling the aperture in the plane parallel to the slit also is essential if maximum radiant power is to be transmitted into the spectrum, but coherence is not so important in this direction.

The aperture required to fill a collimator with light thrown onto the slit by a condensing lens or mirror may be computed most readily for the simple case in which the distance from the source to the condensing lens is the same as that from the condensing lens to the slit. Then, in the horizontal plane, if a broad slit is used, the f number or numerical aperture of the condensing lens must be half that of the collimator lens to fill the collimator with light. If complete filling with light is desired in the vertical plane, the f number of the condenser must be still less than one-half that of the collimator. This setup, giving unit magnification, is frequently used with sources about equal to the slit in length. Often, however, it is desired to form an enlarged image of the source on the slit because the length of the useful emitting area of the source is less than that of the slit. In such instances, the f number of the condensing lens for complete filling of the spectroscope aperture must be smaller than for unit magnification. Conversely, if less than unit magnification is permissible, complete filling of the spectroscope aperture with light may be accomplished with a condenser of greater f number than is required for unit magnification. Application of the simple lens formula enables one to determine the slit-to-condenser distance, x, for these various cases, after which the size of lens required may be computed from Eqs. (6.1) and (6.2).

With arc and spark sources, a magnification of about fourfold is ordinarily found convenient to keep the collimator and dispersing element filled with light while the arc and spark wander.

There is no objection to using a condenser lens of more than sufficient aperture to fill the collimator, provided the light sent into the spectroscope at an angle greater than that necessary to fill the collimator is not scattered into the spectrum. Where scattered light is apt to be troublesome, it is important to stop the condenser down until it just fills the collimator with light.

6.6. Uniform Illumination of the Slit. Uniformity of illumination of the slit along its length is sometimes important, as in certain methods of photographic photometry and in quantitative emission analysis. In other applications, for instance in studying with a stigmatic spectrograph the spectral emission from different areas of a source, it is important that the slit illumination be not uniform but rather that an image of the source be formed on the slit.

Nearly uniform slit illumination may be attained by using a small source, without a condensing lens, placed at a considerable distance from the slit (for example, a 0.5-cm source at 25 cm source-to-slit distance). With this arrangement, each point on the source illuminates every point on the slit, with negligible variation in intensity as a result of variation in angle at which different rays are emitted from the source or of differences in path lengths along different rays. This method does not take full advantage of the resolving power of the spectroscope system unless the slit is narrow enough to fill the collimator with diffracted light. Also, since only that part of the slit length is used which subtends the angle of the collimator at the source, the uniform lines produced are apt to be short.

Uniform slit illumination may be obtained more satisfactorily by the use of a condensing lens placed immediately in front of the slit

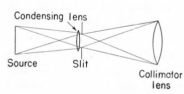

(Fig. 6.6). The source is placed at such a distance from the condensing lens that an image of the source is formed on the collimator. Each portion of the source illuminates the entire condensing lens, and hence the entire length of the slit. Such illumination is not precisely uniform, since the path length and angle of emission vary slightly

Fig. 6.6. Use of a spherical condensing lens immediately in front of the slit to achieve uniform slit illumination.

for rays to different points on the lens, but this effect is almost completely averaged out in the summing up of illumination from all portions of the source. The method is less wasteful of light than the previous one, and the full aperture of the spectroscope will be filled with radiation if the source is magnified to fill the collimator.

A third method of uniform slit illumination involves the use of a cylindrical condensing lens placed with its axis parallel to the slit (Fig. 6.7) at such a position that rays in the horizontal plane focus an image of the source on the slit but rays in the vertical plane pass through the lens approximately undeviated. If the diameter of the cylindrical lens is sufficient, this arrangement fills the width of the collimator with radiation and thereby enables the attainment of optimum resolution.

One can obtain uniform slit illumination and at the same time fill both slit and collimator with radiation by using two cylindrical lenses, as in Fig. 6.8. This method is due to G. Hansen. The first lens is so chosen as to throw a vertical line of light on the slit, focused only in the horizontal direction. The second lens, placed at the slit

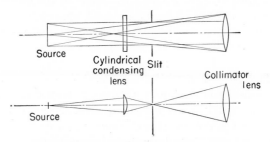

Fig. 6.7. Use of cylindrical condensing lens immediately in front of the slit to achieve uniform slit illumination.

with its axis horizontal, throws an image of the source on the collimator as a horizontal band of light focused in the vertical direction only. With such a system, the maximum resolution of the prism or grating is available, since it is filled with coherent light across its breadth and both slit and collimator are filled with radiation.

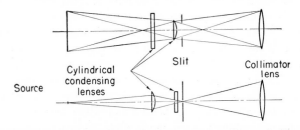

Fig. 6.8. Use of two cylindrical lenses to obtain uniform slit illumination and maximum total illumination.

Desirable focal lengths for the two cylindrical lenses may be computed as follows. The horizontal lens at the slit should fill the collimator vertically. To obtain this result when an arc or spark is used often requires at least fivefold magnification (tenfold might be better but is less practicable). Substituting the slit-collimator distance as v in the lens formula $1/F = 1/u + 1/v$ and in the relation $v = 5u$, we have, in the case of a 21-ft grating, $v = 21$ ft. (approximately),

$u = 50$ in., and $F = 42$ in. Here u is the distance from source to slit and equals $u' + v'$ for the vertical lens which is to focus the source on the slit horizontally. Since it is convenient to magnify an arc or spark about four times on the slit, $v' = 4u'$; and since $v' + u' = 50$ in., $u' = 10$ in. and $v' = 40$ in. Substituting again in the lens equation, we have F', the focal length of the first cylinder, as 8 in. If quartz cylindrical lenses are used, they will serve without correction through the visible and into the ultraviolet. For wavelengths shorter than 3500 A they may be refocused or different lenses may be used, but ordinarily one set of lenses will serve from 2000 to 10,000 A, since the collimator focusing need be only approximate.

6.7. Illumination of the Slit by a Source Extended in Depth. The illumination of the slit by a source of extended depth occurs in Raman spectroscopy and in the use of such sources as a hydrogen discharge tube viewed end on. It is important to obtain the most effective slit illumination under these conditions, since the radiance of any particular section of such a source is usually low. This problem has been considered by Wood[6] and by Nielsen.[7]

Usually, so little absorption or scattering of the radiation by successive layers along the axis of the source occurs that a considerable depth of the source may be made to contribute to the illumination of the slit. If the end of the source is placed close to the slit and if the various sections are extended enough so that each fills the full aperture of the spectroscope system with light, the available radiation will be used effectively. The length of the source is often so great in proportion to its width that layers some distance from the slit are not of sufficient area to fill the spectroscope aperture with light. Under such conditions, a condensing lens may be used and the optimum conditions of illumination determined by trial. One should start with a setup in which the farther end of the source is focused on the slit and then move the condensing lens to bring various sections of the source into focus until maximum brightness of the spectrum is obtained.

6.8. Illumination to Obtain Maximum Radiant Intensity or Total Radiant Power in the Spectral Image. It is often desirable to obtain either (a) the greatest possible radiant intensity (radiant power per unit area) or (b) the greatest possible radiant power in the spectral image. These two requirements should be distinguished

---

[6] R. W. Wood, *Physical Optics*. New York: The Macmillan Company, 1934.

[7] J. R. Nielsen, *Jour. Opt. Soc. Am.*, **20**, 701 (1930); **37**, 494 (1947).

clearly from each other, since they may be accomplished in different ways.

The need for maximum radiant intensity in the spectral image occurs most frequently in spectrography, and to a somewhat more limited extent in photochemical and photobiological investigations by means of monochromatic radiation. In spectrography, the required exposured time is an inverse function of the radiant power per unit area incident upon the photographic plate. Obviously, intensity is what is wanted in this case, since the area of plate illuminated by a spectrum line is likely to be of secondary importance. If the receptor is a photocell, on the other hand, and if all of the incident beam is intercepted by the cell no matter what the optical arrangement, the radiant power rather than the intensity is of importance. In the first case it might be of advantage to use a camera lens of shorter focal length than the collimator lens, to reduce the area of each spectrum line and hence increase its intensity, whereas in the second case this lens would merely increase the difficulty of separating lines, the total radiant power for a given spectral range remaining the same.

Four factors determine the total radiant power available within a given wavelength range of the spectral image: (1) the radiant power per unit solid angle per unit projected area of the source, a factor known as the *steradiancy;* (2) the area of the source effective in illuminating the spectrum; (3) the solid angle of radiation from the source effective in illuminating the spectrum; and (4) the transmission factor, B, of the spectroscopic system as determined by absorption and reflection losses, etc. These factors will be considered in the above order.

For any particular wavelength, the limit to the brightness (radiant power per unit solid angle per unit area) of the spectral image is determined by the steradiancy of the source at that wavelength. This limit arises from the fact that it is impossible with any optical system to form an image of a source that is brighter, or of greater steradiancy, than the source itself.

Lenses or mirrors may, of course, be used to form enlarged or reduced images of the source. The ratio of the area of the image, a_2, to that of the object, a_1, is the same, however, as the ratios of the solid angles, ω_2 and ω_1, within which the radiation leaves the source and enters the image. Thus if a_2 is less than a_1, more radiant power per unit area is delivered into the image than is collected from the source, but this increased power per unit area of the image is accompanied by a proportionate increase in the solid angle through which the radiation illuminates the image (see Fig. 6.9). Insofar as geometrical considerations are concerned, the radiant power per unit area per unit solid angle entering the image therefore remains constant, and no gain in brightness or steradiancy would be accomplished by forming a reduced image. In practice, some loss in steradiancy is always to be expected when an image is formed, as a result of reflection or absorption losses in the image-forming components. These considerations show that for the greatest brightness of the spectral image it is essential to select from otherwise suitable sources the one having highest steradiancy in the wavelength region of interest (see Chapter 8).

Once a source of the highest practicable steradiancy has been chosen, the next step in achieving maximum useful radiant power in the spectral image is to make use of cones of radiation, each of which will fill the entire aperture of the spectroscopic system, from as large

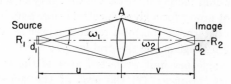

Fig. 6.9. To illustrate that the steradiancy is not increased by forming a reduced image of a source (see text).

an area of the source as feasible. The simplest case to consider is one where the source is placed in juxtaposition to the slit, so that the slit itself effectively acts as the primary source of radiation. Every point on an area of the source corresponding to the slit opening will then illuminate the entire aperture of the spectroscope system (provided the source radiates through a sufficiently wide angle, which is usually the case). Gain in illumination can then be achieved by widening the slit up to the point at which the slit width equals the source width, but this gain is obtained at the expense of loss in spectral purity. In general, there will be some limiting slit width, determined by the required spectral purity, beyond which it is not feasible to go.

If the source cannot be placed in juxtaposition to the slit, a condensing lens or mirror may be used, as described in § 6.5, to form an image of the source on the slit. If we assume that the slit has been opened to the maximum width allowable, the greatest radiant power is then transmitted into the system when (a) the source image is just sufficiently large to cover the slit opening and (b) the condensing lens is large enough to fill the aperture of the spectroscope system with radiation. The proper focal length and size of condensing lens may be computed as described previously.

The fourth factor mentioned above, namely the transmission factor B, is fixed by the choice of the spectroscopic system to be used and cannot be altered greatly by the method of illumination.

6.9. Factors Governing the Radiant Power Transmission of a Spectroscopic System. In the preceding section, it was assumed that a particular spectroscopic system was to be used, and the illumination conditions necessary to transmit maximum radiant power into the spectral image were considered. If some choice between spectroscopic systems is possible or if a new system is to be designed, it may be of considerable importance to consider the factors that determine the total radiant power which can be transmitted by various types of spectroscopic systems under optimum conditions of illumination.

As is discussed in § 6.12, for a given spectral purity the amount of radiant power that can be transmitted by any spectroscopic system is directly proportional to the product of the effective area of the dispersing component, A, the angular dispersion, $d\theta/d\lambda$, and the transmission factor B (determined by absorption and reflection losses, as stated in § 6.8), provided the open area of the slit and the entire aperture of the system are filled with radiation. Thus, if $d\theta/d\lambda$ and B are constant, the radiant power transmission of a spectroscopic system can be increased roughly as the square of its linear dimensions by scaling it up. Theoretically, a size can be reached, of course, beyond which further increase results in such large slit openings and apertures that it is impracticable to fill these with light with usual sources and condensing lenses, but such limits are seldom reached in practice.

It is important to note again the difference between total radiant power and intensity in the spectral image. For a spectroscopic system of given power transmission, the intensity of the spectral image may be increased, within limits, by concentrating the spectrum on a smaller area through the use of a telescope of shorter focal length than the collimator. In a spectrograph for photographing weak sources, this effect may be advantageous, but the extent to which the ratio of telescope to collimator focal lengths can be decreased is limited either (a) by the smallness of the spectral image which is acceptable or (b) by the maximum obtainable relative aperture of the telescope.*

Before considering in greater detail the factors involved in the radiant power transmission of spectroscopic systems, the effect of slit width on spectral purity will be discussed.

6.10.   Effect of Entrance Slit Width on Spectral Purity.   In several types of photographic photometry, it is convenient to use a slit wide enough to produce a flat top on the widest spectrum line to be measured.   Figure 6.10 shows the contours of a spectrum-line image, first with a narrow slit and then with a wide slit.   If two lines are to be compared in intensity, the marked variation in intensity throughout the width of the line image requires careful measurement in the first

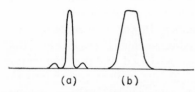

(a)   (b)

Fig. 6.10.   Spectrum-line contours.   (a) For narrow slit. (b) For wide slit.

case.   In the second case, the flat-topped portion of each line contains a contribution from every part of its contour, and hence a single measurement on this flat-topped portion gives a value that is proportional to the intensity of the line.   Widening the slit so as to obtain a flat-topped image results, of course, in some loss of effective resolving power, but this can usually be tolerated without serious difficulty in such applications as quantitative emission analysis.

Slits wider than those which give optimum resolution must also be used with many spectrometers and monochromators employed for spectrophotometry, photochemical investigations, and similar uses. In such applications, the transmission of large amounts of radiant power into the spectrum is often essential, and it is customary to use entrance slit widths many times those required for maximum resolution.

In most applications involving wide slits, the slit width is such that its image is many times the width of the central diffraction maximum.   Under these circumstances, the contributions of diffraction to the slit image may be neglected, and it may be assumed that the spectrum consists of optical images of the slit formed according to the ordinary laws of geometrical optics.   If the plane of the spec-

---

* As the focal length of the telescope is decreased, its diameter must be kept constant if it is to accept the full light beam from the collimator, and thus its relative aperture must be increased.

trum is perpendicular to the axis from it to the collimator (that is, if no plate tilt is necessary), the size of the optical image is equal to that of the slit multiplied by the magnification of the optical system. This magnification equals F_2/F_1, where F_1 and F_2 are, respectively, the focal length of the collimator and telescope. Thus if w and w' are, respectively, the width of the entrance slit and its image, and l and l' are, respectively, the lengths of the slit and slit image, then

$$w' = w \frac{F_2}{F_1} \qquad (6.3)$$

$$l' = l \frac{F_2}{F_1} \qquad (6.4)$$

Or, since the slit area a and the image area a' are, respectively, equal to wl and $w'l'$,

$$a' = a \left(\frac{F_2}{F_1}\right)^2 \qquad (6.5)$$

If the spectral plane is appreciably inclined to the axis of the collimator, the slit images will be broadened as a result, the broadening factor being equal to the cosecant of the angle of inclination.

When a wide slit is used to form images of widths w_1' and w_2' of two spectrum lines of wavelengths λ_1 and λ_2, the line images will just be separated in the spectrum, without overlapping, when $\frac{1}{2}w_1' + \frac{1}{2}w_2' = \Delta l$, where Δl is the distance between the positions in the spectrum corresponding to λ_1 and λ_2 as observed with narrow slits corresponding to maximum resolution. In instances such as a mercury-arc spectrum in which the spectrum lines are widely separated in wavelength, exceedingly wide entrance slits may therefore be employed without causing overlap of the slit images, and this fact is often made use of when monochromators are required to supply large amounts of nearly monochromatic radiant power.

If wide slits are used with a continuous spectrum, there will be an overlapping of slit images corresponding to an appreciable range of wavelengths at each position in the spectrum. The simplest case is that in which the linear dispersion is approximately independent of λ and the spectral plane is approximately perpendicular to the rays from the telescope, as in the case of normal spectra formed by diffraction gratings. The wavelength interval, $\Delta\lambda$, in the spectrum covered by a single slit image may then be computed as follows: If the angular dispersion is $d\theta/d\lambda$ and the focal length of the telescope is F_2, the linear distance in the spectrum corresponding to the wavelength difference $\Delta\lambda$ is $\Delta\lambda(d\theta/d\lambda F)_2$. This value, however, also represents the width, w', of the slit image. Hence

$$w' = \Delta\lambda F_2 \frac{d\theta}{d\lambda} \tag{6.6}$$

But from Eq. (6.3), $w' = w(F_2/F_1)$, where w is the slit width, and therefore

$$w = w'\frac{F_1}{F_2} = \Delta\lambda\, F_2\, \frac{F_1}{F_2}\frac{d\theta}{d\lambda}$$

$$w = \Delta\lambda F_1 \frac{d\theta}{d\lambda} \tag{6.7}$$

$$\Delta\lambda = \frac{w}{F_1 \dfrac{d\theta}{d\lambda}} \tag{6.8}$$

Within the width, w', of the slit image, there is therefore partial overlapping of other slit images corresponding to a range of wavelengths $2\Delta\lambda$; for if λ_m is the wavelength corresponding to the middle of the slit image, images w_2 and w_3 corresponding to wavelengths $\lambda_m + \Delta\lambda$ and $\lambda_m - \Delta\lambda$ will be displaced just sufficiently so as not to overlap the λ_m image at all. For intermediate wavelengths, there will be intermediate amounts of overlap of the corresponding images with that due to λ_m.

6.11. Effect of Exit Slit. In monochromators, a portion of the spectrum is isolated by an exit slit so that this portion only passes out of the system. If a line source is used and the entrance slit is narrow enough so that the images of the lines do not overlap (see § 6.10), the exit slit may be made the full size of the line image in the spectrum plane without passing radiation of other wavelengths except insofar as scattered radiation is concerned. As pointed out in § 6.10, if a continuous source is used, there is always considerable overlapping of slit images corresponding to different wavelengths, provided the entrance slit is of appreciable width, and the radiation passing out of the exit slit will therefore always be somewhat impure no matter how narrow the exit slit is made.

The type of spectral distribution curve to be expected in the radiation from the exit slit when a continuous source is used may be deduced by extending the considerations of § 6.10. As in that section, it will be assumed that the spectrum is uniformly dispersed and lies in a plane perpendicular to rays from the telescope. Let the width of the exit slit be E and that of the image of the entrance slit formed in the spectrum be w'. If these are equal, the exit slit will pass a range of wavelengths from $\lambda_m + \Delta\lambda$ to $\lambda_m - \Delta\lambda$, where $\Delta\lambda$ is the wavelength range covered by w', for w' is partially overlapped by slit images corresponding to wavelengths within this range, as explained in § 6.10. If the spectrum is of constant intensity as a function of wavelength, the intensity-distribution curve of radiation passing through the exit slit will be a triangle rising from zero at $\lambda_m + \Delta\lambda$ to a maximum at λ_m and falling to zero again at $\lambda_m - \Delta\lambda$ (Fig. 6.11). The half-intensity band width of the exit radiation is, accordingly, $\Delta\lambda$, and the full band width is $2\Delta\lambda$. If the exit slit E is wider or narrower than the entrance slit image w', let $\Delta'\lambda$ represent

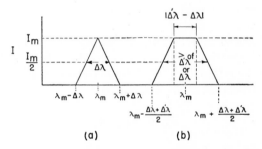

Fig. 6.11. Intensity distribution curves for radiation transmitted by a monochromator with exit-slit and entrance-slit image (a) of equal width and (b) of different width.

the wavelength interval covered in the spectrum by the exit slit, and $\Delta\lambda$ equal that covered by the entrance slit image, as above. The intensity-distribution curve of the exit radiation will then be a trapezoid with a flat top and symmetrically sloping sides (Fig. 6.11b). The full band width of the exit radiation will be $\Delta'\lambda + \Delta\lambda$, the half-intensity band width will be the larger of the two values $\Delta'\lambda$ and $\Delta\lambda$, and the band width of the flat top will be $|\Delta'\lambda - \Delta\lambda|$.

For a given half-intensity band width, the maximum radiant power is transmitted by a spectroscopic system when $w' = E$. However, if an intensity-distribution curve with a broad flat top is desired, w' must be considerably larger or smaller than E.

More complicated cases, in which the dispersion is not linear, the intensity is not a constant function of wavelength, and so on, may be analyzed by extensions of the above considerations. A further discussion of the effect of slit widths in using monochromators is given by Hogness *et al.*[8] and in General Reference 6.3.

6.12. Expression for Radiant Power Transmission of a Spectroscopic System. To obtain an expression for the radiant power transmission of a spectroscopic system, it may be assumed that sources are available for illuminating the system in such a way that the entire entrance slit and collimator aperture are filled with light, as described in § 6.8. Under these circumstances, the radiant power within a given wavelength range $\Delta\lambda$ that enters the system is equal to $R_{\Delta\lambda}wl\omega$, where $R_{\Delta\lambda}$ is the steradiancy (for example, in microwatts per steradian per cm^2) of the source image on the slit within the wavelength range $\Delta\lambda$; w and l are, respectively, the slit width and slit length; and ω is the solid angle (in steradians) subtended by the collimator at the slit. The amount of radiant power $P_{\Delta\lambda}$ of wavelength range $\Delta\lambda$ transmitted through the system into the spectral image is influenced by reflection and absorption losses, and in some instances by vignetting of the beam by apertures farther along in the system than the collimator. If all these factors are lumped together into a single fractional coefficient B, then

$$P_{\Delta\lambda} = BR_{\Delta\lambda}wl\omega \qquad (6.9)$$

The solid angle ω is approximately A/F_1^2, where A is the area of the collimator and F_1 is its focal length. The width w of the entrance slit that can be employed depends on the spectral purity desired. If $\Delta\lambda$ is the wavelength interval in the spectrum that it is permissible for the slit image to cover, then from Eq. (6.7), $w = \Delta'\lambda F_1(d\theta/d\lambda)$, where $(d\theta/d\lambda)$ is the angular dispersion of the system. Furthermore, the length of slit that it is feasible to use is approximately proportional to the focal length F_1 of the collimator, other factors being constant, and hence it is possible to write $l = KF_1$, where K is the allowable slit length per unit collimator focal length. We substitute these values for ω, w, and l in Eq. (6.9):

$$P_{\Delta\lambda} = BR_{\Delta\lambda}\Delta\lambda KA \frac{d\theta}{d\lambda} \qquad (6.10)$$

---

[8] T. R. Hogness, F. P. Zscheile, and A. E. Sidwell, Jr., *Jour. Phys. Chem.*, **41**, 379 (1937).

Thus the relative radiant power transmission, T, of two spectroscopic systems, assuming that $\Delta\lambda$, K, and $R_{\Delta\lambda}$ are the same in the two instances, is

$$T = \frac{P_1}{P_2} = \frac{B_1 A_1 \left(\dfrac{d\theta}{d\lambda}\right)_1}{B_2 A_2 \left(\dfrac{d\theta}{d\lambda}\right)_2} \tag{6.11}$$

The relative power transmission for given spectral purity depends only on the transmission factor B, the area A of the collimator (or of the dispersing component if that is smaller), and the angular dispersion $d\theta/d\lambda$, provided the entrance slit and collimator are filled with light in all instances.

Table 6.1 shows the relative power transmission of several typical spectroscopic systems as computed from Eq. (6.11). In determining the transmission factors B for the various instruments, we have assumed that the transmission of each lens is 0.90 and of each prism 0.85, allowing both for reflection and absorption losses, and that a grating is used which sends 40 per cent of the incident light into the particular spectrum order under consideration. The values of T in the table are based on unity for the small quartz spectrograph, and it is assumed that the dispersing characteristics of the quartz used in the various prisms are the same in all instances.

TABLE 6.1

RELATIVE RADIANT POWER TRANSMISSION OF DIFFERENT SPECTROSCOPIC
SYSTEMS AT 3000 A FOR CONSTANT SPECTRAL PURITY

System	B	$d\theta/d\lambda$, rad./A	A, sq cm	$B\dfrac{d\theta}{d\lambda}A$	Relative power transmission, T
Small quartz spectograph	0.69	6.69×10^{-5}	2.5	12	1
Medium quartz spectrograph	0.69	6.69×10^{-5}	16.8	83	6.9
21-ft grating, Wadsworth mounting, 15,000 lines/inch	0.40	6.0×10^{-5}	75.0	180	15.0
Quartz monochromator (Young-Thollon prisms)	0.59	6.69×10^{-5}	9.0	37	3.1

GENERAL REFERENCES

6.1. R. A. Sawyer, *Experimental Spectroscopy*. New York: Prentice-Hall, Inc., 1944.
6.2. C. F. Meyer, *The Diffraction of Light, X-Rays, and Material Particles*. Chicago: University of Chicago Press, 1934.
6.3. W. E. Forsythe (Ed.), *The Measurement of Radiant Energy*. New York: McGraw-Hill Book Company, Inc., 1937.
6.4. A. C. Hardy and F. H. Perrin, *The Principles of Optics*. New York: McGraw-Hill Book Company, Inc., 1932.
6.5. M. von Rohr, *The Formation of Images in Optical Instruments*. London: His Majesty's Stationery Office, 1920.
6.6. R. W. Wood, *Physical Optics*. New York: The Macmillan Company, 1934.
6.7. F. A. Jenkins and H. E. White, *Fundamentals of Physical Optics*. New York: McGraw-Hill Book Company, Inc., 1937.

CHAPTER 7

Photography of the Spectrum

THE VARIOUS REGIONS OF THE OPTICAL SPECTRUM can be observed
and measured by one or more of four principal methods: photographic, thermoelectric, photoelectric, and visual. Of these, the
photographic method is by far the most important in emission spectroscopy and is useful in many applications of absorption spectroscopy. Photographing the spectrum, which can be done for all
wavelengths shorter than 13,000 A, results in a permanent record
that can be studied at leisure, and makes possible the simultaneous
recording of all lines lying in broad regions of the spectrum. It can
also be used to integrate over a period of time the light from a source
of varying brightness.

In this chapter we consider what may be termed "qualitative
photography," as distinguished from quantitative photography, or
photographic photometry, which will be discussed in detail in Chapter 13. To produce satisfactory spectrograms requires some knowledge of the properties of photographic materials and the most
satisfactory methods of handling them.

The photographic emulsions most commonly used in spectroscopic
work are those classed by the manufacturers as negative materials,
since these are more sensitive to light than positive materials and
have more useful response characteristics. A few positive emulsions
such as ciné positive have recently come into wide use for spectrochemical analysis, however. The light intensities ordinarily involved
in spectrum photography are much fainter than those used in portrait
and landscape photography, and exposure times are likely to range
from a few seconds to several hours. Spectrum photography requires techniques slightly different from those used in ordinary
photography.

7.1. Photographic Plates and Films. Spectrograms from which
precise wavelength determinations are to be made, or with which
permanence and ease of handling are desirable, are ordinarily made

on photographic plates. These consist of moderately flat pieces of glass coated with a thin layer of gelatin containing an emulsion of silver halide salts. Photographic films, which consist of a similar emulsion coated on thin sheets of cellulose nitrate or acetate, are likely to be more uniform in sensitivity over their surface area than plates, and are therefore preferable for making precise intensity measurements. Films may be used with spectrographs that produce a spectrum lying on a steeply curved focal surface to which glass plates could not easily be fitted without breaking. Films and plates each have their own advantages and disadvantages, and their selection in a particular case, apart from the considerations given above, is largely a matter of convenience in cutting and handling.

The negative photographic emulsion is a suspension in gelatin of a mixture of silver bromide with a little silver iodide which has been treated by removal of soluble salts and which has been ripened by carefully adjusted processes to control the sizes of the multitude of silver halide crystals that it contains. These crystals or "grains" vary from 5 μ in diameter down to a size too small to be seen through a microscope, a common diameter being 1 μ. Most of the useful properties of the photographic emulsion depend on the size and size distribution of these grains. The larger the grains, in general, the more sensitive the emulsion.

When a photographic emulsion is prepared in the dark and is then exposed to radiation containing wavelengths to which it is sensitive, a latent image is formed that can be made visible by development. This latent photographic image consists of an aggregation of grains of silver halide that have been altered, presumably in some photo-electric manner, by absorption of incident radiation. Development consists of treating the emulsion with chemicals that reduce to metallic silver the silver salts in those grains which have been affected by light, and do not affect those which have not. The resulting clusters of developed silver grains darken the emulsion locally. To make this darkening permanent on exposure of the whole plate to light, the unreduced silver halide is dissolved, after development, in a suitable chemical solution, usually one of sodium thiosulphate (commonly called *hypo*). This process is known as *fixing*. Also incorporated in the fixer solution is a hardening agent that toughens the gelatin and makes it less sensitive to temperature changes. After being well fixed, the emulsion is washed thoroughly to remove all remaining hypo.

The modern photographic emulsion makes use of chemical amplification, because development involves amplification quite analogous to that produced by vacuum tubes in electronic amplification. Many photochemical processes are known in which absorption of light will produce a change in the color of the chemicals involved, but such reactions are low in sensitivity, since the absorption of one quantum ordinarily does not change more than one molecule.   The photographic emulsion consists of chemicals so arranged that the absorption of a few quanta of light will alter a whole grain of silver halide containing many billions of molecules.   The energy that produces a simple photochemical change comes from the incident light, whereas that which alters a grain in the photographic emulsion comes from the chemicals used in development, the incident light furnishing only enough energy to trigger off the reaction.   Thus a photographic plate or film can be made thousands of times more sensitive than blueprint paper or similar materials which record light and shade by simple photochemical processes.

The latent image, which is detected and made permanent by development, probably consists of minute particles of silver resulting from a change in the positions of electrons in the crystal lattice of the grain.   It is very stable; photographs have been successfully developed years after exposure.

7.2.   Response of the Emulsion to Light.   The degree of blackening of a given spot on a photographic emulsion is usually expressed in terms of its density d, a quantity closely proportional to the amount of metallic silver in a unit area of the image.   Density is easily determined by sending a beam of light through the image with a densitometer (§ 13.12) and measuring the fraction of this light that emerges on the opposite side.   The ratio of the transmitted light to the incident light is called the transmission T of the image.   The reciprocal of transmission is called the opacity O.   Density is the logarithm of opacity to the base 10;   thus

$$d = \log_{10} O = \log_{10} \frac{1}{T}$$

A spot that transmits one-tenth of the light sent through it has a transmission of one-tenth or 10 per cent, an opacity of 10, and a density of 1.

The word *blackening* is sometimes loosely used for opacity, for density, or even for other functions of the transmission, but its commonly accepted definition is as given in § 13.15.

The determination of the response of an emulsion to light is known as sensitometry, and this will be discussed further in Chapter 13. Ordinary emulsions are found to respond as shown in Fig. 7.1, which depicts the densities produced in a given plate by various intensities of light, when the time of exposure and the development conditions were kept constant. A simple S-shaped curve of the type shown is characteristic,[1] though some emulsions show straight-line portions in the center which may be shorter or longer. The curve relating

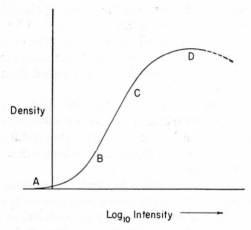

Fig. 7.1. **The characteristic curve of the photographic emulsion.** This curve, sometimes called the Hurter and Driffield or "H & D" curve, shows how the density of the developed image changes with light intensity when exposure time and development conditions are kept constant.

density to $\log_{10}$ intensity is called the *characteristic curve* of the emulsion under the conditions used.

When qualitative considerations only are involved, it is usually immaterial whether density is plotted against $\log I$ or $\log t$, where t is the time of exposure. For this reason it is customary to plot density against $\log E$, where E, the exposure, is $I \times t$. Either the intensity or the time of exposure, whichever is most convenient, can then be varied, when determining characteristic curves like Fig. 7.1. Since time is more easily varied than intensity, a time scale is commonly

---

[1] F. Hurter and V. C. Driffield, *Jour. Soc. Chem. Ind.*, **9**, 455 (1890).

involved when log E is plotted, but in quantitative photometry it is usually essential to vary the intensity rather than the time.

The approximate interchangeability of time and intensity, discovered by Bunsen and Roscoe[2] in 1862, is known as the *reciprocity law*. Although this law holds fairly accurately for certain types of emulsions over a moderately broad range of exposure times, for most emulsions it is only approximate, and for very long or very short exposures to weak or strong light it is apt to be far from exact. Exposure to light of unit intensity for 10,000 seconds, or to light of intensity 10,000 for 1 second, is likely to give a lower density than exposure to light of intensity 100 for 100 seconds. This effect will be discussed further in Chapter 13.

The curve shown in Fig. 7.1 consists of an underexposure region, or "toe," from A to B; a straight-line portion (which may be very short or even nonexistent), which is the so-called *normal exposure* region, from B to C; and a "shoulder," or overexposure region, from C to D. Beyond D the curve may begin to fall again, a phenomenon known as *reversal* or *solarization*.

It is natural to suppose that the most important characteristic of a photographic emulsion is its sensitivity to light. Closer examination shows that this vague concept of sensitivity has only qualitative meaning and that an exact definition of sensitivity is best made after consideration of contrast, speed, and resolving power, which will be discussed individually.

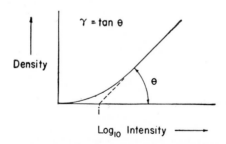

Fig. 7.2.   The contrast, or gamma, of the photographic emulsion.

7.3.   Contrast.   The contrast of a plate or film, usually written γ, is defined as the tangent of the angle θ between the straight-line portion of the characteristic curve and the intensity axis.   (Fig.7.2).

[2] R. W. Bunsen and H. E. Roscoe, *Ann. Physik*, **108**, 193 (1876).

The contrast in an emulsion can be controlled when it is made, by controlling the distribution of grain size. Emulsions in which the grains are more nearly all of the same size have higher contrast than those in which the size variation is great. In emulsions of medium type the contrast is usually near 1, the straight-line portion of the characteristic curve having a slope of 45 deg. In emulsions of very high contrast γ may be as great as 6 or 7, whereas in other emulsions it may be as low as 0.6. An emulsion of extremely high contrast is selected when it is desired to make every part of the picture either black or white, a condition seldom desired in spectrum photography. Use of an emulsion of low contrast gives a response varying only slightly with light intensity, and the resulting spectrogram does not differentiate satisfactorily between weak and strong spectrum lines. Therefore, emulsions of intermediate contrast are most used for spectrum photography.

7.4. Speed, Inertia, and Latitude. The speed of an emulsion has been defined in various ways, but is usually related to the reciprocal

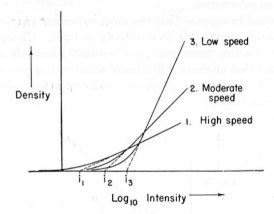

Fig. 7.3. Characteristic curves for typical emulsions of high, moderate, and low speeds.

of the inertia (marked i in Fig. 7.2), which measures the distance between the intercept of the straight-line portion of the characteristic curve with the line of zero density, and the density axis. Most speed ratings have been developed, however, by workers interested in the fields of commercial and artistic photography rather than spectrum spectrography, and hence they involve use of integrated sunlight or artificial light. For our present purpose it is sufficient to remember that speed is an approximate measure of the minimum amount of light required to produce a useful image.

Figure 7.3 shows characteristic curves for typical emulsions of low, moderate, and high speeds. Usually, high speed is associated with low contrast, and low speed with high contrast. High speed arises from the presence of large grains in the emulsion. Since a wide variety of grain sizes usually results if very large grains are present, conditions for producing low contrast often arise.

We think of one emulsion as being more sensitive than another if it will produce a higher density from a given input of light, but it is obvious from Fig. 7.3 that this concept is ambiguous. The high-speed emulsion is seen to be more sensitive to low intensities of light than the others, whereas the low-speed emulsion is more sensitive to high intensities. The concept of sensitivity can be made more rigorous by specifying it in terms of some particular density, for example, $d = 1$. Thus in Fig. 7.4, plotting against wavelength the

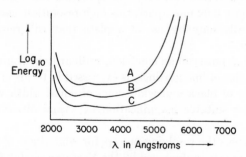

Fig. 7.4. Curves showing the energy required at various wavelengths to produce a fixed emulsion density; curve A, density 1.7; curve B, density 1.0; curve C, density 0.3.

energy required to produce a given density value, we show inverse response curves for an emulsion at three density levels. The concept of sensitivity is useful to indicate the varying response of an emulsion to light of different wavelengths.

The distance along the log E axis subtended by the straight-line portion of the characteristic curve measures the "latitude" of the plate. Strictly speaking, the latitude is defined as the ratio of the exposure at the upper end of the straight portion of the characteristic curve to the exposure at the lower end. Usually, the thicker an emulsion the greater its latitude, and emulsions of low contrast have greater latitude than those of high contrast. In terms of spectrum photography this statement means that selection of an emulsion of too high contrast should be avoided if both weak and strong spectrum lines are to be rendered in densities that are to be directly representative of the log of their intensities.

Latitude depends not merely on the photographic material itself but also on the degree of development used and to some extent on subsequent handling of the plate. Together with speed and contrast, it varies greatly with the wavelength of the light to which the plate is exposed.

7.5. **Resolving Power and Graininess.** A property of the photographic emulsion that is most important to the spectroscopist is resolving power. This property, which measures the ability of a plate to record separately lines that lie close together, depends to a considerable extent on granularity, which also sets a limit to the useful magnification to which a spectrum line can be subjected. If a spectrograph produces two very fine spectrum lines whose intensity maxima are only 0.02 mm apart, this high resolution can be realized photographically only by use of a plate that will resolve 50 lines per millimeter.

The resolving power of an emulsion, ordinarily measured by photographing a series of line gratings, is expressed in terms of the number per millimeter of black and white lines of equal width which can be resolved under suitable magnification by visual observation of the emulsion.

Table 7.1 gives the resolving powers for white light of a number of typical emulsions manufactured by the Eastman Kodak Company.

The resolving power of a photographic material is controlled largely by the contrast of the emulsion and its turbidity. Turbidity, in turn, depends on the light absorption of the emulsion and its scattering power. Resolving power depends greatly on the density that the image attains and is greatest for intermediate densities. Both granularity and resolving power can be improved by using fine-grain developers.

When light in the ultraviolet is photographed, the resolving power of an emulsion is found to be greater than at longer wavelengths. This effect results from the low penetration of the emulsion by short waves, which are strongly absorbed by the silver halide, while wavelengths shorter than 2500 A are also absorbed by the gelatin.

The Eastman Kodak Company has developed emulsions in which graininess has been almost eliminated, but these emulsions are very slow.   When plenty of light is available and a suitable optical system is used they can be made to resolve 500 lines per millimeter or more. The individual grains can be seen only under a microscope of high resolving power, if at all.

In selecting a plate or film on which to photograph the spectrum, one ordinarily decides first whether a fast emulsion is needed, on the basis of the light intensity available and the permissible time of exposure.   If the problem is one of detecting very faint spectrum lines, high sensitivity at low light intensities is needed, which suggests use of a fast plate.   To reproduce both weak and strong spectrum lines on the same spectrogram with correct indication

TABLE 7.1

RESOLVING POWER TO WHITE LIGHT OF TYPICAL EMULSIONS
IN LINES PER MILLIMETER*

Material	P_r
Kodak 50	70
Kodak 40	65
Kodak 33	80
Kodak Panatomic-X	90
Kodak Process	100
Type I-O	60
Type 103-E	60
Type II-C	75
Type III-C	95
Type IV-C	120
Type V-C	160
Type 548	Approx. 500
Type 649	Approx. 1000

* Copied by permission of the Eastman Kodak Co. from *Photographic Plates for Scientific and Technical Use*, Rochester, N. Y., 1948.   The values given apply to an optical image contrast of 20:1, and to the density values for which resolving power is a maximum.   In the case of the last two entries resolution is usually limited by the optical system used rather than by the properties of the emulsion.

of their relative intensities, high latitude and medium contrast are needed.   When a clean, clear background, free from fog, with crisp, sharp spectrum lines is desired, a plate of high contrast is used. Characteristic curves of emulsions suited for these three purposes are given in Fig. 7.5.

Slow contrasty plates show high resolving power.   Such plates are of greatest value for use with spectrographs having low dispersion combined with high resolving power, as is often the case in prism instruments of short focus.   The resolving power of a photographic plate should be approximately matched with that of the spectrograph in which it is to be used.

7.6. **Types of Plates and Films.** Most manufacturers of photographic materials produce plates and films covering a broad range of

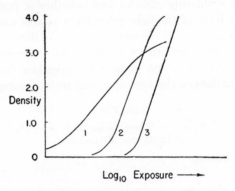

Fig. 7.5. Characteristic curves of emulsions for different spectroscopic purposes. Curve 1 is that of a fast emulsion (Eastman 103–O); curve 2, an emulsion of medium speed and high contrast (Eastman III–O); curve 3, high contrast, fine-grain emulsion (Eastman IV–O).

speed, contrast, and resolving power. Thus at the spectroscopic level of intensity (taken as 0.1 meter candles of sunlight) the Eastman Kodak Company type I–O plate has a speed of 23, and their V–O plate a speed of 0.64. The respective contrast values are 1.3 and 4.5,

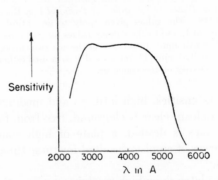

Fig. 7.6. The qualitative variation of the sensitivity of the photographic emulsion through the spectrum. The exact shape of this curve depends on the density level at which the sensitivity is measured.

and the respective resolving powers are 60 and 160 lines per milli-meter.

7.7. Variation of Emulsion Characteristics with Wavelength.
The unsensitized photographic emulsion shows wide variations in sensitivity throughout the spectrum.   Sensitivity becomes negligible at long wavelengths ranging from 4400 to 5200 A, depending on the composition of the silver halide used.   Sensitivity gradually increases toward shorter wavelengths, reaching a maximum in the violet or near ultraviolet between 4100 and 3900 A, and then slowly falling off, as shown in Fig. 7.6, to negligible values near 2000 A.   The broad region of insensitivity between 2000 A and the X-ray region, where the ordinary emulsion again becomes sensitive, results from the absorption of light by the gelatin of the emulsion.

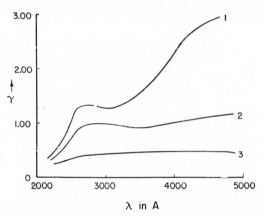

Fig. 7.7. The variation of contrast of several spectrographic emulsion types as a function of wavelength.   Curve 1, typical slow emulsion; 2, medium-speed emulsion; 3, fast emulsion.

The variation of sensitivity with wavelength is usually associated even more closely with variation in contrast than with variation in speed.   Figure 7.7 shows how the contrasts of a number of different photographic emulsions vary with wavelength, and Fig. 7.8 shows the variation in speed of the same emulsions over the same wave-length region.   Sensitivity at longer wavelengths can be greatly increased by adding special dyes to the emulsion as explained in § 7.15.   At shorter wavelengths the Schumann type of emulsion can be used, or fluorescent substances can be coated on an ordinary plate or film (§ 13.7).

7.8. **Storage and Handling of Photographic Materials.** A photographic latent image can be produced, not merely by exposing the emulsion to light, X-rays, or high-speed subatomic particles, but also by applying pressure, heat, or certain chemical fumes such as ammonia. The emulsion deteriorates with age, and unexposed plates that have been stored for a long time are apt to appear dark on development, especially around the edges. The useful life of an unexposed plate can be extended by storing it on edge in a cool, dry place. If plates are stored flat, the weight of other plates may eventually produce a latent image. Plates should never be stored where they are exposed to heat, chemicals, dampness, or burning gases. If they are stored in an electrical refrigerator, some provision should be made for prevention of spoilage by wetting should the power fail and the frost in the refrigerator melt.

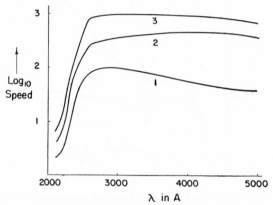

Fig. 7.8. The variation of speed with wavelength for the emulsions of Fig. 7.7.

When possible, plates and films should be obtained in sizes that fit the spectrographic cassettes used, to avoid the necessity of cutting in the darkroom. Standard sizes obtainable for spectrographic work are $1\frac{1}{4} \times 10$ in., 2×7 in., 2×10 in., 2×20 in., $2\frac{3}{4} \times 10$ in., 4×10 in., $3\frac{1}{4} \times 4\frac{1}{4}$ in., $3\frac{1}{4} \times 18$ in., 4×5 in., 5×7 in., 8×10 in., 50×250 mm, and 65×180 mm. Special emulsions designed for spectroscopic use are ordinarily coated on glass, but can be obtained coated on film base on special order.

The flatness of the glass on which photographic plates are coated is of importance, because the sensitivity of the emulsion can be expected to vary over the surface if its thickness varies.   Glass plates are coated by spreading the liquid emulsion over them, chilling to set the gelatin, and drying.   Unless perfectly flat plates are used, the emulsion will vary in thickness.

For accurate measurement of wavelengths in spectrographs in which plates must be bent to high curvature, special glass can be selected which is less than 1 mm in thickness, and plates can be obtained up to 22 in. long coated on such glass.   Even thinner glass plates can be obtained, but they are very fragile.

Photographic plates are usually packed in pairs, with the emulsion sides face to face.   Plates keep better in this way than when the emulsion side is exposed, but it is necessary to prevent adjacent surfaces of emulsion from rubbing together.   For this reason each pair of plates is separated by thin sheets of cardboard at the edges and is then wrapped in black paper.   The emulsion side of the plate can be determined in the darkroom by observing the diffuse reflection in the coated side of a safe light, or in total darkness by applying the edge of the plate to the lips or tongue or biting it gently.

When it is necessary to cut a plate into smaller sections, this can be done in the darkroom by providing a flat board with a rule held in the proper position by pins, so that drawing a glass cutter along the uncoated side of the plate will produce a sharp scratch.   The plates should be laid face down on a piece of paper placed on the board, and only a single cut should be made, the plate then being broken by pressure against the edge of the board.   A sharp scratch rather than a deep one is what is wanted, since the object is not to cut the glass but merely to start the fracture by a high concentration of stresses.   For this purpose a sharp diamond point serves best.

Films may be cut in thin bundles by using a large paper cutter provided with a template so that suitable widths can be selected in the dark.   A number of films can safely be wrapped together without separation if not subjected to abrasion, heat, or humidity.

7.9. The Photographic Darkroom.   The darkroom of a spectroscopy laboratory merits considerable attention.   It should be constructed so that no external light will be admitted unless desired.   If possible, it should be arranged so that it can be entered by means of a double door or lightproof maze.   The former is simpler than the latter, and if provided with an alarm bell that rings when one of the doors is open, safer.   The old-fashioned darkroom, with its walls painted a depressing black, is out of date. If safelight illumination is provided, the walls may be painted light green, cream, or any other pleasing color. When the room lights are on, ample light for good visibility should be available, and when they are off no light should enter the room from outside to be reflected from the walls.

Ordinary plates or films can be developed under a red light, though this should be a safelight, since common red incandescent lamp globes often transmit light in the blue. Panchromatic and other color-sensitive plates must be developed either with a green safelight or in total darkness. A good spectroscopist usually prides himself on developing all spectrum plates in total darkness as a matter of habit.

An Eastman No. 1 red safelight can be used with ordinary plates such as Eastman 33 or type O, if it is desired to observe development, though it is more satisfactory to develop for a predetermined time in developer of a given strength and temperature than to depend on visual observation to determine when sufficient development has taken place. Various filters can be obtained for insertion in the safelights, and green filters can be used with panchromatic emulsions, though total darkness is to be preferred. In developing bromide and other papers, a much greater amount of red light can safely be permitted than with negative materials, and under these circumstances it is desirable to be able to watch development, since it proceeds so rapidly. The safelight can be tested by exposing a section of the emulsion to be developed under the light for twice as long as it would be exposed in development, and comparing it on development with an unexposed portion.

By adopting a definite routine procedure it is quite easy to carry out the standard series of loading and developing operations in the dark. A typical routine for loading a spectrograph plateholder is to place it face down on a dry table, with a closed box of plates on the left. With the back of the plateholder open, turn off the lights and uncover the box of plates, removing two plates in their paper wrapping. Take one of these plates, determine its emulsion side, and place it in the plateholder with this side down. Immediately wrap the remaining plate carefully in its black paper, reinsert it in the box, and close the box. Then close the plateholder, turn on the lights, and load the spectrograph. This procedure eliminates the danger of turning on the darkroom lights to find an open box of plates awaiting disposal.

When possible, it is desirable to provide a "dry" dark room as

well as a "wet" darkroom. Plates should be stored in the dry darkroom, and printing and enlarging equipment can also be installed
there, thus removing it from the corrosive action of chemicals that
may be spilled in the wet darkroom during development or fixing.
An enlarger, properly modified to take long spectrograms, is very
convenient for making reproductions of spectra. Large spectrum
prints are usually made on glossy bromide paper, and contact prints
on ordinary glossy positive paper. When it is very important to
avoid any uneven shrinkage of the print during copying, special types
of photographic paper can be obtained, such as Eastman Aeromapping
paper or Agfa Mapping Special, in which shrinkage has been greatly
reduced.

7.10. Development and Processing. After exposure, the spectrum plates or films are developed, fixed, washed, and dried. Tray
development is ordinarily used for spectrograms. The tray should be
an inch or two longer than the longest plate to be developed in it, and
not much wider than a single plate. It may be necessary to build
special trays to fit plates longer than 10 in. Fresh developer should
be used for each important batch of plates, the plates being placed in
the bottom of the tray, emulsion side up, and the developer being
poured gently over them, the tray then being rocked from end to end
to remove air bubbles on the surfaces of the plates. The developer
should have previously been brought to the correct temperature, as
measured with a thermometer and a time clock should be set to give
an alarm at the end of the selected development period. Provision
should be made for cooling the water to be mixed with the developer
in warm weather, since the temperature of the developer must be
carefully controlled, and the washing water should not be much
warmer than 65° F to avoid peeling or reticulation of the emulsion.

Spectrographic films are not quite so simple to handle in develop
ment and processing as are plates, and manufacturers of spectrographs
that require use of films ordinarily furnish holding devices or special
developing tanks with these as part of the processing equipment.

When quantitative spectrochemical analysis and other work involving photographic photometry is carried on, it is customary to
brush the surface of the emulsion gently back and forth with a
camel's-hair brush to bring fresh developer constantly in contact with
the emulsion and thus reduce the Eberhard effect (§ 7.13).

When the development period is concluded, the plate is removed
from the developer, is held by its edges and dipped once or twice in

the rinsing water (and if desired in a short-stop solution), and then is deposited emulsion side up in the fixing bath.   After it has been in the hypo for a minute or two, the lights can be turned on, but the plate should remain in the fixing bath for at least 10 minutes after the last trace of unexposed emulsion has cleared.   With fresh hypo this should require immersion of not more than 15 min.   Hypo that has become foamy and does not clear up the plate within 20 min should be replaced, but until this foaming occurs the hypo can be used for many batches of plates.

After a plate has been fixed it should be washed in running water. This water should not, however, be allowed to fall on it directly. Fresh water should well up around the surface of the plate in a tray for at least half an hour; then the plate should be "stripped" and placed in a rack for drying.

Stripping consists of holding the plate under the running tap and carefully rubbing it on both sides with the palm of the hand, or with a tuft of moistened cotton, to remove the *bloom*, a filmy layer deposited on it from the tap water.   Remaining droplets of water should then be removed by careful shaking, and the plate should be rinsed on both sides with distilled water and stood in a cool place to dry slowly. When extreme speed is necessary, plates may be measured in the densitometer while wet, but this is usually inconvenient.

When speed is of the greatest importance, the plate may be dried in front of a fan or over a heater, but this should be done carefully. A preliminary rinsing in alcohol to remove some of the surface water and speed up drying is undesirable.   When alcohol is used, the plate should be immersed in it for from 3 to 5 min.   The plate will then dry in 15 sec in a rapid current of air.   However, for most spectrograms it is desirable to use slow drying in a good circulation of dry dust-free air at 75 to 90°F to get uniformity of results.   After drying in racks, in the case of plates, or when hung from clips on a stretched wire, in the case of films, the spectrograms are ready for marking and storing in individual envelopes.

It is especially important that the darkroom be so arranged that hypo will not spatter into the developer tank or get onto the table on which plates are cut and plateholders are loaded, since hypo dust will produce black marks on the emulsion.   Hypo in the developer is much more serious than developer in the hypo, though the plates should be carefully rinsed between development and fixing.   The developing and fixing trays should be so positioned that they can

readily be located in the dark, to avoid the mistake sometimes made
of depositing a spectrogram first in the hypo bath.   Since the developing and fixing processes should be kept rigidly separated, it is common
procedure to provide a sink with a developing tray on one side and a
fixing tray on the other, with washing and rinsing trays between.

The shelves and floor of the darkroom, as well as its walls, should
be kept scrupulously clean, especially from spilled hypo, and the
operator should be able to rinse his hands quickly and dry them on a
towel before he touches anything after his hands have been in the
hypo bath.

7.11.   Developers.   A standard developer consists of a solution of
chemical agents, the most important of which is designed to reduce
to metallic silver the silver halide in the latent image.   Common
developers are amidol, metol or elon, pyrogallic acid, rodinol, and
hydroquinone.   In addition, the developer solution contains an
accelerator such as sodium carbonate or sodium hydroxide, a pre-
servative such as sodium sulfite or bisulfite, and a restrainer, usually
potassium bromide.   The purpose of this restrainer is to minimize
the development of grains which have not been exposed to light.

Probably the most satisfactory type of developer for routine spectroscopic purposes is one that can be kept mixed in large quantities,
so that all the user need do is to dilute it with water just before use.
Dilution is desirable, especially in warm weather, so that the temperature of the diluting water can be chosen to give the proper final
temperature of the developer after pouring into the tray.   A typical
developer of this variety is given in Table 7.2.   This can be mixed
in large quantities but should be kept in stoppered bottles, since
contact with the air will oxidize and darken it.   In large laboratories
developer is often mixed in 10-gal lots, stored in 5-gal bottles, and
when one of these is opened gallon jugs are filled from it.   These, in
turn, are used as needed to fill 8-oz bottles, which can be mixed on
use with 8-oz bottles of water of the proper temperature.   When
three or four spectrograms are to be developed at the same time, a
single batch of developer will suffice, but developer should not be
re-used after it has stood in the tray for a few hours.

When only an occasional plate is to be developed, the standard
commercial M–Q tubes, a metol-quinone developer, will be found
useful.

Most commercial boxes of plates or films contain manufacturers'
formulas for developers recommended for use with the plates.   Many

formulas require that the various solutions be made up in two or three separate parts, which are mixed just prior to use.

For some spectrographic purposes, particularly in high-speed quantitative analysis, rapid development is needed. Under these circumstances it may be worth while to use a two-bath developer in which the degree of development can be more carefully controlled. Neblette[3] gives such a developer, said to produce satisfactory results in 10 sec, which consists of a 5 per cent solution of hydroquinone with 2 per cent sodium sulfite, followed by a 30 per cent solution of potassium hydroxide. The plates are immersed for 8 sec in the first bath and 2 sec in the second bath at a temperature of 80°F. Neblette also gives a high-speed developer which acts within 30 sec to 1 min.[4]

TABLE 7.2

DEVELOPER WITH GOOD KEEPING PROPERTIES*

Distilled water...............................	10 liters
Elon (or metol)..............................	14 grams
Sodium sulphite..............................	212 grams
Hydroquinone...............................	56 grams
Potassium bromide...........................	150 grams
Sodium carbonate............................	300 grams

* This developer can be mixed in large quantities and kept in stoppered bottles for a number of months. When used, it should be diluted with two parts of water to one of developer. Develop in trays for about 5 min at 18° C.

High-speed development or processing of any kind is undesirable unless speed is more important than uniformity, since results will be more precise and more uniform if processing is allowed to proceed at a normal rate.

7.12. Common Defects in Spectrum Photographs. A beginner who is sent into a darkroom to develop a spectrogram is likely to emerge with a sorry-looking product. However, after a few hours of experience and with very little conscious change in procedures, he will produce acceptable spectrograms that are clear, unmarred, and free from fog and dirt. That this change takes place so rapidly emphasizes the great effect of small variations in procedure. Common experiences of the beginner range from putting his carefully taken exposures into the hypo instead of the developer, loading the plateholder backward, or leaving the box of plates open after removing

---

[3] C. B. Neblette, General Reference 7.1, page 540.
[4] C. B. Neblette, General Reference 7.1, page 540.

one for loading, to manipulations that lead to scratching, frilling, and reticulation of the emulsion.

Specks and dark streaks across the plate are likely to have been caused by particles of hypo coming in contact with the emulsion either before or during development. Fingerprints, scratches, and abrasions can be reduced if a plate or film is held by its edges. Blisters are usually caused by the separation of the emulsion from the glass backing under the pressure of water falling directly against the emulsion. Reticulation, or drying of the emulsion in irregular ridges, results when the wash water is too warm or the hardener affects only the surface of the emulsion; thus frilling and reticulation result when there is insufficient hardener in the hypo bath. Transparent spots are usually produced by air bubbles or grease on the surface of the emulsion that keep the developer from coming in contact with it.

Insufficient development gives a spectrogram that lacks contrast, even the densest lines having a gray look rather than appearing black. A similar effect can be produced by underexposure, and experience is needed to differentiate between the two causes.

Fogging, one of the most common defects in spectrum plates, should be particularly watched for in spectrochemical quantitative analysis and photographic photometry. Fogging is produced by a deposit of developable silver grains in addition to those that are included in the latent image. Fogging arises from various causes, and some experience is needed to distinguish among them. Chemical fog is ordinarily quite uniform over the surface of the plate. It may be caused by improper development or by improperly mixed or spoiled developer. The spoilage is usually from contact with metal. However, general fog all over the plate may be caused by exposure to light, either through use of too strong a safelight during development or through a leak in the plate box, spectrograph, or darkroom. Plates that have been exposed to fairly high temperatures become fogged very readily, and may even fog spontaneously. Fog caused by light leaks can usually be detected if it occurs during exposure or during the time the plate was in the plateholder, because it appears strongest near one edge of the plate or in one corner. Fast plates are in general more susceptible to fog than slow plates, and a good contrasty plate makes a much clearer and finer-appearing spectrogram.

In spectroscopic work the finished picture is usually a negative, and the most important consideration is not the accurate rendition of tone values in a positive print to be made from it, but rather the determination of the positions of spectrum lines, and of their densities. Secondary considerations are high resolving power to separate close lines, freedom from fog to increase the accuracy of photometry, sensitivity to weak light so as to bring up faint spectrum lines, and large latitude so as to make possible the recording of both weak and strong lines on the same plate. For this last purpose it is desirable that the emulsion reach a high density before the contrast falls to a value too low to be useful.

7.13. The Eberhard Effect. During the development process, soluble bromide is formed along with the reduction to silver of the silver bromide in the emulsion, so that the concentration of bromide in the developer increases with use. In parts of the emulsion where a particularly dense latent image is being developed, there may be a

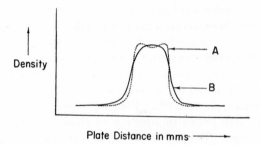

Fig. 7.9. The Eberhard effect in spectra. Curve *A*, measured density in the contour of a strong line; curve *B*, true density in the absence of the Eberhard effect.

high concentration of bromide, which weakens the developer and accelerates the restraining process, causing the so-called Eberhard effect. This effect is of particular importance in quantitative spectrochemical analysis or other processes involving accurate photographic photometry.

The Eberhard effect reduces the density in the center of dense spectrum lines and decreases the background density in the neighborhood of strong lines, as illustrated in Fig. 7.9. The effect can be avoided to a considerable extent by constant brushing[5] of the emulsion surface during development. Motion of the developer by rocking the plate or streaming developer across the emulsion surface ordinarily will not reduce the effect, since it is produced in an extremely thin

---

[5] W. Clark, *Phot. Jour.*, **65**, 76 (1925).

layer of developer that clings to the surface of the emulsion. Some developers are worse offenders than others in this regard.

7.14. Halation and Spreading. Halation, an effect commonly noticed with spectrum lines that have been greatly overexposed, arises from the penetration of light through the emulsion to the glass backing of the plate from which it is reflected and returned back through the emulsion, causing a ring to appear around a dark spot or a rectangle to appear around a line. Halation effects are usually more marked in plates than in films, since in a film the small thickness of the celluloid causes the reflected light to be thrown back directly on the main image. Formerly some plates were painted black on the glass side to reduce halation. Many plates are now backed, the backing being designed to absorb the radiation to which the plate is sensitive, and to be bleached in ordinary processing. Colored dyes on the side of the emulsion next to the glass or film support are also used as antihalation backings. When necessary, halation can be reduced by using a complex developer formula and relatively short development, which confines the image largely to the upper layers of the emulsion.

Spreading is another photographic phenomenon that is important in spectroscopy. The image on a photographic plate will not be confined entirely to the area on which the light strikes, because of halation and irradiation from light scattered in the emulsion so that it strikes grains which otherwise would not be exposed. Spreading and halation both reduce the resolving power of an emulsion and may be of great importance when intense close spectrum lines are studied, since these will be greatly broadened by these effects. To obtain the highest resolving power with a plate it is therefore useful to try surface development. In the ultraviolet region, surface exposure accomplishes the same effect, on account of the decreased penetration of the emulsion by the shorter waves.

7.15. Photography of Various Regions of the Spectrum. Unsensitized photographic plates or films can be used satisfactorily only in the range 2200–5000 A. At longer wavelengths it is necessary to use optically sensitized emulsions. A great number of special dyes have been made for this purpose, providing sensitization as far as 13,000 A. By proper choice of these dyes sensitivities ranging from 50–100 per cent of the sensitivity in the blue may be obtained anywhere in the visible spectrum. Sensitizations for the infrared are weaker, the effective sensitivity generally becoming progressively less with increasing wavelength. The plates sensitized for the infrared are generally improved by hypersensitizing by bathing with water or ammonia shortly before use. A discussion of the chemistry and application of these dyes is given by Mees.[6]

Contrast, and in some cases sensitivity, of ordinary emulsions can be improved in the region 2500 to 2000 A by coating the emulsion with a fluorescent material, such as a mineral oil or one of a number of substances developed for the purpose.[7] Ordinary emulsions can be sensitized to wavelengths as short as 200 A by similar methods. Ultraviolet sensitizing solution can be obtained from the Eastman Kodak Company, who also furnish plates especially sensitized for the short-wave ultraviolet. Ilford, Ltd., of London manufactures "Q" plates that also have excellent characteristics in this region. Schumann emulsions, almost free from gelatin, can also be used. The problem of ultra-short-wave photography is discussed further in Chapter 19.

7.16. Selection of Spectrally Sensitive Emulsions. The sensitivity of an emulsion in various spectral regions can be qualitatively determined by so-called wedge spectrograms, which are made by placing an absorbing optical wedge in front of the slit of a stigmatic spectrograph, thus subjecting a plate to a regular variation in illumination from a continuous source, from top to bottom. Typical wedge spectrograms, obtained for emulsions manufactured by the Eastman Kodak Company, are shown in Fig. 7.10. Approximate wavelengths in angstroms divided by 100 are marked on the spectrograms horizontally, and the height of the light portion at any wavelength gives a qualitative indication of the relative sensitivity of the emulsion at that wavelength. Since such spectrograms are almost always made with glass apparatus, and with incandescent lamps as light sources, wavelengths shorter than about 3800 A are not utilized, and the indication of relative sensitivity at wavelengths less than 4500 A is poor and should be taken as only approximate. The emulsion retains much of its sensitivity from 4200 to 2300 A with almost all dyes.

---

[6] C. E. K. Mees, General Reference 7.2, page 968 *et seq.*

[7] J. Duclaux and P. Jeantet, *Jour. de Phys. et le Radium*, **2,** 156 (1921).

G. R. Harrison, *Jour. Opt. Soc. Am.*, **11,** 113 (1925).

G. R. Harrison and P. A. Leighton, *Jour. Opt. Soc. Am.*, **20,** 313 (1930); *Phys. Rev.*, **36,** 779 (1930).

General Reference 7.5, 5th ed., page 21.

The Eastman Kodak Company manufactures plates sensitive to the various regions of the spectrum, as shown in Table 7.3. From such a table it is possible to choose a suitable emulsion for photographing any desired spectral region at high dispersion. For use in low-dispersion instruments the L type of sensitization covers the entire range from 9000 to 2000 A, but it has rather low sensitivity.

Each of the sensitizations listed is available in various emulsion types, having high, medium, and low sensitivity and medium, high, and very high contrast. The selection of suitable emulsions for a given purpose can be greatly facilitated by consulting the appropriate

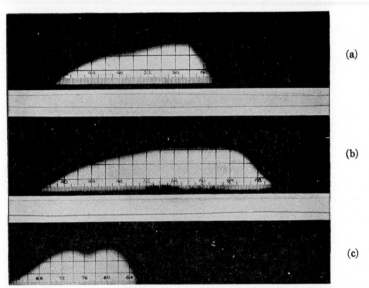

Fig. 7.10. Wedge spectrograms for several spectrographic emulsions. (a) Eastman green-sensitized emulsion G. (b) Eastman Panchromatic emulsion B. (c) Eastman extreme-red-sensitized emulsion N. (Courtesy Eastman Kodak Company, Rochester, New York.)

Eastman Kodak Company publication (General Reference 7.5) and similar publications of other manufacturers.

Most of the dyes now used for sensitization up to 10,000 A are quite stable, but all plates sensitized for the infrared should be kept in a refrigerator as much of the time as is possible. Plates that have been stored thus should be removed some hours before use so that they will reach room temperature before exposure; in this way, surface condensation of moisture will be avoided.

It is sometimes desirable to hypersensitize infrared-sensitive plates with ammonia, particularly those being used for the longer wavelengths. Sensitivity can be increased by bathing the plates for one minute in a 4 per cent solution of 28 per cent ammonia at a temperature of 55°F or less. The plates should then be dried as rapidly as possible in air which is dust-free, and used almost immediately. Hypersensitized plates can be kept for several weeks in a refrigerator, but hypersensitization increases the likelihood of fogging and can be

TABLE 7.3

APPROXIMATE RANGES OF SENSITIVITY OF EASTMAN SPECTROSCOPIC
PLATES

Plate type	Short λ*	Long λ*
O	2,000 A	5,200 A
J	4,600	5,300
H	4,600	5,600
G	4,600	6,000
T	5,500	6,200
D	4,600	6,200
B	4,600	6,600
C	4,600	6,800
E	5,600	6,900
F	4,500	6,900
U	6,600	7,600
N	6,600	8,600
K	7,300	7,900
R	7,400	8,500
L	2,000	8,600
P	8,200	9,200
M	8,600	10,000
Z	10,000	12,000

* All emulsions show some sensitivity in the sensitivity range 2000-5000 A.

carried further if done just before the plates are used.' It is very important that the temperature of the sensitizing bath be controlled accurately.

It is convenient to have available a light-tight box in which sensitized plates can be dried with a blast of air blown from a fan.

The Eastman Kodak Company recommends that the developer whose components are listed in Table 7.4 be used with Eastman spectroscopic plates and states that it is of particular value with infrared sensitive plates. This formula is available in prepared form and can be used without dilution.

Quantitative control and use of the photographic emulsion are discussed in Chapter 13.

TABLE 7.4

KODAK DEVELOPER D-19

(For high contrast on spectroscopic plates)

*Stock Solution**

Water, about 125° F (50° C)..................	500 cc
Elon.......................................	2.2 grams
Sodium sulfite, desiccated.....................	96.0 grams
Hydroquinone..............................	8.8 grams
Sodium carbonate, desiccated.................	56.0 grams
Potassium bromide..........................	5.0 grams
Cold water to make.........................	1 liter

* Dissolve the chemicals in the order given. Use without dilution. Average time of development is about 3 min at 68° F (20° C).

GENERAL REFERENCES

7.1. C. B. Neblette, *Photography: Principles and Practice,* 4th ed.   New York: D. Van Nostrand Company, Inc., 1942.

7.2. C. E. K. Mees, *The Theory of the Photographic Process.*   New York: The Macmillan Company, 1942.

7.3. K. Henney and B. Dudley (Eds.), *Handbook of Photography.*   New York: McGraw-Hill Book Company, Inc., 1939.

7.4. A. C. Hardy and F. Perrin, *The Principles of Optics.*   New York: McGraw-Hill Book Company, Inc., 1932.

7.5. *Photographic Plates for Use in Spectroscopy and Astronomy,* various editions.   Rochester, N. Y.: Eastman Kodak Co., 1933–1948.

CHAPTER 8

Light Sources for Spectroscopy

Light sources, or sources of radiant energy, may be classified according to (a) the method used for exciting radiation, (b) the type of spectrum emitted, or (c) the spectral region to which the source is best adapted (infrared, visible, ultraviolet, or extreme ultraviolet).

In terms of method of excitation, there are four principal categories of sources: (1) *thermal radiators*, (2) *arc sources*, (3) *discharge tubes*, and (4) *spark sources* (see General Reference 8.3). Thermal radiators emit radiation as a result of heating of the radiating surface, as when a current of electricity heats a metal filament to incandescence. Arc sources emit radiation as a result of the maintenance of a comparatively low-voltage ionic electrical discharge between suitable electrodes, under conditions in which the material of the electrodes is evaporated into the arc stream and provides a large proportion of the conducting and radiation-emitting ions. Discharge-tube sources also emit radiation as the result of the maintenance of an ionic discharge, but the source of the ions is a gas at low pressure in an enclosed container, and little, if any, electrode material passes into the ion stream. Spark sources emit radiation as a result of comparatively high-voltage disruptive discharges between suitable electrodes.

The distinction between arc, spark, and discharge excitation is often only approximate. Thus, many carbon arcs depend for their emission primarily on the heating of the tips of the carbons to incandescence as a result of bombardment by the ion stream. Again, when spark sources are operated at progressively higher current densities, they begin to partake more and more of the characteristics of arcs.

In addition to the four principal categories mentioned, there are certain other methods of excitation, such as bombardment by cathode rays or excitation of fluorescence or resonance radiation, that are sometimes useful in spectroscopy.

With respect to the type of spectrum emitted, sources are conveniently classified into three categories according to whether they yield *continuous, line,* or *band* spectra (Fig. 1.5). This distinction is, again, somewhat arbitrary. Continuous spectra often have lines superimposed upon them, and line or band spectra often exhibit an appreciable continuous background. This result is to be expected, since, in general, continuous spectra arise from thermal radiation or nonquantized atomic or molecular-energy transitions (dissociation spectra, for example), line spectra arise from atomic-energy transitions, whereas band spectra arise from molecular-energy transitions; and all these emission mechanisms coexist to some extent in almost every source (see Chapters 10 and 11).

Classification of sources according to the spectral region to which they are best adapted is likewise arbitrary to some extent, but is useful in the choice of sources for special applications. Sources for the infrared are discussed in Chapter 17 and for the vacuum ultraviolet in Chapter 19.

GENERAL CHARACTERISTICS OF SOURCES

8.1. Spectral Energy Distribution. In choosing a source for a particular application, it is desirable to select one that emits radiant energy predominently in the spectral region to be explored. This selection is frequently difficult to achieve in practice. For example, incandescent lamps are excellent sources for many applications in the visible region, yet they radiate more total energy in the infrared than in the visible. The greater the atomic or molecular energy transitions involved in the excitation, the shorter the wavelength region in which the radiant energy may be expected to predominate (see Chapter 10). Thus thermal-emission sources are mainly useful for the infrared and visible regions, arcs for the visible and near ultraviolet, and discharge tubes and sparks for the visible, ultraviolet, and extreme ultraviolet regions.

Sources emitting continuous spectra are particularly useful in making absorption measurements (Chapters 14 and 17). Those emitting line spectra are useful in studying atomic structure and in qualitative and quantitative emission spectrum analysis (Chapters 15 and 16), and in applications in which it is desired to isolate approximately monochromatic radiation.

The general spectral-emission characteristics of various sources are summarized in Table 8.1.

TABLE 8.1

General Spectral Characteristics of Principal Types of Sources

Source	Principal spectral range	Type of spectrum	Principal applications
Blackbodies	Infrared, visible, near ultraviolet	Continuous	Radiation standards
Incandescent lamps	Infrared, visible, near ultraviolet	Continuous	Absorption spectrophotometry, secondary radiation standards
Metallic arcs with incandescent electrodes	Infrared, visible, near ultraviolet	Continuous with lines superposed	Absorption spectrophotometry
Low-temperature thermal radiators	Infrared, visible	Continuous	Infrared spectroscopy
Open carbon arcs and metallic arcs	Infrared, visible, ultraviolet	Line, with more or less continuous background	Qualitative and quantitative spectrum analysis; wavelength standards
Mercury arcs	Visible, ultraviolet	Line, with more or less continuous background	Excitation of Raman effect and fluorescence; absorption spectrophotometry
Discharge tubes	Visible, ultraviolet	Line, band, or continuous, depending on source	Absorption spectrophotometry; spectroscopy of extreme ultraviolet; secondary wavelength standards
Sparks	Visible, ultraviolet	Line	Qualitative and quantitative spectrum analysis; absorption spectrophotometry; spectroscopy of extreme ultraviolet; secondary wavelength standards.

8.2. The Power Output of Sources. The total *radiant* or *luminous power output* is sometimes of importance in choosing a source for spectroscopic applications. The *steradiancy* (radiant power output per unit projected area of source per unit solid angle) or *brightness* (luminous power output per unit projected area of source per unit solid angle) is, however, usually more important, since this is the limiting factor that ordinarily determines the amount of radiant power transmitted through the spectroscopic system onto the radiation receiver (photographic plate, photocell, eye, and so on), as discussed in Chapter 6. For example, an ordinary fluorescent lamp is an excellent source for general illumination but a very poor source for visual absorption spectrophotometry, for precisely the same reason in both instances: while its total luminous power output is comparatively high, its brightness is comparatively low.

Radiant power is measured in *watts*, *milliwatts* (mw), or *microwatts* (μw). Luminous power is measured in *lumens*. One lumen is the luminous flux in unit solid angle from a uniform source of 1 candle power. Since the luminous effect of a given amount of radiant power depends on the wavelength of the radiation and the spectral sensitivity of the observer's eye, the ratios *lumens/watt* and *watts/lumen* can be expressed only for each particular wavelength and in terms of a particular spectral visibility curve (Fig. 1.1). Data representing the lumens/watt at various wavelengths for a "standard observer" have been adopted by the Illumination Engineering Society on the basis of the average spectral visibility curves of a large number of normal persons. From such data and from data on the spectral energy distribution of a source, the luminous power of the source may be determined by step-by-step or graphical methods.[1] *Steradiancy* is measured in watts (or mw or μw)/cm^2/*steradian*, where the area in cm^2 refers to the projected area of the source on a plane perpendicular to the direction in which the radiance is taken. *Brightness* is measured in *lumens/cm^2/steradian*, or in *candles/cm^2*, the area in cm^2 having the same significance as in the case of steradiancy.

The radiant or luminous power output deteriorates with time in some sources, such as incandescent lamps and mercury arcs, but not in others, such as open carbon arcs and sparks wherein provisions are made to keep the interelectrode gap constant as the electrodes wear away. Such long-time changes are usually not important, but

---

[1] A. C. Hardy and F. H. Perrin, *The Principles of Optics*. New York: McGraw-Hill Book Company, Inc.. 1932.

if emission must be kept at or near the maximum, it is desirable to replace deteriorating sources routinely after a fixed, limited period of operation. Short-time fluctuations of radiance or brightness are often significant in spectroscopic measurements, particularly if the radiation-measuring system is not an integrating device like the photographic plate, which averages out random fluctuations.

Radiance or brightness is more uniform over extended areas of some sources, such as ribbon-filament lamps, than others, such as coil-filament lamps. A uniform source is to be preferred in instances in which different portions of a final image field, formed by radiation emitted from different portions of the source, are to be compared.

8.3. Practical Considerations. Practical factors in the choice of sources include simplicity of construction and operation, ruggedness, useful life, availability, and cost. Special considerations regarding the choice of sources for absorption spectrophotometry, qualitative and quantitative emission spectrum analysis, infrared spectroscopy, spectroscopy of the extreme ultraviolet, and Raman spectroscopy are discussed in the chapters dealing with these subjects.

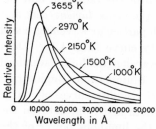

Fig. 8.1. Intensity distribution as a function of wavelength for blackbody radiators of the same total wattage output.

THERMAL EMISSION SOURCES

8.4. Spectral Characteristics of Blackbody Radiation. A blackbody is a body that absorbs all radiant energy incident upon it, neither transmitting nor reflecting any of this radiant energy.* No substance behaves as a perfect blackbody, but very close approximations to blackbodies can be constructed (see § 8.5).

The spectrum of a blackbody radiator is continuous. From the short-wave end, the spectral intensity curve rises rather sharply to a maximum and then tapers off more gradually toward still longer wavelengths (Fig. 8.1). The position of the maximum depends on the temperature of the radiator, in accordance with Wien's displacement law:

$$\lambda_m T = b \tag{8.1}$$

---

* It should be recalled that this discussion is confined to the optical region of the spectrum (infrared, visible, and ultraviolet), hence we are here concerned with blackbody characteristics within the optical region.

where λ_m is the wavelength, in angstroms, of maximum intensity; T is the temperature, in degrees Kelvin; and b is a constant $= 2.884 \times 10^7$. The total radiation depends on the temperature of the radiator in accordance with the Stefan-Boltzmann law:

$$W = \sigma T^4 \tag{8.2}$$

where W is the total radiant power, in watts/cm^2 area of source, and σ is a constant $= 5.735 \times 10^{-12}$. The distribution of intensity as a function of wavelength is given closely by Planck's radiation law (shown here as applied to spectral energy measurements of band width $d\lambda$):

$$J_\lambda d\lambda = \frac{A c_1 \lambda^{-5}}{e^{\frac{c_2}{\lambda T}} - 1} d\lambda \tag{8.3}$$

where J_λ is the spectral radiant intensity (watts per steradian per cm wavelength), $d\lambda$ the spectral band width (in cm), A the area of the source (in cm^2), c_1 the first radiation constant (1.177×10^{-12} watts cm^2), c_2 the second radiation constant (1.4320 cm deg), and e the base of natural logarithms (2.718+). The curves of Fig. 8.1 were computed from Eq. (8.3).

The Planck radiation formula is somewhat cumbersome to handle, and for many practical purposes the Wien formula, which is an approximation of simpler form, may be used without causing appreciable error. This is of the form

$$J_\lambda d\lambda = A c_1 \lambda^{-5} e^{-\frac{c_2}{\lambda T}} d\lambda \tag{8.4}$$

the constants having the same values as in Eq. (8.3). The errors introduced by using the Wien equation are smallest for small values of λT. When λT is less than 0.5 cm deg, these errors are less than probable errors of measurement. Extensive tables giving the radiant power per unit wavelength interval at various wavelengths will be found in the International Critical Tables.[2] Methods of applying the radiation laws to the sensitivity standardization of photographic plates and photocells are discussed in § 13.5.

Those thermal radiators which are not blackbodies do not radiate precisely in accordance with the above laws, but the correspondence is

---

[2] *International Critical Tables.* New York: McGraw-Hill Book Company, Inc., 1929.

sufficiently close to permit computation of the approximate characteristics of the radiation to be expected from such sources when their
operating temperatures are known.

In presenting data regarding nonblackbody thermal radiators,
reference is frequently made to the brightness temperature, radiation
temperature, or color temperature. The *brightness temperature* or
radiation temperature is the temperature at which a blackbody would
have the same brightness or radiate the same power in a particular
wave band as the given nonblackbody radiator. Since blackbodies
are more efficient radiators than nonblackbodies, brightness or
radiation temperatures are less than the true temperatures of nonblackbody radiators. The *color temperature* is the temperature at
which a blackbody would have to be maintained to match the visible
color of a particular nonblackbody radiator, for example a metal.
The color temperature may be much higher than the actual temperature of the nonblackbody radiator, since there is a tendency for the
spectra of such nonblackbody radiators as metals to be shifted toward
the blue as compared with those of blackbody radiators. Optical
pyrometers of the vanishing-filament type measure brightness
temperatures.

8.5. Blackbody Radiators. Blackbody radiators are useful as
standards in the visible and infrared regions because their radiation

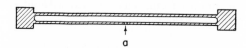

Fig. 8.2. Cross section of a simple blackbody, consisting of an electrically heated
metallic tube with small hole, *a*, through which radiation is observed.

distribution is completely determined by their temperature, as indicated by Eqs. (8.1) through (8.4). A close approximation to
blackbody radiation is obtained by viewing a uniformly heated cavity
of opaque material through a hole that is small in proportion to the
size of the cavity.[3] Various designs of practical cavity-type blackbodies have been described (General Reference 8.1). One of these
is illustrated in Fig. 8.2.

---

[3] F. K. Richtmyer and E. H. Kennard, *Introduction to Modern Physics.*   New York.
McGraw-Hill Book Company, Inc., 1942.

8.6. Incandescent Electric Lamps. These are useful sources for visible, near infrared, and near ultraviolet radiation, because they have highly uniform and predictable spectral intensity characteristics. Thus according to Forsythe (General Reference 8.1), a new gas-filled, single-coil, 115-volt, 100-watt lamp, operated at a color temperature of 2870°K with a rated life of 750 hr and a luminous efficiency of 15.4 lumens per watt, has a spectral intensity distribution in the visible region that can be matched by that of a blackbody operated at a temperature somewhere in the range from about 2865 to 2875°K. Since the radiation characteristics of incandescent lamps are well known and are reliably constant when the lamps are new and are operated at rated voltage, such sources serve as good secondary standards, when calibrated in comparison with blackbodies, for determining the sensitivities of thermopiles and other radiation-sensitive devices.

Data on the brightness and radiance of tungsten filaments are shown in Tables 8.2 and 8.3. Table 8.4 shows the color temperatures and maximum brightnesses of various lamps.

TABLE 8.2

DATA FOR BRIGHTNESS AND RADIANCE OF TUNGSTEN[4]

Temperature, °K	Color temperature, °K	Candles per cm² *	Total lumens per watt input	Radiant flux, watts per cm²
2500	2557	237.5	11.67	67.2
2600	2663	347.0	14.28	80.6
2700	2770	498.0	17.26	95.6
2800	2878	694.0	20.43	112.5
2900	2986	949.0	23.80	132.5
3000	3094	1257.0	27.10	154.5
3100	3202	1647.0	31.0	177.5
3200	3311	2110.0	34.6	203.0
3300	3422	2685.0	38.5	232.0
3400	3533	3370.0	42.6	264.0
3500	3646	4220.0	45.9	300.0
3655†	3817	5740.0	53.1	360.0

[4] W. E. Forsythe and E. M. Watson, *Jour. Opt. Soc. Am.*, **24**, 114–118 (1934).
* Equivalent to lumens per cm² per steradian.
† Melting point of tungsten.

TABLE 8.3

DATA FOR STERADIANCY OF TUNGSTEN[4] AT 2800 °K

λ in A	Watts/cm^2/steradian in 100 A band
3,000	8.8×10^{-4}
4,000	1.46×10^{-2}
5,000	5.98×10^{-2}
6,000	1.29×10^{-1}
7,000	1.95×10^{-1}
8,000	2.44×10^{-1}
9,000	2.66×10^{-1}
10,000	2.70×10^{-1}

TABLE 8.4

COLOR TEMPERATURE AND MAXIMUM BRIGHTNESS OF VARIOUS INCANDESCENT LAMPS

Lamp	Color temp., °K	Max. brightness, candles/cm^2
Regular 50-watt	2670	469
75-watt	2705	563
100-watt	2740	605
200-watt	2810	781
1000-watt stereopticon	3175	2065
Photoflood	3360	3100*
6.4-volt auto	2905	965*
Ribbon filament	2800	694*
Projection	3311	2110*

* Computed.

For spectroscopic applications, concentrated, uniform sources of high brightness (or radiance) are desirable. These requirements are most closely met by projection lamps, automobile headlight bulbs, and ribbon-filament lamps. The latter two types may be used advantageously in applications in which the emission is required to be free from short-time fluctuations, since they are low-voltage devices that may be operated from storage batteries.

The radiant power output of incandescent lamps decreases with time, as a result of evaporation of metal from the filament onto the inside of the bulb. The life L is markedly decreased by increase in the operating voltage V, as shown by the following expression (General Reference 8.1):

$$\frac{L_1}{L_2} = \left(\frac{V_1}{V_2}\right)^{-13} \tag{8.5}$$

8.7. Enclosed Metallic Arcs with Incandescent Electrodes. In this category are several sources in which the bombardment of electrodes by ions in an arc stream raises the temperature of one or more electrodes to incandescence, causing them to emit radiation. These might be classed as arc sources, but since the radiation they emit is principally from the incandescent electrodes, they are included here with thermal radiators. All these sources must be operated in series with ballast resistors or reactors, since they have the negative potential-current characteristics of arcs (see § 8.10).

The *Pointolite* is an enclosed tungsten-electrode arc in an argon atmosphere. For DC operation, it is constructed with a tungsten ball as anode and a tungsten rod-and-coil filament in series as cathode (Fig. 8.3). The AC Pointolite is similar in principle but has two tungsten balls that operate alternately as anodes on successive half cycles. Usual sizes for

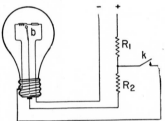

Fig. 8.3. DC Pointolite. b, Bimetallic strip; K, key for starting; R_1 and R_2, ballast resistors.

the DC Pointolites are 30, 100, 500, and 1000 candle power, and for the AC, 150 candle power. Further data are given in Table 8.5.

The *General Electric photomicrographic lamp* is a variant of the S–1 sun lamp, described in § 8.14. It contains a small cup-shaped electrode, about 0.25 cm in diameter, placed slightly behind a tungsten ring of somewhat larger diameter. These electrodes, between which the arc is maintained, are connected by a V-shaped coiled-tungsten filament. The atmosphere in the bulb is argon together with mercury vapor from an excess of metallic mercury. The bulb must be burned base up, so that the mercury pool remains near the tip. The lamp is operated on alternating current from an autotransformer. The cup-shaped tungsten electrode becomes very hot during operation, emitting visible radiation of intense brightness (see Table 8.5). Considerable radiation also arises from the arc stream, the mercury lines being clearly visible in the spectrum.

TABLE 8.5

CHARACTERISTICS OF VARIOUS ENCLOSED METALLIC ARCS WITH INCANDESCENT ELECTRODES

Source	AC or DC	Watts	Volts	Amp	Source diameter, mm	Brightness, candles/cm²		Candle power	Average life, hr
						Maximum	Average		
Pointolite	DC	60	45	1.35	2.5		1900	100	1000
Pointolite	AC	100	50	2.0	2.5		1300	150	1000
G.E. photomicrographic	AC	330	11	30.0	2.5		4800	600	400
W.U. arc	DC	2	37	0.055	0.085	9600	5600	0.32	175
W.U. arc	DC	10	21	0.5	0.4	5500	2200	2.7	700
W.U. arc	DC	25	20	1.25	0.73	4000	2100	8.7	800
W.U. arc	DC	100	15.4	6.25	1.50	5200	3900	77.0	1000

The data in the above table are in general those given by the manufacturers; in some instances independent measurements have been made.

The *Western Union concentrated arc*[5, 6] operates in argon at atmospheric pressure by ionic bombardment of a metallic film of metallic zirconium or zirconium oxide.   It is a DC lamp, operated from a suitable rectifier that provides high voltage for starting and low voltage for operation.   Alternatively, it may be operated in series with a suitable ballast resistor and r-f choke directly from 110-volt DC mains.   Means such as a Tesla-coil vacuum leak tester must then be provided for starting.   The cathode consists of a cup of tungsten, molybdenum, or tantalum packed with zirconium oxide; the anode is a sheet or plate of similar metal.   The lamp is operated under suitable conditions until a thin metallic film of molten zirconium forms on the surface of the oxide in the cathode cup, after which it is ready for service.   The spectrum exhibits a continuum from the incandescent zirconium metal (temperature about 3000°K), superposed upon which are argon and zirconium lines from the arc stream.   The brightness, which is very high initially (Table 8.5), increases with age, whereas the spot size and total candle power decrease.   The current density is about 900 amp/cm² for the 2-watt size, whereas the diameter of the luminous spot is only a few thousandths of an inch.

Descriptions of several special incandescent-electrode metallic arcs in addition to those described herein, are given in General Reference 8.1.

8.8.   Low-Temperature Thermal Radiators.   Several thermal radiators that operate at comparatively moderate or low temperatures (about 2000°K or less) are useful as emitters of infrared radiation (see Chapter 17).

The *Nernst glower* (§ 17.1) is a high-resistance element made principally from zirconium, yttrium, and thorium oxides, which is maintained at an appropriate radiation temperature by passage of an electric current after preheating to make it conducting.   The preheating may be accomplished automatically by an electric heater, or a Bunsen flame may be used.   To ensure constancy of output, photocell-electronic regulating circuits may be employed.   It is claimed that one such device maintains the radiant emission to within 0.1 per cent of the average value.   A typical glower for 110-volt AC or DC operation is in the form of a rod 1 mm in diameter and 10 mm long, and consumes 1 amp at 95 volts.   This source has

---

[5] W. O. Buckingham and C. R. Deitert, *Jour. Opt. Soc. Am.*, **36**, 245 (1946).

[6] *The Concentrated-Arc Lamp: A New Type of Light Source.* Water Mill, N. Y.: The Western Union Telegraph Co.

a negative temperature coefficient and must be operated in series with a ballast resistor. The radiant emission is high in the near infrared but low in the far infrared. The visible emission is sufficiently high to permit use in this region when a uniform source of moderate brilliance in the form of a rod is desired.

The *Globar rod* (§ 17.1) is a resistance heating element commonly used in electric furnaces and heaters. It has a high emissivity in the far infrared and is advantageous for measurements beyond 10 μ. If operated at above-normal voltages, it may have a radiance as high as 60 watts/cm^2, at a brightness temperature of about 1800°K.

The *Welsbach mantle* has high emissivity in the infrared beyond 8 μ as well as in the visible, whereas its near infrared emissivity is relatively low. A piece of Welsbach mantle heated by a gaseous discharge serves as a satisfactory source for far infrared work.

Hot glass, which may be heated by embedded wires carrying an electric current, is a good emitter in the far infrared.[7] *Heated films of crystalline powders*[8] have been used as selective radiators in the infrared.

8.9. Other Thermal Radiators. W. M. Cohn[9] has developed a thorium lamp that depends for its emission on bombardment of a thorium target with an electron stream at 25 kv, 1 ma. This source is nearly free from infrared and red radiation and has a continuous spectrum extending well into the ultraviolet.

Photoflash lamps[10] have maximum intensities of about 360,000 candles and flash durations of 0.03 to 0.06 sec. They emit radiation through the electrical ignition of a thin sheet of crumpled aluminum in an atmosphere rich in oxygen. The maximum temperature reached is about 9500°K.

Luminous flames, such as those of the kerosene lamp, yield continuous spectra as a result of the heating of carbon particles in the flame. They are of insufficient brightness or steadiness to be of interest in modern spectroscopy. Nonluminous flames, such as that of the Bunsen burner, are often used to excite characteristic emission-spectrum lines of Ba, Ca, Na, Sr, and other elements by the insertion of salts of these substances in a hot portion of the flame. This method is mainly useful for demonstrations or as a source of alkali-metal lines

[7] C. H. Cartwright, *Phys. Rev.*, **35**, 415 (1930).

[8] A. H. Pfund, *Jour. Opt. Soc. Am.*, **23**, 270 (1933).

[9] W. M. Cohn, *Physik. Zeitschr.*, **32**, 559 (1931).

[10] W. E. Forsythe and M. A. Easley, *Jour. Opt. Soc. Am.*, **21**, 685 (1931).

when a suitable discharge lamp is not available. Many methods of introducing the materials into the flame have been suggested; one of the simplest and most effective is to soak a strip of filter paper in a solution of the salt and wrap the paper around the Bunsen burner so as to form a tube extending about half an inch above the top of the burner. By the use of oxyacetylene or oxypropane flames, sufficient temperatures may be obtained to excite the characteristic line spectra of more than a dozen elements for quantitative emission analysis, and such sources are used in flame photometry.

A graphite-tube furnace has been developed by King (General Reference 8.1) for studying the high-temperature emission spectra of various substances.

Exploded wires afford a means of obtaining radiation of high intensity, particularly in the ultraviolet. The method consists in discharging a high voltage (about 50,000) from a condenser (of say 0.2 to 0.5 μf) through a thin wire[10] or through an asbestos fiber saturated with a solution of metallic salt,[11, 12] with a minimum of inductance in the circuit. The wire or fiber may be mounted in a groove in a block of insulating material. The discharge is extremely noisy. The spectrum is continuous at ordinary atmospheric pressures except for absorption lines arising from the vapor of the metal exploded.

OPEN ARCS

8.10. Electrical Characteristics.   Arcs between electrodes of materials having high thermal conductivity, such as metals, tend to extinguish more readily than those between materials of low conductivity, such as graphite. This characteristic accounts for the fact that it is very difficult to maintain an arc between metallic electrodes on alternating current, whereas with carbon electrodes this is not true.

The equation relating voltage and current in an open arc is:[13]

$$V = A + \frac{B}{I^x} \tag{8.6}$$

where A and B are constants, I is the current, and x depends on the anode material and is equal to 1 for carbon, 1.38 for tungsten, and 0.67 for copper. It will be noted that this equation indicates a

---

[11] J. A. Anderson, *Astrophys. Jour.*, **51**, 37 (1920).

[12] R. A. Sawyer and A. L. Becker, *Astrophys. Jour.*, **57**, 98 (1923).

[13] W. B. Nottingham, *Am. Inst. Elect. Eng.*, **42**, 12 (1923); *Phys. Rev.*, **28**, 764 (1926).

negative potential-current characteristic; as the voltage increases, the current decreases, and vice versa. It is generally necessary, therefore, to use a suitable ballast resistor (or a reactor for AC operation) in series with the arc to achieve stability of operation. When a DC arc is operated from a suitable rectifier, the ballast resistor may be dispensed with by designing the transformer supplying the rectifier tubes to have effective regulation in controlling the DC output. It is often useful to include a suitable reactor in series with a DC arc to damp out incipient oscillations and to build up a voltage if the arc starts to die out.

Direct-current carbon arcs operate at voltage drops of from 30 to 60 volts across the arc terminals, AC carbon arcs at 80 volts or more, and DC iron and copper arcs at 20 to 90 volts.

8.11. Carbon Arcs. There are two principal types of carbon arcs: *incandescent arcs*, in which the incandescent ends of the electrodes are the main source of radiation, and *flame arcs*, in which the radiation comes primarily from the arc space.

Incandescent arcs may use solid or cored carbons. In DC arcs, the maximum brightness is in the positive crater. The total candle power is directly proportional to the current. The brightness is proportional to the current density. The carbon diameter must be increased as the current is increased to achieve effective stable operation, but higher current densities are attainable, in general, with the larger carbon sizes. The *plain carbon arc* operates at about 55 volts, 4 to 8 amp for small laboratory arcs and 20 to 40 amp for projector arcs. The spectrum of the incandescent carbon arc consists of a continuum arising from the approximately blackbody emission of the hot electrodes (principally the anode in DC arcs), upon which is superposed a series of lines characteristic of the materials vaporized into the arc stream.

Flame carbon arcs use hollow carbons packed with core materials of various substances; salts of strontium, calcium, cobalt, or sodium are frequently employed. The usual burning position is vertical. The highly luminous area is an extended arc stream, roughly ellipsoidal in shape, the projected area of which is approximately equal to that of a circle twice the diameter of the carbons used. For the same current consumption, the carbon size used is generally somewhat larger than that for incandescent arcs (see Table 8.6). The spectrum consists principally of closely spaced lines emitted by excited atoms in the arc stream. By varying the core material, it is possible to modify the spectral emission in particular regions substantially. Appropriate cores give high emissivity in the ultraviolet.

TABLE 8.6

CHARACTERISTICS OF CARBON ARCS AS LUMINOUS SOURCES
(Based on data in General Reference 8.1)

Type	Volts	Amp	Carbon diam., cm	Candle power*†
Plain carbon				
(low intensity)	55	5	0.8	1,350
	55	30	1.2	8,500
	55	40	1.3	11,900
Suprex carbons	32	40	0.6	8,150
	34	50	0.7	11,600
	35	65	0.8	17,100
High intensity	90	195	1.6	88,400
Flame arcs, white flame	55	60	1.5	15,900

* Mean spherical candle power for flame arc; candle at 20° for high intensity arc and at 30° for Suprex 0.7 and 0.8 cm carbons; horizontal candle power in all other cases.

† Emission from crater of positive carbon only in the case of plain and high-intensity arcs; from the entire area of the positive carbon in the case of Suprex arcs.

In continuously operated arcs, the maintenance of constant inter-electrode distance as the electrodes wear away may be accomplished by hand-feed devices or by automatic clockwork or motor-drive mechanisms. Very reliable feeding mechanisms, which should find application in the spectrographic laboratory, have been developed for motion-picture projector arcs.

For AC operation, high voltages (about 2500 to 5000) are sometimes used in spectrographic work to trigger the discharge on each half cycle, the supply circuit being designed so that the voltage drops almost instantaneously to normal arc-operation values as soon as the arc is established.[14]

8.12. Metallic Arcs. Arcs of many metals, such as copper, nickel, cadmium, thallium, and tungsten, are used as spectroscopic sources in the study of emission spectra (Chapters 9 and 15). As an alternative to placement of the sample in a hollow carbon electrode,

---

[14] O. S. Duffendack and K. B. Thomson, *Proc. Am. Soc. Testing Materials*, **36**, II, 301 (1936); commercial arcs of this type are available for use in spectrochemical analysis.

arc electrodes may be formed directly from metallic samples for qualitative and quantitative emission-spectrum analysis (Chapters 15 and 16). Horizontal rotating electrodes have been used in iron arcs to permit long-continued operation. King[15] and Gerdien and Lotz[16]

Fig. 8.4. Pfund arc.

developed special arcs for studying the spectrum of iron and other metals, in which water-cooled electrode holders permit the use of extremely high current densities.

Pfund [17] developed a very steady type of metallic arc, shown in Fig. 8.4, which though ordinarily used with iron electrodes can also be used with electrodes of copper and some other metals. Owing to

[15] A. S. King, *Astrophys. Jour.*, **62**, 238 (1925).

[16] H. Gerdien and A. Lotz, *Zeitschr. tech. Physik*, **4**, 157 (1923); **5**, 515 (1924).

[17] A. H. Pfund, *Astrophys. Jour.*, **27**, 298 (1908).

the reproducibility of the lines produced by the iron arc of the Pfund type, it has been adopted as a source for secondary standard lines (§ 9.8). The source is specified by the International Astronomical Union as "the Pfund arc operated between 110 and 250 volts, with 5 amps or less, at a length of 12–15 mm used over a central zone at right angles to the axis of the arc, not to exceed 1–1.5 mm in width, and with an iron rod 6–7 mm diameter as the upper pole and a bead of oxide of iron as the lower pole." With protection from air currents the Pfund arc can be drawn out to lengths of 20 mm or more. The lower electrode is usually made half an inch in diameter, tapered conically to a cup that holds the bead of iron oxide. To avoid deforming the cup when the arc is first struck, a small bead of iron may be deposited in the cup, the arc being struck with a nail held in an insulating handle. The upper electrode should be made negative, and a suitable ballast resistor and reactor should be used to operate the arc from 220 or more volts direct current, to ensure stability.

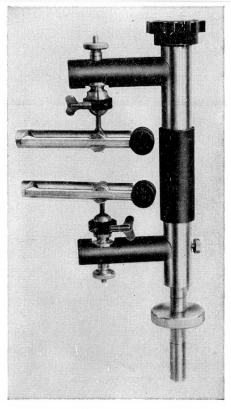

Fig. 8.5.   Arc or spark electrode holder.
(Courtesy Baird Associates, Cambridge, Mass.)

Figure 8.5 shows a convenient type of arc holder for use with rod electrodes. It is characterized by having adjustments that give vertical control of the arc height, and horizontal and arc-length adjustments, so that the operator can keep an arc of proper length centered on the spectroscope slit.

ENCLOSED ARCS

8.13. Electrical Characteristics. Enclosed arcs, like open arcs, have negative potential-current characteristics and must be operated with series resistors and reactors, or from special transformer or rectifier circuits having appropriate regulation characteristics.

The potential drop across a particular arc and the current through it depend on the pressure of the conducting vapor between the electrodes. After the arc is started, a rise in temperature ensues, resulting in an increase in the pressure of the vapor, a decrease in the current, and a rise in the potential drop between the electrodes. The final operating condition depends on the equilibrium temperature between the arc and its surroundings. This temperature in turn depends on whether the arc is ventilated or is cooled by an air blast or by running water. The equilibrium condition is apt to be rather unstable unless the operating temperature is controlled automatically within narrow limits by such means as an intermittent or variable air blast.

The usual operating voltages and currents for low-pressure metallic-vapor enclosed arcs are respectively about 30 to 200 volts and 3 to 8 amp. For high-pressure metallic-vapor arcs, the operating voltage may be 800 or more. The excitation in the arc stream increases as the pressure is lowered, so that vacuum arcs may show higher excitation than sparks.

8.14. Low-Pressure Mercury Arcs. These arcs usually operate at pressures of about 1 atmosphere or less. They are good sources for isolation of monochromatic radiation corresponding to the principal mercury lines, for example in the excitation of the Raman effect or in monochromatic irradiation experiments. Water-cooled arcs, such as the Kromayer and Burdick therapeutic lamps, operate at lower temperatures and pressures than air-cooled arcs, and yield spectra comparatively free from continuous background.

There are three principal types of low-pressure mercury arcs: (1) those with two liquid mercury electrodes, (2) those with a cathode of liquid mercury and an anode consisting of a spiral of tungsten wire (DC Uviarcs), and (3) those with tungsten or oxide-coated metal electrodes and an atmosphere that contains, in addition to mercury, a small amount of argon or neon for starting the arc by ionization.

The first two types of lamps are normally started by tilting the arc mechanically until contact is established between the electrodes, as a result of the flow of metallic mercury through the arc tube, and then restoring the tube to its initial position so that the contact is broken. The tungsten coil must be made positive in the Uviarc; otherwise the arc will go out or the coil will quickly be burned out by bombardment with mercury ions.   A reactor should be used in the circuit to provide an induced high voltage to help maintain the discharge when contact is broken.   Many ingenious electrical and electromechanical devices have been designed for starting arcs of the first two types automatically.   However, when automatic starting is desired, it is now more customary to employ arcs of the third type.   These depend on thermionic emission from the electrodes (or from an auxiliary filament) to excite ions in a gas such as argon, and on the use of sufficiently high interelectrode potentials so that the accelerated argon ions excite mercury ions by collision.   Such arcs, if properly designed, will operate on 60-cycle alternating current with extinction of the arc at each half cycle.

Arcs of the third type are obtainable in envelopes of quartz or of ultraviolet-transmitting glasses, such as Corning Corex.   The latter are frequently used for "sun lamps" in order to restrict the transmitted radiation approximately to the spectral range of sunlight, the short-wave limit of which is about 2900 A.

Data regarding the radiant emission of low-pressure mercury arcs at wavelengths corresponding to the principal mercury lines have been published by McAlister[18] and others (see General Reference 8.2).

Alternating-current Uviarcs[19] in quartz are convenient line sources of ultraviolet radiation down to about 1850 A.   The electrodes are helices of wire, the interstices of which are filled with rare-earth oxides.   The electrode material contributes little to the nature of the arc stream, so these lamps are sometimes classed as discharge tubes rather than arcs, but their operating pressure ($\frac{1}{2}$ to 1 atmosphere) is higher and their potential gradient (about 12 volts/cm) lower than those characteristic of discharge tubes.   A small amount of argon, added to the completely vaporized mercury in the tube, serves to initiate the discharge.   The quantity of mercury to be used is determined by the fact that the voltage gradient varies directly as the $\frac{7}{12}$ power of the mass of mercury per unit tube length and inversely as the $\frac{3}{2}$ power of the inside tube diameter.[20]   Alternating-current

[18] E. D. McAlister, *Smithsonian Misc. Collect.*, **87**, No. 17, 1 (1933).
[19] L. B. Johnson and S. B. Webster, *Rev. Sci. Inst.*, **9**, 325 (1938).
[20] W. Elenbass, *Physics*, **4**, 747 (1937).

Uviarcs are operated from high-reactance transformers, which provide the necessary ballast for stable operation. Maximum output is attained in about 4 min after the arc starts. The lamps may be burned in any position. In all cases it should be remembered that the radiation from a mercury arc changes greatly as it warms up.

The General Electric S–1 sun lamp employs tungsten electrodes, connected by a tungsten filament, in an atmosphere of mercury and argon. Its spectrum shows the mercury emission lines superposed upon a continuum from the tungsten filament and electrodes. The lines of shorter wavelength than 2664 A are absorbed almost completely if the bulb is Corex D glass; this transmission limit is shifted to the 2894 A line if Corning glass No. 690 is used.

8.15. High-Pressure Mercury Arcs. Several high-pressure mercury arcs have been developed for use primarily as luminous sources.[21–24] These operate at comparatively high current densities and at pressures ranging from 1 to 80 atmospheres (Table 8.7). Their spectra exhibit, in general, much stronger continua and a greater

TABLE 8.7

DATA ON HIGH-PRESSURE MERCURY ARCS[24]

Type	H-3	H-4	H-5	H-6
Watts (lamp)	85	100	250	1,000
Lumens (100 hr)	3000	3500	10,000	65,000
Pressure (atm)	30	8	4	80
Maximum lumens/cm²/steradian	900	400	300	30,000*
Source length (cm)	1.8	2.4	4.3	2.5
Source diameter (cm)	0.4	0.75	1.3	0.2

* The average value appears from computation to be about 6500.

proportion of energy in the visible region than is characteristic of low-pressure mercury arcs. Like AC Uviarcs (§ 8.14), they employ oxide-coated electrodes, together with an atmosphere of argon for starting the arc, and are operated on alternating current from transformers with sufficient reactance to serve as ballast. After starting, these sources require several minutes of operation to reach maximum total radiant output.

[21] B. T. Barnes, W. E. Forsythe, and W. J. Karash, *General Electric Rev.*, **42**, 540 (1939).

[22] E. B. Noel, *Jour. Appl. Physics*, **11**, 425 (1940).

[23] B. T. Barnes and W. E. Forsythe, *Jour. Opt. Soc. Am.*, **27**, 83 (1937).

[24] L. J. Buttolph, *Jour. Opt. Soc. Am.*, **29**, 124 (1939).

The arc envelopes are of quartz.   These are surrounded by jackets of glass except in the case of the H–6 water-cooled lamp (Fig. 8.6), for which outer jackets of either quartz or glass may be obtained. Some of the lamps with glass outer jackets cannot be operated with the outer jacket removed without damage to the arc envelope seal and hence are useful only for visible radiation and ultraviolet to about 3000 A.   With a quartz outer jacket, the H–6 lamp gives a

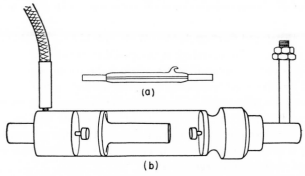

Fig. 8.6.   High-pressure, water-cooled, 1000-watt quartz mercury arc. (*a*) Quartz-arc capillary tube containing mercury vapor. (*b*) Housing, consisting of quartz or glass tube with metal end fittings, to permit cooling the arc tube with flowing water.

strong continuum in the ultraviolet to about 2270 A, with reversals at 2350 and 2537 A.   The lines are superposed upon the continuum but are not prominent.   The H–3 and H–4 lamps with outer jackets removed (or with holes punctured in the jacket for transmission of radiation) yield the mercury line spectrum in the ultraviolet superposed upon strong continua.   The short-wave limit of emission is about 2120 A, and the 2537 A line is reversed.

Because of its high radiant emission from a small emitting area (Table 8.7), the H–6 arc is an excellent source for applications in which high radiance is required in the range from about 2700 A through the visible and near infrared regions, and in which a strong continuous spectrum is desirable.   For shorter wavelengths or for the isolation of monochromatic radiation, other sources may be preferable even when the highest radiance is required.   On alternating current, the H–6 arc must be operated in the horizontal position; on direct current, it may be operated vertically, with the cathode as the upper electrode, using a supply capable of delivering 1220 volts at 1.2 amp and a ballast resistor which, at 1.2 amp, will reduce the potential across the arc to about 840 volts.

8.16.   Other Enclosed Metallic-Vapor Arcs.   The 200-watt G.E. sodium-vapor arc has an output of 10,000 lumens and a brightness of about 6 candles/cm^2, the radiation being concentrated primarily in the sodium lines near 5890 A.[24] Commercial enclosed metallic-vapor arcs yielding spectra of cadmium and zinc, as well as sodium are available.[25]   Enclosed metallic-vapor arcs have been designed for emission of characteristic lines of antimony, bismuth, iron, lead, potassium, selenium, tellurium, and tin (General References 8.1, 8.2).

8.17.   Enclosed Carbon Arcs.   With suitably designed enclosures, carbon arcs may be operated at increased pressures in various inert atmospheres[26] (including nitrogen, argon, helium, and hydrogen) or at reduced pressures as compared with the normal operating pressures of open arcs.   The effect of increasing the pressure is to increase the operating temperature, accentuate the continuous background, and broaden the characteristic spectrum lines.   The effect of reducing the pressure is to narrow the emission lines and to yield lines characteristic of higher excitation energies.

DISCHARGE TUBES

8.18.   General Characteristics.   A distinction has been made between arcs and discharge tubes on the basis that arcs are characterized by appreciable contribution of the electrode material to the ionic discharge stream and to the emission of radiation.   This distinction is not always clear-cut.   There are, however, other distinguishing characteristics that mark discharge tubes as different from arcs: (a) they operate at lower pressures (usually less than 0.01 atmosphere), lower current densities, and lower temperatures than arcs;   (b) a higher potential gradient (up to several hundred volts per cm) may be required to maintain the discharge;   and (c) the spectra emitted show lines of higher excitation energy and other differences.

Discharge tubes are usually operated from spark coils or transformers supplying high voltage (2000 to 20,000 volts) and low current (4 to 60 ma).   Spark coils have the advantage for some applications of supplying unidirectional pulses, the induced voltage developed

---

[25] *Electric Discharge and Other Lamps.*   London: Adam Hilger, Ltd., 1940.
[26] F. Paschen, *Ann. d. Physik*, **12**, 509 (1932).

when the primary interrupter makes contact being much less than that when it breaks contact. Transformers for operating discharge tubes should have sufficient reactance to limit the secondary current to a safe operating maximum. Sign-lighting transformers are designed with such characteristics and are available in a sufficiently wide variety of specifications to meet most needs for AC discharge-tube operation. High-voltage rectifier circuits may be used in special instances in which direct current is required. Finally, electrodeless discharge tubes may be excited by placing them in a high-frequency field.

As a general rule, the brightness or radiance of discharge tubes is comparatively low. With certain exceptions, therefore, they are not so well adapted to spectroscopic applications requiring highly concentrated light sources of great intrinsic brightness or radiance as to applications in which extended sources of high total radiant output are desired.

8.19. Glow–Discharge Tubes. A convenient form of Geissler tube for spectroscopic use has two enlarged portions, containing the electrodes, connected by a constricted tube (Fig. 8.7). Such tubes

Fig. 8.7. Geissler tube.

are made either of glass or quartz, and may be obtained unfilled (with stopcocks for filling) or filled with various gases such as argon, helium, hydrogen, neon, nitrogen, or mercury vapor. The electrodes may be of a plain metal, such as tungsten, or may be oxide-coated. Excitation is often supplied by a spark coil, but a small sign-lighting transformer (about 3000 volts, 6 ma) serves equally well. Geissler tubes are chiefly useful for demonstration purposes and to obtain narrow lines for reference standards or for interferometry (see Chapter 20).

Another type of discharge tube that is commercially available and has somewhat greater brightness, or radiance, than the usual Geissler tube has been described by Ryde.[27] It contains two closely spaced electrodes in a compact envelope, the discharge being viewed through

---

[27] J. W. Ryde, *Nature*, **112**, 944 (1923).

a window in one electrode.   Glass or quartz envelopes may be obtained, with atmospheres of argon, CO_2, helium, neon, nitrogen, or
oxygen.   The spectrum of the neon tube is rich in sharp lines that
are useful as secondary wavelength standards.   These lamps are
intended primarily for DC operation at 300 to 450 volts with oxygen,
nitrogen, and CO_2, and at 200 to 250 volts with helium, argon, and
neon.   They may, however, be operated on alternating current.
The current consumption is 5 to 15 ma.

Hollow-cathode tubes,[28, 29] with an atmosphere of inert gas, have been
designed in which radiation is emitted almost exclusively from the
cathode glow inside a hollow electrode closed at one end (Fig. 8.8).

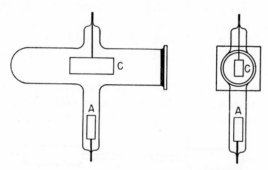

Fig. 8.8.   Hollow-cathode discharge tube.   *A*, Anode; *C*, cathode.

Spark lines of the metal comprising the cathode occur in the spectrum.   These tubes are especially valuable for producing sharp lines
for interferometry (§ 20.2), or for spectroscopic analysis of small
quantities of material (Chapter 15).

Mercury-Vapor Discharge Tubes.   When mercury vapor at low
pressures is admixed with a small amount of neon or argon in a discharge tube with oxide-coated electrodes, an easily started source is
obtained in which the ultraviolet radiation is largely concentrated
in the 2537 A mercury resonance line.   This fact has been made use
of in the design of a large variety of discharge tubes for supplying
(together with appropriate filters), approximately monochromatic
radiation at 2537 A (see General Reference 8.2), to be used, for
example, in the excitation of Raman spectra or in ultraviolet pho-
tomicrography.   With appropriate cooling it is possible to operate

---

[28] F. Paschen, *Ann. d. Physik*, **50**, 901 (1916).
[29] H. Schüler, *Physik. Zeitschr.*, **22**, 264 (1921).

such tubes at moderately high-current densities that, together with the concentration of emission in the resonance line, give radiance at 2537 A as great as 10 times that achievable with usual mercury arcs.[30]

Hydrogen Discharge Tubes.   One of the most convenient and practical sources for providing a continuous spectrum throughout the visible and ultraviolet regions (especially useful in absorption spectrophotometry) is the hydrogen discharge tube.[31, 32]   Such tubes are

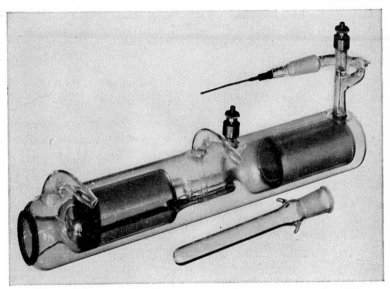

Fig. 8.9.   Hydrogen discharge tube for absorption spectroscopy.   (Courtesy Adam Hilger, Ltd., London.)

operated at hydrogen pressures ranging from 1 to 10 mm of mercury, at applied voltages from 3000 to 5000 and at currents from a fraction of an ampere to several amperes.   At the higher current densities the tubes must be jacketed and cooled by running water.   The discharge is usually viewed end on through a quartz window to increase the effective brightness.[33]   Several commercial hydrogen discharge tubes are available for spectroscopic use (Fig. 8.9).

[30] G. Kornfeld and F. Müller-Skjold, *Zeitschr. physik Chem.*, **B31**, 223 (1936).

[31] E. O. Lawrence and N. E. Edlefson, *Rev. Sci. Inst.*, **1**, 45 (1930).

[32] G. B. Kistiakowsky, *Rev. Sci. Inst.*, **2**, 549 (1931).

[33] R. W. Wood, *Physical Optics*.   New York: The Macmillan Company, 1934.

Electrodeless Discharge Tubes.   If an electrodeless tube containing an appropriate gas at low pressure is placed in a high-frequency electromagnetic field, such as that of a Tesla coil or radar transmitter, a glow discharge in the gas will be excited under proper conditions. Various methods of construction and operation have been described.[34] One method of excitation is to surround the tube with a close-fitting coil of wire carrying the high-frequency electrical current.   Sources of this type have been used in therapeutic applications and as probes to determine the extent of high-frequency fields.   They have found use in spectroscopy for the production of spectra of multiply ionized atoms or gases or metallic vapors and are particularly useful in the vacuum ultraviolet.

ELECTRIC SPARKS

8.20.   General Characteristics.   The electric spark is an electrical discharge across a gap separating two electrodes between which a high potential difference exists.   The potential gradient necessary to initiate such a discharge depends on the gas pressure in the gap, the ionization potential of the gas, the shape of the electrodes, and other factors.   For sharply pointed electrodes in air at atmospheric pressure the required gradient is about 12,000 volts/cm.

Cold emission of electrons from the cathode as a result of the high potential gradient plays an important part in starting the discharge. In this respect, sparks differ from arcs, in which thermionic emission accounts primarily for the contribution of electrons to the discharge stream.   After breakdown occurs, an oscillatory discharge takes place, the frequency and duration of which depends upon the constants of the electrical circuit.   Once the train of succeeding oscillations and sparks has died out, the gap remains quiescent until the potential gradient has been built up again to the point at which a disruptive discharge occurs.   During the oscillatory discharge, electrode material enters the discharge stream as a result of ionic bombardment of the cathode.   This effect, again, distinguishes sparks from arcs (see General Reference 8.3), in which vaporization by heat is largely responsible for the entry of electrode material into the arc stream.[35]

---

[34] J. G. Winans, *Rev. Sci. Inst.*, **9**, 203 (1938); see also General Reference 8.2.

[35] H. Kaiser and A. Wallraff, *Ann. d. Physik*, **34**, 297 (1939).

As sparks are operated at higher current densities and higher electrode temperatures, they begin to behave more and more like arcs. Indeed, under suitable circumstances the transition to an arc discharge may be complete.

Spark spectra show the emission lines of singly and multiply ionized atoms in addition to those of neutral atoms which are characteristic of arc spectra (see Chapter 10). The emission lines of atoms of the electrode material normally predominate, in terms of total radiant emission, over those of any gases present in the gap, and the latter may be suppressed almost entirely by use of a series inductance (Chapter 15).

8.21. The Spark in Air and Other Gases. For spectroscopic use, it is convenient to employ electrodes about 3 to 4 mm in diameter with wedge-shaped opposing ends (Fig. 8.10). The electrodes are mounted with the formed edges parallel to each other and to the optical axis of the spectrograph, so that wandering of the spark along the edges does not displace it laterally with respect to the axis. The gap between the electrodes may be from 2 to 8 mm.

Fig. 8.10. Wedge-shaped spark electrodes.

A spark of these specifications may be operated from an induction coil ("spark" coil) but is much more convenient to use with a high-voltage transformer, the primary of which is supplied with power from a 110- or 220-volt AC line. The transformer should be rated at 0.25 to 1.0 kva and should develop a secondary voltage of at least 10,000 and preferably 15,000 or 20,000 volts.

If a spark is operated directly from a spark coil or transformer, the capacitance of the circuit is insufficient to permit appreciable storage of electrical energy at the discharge potential. Under this circumstance, discharges occur quite frequently, the spark is "thin" and comparatively nonluminous, and the radiance is low, being primarily from emission by atoms of the gas in the gap rather than from those of the electrode material. If, however, a capacitor of appropriate value is connected in parallel with the spark gap (Fig. 8.11), the energy dissipated during each oscillatory discharge is greater, and appreciable quantities of electrode material appear in the gap and contribute to the radiant emission. Although the discharges occur less often (and with lower oscillation frequency), they are of so much greater radiance that the integrated radiation during a given period of time is con-

siderably larger. It is customary, therefore, to use a capacitor in
the circuit so as to obtain a "hot," bright spark in which the spark
lines of the electrode material predominate.

Increasing the value of the capacitor augments the brightness of
each disruptive discharge. Obviously, however, the capacitance
cannot be increased indefinitely. With any transformer of given
power rating and a circuit of given resistance, ultimately a capacitance
will be reached which is so great that the transformer cannot charge
it to a potential sufficient to cause breakdown of the spark gap
within the time of a half cycle. Then the condenser will simply be
charged with opposite polarities during succeeding half cycles, without
any disruptive sparks taking place. Before this condition is reached,
the spark will become irregular. The appropriate circuit constants

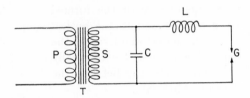

Fig. 8.11. **Electrical circuit for operating a spark.** T, High-voltage step-up
transformer; P, primary; S, secondary; C, condenser; L, self-inductance (used
if it is desired to suppress air lines); G, spark gap.

may be computed from principles set forth in standard electrical
engineering texts. For example, if P is the power in watts required
to charge a condenser of capacity C in farads to a maximum voltage V_0
at every half cycle from an AC circuit of frequency F cycles per
second, then $P = CV_0^2F$. If C is 0.02 μf, V_0 is 15,000 volts, and
F is 60 cycles per second, $P = 270$ watts, or approximately 0.25 kva.

Actually, the power rating of the transformer used should be considerably greater than this for satisfactory operation. The practical
approach to the problem of optimum capacitance is to use a capacitor
of multiple sections and, with a particular transformer and gap, to
determine by trial the capacitance which gives a bright but regular
spark. For use with 0.25 to 1.0 kva, 15,000- to 20,000-volt transformers and gaps of 4 to 5 mm, the optimum capacitance usually lies
between 0.003 and 0.03 μf.[36]

---

[36] J. A. Anderson, *Astrophys. Jour.*, **59**, 76 (1924).

The introduction of an inductance coil in the oscillatory circuit (Fig. 8.11), which reduces the frequency of oscillation since $F = \dfrac{1}{2\pi\sqrt{LC}}$, tends to reduce the intensity of emission lines arising from the atmosphere in which the spark operates, and gives rise to a hotter spark. With large values of inductance and capacitance, essentially the entire arc spectrum of the electrode material appears, in addition to spark lines. Usual values of the self-inductance L of the coil range from 15 microhenries to 1 millihenry; the value essential for effective suppression of the air lines in any particular case may be determined by trial. A suitable coil may be made by winding 40 turns of No. 18 copper wire in a single layer on a 4-in.-diameter insulating tube and providing a tap every five turns.

One difficulty with sparks is their tendency to be irregular. Methods of overcoming this difficulty include the use of a rotating synchronous spark gap in series with the gap used as a source[37] and the use of a low-power, high-voltage interrupted spark to ignite and control a high-power, low-voltage spark connected in parallel with it.[38]

8.22. The Hot Spark in Vacuum. The average excitation energies in the spark discharge increase as the voltage and capacitance are increased. By operating a spark in a vacuum, under which conditions high breakdown potentials are required, and by using large capacitors and transformers of high power and voltage rating, it is possible to obtain bright sparks high in emissivity in the far ultraviolet.[39–43] Millikan and Sawyer[39] and Edlén[40] used gap lengths from 0.2 to 2 mm, voltages of 50,000 or more, and capacitances of 0.01 to 0.5 μf. A fixed or rotating external gap is used in series with the vacuum gap to obtain uniform discharges (see Chapter 19).

If wires are exploded (§ 8.9) in vacuum instead of air, the spark spectrum of the wire material is obtained instead of a continuum.

8.23. The Underwater Spark. A spark between metallic electrodes under water yields a continuous spectrum extending to about

---

[37] O. Faussner, *Archiv f. Eisenhüttenwesen*, **6**, 551 (1932).

[38] M. F. Hasler and H. W. Dietert, *Jour. Opt. Soc. Am.*, **33**, 218 (1943).

[39] R. A. Millikan and R. A. Sawyer, *Phys. Rev.*, **12**, 167 (1918).

[40] B. Edlén, *Zeitschr. f. Physik*, **100**, 621 (1936).

[41] R. A. Millikan, *Astrophys. Jour.*, **52**, 47 (1920).

[42] R. A. Sawyer, *Astrophys. Jour.*, **52**, 286 (1920).

[43] E. Carter, *Astrophys. Jour.*, **55**, 162 (1922).

2000 A in the ultraviolet.[44-46]   The source is of high intrinsic brightness and is of particular value in absorption spectrophotometry of the
ultraviolet (Chapter 14).   Electrodes of various metals may be used,
tungsten steel being particularly satisfactory.   The spark gap (3 or
4 mm in length) is housed in a watertight container, with a quartz
window.   Distilled water is used in the container.   A high-frequency,
high-voltage electrical supply from a Tesla coil is used to energize the
spark.   The primary of the Tesla coil is connected through a spark
gap to a circuit consisting of a capacitor in parallel with the secondary
of a high-voltage transformer (about 20,000 volts, 1 kva), with a
primary for operation from 110 or 220 volts alternating current.)   If
an open spark gap is used in the oscillatory exciting circuit for the
Tesla coil, operation is extremely noisy;   quieter operation may be
achieved by the use of a quenched gap.

   **8.24.   The Spark as a Source in Qualitative and Quantitative
Analysis.**   If it is desired to observe the spark spectra of solid conducting materials for purposes of identification or quantitative analysis, these may be made the electrodes of a spark gap.   The spectra
of nonconductors or of liquids may be observed by introducing them
into suitable spark gaps having electrodes of appropriate materials;
alternatively, conducting liquids may be made to serve as the electrodes.   Various methods of applying spark spectra to qualitative
and quantitative analysis are discussed in Chapters 15 and 16.

MISCELLANEOUS SOURCES

   8.25.   Cathodoluminescence Devices.   Radiation may be excited
by bombarding a gas or vapor with accelerated electrons.   The principal problem in so doing is to provide an evacuated space for the
acceleration of the electrons, and a gas space in which impacts may
occur, without the use of a barrier between them.   This result has
been accomplished in various cathodoluminescence devices[47, 48] by
bombarding a metal with electrons in an enclosure that may be con-

---

[44] H. J. McNicholas, *Nat. Bur. Standards Jour. Res.*, **1**, 939 (1928).

[45] I. Wyneken, *Ann. d. Physik*, **86**, 1071 (1928).

[46] B. Wrede, *Ann. d. Physik*, **3**, 823 (1929).

[47] H. Hertz, *Wied. Ann.*, **19**, 809 (1883).

[48] A. S. King and E. Carter, *Astrophys. Jour.*, **44**, 303 (1916);   E. Carter and A. S.
King, *Astrophys. Jour.*, **49**, 224 (1919).

tinuously evacuated. Small amounts of the metal are vaporized; under appropriate conditions the vapor can be confined largely to the immediate vicinity of the metal target. The atomic beam for producing very narrow lines by this method is discussed in § 20.2.

8.26. Fluorescence, Phosphorescence, Resonance Radiation, and Chemiluminescence. Sources involving these mechanisms for the emission of radiation are of low intrinsic brightness and are of interest in spectroscopy primarily from the standpoint of studying the spectra characterizing the phenomenon concerned. Fluorescence is readily excited in many substances by irradiating them with ultraviolet radiation. The 3650 A and 2537 A mercury arc or discharge-tube lines are particularly convenient for this purpose.

8.27. Pulsed Discharge Tubes. By discharging a condenser through a suitable tube with a minimum of inductance and resistance in the circuit, it is possible to obtain brilliant flashes of light of extremely short duration. Anderson[49] used this method to excite hydrogen discharge tubes, employing a 2-μf condenser charged to 35,000 volts. Current densities of the order of 25,000 amp/cm^2 were obtained. The brightness was extremely high, approximating that of a blackbody at 40,000°K. Edgerton[50] has carried out extensive investigations of pulsed discharge tubes for application to high-speed photography, for aerial photography at night, and for other uses. In applications in which a maximum of radiance is required and a minimum duration of radiation is unobjectionable, such sources are extremely useful.

8.28. The Sun as a Source of Radiation. The sun is a source of high intrinsic brightness, yielding radiation extending from the far infrared through the visible and ultraviolet regions. Its spectrum is continuous but contains thousands of absorption lines, the Fraunhofer lines. As the sun's radiation reaches the earth, it is modified further by absorption by CO_2, O_2, water vapor, and ozone in the various layers of the atmosphere. Typical values for the radiant power of sunlight at the earth's surface in various spectral regions at noon on a clear day are given by Luckiesh.[51]

---

[49] J. A. Anderson, *Astrophys. Jour.*, **75**, 394 (1932).

[50] H. E. Edgerton, *Elec. Eng.*, **50**, 327 (1931); H. E. Edgerton and K. J. Germeshausen, *Rev. Sci. Inst.*, **3**, 535 (1932).

[51] Matthew Luckiesh, *Germicidal, Erythemal, and Infra-Red Energy*. New York: D. Van Nostrand Company, Inc., 1946.

GENERAL REFERENCES

8.1.   W. E. Forsythe (Ed.), *Measurement of Radiant Energy.*   New York: McGraw-Hill Book Company, Inc., 1937.

8.2.   F. F. Heyroth, *The Chemical Action of Ultraviolet Rays.*   New York: Reinhold Publishing Corporation, 1941.

8.3.   Leonard B. Loeb, *Fundamental Processes of Electrical Discharge in Gases.* New York: John Wiley & Sons, Inc., 1939.

CHAPTER 9

Identification of Spectrum Lines

THE ATOMS OF THE CHEMICAL ELEMENTS that have been studied spectroscopically are found to emit, in their various stages of ionization, millions of spectrum lines of different wavelengths. Some of these lines are much stronger than others, so that most of the light emitted by atoms appears in a smaller number of lines, of which some 350,000 have been measured and listed as to parent atom. Less than half of these have been classified as to exact mode of origin in the atom.

Each of the hundreds of thousands of molecules produced by combinations of the elementary atoms emits many characteristic bands. The study and elucidation of band spectra is a very important aspect of spectroscopy that is still in its infancy. Only in the case of diatomic molecules have many bands been classified.

Every spectrum line has a definite wavelength, characteristic of the atom or molecule that emits it and dependent to only slight degree on the electrical and magnetic surroundings of that atom or molecule. The most precise means of identifying a spectrum line is by its wavelength, which in much of the spectrum can be determined to seven significant figures, in some cases to eight. Other less positive means of identification are by observation of the intensity of the line relative to other lines in the same spectrum, of the patterns formed in the spectrum by groups of related lines arising from the same atom, and of the behavior of the line when the source of light from which it is emitted is subjected to various external influences, such as variations in temperature, pressure, excitation, or electric or magnetic field.

In general, elements on the left-hand side of the periodic table emit comparatively simple spectra. The complexity of the spectra emitted increases for the elements in the middle of the table and diminishes again slightly for those on the right. The breadth of spacing of lines in the patterns formed by groups of spectrum lines,

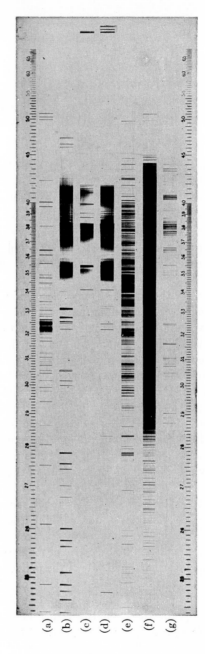

Fig. 9.1. Characteristic spectra. (a) Copper arc; (b) zinc in graphite electrodes; (c) potassium in graphite electrodes; (d) rubidium in graphite electrodes; (e) nickel arc; (f) titanium arc; (g) vanadium in graphite electrodes. The cyanogen bands in the near ultraviolet can be seen clearly in (b), (c), and (d).

called *multiplets*, emitted by an element increases from top to bottom of the periodic table. This widening causes overlapping of patterns and an apparent increase in complexity for the elements lying low in the table. Thus the simplest spectra are emitted by the elements in the upper left-hand corner of the table, and the most complex by those in the middle bottom region. The two extremes are well represented by hydrogen and uranium.

9.1. Identification of Lines and Bands by Appearance. Experience soon brings the practicing spectroscopist considerable familiarity with the appearance of characteristic spectra, so that he can readily identify groups of lines at a glance. The color of the visible lines as seen in a spectroscope gives a first clue; thus the two yellow lines of sodium, at 5896 and 5890 A, known as the *D* lines, are familiar to almost every scientist. On a spectrogram the color is lost, but a much more precise means of identification is substituted—the position of the line on the plate relative to other lines. In Fig. 9.1, several characteristic spectra are shown. The spectra of zinc and cadmium show triple groups of lines, of intensity diminishing toward shorter

Fig. 9.2. Comparison spectrum for identification purposes. The upper spectrum is that of iron, and the lower that of copper.

wavelengths, the triplets of cadmium being somewhat more widely separated than those of zinc. The spectra of copper, potassium, and rubidium contain obvious doublets, and the spectra of titanium and vanadium show more complex regularities. Iron shows few regularities that are immediately obvious, yet they exist in profusion. The cyanogen bands are emitted strongly by CN molecules formed in the carbon arc burning in air and are easy to identify by their appearance.

9.2. Identification by Comparison Spectra. Lines in an unfamiliar spectrum can conveniently be identified by using the method of comparison spectra. The spectrum of the unknown material is photographed on the same plate as that of some material whose spectrum is well known, as in Fig. 9.2. Known lines of the familiar spectrum can then be identified at intervals across the spectrogram, and by

approximate interpolation the wavelengths of the unknown lines can
be determined.   The unknown may then be identified by the use of
wavelength tables.   In preparing such spectrograms, it is important
to avoid lateral displacement of the plate between the recording of
the known and the unknown spectra.   If the plate is racked up or
down, one cannot be sure that this condition is fulfilled, and so use
is made of diaphragms or occulters to cover different parts of the slit
or the plate during each of the exposures.   The Hartmann diaphragm,[1] shown in Fig. 5.4, can be used on the slit of a stigmatic
spectrograph and produces a spectrogram of the type shown in
Fig. 9.3.   It is important to remember that the image of the slit

Fig. 9.3.   Comparison spectrogram taken with a Hartmann diaphragm.   Top
and bottom spectra are of the iron arc.   The center spectrum is lead.

on the plate is inverted; hence the upper portion of the slit corresponds to the lower spectrum.   Care should be taken not to jar the
spectrograph when adjusting the diaphragm.

Even with astigmatic instruments, sufficient separation between
two spectra can be obtained with a Hartmann diaphragm at the slit
to make identification possible if the astigmatism is small.   With
spectrographs having great astigmatism, it is useful to provide an
occulter directly in front of the plate and as close to it as possible.
This diaphragm can be moved up and down to uncover various portions of the line length on the plate for the production of comparison
spectra.

For quick identification by comparison spectra, a low- or medium-
pressure quartz mercury arc such as the Lab-arc or Uviarc is a useful
source, because it can be kept readily available and furnishes a
limited number of intense lines well distributed throughout the
visible and ultraviolet regions.   The beginning spectroscopist should

---

[1] J. Hartmann, *Zeits. f. Instrumentenkunde,* **20,** 57 (1900).

acquaint himself with the approximate wavelengths of the principal groups of mercury lines, as given in Table 9.1.

To provide comparison spectra having greater numbers of lines, a copper arc or spark or an iron arc will be found useful, the latter having the more complex spectrum. The wavelengths of the principal iron lines have been very carefully measured, and the spectrum is so rich that a known line can be found every few angstroms.

In many cases it is useful to expose a spectrogram to light from both a quartz mercury arc and an iron arc, the spectrum of the former being used for preliminary orientation and that of the latter for precise determination of the wavelengths of unknown lines.

TABLE 9.1

Groups of Mercury Lines Useful for Wavelength Identification

Group	Color	Wavelengths	Approximate intensity
1	Red	6234 A	10
		6152	20
2	Yellow	5790	50
		5770	50
3	Green	5461	100
4	Blue	4359–4348	20
5	Violet	4078	8
		4047	10
6	Ultraviolet	3663–3654–3650	70
7	Ultraviolet	3342	10
8	Ultraviolet	3132–3126	40
9	Ultraviolet	3026–3022	30
10	Ultraviolet	2967	10
11	Ultraviolet	2893	10
12	Ultraviolet	2804	20
13	Ultraviolet	2753	10
14	Ultraviolet	2652	8
15	Ultraviolet	2537	30
16	Ultraviolet	2482	5
17	Ultraviolet	2399–2378	3

9.3.   Spectrum Charts for Comparison.   Each spectrograph has its own characteristic dispersion curve, relating the wavelengths of spectrum lines to their positions on a spectrogram. Users of spectrographs find it convenient to accumulate a set of standard spectrograms on which wavelengths are marked for quick identification of lines on future plates. Spectrograms of unknown materials produced with the same instrument can then be fitted over these standard plates, corresponding known lines being superimposed, and other lines identified by inspection.   Lines of striking intensity or pattern can be

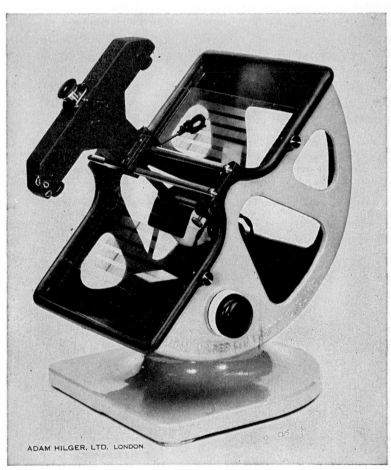

ADAM HILGER, LTD. LONDON.

Fig. 9.4.   The Judd-Lewis spectrum comparator.

quickly identified by this means, and key lines can be marked on the new spectrogram.

The spectra on such standard plates should not be crowded together, but a sufficient width of clear plate should be left between to permit recording wavelengths of important lines in India ink.   When a mark is to be permanent it should be placed on the emulsion side of the plate, but if temporary only, on the glass side.   The dry emulsion will take ink better if roughened with a rubber eraser.

Comparison of plates taken on the same spectrograph can be accomplished by superposing plates on a viewing box, but various devices are manufactured commercially for doing this without introducing actual contact between the plates.   Of these, the Judd-Lewis Spectrum Comparator, Fig. 9.4, is typical.   A suitable optical system enables the observer to see the image of one spectrogram superposed on that of the other, and by adjusting the position of one plate with a horizontal and a vertical screw or rack and pinion he can bring any spectrum line on this plate into coincidence with the corresponding line on the other.   A library of standard films with wavelengths of important lines marked on them is provided with the spectrum comparator manufactured by the Applied Research Laboratories, for use with their grating spectrograph.   These films can be projected directly on the screen of the spectrum comparator for rapid identification of lines.

Although a set of marked spectrograms built up about a given instrument forms the most useful type of reference library for identification of lines by comparison, charts and atlases of spectra are obtainable which can be of considerable assistance.   These are of greatest use for visual comparison of line patterns.   The value of the published charts is somewhat limited by variation in the dispersion characteristics of different spectroscopic instruments.   Grating spectrographs, however, give dispersion that is nearly uniform with wavelength; and by varying the magnification in a projection device, one can provide any dispersion desired.   Hence grating spectrograms can usually be projected directly on commercial charts made with grating instruments and can be compared with them with relatively little error as a result of differences in dispersion.

The principal atlases of spectra that have been printed or are available as photographic reproductions are listed in Table 9.2.   Probably the most generally useful of the charts are those of the spectrum of iron, since iron lines are so frequently used for purposes of wavelength identification.   Many of these iron charts have marked on them the positions of the principal lines of other elements, so that these can be identified by projecting unidentified lines directly on the chart.

TABLE 9.2
LIST OF CHARTS AND ATLASES OF SPECTRA*

1. J. M. Eder and E. Valenta, *Atlas typischer Spektren*. Vienna: A. Hölder, 1911. Contains reproductions of more than 600 photographs of flame, arc, and spark spectra, taken with glass and quartz prism spectrographs and with low-dispersion gratings. Note Rowland scale of wavelengths.

2. J. Bardet, *Atlas de Spectre d'Arc*. Paris: G. Doin, 1926. Contains 54 charts of sensitive lines of the elements, with the iron spectrum, taken with a prism, from 3500 to 2500 A.

3. F. Löwe, *Atlas der Letzten Linien der Wichstigsten Elemente*. Dresden: Steinkopf, 1928. Contains charts of sensitive lines for 43 elements taken with a small quartz spectrograph in the region 4700 to 2200 A.

4. G. Scheibe and C. F. Lindström, *Tabellen des Funken- und Bogenspectrum des Eisens*, etc. Berlin-Steglitz: R. Fuess, 1933. Charts of arc and spark spectra, in the range 3700 to 2300 A.

5. W. J. Crook, *Metallurgical Spectrum Analysis*. Stanford University Press, 1935. Gives 20 charts of sensitive lines of the elements in the range 5670 to 2796 A, and the iron spectrum in the ranges 5671 to 5058 A and 3433 to 2794 A, using grating.

6. A. Gatterer and J. Junkes, *Atlas der Restlinien*. Castel Gandolfo, Italy: Specola Vaticana, 1937. Contains 28 photographs of spectra in the range 8000 to 2200 A, in arc and spark for 50 elements.

7. W. R. Brode, *Chemical Spectroscopy*. New York: John Wiley & Sons, 1939. Contains 35 charts for the range 5090 to 2310 A, in the arc, showing the spectral lines of iron, with indicated positions of lines of other elements.

8. A. Gatterer and J. Junkes, *Spektren der seltenen Erden*. Castel Gandolfo, Italy: Specola Vaticana, 1945. Contains 45 pages of spectrum charts of the rare earths taken with prism spectrograph. Arc spectra, 7600 to 2265 A; spark spectra, 4350 to 2265 A.

9. A. Hilger, Ltd., London. Charts of spectra taken with a quartz prism spectrograph of R.U. powder (mixture of 50 elements) and of iron, copper, neon, and helium.

10. *Charts of the Iron Spectrum Photographed at the Massachusetts Institute of Technology*. Cambridge, Mass.: Jarrell-Ash Co. Contains 10 marked and mounted spectrum charts, each 20 in. long, of the iron arc taken with a 35-ft concave grating.

Adam Hilger, Ltd., has issued a set of spectrum charts showing at least seven important lines of each included element. This firm also furnishes a so-called R. U. (*raies ultimes*) powder, which contains a mixture of chemical elements in such proportions that seven or more lines of the most important elements will appear when the material is burned in an arc. This powder is convenient for use in qualitative

---

* Based on an article by G. R. Harrison, *Jour. App. Phys.*, **10**, 760 (1939), by permission of that Journal.

spectrographic analysis, to determine the presence or absence of any given chemical element.

9.4. Identification of Lines by Wavelength Determination. Spectrum lines can be identified most accurately by measurement of their wavelengths. In a simple spectrum, a line can usually be identified if its wavelength is determined with a precision of a few tenths of an angstrom, or even more. Several other strong lines of the element can be looked for to establish the presence or absence of the element in the source. In more complex spectra it often becomes important to know wavelengths to within ±0.01 A, whereas for term analysis of a really complex spectrum, wavelength precision to ±0.001 A is desirable. Fortunately, the broadest lines, whose wavelengths are most difficult to determine precisely, usually arise from the simplest spectra. Lines emitted by such atoms as the rare earths or uranium are usually sharp and well defined. Sharp lines can be measured with large diffraction gratings to within a few thousandths of an angstrom, and when improved standard lines become available, precision to ±0.001 A should not be unusual. With interferometers, wavelengths of sharp lines can be measured to ±0.0001 A, or 1 part in 50 million or better (Chapter 20).

Wavelength measurement with an ordinary spectrograph involves determining the location of a line on the plate relative to known lines and also determining the positions of the known lines so the dispersion of the plate can be computed. The dispersion of a prism spectrograph varies so rapidly with wavelength that it is necessary to use a carefully plotted dispersion curve, or if very precise determinations are needed, to make interpolation calculations of the type discussed in § 9.6. Known comparison lines are then needed on the plate at very close intervals. For a small prism spectrograph, where precision to only 0.1 A is required, a dispersion curve similar to that shown in Fig. 9.5 can be plotted on cross-section paper. The scale of the plot should be fairly large, 0.1 mm on the position scale corresponding to 0.1 A if the fifth figure of the wavelength is to be considered significant. Thus a sheet of paper a meter long would be required to cover 3000 angstroms, and to reach greater accuracy would require use of an inconveniently large sheet.

Since a long narrow sheet of paper is more readily obtainable and handled than a large square sheet, it is useful to break up the interpolation process into two parts, a linear portion, marked A in Fig. 9.6, and a residual part. Part A need not be plotted, since linear computations are readily carried out, and the residual can be plotted as a correction curve in a form similar to Fig. 9.7.

Wavelength measurements should always be supplemented by

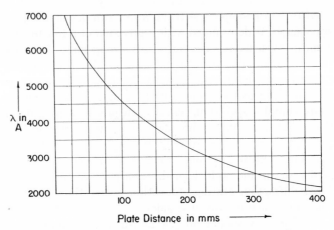

Fig. 9.5. Dispersion curve for a prism spectrograph.

intensity estimates, since the intensity of a line often gives secondary information that is revealing and confirmatory (§ 9.9).

9.5. Measurement of Spectrograms. Distances along the plate can be measured with a celluloid rule calibrated in centimeters, if

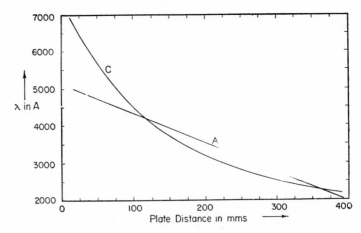

Fig. 9.6. Approximation of a dispersion curve C by a straight line, A.

estimates to 0.1 mm will suffice for the desired precision.   Lines produced by small prism spectrographs can be measured in this way with an uncertainty of 1 to 10 angstroms, depending on the spectral region involved, and those produced by large grating spectrographs to within 0.05 A.   Some spectrographs are provided with wavelength or frequency scales.   These are inferior in accuracy to separate millimeter scales but reduce the necessary computation.

Improved precision can be obtained by using a spectrum magnifier. A typical instrument of this sort, with 20 mm scale calibrated to 0.1 mm, is manufactured by Bausch & Lomb.   It is arranged to be placed directly against the emulsion side of the plate, thus avoiding errors due to parallax.   This scale can be read to ±0.01 mm.   The eyepiece is adjustable and should be carefully focused on the scale by each observer.

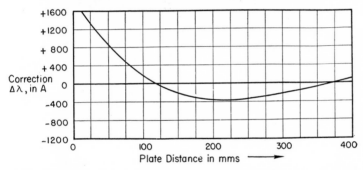

Fig. 9.7.   Correction curve, B, to be used with the linear approximation of Fig. 9.6.

For measurement of Raman spectra, in which weak and diffuse lines are common and extreme precision is unnecessary, positive prints enlarged approximately 10 times are useful.   Such lines are difficult to measure on the negative under magnification, especially on the fast and grainy plates used in photographing Raman spectra.

9.6. Use of the Comparator.   Precise wavelength measurements are carried out on a spectrum-measuring engine or wavelength comparator.   A typical comparator, manufactured by Adam Hilger, Ltd., is illustrated in Fig. 9.8.   Comparators are of two basic types, those in which the microscope (and the observer's eye) is moved, and those in which the plate is moved.   The former is the simpler method, since the microscope can be carried on a comparatively short carriage

Fig. 9.8.   Hilger wavelength comparator, Model L76.

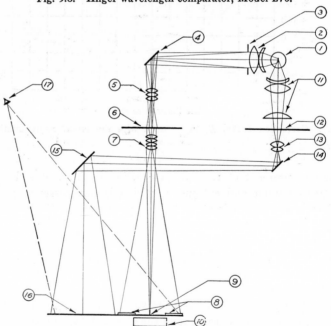

Fig. 9.9.   Optical diagram of Jarrell-Ash projection comparator JA-200.   1, Lamp; 2, 11, condensing lenses; 3, slit and filter; 4, 14, 15, first-surface mirrors; 5. 7, 13, projection lenses; 6, plate being measured; 12, comparison plate; 8, screen occulter; 9, adjustable slit; 10, photocell (barrier-layer type); 16, screen; 17, observer's eye.   (Courtesy Jarrell-Ash Company, Boston, Massachusetts.)

which slides on ways that need be only as long as the length of this carriage plus the amount of motion desired. When the entire plate is moved, the length of the ways must be at least equal to the length of the plate carriage plus the amount of motion required. Thus, to read from end to end of a 10-in. plate without resetting would require a comparator more than 20 in. long. However, this arrangement results in higher over-all precision and greater convenience.

Fig. 9.10.   Jarrell-Ash projection comparator, Model JA200.

The plate is usually observed through a microscope provided with an eyepiece in which cross hairs are mounted to serve as fiducial marks. This microscope should magnify the spectrum lines by not more than 15 diameters, and $10\times$ will be found satisfactory for all spectra but those containing the sharpest lines. It is undesirable to magnify spectrum lines by more than this amount, since the line consists merely of an elongated array of silver grains, and the eye must be able to estimate the center of gravity of this array. Contrast, as well as density and symmetry, enters into this judgment. Observation of a very diffuse line is sometimes facilitated by use of a diminishing lens.   Usually, however, a change in magnification during a series of measurements along a plate is not practicable.

Some modern comparators use the projection system.   A beam from a low-power lamp is sent through the plate as in a projection lantern, and an image of the plate is thrown on a screen in front of the operator.   A typical optical system of this sort is shown in Fig. 9.9, and a commercial instrument using this principle in Fig. 9.10. Advantages of this method are ease of superposing comparison spectra; improved comfort of the operator, who need not refocus his eyes between setting on the line and reading the comparator scales; and the possibility of using a fiducial mark of any desired shape, this being change- able at will by drawing an India-ink line on the ground-glass projection screen. Favorite forms of fiducial mark are shown in Fig. 9.11.   The chief disadvantages of projection comparators are lack of compactness and susceptibility to errors introduced by the heat from the projection lamp.

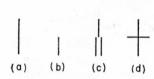

(a)   (b)   (c)   (d)

Fig. 9.11. Convenient forms of fiducial marks for use in projection comparators.

Before measuring a plate, it is desirable to place dots at the ends of a few identified lines, to serve as reference marks.   The plate to be measured (or film fastened on a glass plate) is clamped, emulsion side up, on the comparator carriage.   This carriage is moved on ways by means of a screw, usually of 1 or 2 mm pitch.   The screw is turned by a handle mounted on a drum that is usually calibrated with divisions marking 0.01 mm plate travel.   Verniers make estimates possible to 0.001 mm.

During measurement of a spectrogram it is important that the plate be mounted so that the spectrum being measured is closely parallel to the ways of the comparator and so that the distance from the emulsion surface to the microscope or projection lens remains sufficiently constant to ensure that the plate will not go out of focus while being traversed from one end to the other.   The plate should be mounted with the emulsion side up, since measuring the lines through the glass may introduce errors due to variations in refraction. In some comparators a means is provided of freeing the carriage from the screw that drives it, so that the plate can be slid rapidly from one end to the other to make sure that the lines remain in focus and in the field.

The eyepiece of the comparator should first be focused on the cross hairs, and then the microscope should be carefully focused on the lines by the parallax method, in which one moves the eye slightly from side to side to make sure that the image of a cross hair moves with that of the spectrum line.   One cross hair should be adjusted to be closely parallel to the lines (though it is not necessary that these be at right angles to the screw), to ensure that the same part of each line will be measured from one end of the spectrum to the other.   Change of inclination of the line of traverse across the plate will obviously change the observed dispersion.

With measurements being started at one end of the plate, a line is brought into view and the comparator is adjusted until an accurate setting of the vertical cross hair on the center of the line is achieved. The observer then makes entries in his notebook, recording the screw reading in millimeters and the drum reading in thousandths of a millimeter followed by an estimate of the intensity of the line.   Intensity estimates may be made on a scale of 0 to 10, 0 to 100, 0 to 1000, or even greater.   At first, intensity estimates will be haphazard, but after some practice the observer should be able to make fairly self-consistent estimates.   After deciding on the line intensity, he may put down in a Remarks column some comment such as d, R, s, h, or other notation as given in Table 9.3, to describe the character of the line.

TABLE 9.3

DESCRIPTIVE NOTATION FOR SPECTRUM LINES*

bh	Band head
c	Complex line
d	Double line
h	Hazy, diffuse, nebulous
a_l	Asymmetrical, heavy toward long wavelengths
a_s	Asymmetrical, heavy toward short wavelengths
r	Slightly self-reversed
R	Heavily self-reversed
s	Sharp
w	Wide
W	Very wide

* Adapted from *Massachusetts Institute of Technology Wavelength Tables*, General Reference 9.3.

Comparators usually have a certain amount of backlash between the screw and the nut, and settings should be made by approaching all lines from the same side. If the operator decides that he has overshot the center of gravity of a line, he should reverse the screw by at least half a turn and approach the line again.

To reduce backlash, comparators are sometimes provided with counterweights which keep the carriage pushed against the screw which drives the nut. Others are provided with split nuts with built-in springs that automatically keep the tension uniform and reduce the backlash. Even when one of these provisions is made, however, it is desirable to approach all spectrum lines from the same side in any series of measurements.

With a carefully made comparator, it should be possible to repeat single readings to within 0.002 mm or even better, but this limit will depend on many factors besides the judgment of the operator, such as backlash, the thickness and viscosity of the oil film separating the nut from the screw, friction in the bearings, elasticity in the metal, and so on. Comparators are available for astronomical work in which motions in two directions can be measured. Additional data on comparator construction are given in § 9.11.

9.7. Calculation of Wavelengths. When wavelengths are to be determined to a precision greater than ±0.1 A, they must be calculated unless an automatic comparator is used (§ 9.11). If standard reference lines are close together, linear interpolation can be used, especially with grating spectrograms for which the dispersion curve is almost linear when wavelength is plotted against position on the plate. With prism spectrograms, the wavelength-dispersion curve is far from linear, though a somewhat flatter curve is obtained when wave numbers or frequency units are plotted instead of wavelengths.

The plate factor of a spectrogram should always be measured in angstroms per millimeter. The tendency of some beginning spectrographers to calculate "dispersion" in angstroms per inch is to be discouraged because of the convenience of using a common system among all spectroscopists.

As an example of linear interpolation, take the case of two lines A and B, shown in Fig. 9.12, lying between two known lines whose wavelengths are as given in the figure. By means of a comparator, the distance from standard 1 to line A is measured as 4.88 mm, to line B as 7.96 mm and to standard 2 as 11.21 mm. Since the distance between the two standards is 11.21 mm and the difference in their wavelengths is 13.56 A, the plate factor in this region is 1.209 A per millimeter. The distance from standard 1 to line A can then be multiplied by this plate factor to give a wavelength difference of 5.90 A, which, when added to the wavelength of standard 1, gives 4696.21 A as the wavelength of line A. This process may be repeated to determine the wavelengths of unknown lines by extrapolation for a short distance beyond the second standard, the limitation being

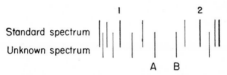

Fig. 9.12. Wavelength measurement by linear interpolation.

that the departure from linearity must not be greater than the maximum error that can be tolerated in the wavelength determinations.

Where greater precision is desired, nonlinear interpolation formulas can be used with either grating or prism spectrograms.   Hartmann's[2] interpolation formula is the best known of these.   It may be written simply as

$$\lambda = \lambda_0 + \frac{C}{d - d_0}$$

where λ is the wavelength of the unknown line, λ_0 is a wavelength which is constant for a given plate, C is a constant for the plate, and d is the distance measured along the plate from d_0, which is some definite point on a linear scale.   The three constants λ_0, C, and d_0 can be calculated by substituting the wavelengths and comparator readings of three known lines in the above equation and then solving the three equations simultaneously.   On substituting in the equation the values of the constants so determined, the wavelength of any unknown line can be calculated from its position.

Hartmann's formula is used much less frequently nowadays than formerly, since the wavelengths of so many lines are known with high precision that linear interpolation between known lines suffices for most wavelength determinations.   Furthermore, prism spectrographs are seldom used for precise wavelength determinations, and linear interpolation serves with diffraction gratings.

The *method of coincidences* is sometimes used in measuring wave-

[2] J. Hartmann, *Astrophys. Jour.*, **8**, 218 (1898).

lengths with diffraction gratings, though it has been restricted in the past principally to setting up wavelength scales, and the modern interferometer has made this procedure unnecessary. The method of coincidences makes use of the fact that in diffraction-grating spectra a first-order line of wavelength λ should theoretically occur in the same position as a second-order line of wavelength $\lambda/2$, a third-order line of wavelength $\lambda/3$, and so on. Since diffraction gratings are imperfect optical instruments, this method gives only approximate results, and gross errors may result if it is relied on entirely. Rowland's original wavelength scale,[3] built up by this system, ultimately was found to have errors in some regions of the spectrum of several tenths of an angstrom. Errors produced by using the method of coincidences vary from grating to grating but are usually of the order of a few thousandths or hundredths of an angstrom. With a given grating, such errors depend on the density of exposure. This effect is closely related to target pattern and to the variation of line shape with order and with density of exposure.

Overlapping orders are sometimes of value in identifying spectrum lines obtained with diffraction gratings, since it is often possible to identify lines of different orders by their appearance. Thus a second-order line at 2300 A can readily be distinguished from a first-order line at 4600 A, because the contrast of the photographic emulsion is less for the shorter wavelength than for the longer; one line will have a grayish tone and the other will be a dense black. The appearance of the Rowland ghosts (§ 5.3) and the lengths of lines can also be used on occasion to identify lines from different orders.

For very accurate measurements of wavelengths, interferometers should be used, as discussed in Chapter 20.

9.8. Standards of Wavelength. The lengths of light waves can be measured directly by means of interferometers (§ 20.2). Since the determination of a wavelength to 1 part in 5,000,000 or better is a very delicate and lengthy process, the procedure has been adopted of determining the wavelengths of a few lines very precisely and then making measurements relative to these standard lines with ordinary spectrographs. In practice, the red cadmium line at 6438.4696 A is taken as the primary standard of wavelength, and several hundred other lines have been measured relative to this with interferometers, and defined as secondary and tertiary standards.

---

[3] H. A. Rowland, *Collected Physical Papers.*

If new measurements of the wavelength of the primary standard were always made in terms of the standard meter bar, the accepted wavelengths of all spectrum lines would have to be changed every time improved measurements of either were made. To avoid the necessity of making such corrections, the International Union for Cooperation in Solar Research[4] in 1907 adopted the following resolution: "The wavelength of the red ray of light from cadmium produced by a tube with electrodes is 6438.4696 A, in dry air, at 15°C on the hydrogen thermometer, at a pressure of 760 mm of mercury, the value of g being 980.67. This number will be the definition of the unit of wavelength." Hence the International Primary Standard of Wavelength Cd 6438.4696 A is exactly correct by definition, even though its value is known in terms of the standard meter bar to only about 1 part in 10,000,000. An angstrom, written A, is thus defined to be $\dfrac{1}{6438.4696}$ of the wavelength of the cadmium red line, and not, as previously, 10^{-8} cm (written Å).

The International Astronomical Union[5] has set up a number of international secondary standards of wavelength, using only lines that have been measured concordantly and independently in at least three laboratories, usually with Fabry-Perot etalons (§ 20.6). Many of these secondary standards are lines of neon and krypton, and are known relative to each other and to the primary standard to within 0.0001 A, or about 1 part in 50,000,000. A still larger number of iron lines have been measured with the etalon interferometer, and some of these have been adopted as secondary standards. These lines are broader than those of the rare gases and presumably are correct only to within 0.001 A. Table 9.4, page 218, contains a list of publications giving the adopted secondary standards.

The standard Pfund arc (§ 8.12) is used for producing the iron secondary standards, light being taken only from regions not closer than 7 mm to an electrode (to avoid wavelength shifts due to strong electric fields near the electrodes, known as *pole effect*). This precaution can be observed only at wavelengths below 4500 A, however, since at longer wavelengths it is found necessary to use a shorter arc to bring out the desired lines; but pole effects are less likely to occur to lines in this spectrum region.

The secondary standards leave little to be desired with respect to

[4] *Trans. Int. Union Solar Res.*, **2**, 109 (1907).
[5] *Trans. Int. Astron. Union*, **6**, 79 (1938).

TABLE 9.4

TABLES OF STANDARD WAVELENGTHS*

1. Commission 14, Wavelength Standards, *Trans. Int. Astron. Union*, **1**, 35 (1922), contains 402 secondary and tertiary standards in the range 7032 to 3370 A, for iron and neon, given to 0.001 A, with intensity range 1 to 10. *Trans. Int. Astron. Union*, **2**, 40 (1925), contains 4 neon lines in range 7537–6929 A, given to 0.001 A, adopted as secondary standards. Other lines listed but not adopted. *Trans. Int. Astron. Union*, **3**, 77 (1928), contains 384 lines in the range 7535 to 3370 A, in arc and discharge for iron and neon, given to 0.001 A, with intensity range 1 to 10. Revision of standards, including provisional standards as well as adopted standards. *Trans. Int. Astron. Union*, **4**, 58 (1932), contains 312 lines in range 8662 to 341 A, in standard arc, vacuum arc, and discharge, for six elements, given to 0.001 and 0.0001 A, 3 iron and 10 krypton standards adopted. Corrections to 1922 table given. *Trans. Int. Astron. Union*, **5**, 81 (1935), contains 201 lines in the range 10,216 to 580 A, in standard arc, vacuum arc, and discharge, for seven elements, given to 0.001 and 0.0001 A, with intensity range 1 to 1500. Krypton and neon standards adopted. *Trans. Int. Astron. Union*, **6**, 79 (1938), contains 271 lines in the range 3845 to 2100 A, in arc and discharge, for iron and krypton, given to 0.001 and 0.0001 A, with those adopted as standards.

2. W. F. Meggers, *Nat. Bur. Standards Jour. Res.*, **14**, 33 (1935), contains 91 lines in the range 10,216 to 7164 A, in the short iron arc, given to 0.001 A, with intensity range 1 to 1500. *Nat. Bur. Standards Jour. Res.*, **18**, 543 (1937), contains 242 lines in the range 3497 to 2100 A, in the standard iron arc, given to 0.001 and 0.0001 A.

3. W. F. Meggers, *Proceedings Sixth Conference on Spectroscopy* (Wiley, New York, 1939), page 116, contains 346 lines in the range 7032 to 2447 A, in arc and discharge, for iron, neon, and krypton, given to 0.001 and 0.0001 A. Collection of all adopted secondary standards.

4. F. Twyman and D. M. Smith, *Wavelength Tables for Spectrum Analysis*, 2d ed. (Hilger, London, 1931), page 12, contains 505 lines in the range 6750 to 2327 A, for standard arc and discharge, for iron, helium, and neon, given to 0.001 A, with intensity range 1 to 10. Collection of adopted standards and other accurate measurements.

5. W. R. Brode, *Chemical Spectroscopy* (Wiley, New York, 1939), page 387. In list of principal iron lines, gives adopted secondary standards.

precision but are somewhat lacking in number, distribution, suitability for obtaining various forms of excitation, and desirable variety and uniformity of physical characteristics. A discussion of the 1938 status of wavelength standards has been given by W. F. Meggers,[5] president of that commission of the I.A.U. charged with the responsibility for these standards.

---

* Based on a list given by G. R. Harrison, *Jour. App. Phys.*, **10**, 760 (1939), by permission of that Journal.

Spectral regions shorter than 2447 A and longer than 6678 A are thus far unprovided with official wavelength standards, but for most routine purposes wavelengths of known spectrum lines suitable for use as standards in these regions can be obtained from wavelength tables.

Wavelengths measured before 1910 or thereabouts are on a different scale from that of the international angstrom and should be corrected before use. Most such measurements are on Rowland's scale. Kayser (General Reference 9.1, Vol. VI, page 891 (1912)), gives corrections that should be applied to change original angstroms (Å) to international angstroms (A).

In addition to the International Secondary Standards, a group of tertiary standards has been set up, but these are relatively unimportant, and many wavelengths given in spectroscopic tables are of comparable accuracy. The tertiary standards hǎve been measured with large diffraction-grating spectrographs. Such wavelength determinations are limited in precision by several factors, most of which are related to the fact that many diffraction gratings produce unsymmetrical spectrum lines, which vary in shape with density of exposure. The center of gravity of the line may shift with density owing to the nonlinearity of the characteristic curve of the emulsion and the complex forms of the lines produced by the grating. It is usually necessary to photograph at one time many lines of widely different intensities. When a broad region of the spectrum is covered in a single exposure, as is becoming increasingly common, it is difficult to have all standard lines of the proper density.

Standards measured by interferometers can be effectively supplemented by those obtained by computation, if we make use of the Ritz combination principle, that each spectral line corresponds to the difference in energy between two levels (§ 10.1). In a complex atom each energy level may give rise to many spectrum lines, and when the wavelengths of a number of lines have been measured with sufficient accuracy to determine a large number of the energy levels precisely, the wavelengths of other lines arising from these levels can be computed with a high degree of accuracy. By this means, wavelength scales can be smoothed out and made self-consistent. This procedure is particularly valuable for the infrared region.

9.9. Intensity Estimates. An important part of the description of a spectrum line is an estimate of its intensity relative to other lines in the same spectrum. Ability to estimate intensities on a uniform scale can be acquired only by experience. A good intensity estimate is often more satisfactory than a very precise intensity determination, because the actual intensity of a spectrum line depends on many factors, including the type of spectrograph and photographic emulsion used, the method of source excitation, and the characteristics of the atom emitting the line.

It is important to differentiate clearly between two needs for intensity estimates. The fundamental need is that of determining the probability that an atom will emit a certain spectrum line under certain conditions, relative to its probability of emitting another line. The second need is that of the spectroscopist who is interested merely in the actual density of a line as it can be expected to appear on his spectrum plate. For this purpose, no method of determining spectral intensities has been developed which is more satisfactory than a good visual estimate.

One of the most uniform intensity scales is that of A. S. King, who, in the course of a long lifetime spent at Mount Wilson Observatory in measuring spectrograms and estimating intensities, developed a remarkably uniform and self-consistent scale. Russell [6] has shown that King's intensity estimates vary approximately as the square root of the true intensity of the line.

The older intensity scales ordinarily ran from 1 to 10, with additions at both ends. When a spectroscopist found lines fainter than those he had been calling 1 he called them 0 or 00, and often progressed as far as 0000. If the line were stronger than 10, he might call it 12 or 15. Modern workers have found that an expanded scale is useful, particularly since the tendency in making an eye estimate is to compress the true intensity scale, strong lines appearing relatively weaker than is justified. Meggers and other workers at the Bureau of Standards use a scale that goes up to 10,000, and the intensity scale in the *Massachusetts Institute of Technology Wavelength Tables* runs from 2 to 10,000, lines fainter than 2 having been arbitrarily excluded. Even on these expanded scales all numbers are not used, the numbers most commonly used by spectroscopists being 0, 1, 2, 3, 5, 8, 10, 12, 15, 20, 25, 35, 50, 60, 70, 80, 100, 120, 150, 200, 300, 400, 500, 700, 1000, 1200, 1500, 2000, 3000, 5000, and 10,000, with occasional interpolations between these.

When one estimates the intensity of a line, its width and shape

---

[6] H. N. Russell, *Proc. Nat. Acad. Sci.*, **11**, 314 and 322 (1925).

probably contribute as much to the estimate as its maximum density. A skillful estimator takes into account the general integrated intensity of the line, including something for self-absorption (§ 10.9), as shown by the changed shape of the line.

The precise determination of intensity is a complex and difficult process, since so many variables must be taken into account.[7] This precision is not needed and, in fact, is not what is wanted for spectral intensities to be used in connection with wavelength tables.

9.10. Catalogues of Wavelengths. Wavelengths are conveniently listed in two types of catalogues, the first giving in order of wavelength the lines known to be emitted by a particular type of atom or molecule, and the second listing wavelengths in order, followed by the atom or molecule of origin.

Spectrochemical qualitative analysis requires use of only a few of the most sensitive lines of each element, and these are most conveniently obtained from brief tables listing from 500 to 5000 lines. Such tables are given in Appendices I and II of this book.

The best-known inclusive tables of spectrum wavelengths for atomic lines are listed in Table 9.5. Outstanding is Kayser's monumental *Handbuch der Spectroscopie*, General Reference 9.1, with data on 180,000 lines. Many wavelength data included in this are now outdated, however. Although parts of Volumes VII and VIII contain data obtained for certain elements as recently as 1934, no data obtained later than 1911 are included for some 40 elements.

TABLE 9.5

INCLUSIVE TABLES OF SPECTRUM LINES*

1. H. Kayser, *Handbuch der Spectroscopie* (Hirzel, Leipzig), Vol. V (1910), contains about 20,000 lines in the range 39,100 to 1030 A, in arc, spark, discharge and flame, for 45 elements, A to N, given mostly to 0.01 A, with intensity range 1 to 500.   Contains table of air lines and also some band heads. Note Rowland scale.   Volume VI (1912) contains about 50,000 lines in the range 8000 to 2000 A, in arc, spark, discharge, and flame, for 41 elements, Na to Zr, given mostly to 0.01 to 0.001 A, with intensity range 1 to 10.   Also contains tables of iron lines, wavelength range 9000 to 2200 A, principal lines, wavelength range 91,000 to 1850 A, and band heads.   Note mostly Rowland scale.

---

[7] See G. R. Harrison, *Jour. Opt. Soc. Am.*, **17**, 389 (1928); G. R. Harrison and H. Engwicht, *ibid.*, **18**, 287 (1929); R. S. Seward, *Phys. Rev.*, **37**, 344 (1931).

* Based on an article by G. R. Harrison, *Jour. App. Phys.*, **10**, 760 (1939) by permission of that Journal.

2. H. Kayser and H. Konen, *Handbuch der Spectroscopie* (Hirzel, Leipzig), Vol. VII (Parts 1, 2, 3, 1923–1934), contains about 54,000 lines in the range 75,000 to 70 A, in arc, spark, discharge, and flame for 49 elements, given to 0.01 or 0.001 A, with intensity range 1 to 10. Also table of air lines. Volume VIII (1932) contains about 22,000 lines in the range 29,300 to 250 A, in arc, spark, and discharge, for 19 elements Ag to Cu, given to 0.01 or 0.001 A, with intensity range 1 to 10.

3. Landolt-Börnstein, *Physikalisch-chemische Tabellen*, Ergänzungsband I, page 336, II, page 529, III, page 763 (Springer, Berlin, 1931–1935), contains about 10,000 lines in the range 74,360 to 291 A, in arc, spark, and discharge, for 81 elements, given mostly to 0.01 A. Contains also some band heads and tables of intense and ultimate lines.

4. G. R. Harrison, *Massachusetts Institute of Technology Wavelength Tables* (Wiley, New York, 1939), contains 109,275 lines, listed according to wavelength, in the range 10,000 to 2000 A, in the arc, spark, and discharge, for 87 elements, given mostly to 0.001 A, with intensity range from 1 to 9000. Air lines and some band heads included.

5. F. Exner and E. Haschek, *Die Spektren der Elemente bei normalem Druck* (Deuticke, Leipzig and Vienna, 1911), Vol. II, contains about 60,000 lines in the range 6800 to 2200 A, in the arc, for 67 elements, given to 0.01 A, with intensity range 1 to 1000; 214 band heads also listed   Volume III contains about 56,000 lines in the range 6800 to 2200 A, in the spark, for 78 elements, given to 0.01 A, with intensity range 1 to 1000; 107 bands also listed.   Note Rowland scale.

6. P. Auger and others, *Données numériques de spectroscopie* (Gauthier-Villars, Paris, 1910–1936), contains about 150,000 lines (including duplicates) in the range 10,000 to 2000 A, in the arc, spark, flame, and discharge, for 76 elements, given to 0.1 and 0.01 A, with intensity range 1 to 1000.   Some bands also included.

7. W. Jevons, *Report on Band Spectra of Diatomic Molecules* (The Physical Society, London, 1932), contains data on bands of 142 molecules.

8. W. Weizel, *Handbuch der Experimentalphysik*, Ergänzungsband I (Akademische Verlagsgesellschaft, Leipzig, 1931), contains data on bands of about 150 molecules.

A catalogue containing more than 300,000 entries, comprising all wavelength measurements on atomic lines given in the literature up to 1939, has been compiled at the Massachusetts Institute of Technology by WPA workers, but this has not appeared in printed form.

Kayser's *Tabelle der Hauptlinien der Linienspektren aller Elemente*, appearing in its latest edition in 1939 under the editorship of Kayser and Ritschl (General Reference 9.2), lists 27,000 lines in the order of wavelengths in the range 90,850 to 33 A, in arc, spark, and discharge tube for 88 elements, with wavelengths given to one or two figures after the decimal.

In 1939, the *Massachusetts Institute of Technology Wavelength Tables* (General Reference 9.3), giving the 109,275 strongest lines lying between 10,000 and 2000 A from neutral atoms and those in their first stage of ionization, were published. In these tables, the lines are listed in order of wavelength, followed by the parent element. Abbreviated tables of wavelengths useful in spectrochemical analysis are listed in Table 15.2.

Which lines of a given element will appear strongest when vanishingly small concentrations of the element are caused to emit light depends to some extent on the type of spectroscopic equipment used, on the methods of recording and observing the spectrum, and on the type of excitation used. Tables of the most sensitive spectrum lines will be found to differ somewhat, depending on whether they are based principally on lists compiled by the earlier workers (see § 15.2), whether they depend on theory,[8] or whether they involve observations made with modern equipment and the new ultraviolet and infrared photographic emulsions of increased sensitivity.

The published descriptions of spectra are far from complete, even for comparatively strong lines. Most complex elements have not been thoroughly studied at wavelengths longer than 6000 A, in the range 2000–2500 A, and in the vacuum ultraviolet. Such elements as ruthenium, rhodium, thorium, and uranium have been fairly thoroughly studied in recent years, but much work remains to be done on many similar elements.

9.11. The Harrison Automatic Comparator. The measurement and reduction of spectrograms can be greatly facilitated by the use of an automatic comparator. Such a measuring engine,[9] in use at the Massachusetts Institute of Technology since 1938, is capable of measuring in 120 sec an entire 20-in. plate containing perhaps 2000 spectrum lines, recording on a motion-picture film to seven-figure precision the wavelengths in angstroms of all lines, and providing on the same film a density trace of the lines. Such a machine is of great value when large numbers of measurements are to be made from a number of plates taken with a given spectrograph. For the measurement of occasional single plates taken on different spectrographs, it is of value in giving results in terms of distance along the plate, the

---

[8] W. F. Meggers, *Jour. Opt. Soc. Am.*, **31**, 39 (1941).

[9] G. R. Harrison, *Jour. Opt. Soc. Am.*, **25**, 169 (1935); G. R. Harrison and J. P. Molnar, *ibid.*, **30**, 343 (1940).

reduction from linear measurement to wavelength being carried out with a computing machine.

A spectrum plate is clamped to the carriage shown in the rear center of Fig. 9.13 and is moved by the comparator screw at constant speed across a beam of light, which throws on the circular white screen an image of that portion of the plate passing across it at any moment. The operator can move the plate in either direction by turning the handle shown in the lower right-hand corner of Fig. 9.13 or by operating an electric drive in the forward or reverse directions.

Fig. 9.13. The Harrison automatic comparator.

An automobile headlamp operated by a storage battery is mounted below the comparator case. Light from this lamp is projected by a condenser lens through the plate being measured, on to a micro-Tessar lens, which produces an enlarged image of the plate on the screen some 6 ft distant.

Figure 9.14 shows the appearance of a portion of a wavelength record obtained with the automatic engine. The wavelength of a line which is passing across a scanning slit in the screen is recorded with a single flash of a stroboscope lamp as the density peak passes. Condensers discharge through this lamp when a signal is received from an electrical circuit, indicating that the maximum of the spectrum line is passing across the slit.

Though the relation between distance along the plate and wavelengths of the lines recorded thereon is not linear, the instrument is arranged to record wavelengths directly in angstroms. By means of decimal gears, the first two figures of the dispersion of the plate can be set into the machine. The next four figures are controlled by a variable-speed unit driven by a cam specially cut for the spectral region being covered, each cam having been laid out initially in terms of standard iron spectra obtained with the spectrograph used. The seventh figure is controlled by a photoelectric device that automatically follows the outer edge of an inked curve. Plate after plate taken

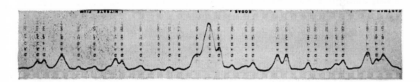

Fig. 9.14. Wavelength record obtained with the automatic comparator.

in the same region of the same spectrograph can be measured with a single cam and curve. When plates are changed, small variations may be found, but these can be reduced to any desired value. Variations as great as 0.01 A may be tolerated if necessary, since standard lines are recorded on all plates and these are measured with the unknowns. Wavelength values read from the film can then be changed in the seventh figure in accordance with the error found in the seventh figure of the standard line readings.

An electron multiplier tube is used behind the slit of the projection system to measure the light passing through it. The output of the multiplier is fed to an electrical network which causes the stroboscopic lamp to flash at the instant when the peak of a spectrum line is symmetrically disposed across the slit.

The *maximum picker*, as the electrical line-measuring device is called, does not, as might be supposed, operate on the slope of the density curve of the line. The graininess of the plate makes such operation undesirable, and the saturation of the photographic emulsion at high densities flattens the tops of dense lines. Instead, the line peak is taken as being halfway between two areas of equal density measured at the points of approximately maximum contrast for the narrowest line that can be resolved by the spectrograph on which the plate was exposed.

This automatic comparator has been found to possess several advantages beyond the more than hundredfold gain in speed of measurement and computation which it provides. The comparator screw does not change temperature during the few seconds required to measure a plate, and its nut is pushed with uniform speed, so that an oil film of constant thickness is kept in the screw-nut contact. Wavelength values are available instantaneously so that any line can be identified by inspection if the machine is stopped or is operated by hand. If the operator prefers, he can run the comparator by hand, using hand settings, and pressing a button whenever he has set the center of a line on the fiducial mark.

It is found that the reproducibility of setting on narrow lines by the automatic method is from three to five times more precise than that of eye setting. In a test spectrum, lines of various breadths were picked by the machine 30 times in each direction with an average deviation of ±0.0004 A, whereas the average internal deviation of hand-and-eye setting by an experienced operator was ±0.0020 A on the same machine and plate.

9.12. Limitations of Wavelength Measurement with Diffraction Gratings. The principal sources of errors in wavelength determinations by means of gratings are as follows (see also § 20.4):

1. The inadequacy of wavelength standards in certain spectral regions, particularly of standard lines of suitable intensity.

2. The displacement on spectrograms, relative to standard lines, of lines to be measured.

3. Displacements caused by strong neighboring lines or by blends with impurity lines due to bands.

4. The natural breadths of some lines and the complex structures of others (§ 20.1).

5. Actual variations of wavelengths, in standards or unknowns, with excitation conditions.

6. Incorrect identification of lines.

7. Uncertainties of setting on line maxima.

8. Comparator errors.

9. Errors in computation.

10. Corrections required to express all measured wavelengths in air of standard density.

Great gaps still exist in our knowledge of spectrum lines.   Accurate wavelengths of approximately a million atomic and ionic lines will probably be needed in order to give astronomers, physicists, and chemists all the material of this sort that they can effectively use. Fewer than one-third of these spectrum lines have been measured and assigned to parent atoms.

GENERAL REFERENCES

9.1.   H. Kayser, *Handbuch der Spectroscopie*, Vols. 1–6, to 1912; H. Kayser and H. Konen, *ibid.*, Vols. 7–8, to 1932.   Leipzig: S. Hirzel.

9.2.   H. Kayser and R. Ritschl, *Tabelle der Hauptlinien der Linienspektren aller Elemente.*   Berlin: Springer, 1939.

9.3.   G. R. Harrison, *M.I.T. Wavelength Tables.*   Cambridge, Mass: Technology Press.   New York: John Wiley & Sons, Inc., 1939.

9.4.   G. R. Harrison, "Compilations of Spectroscopic Data".   *Jour. App. Phys.*, **10**, 760 (1939).

9.5.   G. R. Harrison, "The M.I.T. Wavelength Project," *Reports on Progress in Physics, Phys. Soc. Lond.*, **8**, 202 (1941).

CHAPTER 10

The Origins of Atomic Spectra

ANY THEORY OF THE ORIGIN OF SPECTRAL LINES must explain observed spectra quantitatively in terms of models of the atoms from which the spectra arise. It is necessary not only to explain the intensity of emitted or absorbed radiation as a function of wavelength but also to give a quantitative basis for the understanding of such details as the effects on the spectrum of temperature and of electric and magnetic fields. Spectroscopic theory has contributed much to our ideas about the structure and mechanics of atoms. Some familiarity with the elementary aspects of the theory is therefore helpful in visualizing the processes involved in the emission and absorption of radiation.

SPECTRAL SERIES AND ATOMIC ENERGY STATES

The most striking regularity in the spectra of many atoms is the classification of the spectral lines into *series*. The frequencies of the several members of a given series can be represented numerically by a simple formula such as

$$\nu_i = \nu_\infty - \frac{R}{(i + C_1)^2} \tag{10.1}$$

Here ν_i is the frequency of a line in the series, a so-called *series member;* ν_∞ is the *series limit*, or series member of highest frequency; R and C_1 are constants for the entire series; and i is an integer that runs from 1 to infinity. As i gets larger and larger, the spacing of the lines in the series gets smaller and smaller, until the series finally converges on the series limit. Such series, of which an example is shown in Fig. 10.1, are frequently found and are called *Rydberg series* after the proposer of Eq. (10.1). R is called the *Rydberg constant*.

The relationship between different series in the same spectrum is significant inasmuch as the frequency ν_∞ for one series is equal to the expression $R/(i + C_1)^2$ for another series, i being some small integer. Thus a more general form of Eq. (10.1) is

$$\nu_{ij} = R\left(\frac{1}{(i + C_1)^2} - \frac{1}{(j + C_2)^2}\right) \tag{10.2}$$

by which all the series for certain atoms may be represented. Here the value of i is fixed at some small integer for a particular series, and j takes on integral values up to very large numbers to give the frequencies for the various members of that series.

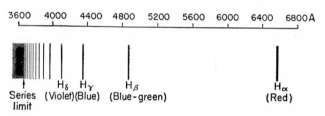

Fig. 10.1. The Balmer series in the spectrum of the hydrogen atom.

10.1. The Hydrogen Atom. The empirical formula for the various series in hydrogen has a particularly simple form:

$$\nu_{ij} = R_H\left(\frac{1}{i^2} - \frac{1}{j^2}\right) \tag{10.3}$$

The constant R_H is the Rydberg constant for hydrogen. If we set $i = 1$ and $j = 2, 3, 4, 5, \ldots$, we get the members of the Lyman far ultraviolet series in hydrogen, beginning with a strong line at 1216 A. Similarly, $i = 2$, and $j = 3, 4, 5, 6, \ldots$, gives the Balmer series (visible and near ultraviolet) and $i = 3$, $j = 4, 5, 6, 7, \ldots$, the Paschen series (near infrared). Thus the frequencies of the members of all the known series in hydrogen can be expressed as the difference between two terms, the frequency value of each term being expressed as

$$\nu_n = \frac{R_H}{n^2} \qquad\qquad (\cdot$$

in which n is an integer.

As we shall see in § 10.5, terms such as those can be identified with stationary energy states or l spectral lines associated with the transitions betw

The hydrogen terms are plotted on an energy-level diagram in Fig. 10.2, and the transitions between them, which give rise to the various hydrogen series, are indicated by arrows connecting the initial and final levels for each transition.   Thus each arrow indicates the transi-

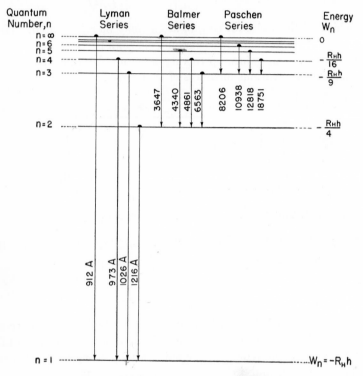

Fig. 10.2.   The energy levels of the hydrogen atom.

tion giving rise to a particular spectral line.   Expression (10.4) can be rewritten in energy units as

$$W_n = \frac{-R_H h}{n^2} \qquad (10.5)$$

where W_n is the energy of a stationary state, the factor $-h$ (Planck's constant) being necessary to convert frequency units into ergs and to conform to the useful convention of having the *highest* energy that which corresponds to $n = \infty$ and the lowest that for $n = 1$ (compare Fig. 10.2).

The concept of stationary energy states in atoms was first put forth by Bohr.[1]   The mechanics used by Bohr has since been superseded by quantum mechanics, but the expression he obtained for the energies of the stationary states in the hydrogen atom is also given by quantum mechanics.   It is

$$W_n = \frac{-2\pi^2\mu e^4 Z^2}{n^2 h^2} \tag{10.6}$$

In this expression, μ is the reduced mass of the central nucleus and electron [in the hydrogen atom $\mu = m_e m_p/(m_e + m_p)$, m_e = electron mass, m_p = proton mass], e is the electronic charge, and Z the atomic number of the central nucleus (which is 1 for the proton).   The constant R_H can thus be expressed* in terms of fundamental constants:

$$R_H = \frac{2\pi^2\mu e^4}{h^3} \tag{10.7}$$

It is interesting to consider the physical significance of the energy levels shown in Fig. 10.2.   The lowest level ($n = 1$) is the so-called *ground state*, and in a collection of hydrogen *atoms* in a gas, it will be the stationary state in which most of the atoms exist for most of the time.   To raise a hydrogen atom to a higher level, energy has to be supplied to the atom, the amount of energy required for elevation to a particular level W_n being known as the *excitation potential*† of that level.   This excitation energy can be supplied by radiation, in which case the atom absorbs radiation of frequency

$$\nu = \frac{W_n - W_1}{h}$$

It can also be supplied by collision with atoms, ions, or electrons.   If it is supplied by collision with electrons in an electrical discharge, the electrons must necessarily have a kinetic energy at least as large as $W_n - W_1$.   Since the kinetic energy is imparted to the electrons by their falling through a potential drop of a certain number of volts, the kinetic energy of the electrons can be expressed in terms of volts.

---

[1] N. Bohr, *Phil. Mag.*, **26**, 1 (1913).

* Equation 10.7 gives R_H in frequency units (ν).   It is often expressed in wavenumber units (σ). $\sigma = \nu/c$.   In wave-numbers the value of R_H is 109,677.76 cm^{-1}.

† Also sometimes called *critical potential*.

In turn, an excitation potential can be expressed in volts, since this potential corresponds to the minimum kinetic energy that an electron must have to cause the transition to the upper state. Electron volts are frequently used as units for energy levels, because the numerical values of the levels then lie in the range from 1 to 100 volts. One volt corresponds to 8066 cm^{-1}, so the wavelength region from 12,500 A (8000 cm^{-1}) to 125 A (800,000 cm^{-1}) corresponds to the range 1 to 100 volts.

The excitation potential of the level for $n = \infty$ has a special significance. It corresponds to the energy required to remove the electron in the hydrogen atom to an indefinitely large distance from the proton, in other words, to ionize the atom. This energy, called the *ionization potential*, is $W_\infty - W_1$, or $R_H h$, and has the value 13.59 electron volts. Ionization potentials for other atoms are listed in Table 10.1.

Several other atomic systems are known whose energy-level scheme is that of Fig. 10.2 except for a change of scale. These are all ions consisting of one electron and a heavy atomic nucleus. As one can see from Eq. (10.6), the energy levels differ from those of hydrogen only in the values of Z^2 and μ. If the atomic nucleus is that of helium, μ is only slightly different (about 0.05 per cent) from μ in the hydrogen atom, but Z^2 has the value 4. If the nucleus is lithium, $Z^2 = 9$, and so on. Hence the scale in Fig. 10.2 has to be changed by about a factor of 4 for the He$^+$ ion, 9 for the Li^{++} ion, and so on. The various series for these ions lie in the far ultraviolet, as can readily be verified by calculation from Eq. (10.3). The ionization potentials are also increased by the approximate factors 4 for the ionization of He$^+$ to He^{++}, 9 for Li^{++} to Li^{+++}, and so on (see Table 10.1). The series for ionized helium were known before Bohr's work on the hydrogen spectrum, but to what atom or ion they were due was not clear. Bohr's highly exact calculation of the frequencies of the lines in the He$^+$ series was simultaneously a satisfying solution to a puzzling problem in the origin of spectra and a highly convincing corollary to his theory of the hydrogen spectrum.

10.2. Quantum Numbers in Atomic Spectra. The number n in Eq. (10.6) is a *quantum number*. It is not the only quantum number, however, associated with the various energy states; but because it is the most important insofar as the energy values in the hydrogen atom are concerned, it is called the *principal quantum number*. There are three other quantum numbers associated with each electron in an atom, usually designated l, m, and s. Each of these is concerned with one of two types of angular momentum which every electron in an atom possesses. The quantum numbers l and m are related to the orbital angular momentum of the electron in its motion about the atomic nucleus, whereas the quantum number s is associated with the spin of the electron. If the atom be compared to a miniature solar system with the sun and earth in the roles of nucleus and electron, respectively, the orbital angular momentum of the earth is that associated with its annual trip around the sun, whereas its spin angular momentum is due to its daily rotation on its own axis.

The quantum numbers l and m take on integral values, just as does n, but these values are not completely independent of n The numerical values that l can have range between $n - 1$ and 0. Similarly, m can never be larger than l, but in contrast to l, it can assume *negative* values down to $-l$. The physical interpretation of l and m pictures l as a numerical factor expressing the orbital angular momentum in terms of the quantum mechanical unit of angular momentum, $h/2\pi^*$; m, on the other hand, is the number related to the orientation of the orbit in space. A positive and negative pair of values of m correspond to the same orbital orientation, but one (say the positive m) corresponds to a clockwise motion of the electron in its orbit, and the other to a counterclockwise motion.

Before we consider the quantum number s, we must discuss the spectra of some relatively simple atoms, in which the energy levels depend not only on n but also on l.

10.3. Series in Atoms with Many Electrons. An atomic spectrum increases in complexity as the number of electrons directly involved in its production increases. However, the number of electrons involved need not be the total number of electrons in the atom. It frequently happens that the energy-level scheme for an atom depends primarily on one or two electrons only, the other electrons maintaining a constant set of quantum numbers (and therefore energies), regard-

---

* The reader can readily verify that the units of h (erg-seconds) have the dimensions of angular momentum, which is linear momentum (dimensions mass $\times$ velocity) multiplied by a moment arm (dimension length). The numerical relationship between l and orbital angular momentum is

$$\text{Orbital angular momentum} = \sqrt{l(l + 1)} \left(\frac{h}{2\pi} \right)$$

Atomic number	Symbol	Ionization potentials		
		I	II	III
1	H	13.59	—	—
2	He	24.46	54.38	—
3	Li	5.36	75.26	121.8
4	Be	9.28	18.12	153.1
5	B	8.26	25.00	37.75
6	C	11.22	24.27	47.65
7	N	14.48	29.47	47.40
8	O	13.55	34.93	54.87
9	F	17.34	34.81	62.35
10	Ne	21.45	40.9	63.2
11	Na	5.12	47.06	70.72
12	Mg	7.61	14.96	79.72
13	Al	5.96	18.74	28.31
14	Si	8.12	16.27	33.35
15	P	10.9	19.56	30.0
16	S	10.30	23.3	34.9
17	Cl	12.95	23.67	39.69
18	A	15.68	27.76	40.75
19	K	4.32	31.66	46.5
20	Ca	6.09	11.82	50.96
21	Sc	(6.7)	(12.8)	24.61
22	Ti	6.81	(13.6)	(27.6)
23	V	6.71	14.1	(29.6)
24	Cr	6.74	(16.6)	(32.1)
25	Mn	7.41	15.70	(34.0)
26	Fe	7.83	16.16	(31.7)
27	Co	7.81	17.3	(33.8)
28	Ni	7.61	18.2	(35.9)
29	Cu	7.68	20.2	(29.5)
30	Zn	9.36	17.89	40.0
31	Ga	5.97	20.43	(30.6)
32	Ge	8.09	15.86	(32.0)
33	As	10.5	20.1	28.2
34	Se	9.70	21.3	33.9
35	Br	11.80	19.1	25.7
36	Kr	13.93	24.4	31.4
37	Rb	4.16	27.36	(47.0)
38	Sr	5.67	10.98	(43.0)
39	Y	6.5	12.3	20.4
40	Zr	6.92	13.97	24.00
41	Cb	?	(13.5)	24.2
42	Mo	7.35	(15.2)	(27.0)
43	Tc	(4.8)	(14.6)	(29.3)
44	Ru	7.5	(16.4)	(28.6)
45	Rh	7.7	(18.0)	(31.0)
46	Pd	8.3	19.8	(33.4)
47	Ag	7.54	21.4	35.9
48	Cd	8.96	17.30	38.0
49	In	5.76	18.79	27.9
50	Sn	7.30	14.53	30.5

OF THE ATOMS IN VOLTS*

Atomic number	Symbol	Ionization potentials		
		I	II	III
51	Sb	8.35	18.8	24.7
52	Te	8.96	(19.3)	30.5
53	I	10.6	19.4	(31.4)
54	Xe	12.08	(21.1)	(32)
55	Cs	3.87	23.4	(35)
56	Ba	5.19	9.95	?
57	La	5.6	11.4	(20.4)
58	Ce	6.54	14.8	?
59	Pr	5.76	?	?
60	Nd	6.31	?	?
61	—	?	?	?
62	Sm	6.55	11.4	?
63	Eu	5.64	11.4	?
64	Gd	6.65	?	?
65	Tb	6.74	?	?
66	Dy	6.82	?	?
67	Ho	?	?	?
68	Er	?	?	?
69	Tm	?	?	?
70	Yb	7.06	?	?
71	Lu	?	?	?
72	Hf	?	?	?
73	Ta	?	?	?
74	W	?	(14.0)	24.1
75	Re	(7.8)	(13.2)	(26.0)
76	Os	(8.7)	(14.6)	(24.8)
77	Ir	?	(16.0)	(26.7)
78	Pt	8.88	(17.4)	(28.6)
79	Au	9.18	19.95	(30.46)
80	Hg	10.38	18.65	34.3
81	Tl	6.07	20.32	29.7
82	Pb	7.38	14.96	(31.9)
83	Bi	7.25	16.6	25.42
84	Po	(8.21)	(18.6)	(27.8)
85	At	(9.59)	(18.1)	(30.3)
86	Rn	10.70	(20.0)	(30.0)
87	Fr	(4.0)	(21.5)	(32.3)
88	Ra	5.25	10.10	(34.3)
89	Ac	?	?	?
90	Th	?	?	29.4
91	Pa	?	?	?
92	U	?	?	?
93	Np	?	?	?
94	Pu	?	?	?
95	Am	?	?	?
96	Cm	?	?	?

* The values in Table 10.1 have not been critically reviewed; uncertain or estimated values are given in parentheses. Higher ionization potentials may be found in General Reference 10.3, p. 200, and in E. Lisitzin, *Soc. Scient. Fennica, Comm. Phys.-Math.*, X, No. 1 (1938). The latter reference contains an extensive bibliography of papers dealing with ionization potentials.

less of changes in the quantum numbers of the one or two electrons. The reason is that electrons in an atom tend to arrange themselves in concentric shells about the atomic nucleus according to their quantum numbers, all the electrons in a given shell having the same value of n. Because each shell has a limited quota of electrons (as we shall see in § 10.9), electrons in excess of this quota are forced into shells of larger radius (higher n). A shell whose quota is filled has on the average a symmetrical arrangement of electronic orbits that corresponds to a spherical distribution of electric charge. The term *shell* originates from this fact.

A spectroscopically important situation occurs when the total number of electrons in a neutral or in an ionized atom exceeds by 1 the number just needed to fill the quota of a shell. In this case, the excess electron moves approximately as does the electron in the hydrogen atom, that is, in the field of a charged central nucleus, because the spherical charge distribution of the other electrons acts approximately as though the whole charge were concentrated at the nucleus. Such an electronic arrangement is characteristic of the atoms of the alkali metals lithium, sodium, potassium, rubidium, and cesium. The series found in the spectra of such atoms are similar to the hydrogen series but follow Eq. (10.2) instead of Eq. (10.3). The number of series is larger, however, because a distinct series is obtained for each value of the constants C_1 and C_2 in Eq. (10.2). Moreover, two series can converge on the same wavelength if they share in common the constant C_1 but have different C_2 values.

The various energy levels of the alkali atoms that give rise to these series correspond to various values of the quantum numbers of the single outermost electron, the quantum numbers of all the other electrons in the atom (those in the filled shells) staying fixed. The numbers i and j in Eq. (10.2) are the values of the principal quantum number n for this electron, in strict analogy with the case of the hydrogen atom. The constants C_1 and C_2, however, intrude because the energy levels depend on the quantum number l of the outer electron as well as on n, in contradistinction to the energy levels in hydrogen. The reason can be seen qualitatively with the help of the orbital picture, if we recall that the quantum number l is a measure of the orbital angular momentum of the electron, larger l corresponding to larger angular momentum. A value of l small compared with the value of n therefore means that the angular momentum is small and indicates that the electron's orbit is not circular but a highly eccentric ellipse. In a circular orbit (maximum l) the outermost electron moves at a uniform distance from the inner, filled shells (Fig. 10.3a), and the situation resembles hydrogen. In the eccentric orbits, however, the electron orbit "penetrates" the shells to a greater or lesser extent (Fig. 10.3b) and during the penetration is attracted much more strongly by the positively charged nucleus. The energy of the electronic orbit is thereby lowered, the reduction depending on the extent of the penetration, that is, on the eccentricity, which in turn is determined by the quantum number l for a given value of n.

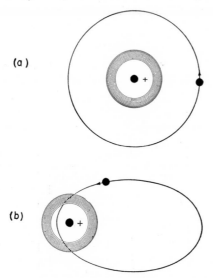

Fig. 10.3. The penetration of an inner shell by an electron moving in an eccentric orbit. (a) Circular orbit (l equal to $n - 1$). (b) Elliptical orbit (l smaller than $n - 1$).

These effects are illustrated in Fig. 10.4, where the energy levels of the sodium atom are plotted to scale with those of hydrogen. The filled shells in sodium contain 10 electrons, the eleventh or outermost being forced into orbits with n equal to 3 or larger. The energy levels* depend on both n and l. If $n = 3, 4, 5, \ldots$, and $l = 0$, the energies are

$$W = \frac{-R_{\mathrm{Na}}hc}{(n - 1.35)^2} \tag{10.8}$$

---

* The units of the energies in Eqs. (10.8)–(10.11) will be ergs per atom if R_{Na} is in reciprocal centimeters. R_{Na} has the value 109,735 cm^{-1}.

When $l = 1$, the expression is

$$W = \frac{-R_{Na}hc}{(n - 0.87)^2} \tag{10.9}$$

When $l = 2$, the expression is

$$W = \frac{-R_{Na}hc}{(n - 0.01)^2} \tag{10.10}$$

When $l = 3$ or larger $(n > 3$, since l is always less than $n)$, the expression is

$$W = \frac{-R_{Na}hc}{n^2} \tag{10.11}$$

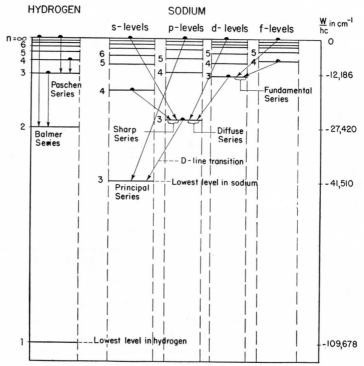

Fig. 10.4.   Comparison of the energy levels of the hydrogen and sodium atoms

This last expression agrees exactly with Eq. (10.5), which means that the energies of orbits not eccentric enough to penetrate the filled shells (that is, orbits with large l) do not depend appreciably on l but only on n.

The various series arising from these levels in the sodium atom are summarized in Table 10.2, in which the numerical values of n and l for the upper and lower levels of each transition are indicated. It will be noticed that the lower level for each series has a value of 3 for n. Accordingly, each series is analogous to the Paschen series in hydrogen, for which the lower level has $n = 3$, but the different series in sodium arise from the differences in energy associated with different l values.* The short wavelength limit of the Paschen series occurs in the near infrared at 8206 A, which is also approximately the limit of the fundamental series in sodium, but the other series all have limits in the violet or ultraviolet. The shift is illustrated in Fig. 10.4, which shows the drop in energy of the levels of small l value in comparison with the corresponding levels in hydrogen.

TABLE 10.2

SERIES IN SODIUM

Series	Value of l		Δl, differ-ence	Value of n		Constants (Eq. 10.2)	
	Upper level	Lower level		Upper	Lower	C_2 (upper)	C_1 (lower)
Sharp	0	1	-1	4, 5, 6,...	3	-1.35	-0.87
Principal	1	0	$+1$	3, 4, 5,...	3	-0.87	-1.35
Diffuse	2	1	$+1$	3, 4, 5,...	3	-0.01	-0.87
Fundamental	3	2	$+1$	4, 5, 6,...	3	0.00	-0.01

Because all the lines in the sharp series of the alkali metals originate from upper levels with $l = 0$, spectroscopists have fallen into the practice of calling all electrons with $l = 0$, s electrons (s for sharp); similarly, electrons with $l = 1$, p electrons (p for principal); with $l = 2$, d electrons; with $l = 3$, f electrons. For higher values of l, the notation proceeds alphabetically (g for $l = 4$, h for $l = 5$, and so on). It will be noticed from Table 10.2 that the several series result from transitions during which l changes by one unit, either plus or minus, never by zero, two, or three. This result may be

* There are two spectral lines for which this analogy does not hold, however: the first line in the so-called principal series (transition from $n = 3$, $l = 1$ to $n = 3$, $l = 0$) and the first line in the diffuse series (transition from $n = 3$, $l = 2$ to $n = 3$, $l = 1$). The upper and lower levels for each of these two transitions have the same value of n and accordingly in the hydrogen atom would have identical energies.

summarized by giving the *selection rule* (§ 10.6) for l: In any one-electron spectrum, the change in l, Δl, during a transition is always plus or minus 1.

$$\Delta l = \pm 1 \tag{10.12}$$

Similarly, one may say

$$\Delta n = 0, 1, 2, 3, \ldots, \infty \tag{10.13}$$

that is, there is no restriction on the amount by which n may change during a transition. In particular, these selection rules hold for the other alkali metals, all of which have series similar to those of sodium but with different values of n for the ground state.

10.4. Multiplicity in Atomic Spectra. One important feature of the sodium spectrum has not been mentioned—the double character of the individual lines. For instance, the first "line" in the principal series—the famous D lines of sodium—is well known to be a doublet whose individual wavelengths are 5890 and 5896 A. A composite "line" such as this one, consisting of several components of related origin that are usually closely spaced, is known as a *multiplet*. Multiplicity is the rule rather than the exception in atomic spectra, although in very complicated spectra it may be difficult to discern in the rich assortment of lines those which are associated as the components of a particular multiplet.

Multiplicity arises from electron spin. The spin of the electron produces a magnetic field, and between this field and the electron moving in its orbit there is electromagnetic interaction that affects the energy of the electron. This effect depends quantitatively on the size and direction of the spin magnetic field, both of which properties are severely restricted. The spin field always has the same size (that is, the electron spin has a constant angular velocity), and its direction is limited to one of two specific directions, namely, parallel or anti-parallel to some other field that serves as a reference direction. The other field may be the magnetic field of the electron moving in its orbit, the field of another spinning electron, or an external field due to an electromagnet. Associated with these two directions are the two possible values of the spin quantum number s, namely, $s = +\frac{1}{2}$ for parallel direction and $s = -\frac{1}{2}$ for antiparallel direction.*

---

* The reason for $s = \pm\frac{1}{2}$, rather than $s = \pm 1$, is that the spin angular momentum is $\dfrac{1}{2} \times \dfrac{h}{2\pi}$, not $\dfrac{h}{2\pi}$.

In the sodium and other alkali atoms the orbital magnetic field of the single outermost electron provides the reference direction.   If the spin field is parallel to the orbital field, $s = +\frac{1}{2}$.   Thus each energy level in Fig. 10.4 becomes two levels,* the higher one with $s = +\frac{1}{2}$, the other with $s = -\frac{1}{2}$.   The difference between the two levels $n = 3$, $l = 1$, $s = +\frac{1}{2}$ and $n = 3$, $l = 1$, and $s = -\frac{1}{2}$ in sodium is about 17 cm^{-1} (or 0.002 volt), and this is the order of magnitude of multiplet separation in light atoms.   In heavy atoms such as mercury the separations may be a hundred times larger.

Whereas a single electron produces a doubling of the energy levels, two or more electrons have a more complicated effect.   Fortunately, the fact that the spin quantum number s for each electron can have only two values simplifies matters.   The multiplicity or splitting up of each level on account of spin depends on the numerical values of the sum, S, of the spin quantum numbers.   The multiplicity is

$$M = 2S + 1 \qquad\qquad (10.14)$$

The sum S, which is always taken to have a positive sign, can have various values, of course, and the multiplicities M will vary accordingly.   For two electrons, $S = 0$ or 1, depending on whether the two spins are antiparallel or parallel.   Hence atomic spectra that arise from two electrons (helium and the alkaline-earth metals Be, Mg, Ca, Sr, and Ba) can have multiplicities of 1 (that is, no splitting of levels because of spin) or 3 (splitting of each level into three).   Spectra depending on three electrons can have $S = \frac{1}{2}$ or $\frac{3}{2}$ (hence $M = 2$ or 4).   It can readily be seen that the values of S will range in steps of one from 0 to $N/2$ for N electrons if N is even, and from $\frac{1}{2}$ to $N/2$ if N is odd.   Hence an atom or ion containing an even number of electrons will have only *odd* multiplicities, and one containing an odd number will have only *even* multiplicities.

The summing process by which the individual spin quantum numbers s add up algebraically to give a total spin S for the atom also is applicable to the individual orbital quantum numbers l, which add up to a total orbital quantum number L.   The addition process, however, depends on the quantum numbers m, which, as we have mentioned, indicate the orientation of the orbit in space, and can have negative values (*counterclockwise orbits*) as well as positive ones (*clockwise orbits*).   The sign of L is taken as positive, but its numer-

---

* This doubling does not occur in the set of levels for which $l = 0$, since there is no orbital magnetic field when $l = 0$, and hence no effect of spin on the energy.

ical values cannot be so succinctly given as can those for S because of the greater variety of possibilities of the individual m values. The maximum possible value of L, however, is the arithmetical sum of the individual l's. By way of example, we can consider three electrons with the respective sets of quantum numbers as follows:

$$n_1 = 2,\ l_1 = 1,\ m_1 = +1,\ s_1 = +\tfrac{1}{2}$$
$$n_2 = 3,\ l_2 = 2,\ m_2 = +2,\ s_2 = +\tfrac{1}{2}$$
$$n_3 = 4,\ l_3 = 3,\ m_3 = +3,\ s_3 = +\tfrac{1}{2}$$

Here $$S = s_1 + s_2 + s_3 = \tfrac{3}{2}$$

and $$L = m_1 + m_2 + m_3 = 6$$

The total energy of a given level depends on S and on L, and also on the way in which the total spin interacts or "couples" with the total orbital angular momentum. S and L couple to give a total angular momentum for the atom. This angular momentum is called J, is taken as positive, and lies between a minimum value of the numerical difference between L and S and a maximum value of the sum $L + S$.

It is customary for spectroscopists to symbolize a given atomic-energy level or term by a *term symbol*. The term symbol represents the numerical values of the different quantities L, S, and J on which the energy depends, and for which the selection rules are stated. The term symbol is

$$^{M}L_J$$

in which M, the multiplicity, is written as a number calculated from Eq. (10.14); that is, $M = 2S + 1$. J is also written as a number and varies with the coupling between L and S, but has a definite value for a particular energy level. L is not written as a number but as a capital letter. The letter symbol is S if $L = 0$, P if $L = 1$, D if $L = 2$, and so on, in strict analogy with the previously discussed convention of writing s for $l = 0$, and so on. The term symbol is sometimes written with a principal quantum number n as a prefix when there is no ambiguity as to which electron or electrons possess that value of n. For example, the two upper levels of the D lines in sodium (Fig. 10.4), which arise from one electron for which $n = 3, l = 1, s = \tfrac{1}{2}$, so that $L = 1, S = \tfrac{1}{2}, M = 2, J = 1 - \tfrac{1}{2}$ and $1 + \tfrac{1}{2}$, will have the symbols

$$3\,^2P_{\tfrac{1}{2}} \qquad \text{and} \qquad 3\,^2P_{\tfrac{3}{2}}$$

The lower level of the D lines arises from an electron with $n = 3$, $l = 0$, $s = \frac{1}{2}$, so that $L = 0$, $S = \frac{1}{2}$, $M = 2$, $J = \frac{1}{2}$. Hence this level will have the term symbol $3\,^2S_{\frac{1}{2}}$. The two D-line transitions can then be represented briefly by the symbols

$$3\,^2S_{\frac{1}{2}} - 3\,^2P_{\frac{1}{2}} \quad \text{and} \quad 3\,^2S_{\frac{1}{2}} - 3\,^2P_{\frac{3}{2}}$$

It is customary to write the lower level of the transition first.

Three spectroscopically useful rules about the energy relationships among multiplet levels can be stated with the help of the L, S, J quantum numbers.

1. *Hund's rule:* Of the energy levels associated with a given electronic configuration (that is, a set of electrons with their n and l quantum numbers fixed but with m and s not fixed), the levels of highest multiplicity (highest value of S) will have the lowest energy. Of the levels with highest multiplicity, that one with maximum L will have the lowest energy.

2. *Landé's interval rule:* The energy difference between two adjacent levels in a multiplet (same L and S, various J values) is proportional to the J value of the higher of the two levels.

3. *Inversion rule:* In electronic configurations in which a shell of electrons is less than half full, the lowest J value in a multiplet has the lowest energy; when a shell of electrons is more than half full, the highest J value in a multiplet has the lowest energy.

These rules are exceedingly useful in understanding the spectra of polyelectronic atoms and ions, but their application requires some information about the quantum numbers n and l of the various electrons in the atom. Fortunately, this information is usually available with the help of the basic rule known as the Pauli principle, which is discussed in § 10.9.

LINE INTENSITIES IN ATOMIC SPECTRA

Although line intensities cannot be determined with the precision of wavelength measurements, they are an important property of the spectrum, and the theory must deal with them quantitatively. It is beyond the scope of such a brief discussion as this to include any of the details of the quantum mechanics on which the theory is based. Our discussion will therefore merely summarize some results of quantum mechanics with the help of which a simplified treatment of intensities can be given.

10.5. Some Basic Results of Quantum Mechanics. When the equations of quantum mechanics are set up and solved for a simple atom or molecule, they lead to the result that the total energy of the atom or molecule cannot have every value between minus infinity and plus infinity but *is restricted to a relatively small set of special values.* These are the energy levels, or stationary states, of the atom or molecule. Ordinarily a stationary state is described in terms of a set of quantum numbers upon which the energy, W, of the stationary state depends in some definite algebraic way. However, in those instances in which the energy expression does not contain all the quantum numbers, more than one set of quantum numbers will correspond to the same energy levels. For example, if the states of an atom are described in terms of four quantum numbers n, l, m, s, and the energy expression has the simple form

$$W = \text{constant} \div n^2 \tag{10.15}$$

then all states with the same value of n have the same energy, regardless of the values of the other quantum numbers.

It is usually customary to lump together all the various states in an atom or molecule having the same energy. The number of states of equal energy so grouped together is termed the *degeneracy* of the resultant state. Synonymous terms for degeneracy are *statistical weight* and *a priori probability.* It is usually denoted by g_i, where i is an index number referring to the particular group of states lumped together.

It is helpful in considering the energy levels of an atom or molecule, whether these be known from experiment or from theory, to make a diagram of them. Such diagrams, of which Figs. 10.2 and 10.4 are simple examples, are widely used in the systematic understanding of spectra of all kinds. If the energy levels depend on a quantum number n in the way expressed by Eq. (10.5), in which the constant is given a *negative* value, then the energy for $n = \infty$ will be zero and that for $n = 1$ will be lowest (that is, largest negative number). As was mentioned in § 10.1, the horizontal lines in the figure represent the energies of the various stationary states, and the energy values other than those represented by horizontal lines are energies that the atom under consideration cannot possess.

As long as an atom or molecule remains in a given stationary state,

its energy is fixed and it neither loses nor gains energy from its surroundings. Therefore, if it is to emit or absorb radiation, it must
change to another energy level. Because the various energy levels
differ from one another by fixed amounts, the amounts of radiant
energy which the atom or molecule can gain or lose are fixed in size.
It is a result of quantum mechanics that there is a definite relationship
between the *frequency* of the emitted or absorbed radiation and the
change in energy of the atom or molecule. As was mentioned in
§ 10.1, this relation is

$$\nu_{1,2} = \frac{W_1 - W_2}{h} \tag{10.16}$$

where $\nu_{1,2}$ is the frequency of the radiation, h is Planck's constant
$(6.6 \times 10^{-27}$ erg-seconds), and W_1 and W_2 are, respectively, the
energy levels of the atom before and after the atom has emitted (or
absorbed) light. If W_1 is smaller than W_2, the atom has gained
energy, that is, has absorbed radiation. If W_1 is larger than W_2,
the atom has lost energy in the process, that is, has emitted radiation.

10.6. Selection Rules and Intensities of Spectral Lines. The
change from one energy level to another is termed a *transition*. It is
clear that the *frequency* of radiation emitted or absorbed during a
transition depends not on the properties of the system before or after
the transition but only on the energy difference between the two
stationary states. The *intensity* with which radiation is emitted or
absorbed, on the other hand, is very much dependent on the nature
of the initial and final states. Suppose we have a container full of
similar atoms all in a stationary state W_1. These atoms can conceivably radiate energy of a particular frequency $\nu_{1,2}$ if there is a
lower energy level W_2 such that

$$\nu_{1,2} = \frac{(W_1 - W_2)}{h} \tag{10.17}$$

The *rate* at which radiation of frequency $\nu_{1,2}$ is emitted depends on
the *number* of atoms making the transition from W_1 to W_2 per second.
In fact, the intensity of radiation of frequency $\nu_{1,2}$ will be

$$I = \text{constant} \times N_{1 \to 2} h \nu_{1,2} \tag{10.18}$$

where $N_{1 \to 2}$ is the number of atoms going from state W_1 to state W_2
per second, and $h\nu_{1,2}$ is the energy given out by each transition. To
understand what $N_{1 \to 2}$ depends on, let us consider the behavior of

the atoms in our container in state W_1. They can make transitions to W_2, of course, but it is also likely that there are a good many other stationary states W_3, W_4, W_5, and so on, to which transitions are possible. Since these states have different energies, transitions to them will not result in radiation of frequency $\nu_{1,2}$; moreover, if an atom makes a transition from W_1 to W_3, for example, it will no longer be able to make the transition W_1 to W_2. Hence the number $N_{1\rightarrow 2}$ will depend on the relative chance that an atom in state W_1 will go to state W_2 in preference to states W_3, W_4, W_5. . . . This relative chance is termed the *transition probability* for the transition $W_1 \rightarrow W_2$ and is found to depend on the characteristics of the two stationary states.

The calculation of transition probabilities by quantum-mechanical methods leads to the interesting general result that for a given atomic system there are a great many transitions for which the transition probability is zero; that is, the two states concerned do not *combine* to emit or absorb radiation. Since the characteristics of the two states are determined by their quantum numbers, it is possible to express transition probabilities in terms of quantum numbers, and in particular, to state what the relationships are between the quantum numbers of two states that do not combine. A generalization of transition probabilities expressed in terms of the quantum numbers is termed a *selection rule*, because the rule enables one to make a selection of the pairs of states which combine (the so-called *allowed* transitions), and of the pairs which do not combine (*forbidden* transitions) from the various pairs. Selection rules usually take the form of a statement of the changes in quantum numbers associated with allowed transitions. In terms of the quantum numbers L, S, J (§ 10.4), the selection rules* governing allowed transitions are

$$
\left.
\begin{aligned}
\Delta L &= 0, \pm 1 \\
\Delta S &= 0 \\
\Delta J &= \pm 1 \text{ (all } J \text{ values)} \\
\Delta J &= 0 \text{ (all } J \text{ values except } J = 0)
\end{aligned}
\right\} \qquad (10.19)
$$

---

* The rules are valid only for atoms in which the L,S coupling (Russell-Saunders coupling) holds. L,S coupling is a good approximation for atoms of low atomic number but is not so good for heavy atoms. For heavy atoms, in which the so-called j,j coupling or intermediate types of coupling obtain, the rules hold only roughly. Especially the selection rule $\Delta S = 0$ is no longer strictly valid, and many "intercombination" lines, corresponding to transitions in which $\Delta S = 1$ or more, are observed. The well-known "resonance line" in mercury at 2537 A is an example. Here $\Delta S = 1$.

The symbol ΔL stands for the difference between the value of L in the initial state and that in the final state. ΔS and ΔJ have analogous significance.

An interesting situation arises when a given energy state in an atom or molecule may not combine with the lowest energy state (the so-called *ground state*) in the atom, or with any of the intermediate energy states between it and the ground state. If, in such a case, the atom by some means gets into the given energy state, it will be unable to drop to a lower state by the emission of radiation and hence will remain in the upper state for an indefinite length of time. It may ultimately change from the state by the absorption of radiation, or by a collision with another atom, but transitions by these mechanisms are usually slow compared with those which emit radiation. When an atom remains in an excited stationary state for a long time, that state is said to have a long "lifetime" and is called a *metastable* state. The lifetime of an atomic state generally is of the order of magnitude of 10^{-8} sec, but for metastable states it may be many orders of magnitude larger.

Evidently, from the foregoing remarks, it is desirable to have some knowledge of what energy states are occupied by the atoms or molecules in a system whose spectra we wish to understand. Atoms and molecules may be raised to upper states (*excited states*) from the ground state by various means, including electrical discharge and heating. If the excitation occurs by heating and if thermal equilibrium among the atoms or molecules is approximately established, the number of atoms or molecules in a stationary state of energy W_2 compared with the number in the ground state W_1 is given by the expression

$$\frac{N_2}{N_1} = \frac{g_2}{g_1} e^{(W_1 - W_2)/kT} \tag{10.20}$$

in which N_1 and N_2 are the numbers of atoms in states 1 and 2, g_1 and g_2 the respective degeneracies of states 1 and 2, k is Boltzmann's constant $(1.371 \times 10^{-16}$ erg per degree per molecule), and T is the absolute temperature. The right-hand side of Eq. (10.20) is sometimes referred to as the Boltzmann factor for state 2, when state 1 is the ground state.

The same quantum-mechanical calculations that lead to the selection rules also provide certain generalizations about intensity relationships within multiplets. These intensity rules are as follows:

A. *The sum rules*:

1.   The sum of the intensities of all lines of a multiplet that begin their transitions from the same energy level is proportional to the degeneracy g_i of that level.   In terms of J, $g_i = 2J + 1$.

2.   The sum of the intensities of all lines of a multiplet that end their transitions on the same energy level is proportional to the degeneracy g_i of that level $(g_i = 2J + 1)$.

B. *The rules for relative intensities within a multiplet* (all L, S, J values are those of the *final* state):

For $\Delta L = +1$, $\Delta J = +1$:

$$I_{rel} = \frac{(L + J + S + 1)(L + J + S)(L + J - S)(L + J - S - 1)}{J}$$

For $\Delta L = +1$, $\Delta J = 0$:

$$I_{rel} = \frac{-(L+J+S+1)(L+J-S)(L-J+S)(L-J-S-1)(2J+1)}{J(J+1)}$$

For $\Delta L = +1$, $\Delta J = -1$:

$$I_{rel} = \frac{(L - J + S - 1)(L - J + S)(L - J - S - 1)(L - J - S - 2)}{(J + 1)}$$

For $\Delta L = 0$, $\Delta J = +1$:

$$I_{rel} = \frac{-(L + J + S + 1)(L + J - S)(L - J + S + 1)(L - J - S)}{J}$$

For $\Delta L = 0$, $\Delta J = 0$:

$$I_{rel} = \frac{[L(L + 1) + J(J + 1) - S(S + 1)]^2 (2J + 1)}{J(J + 1)}$$

For $\Delta L = 0$, $\Delta J = -1$:

$$I_{rel} = \frac{-(L + J + S + 2)(L - J + S)(L + J - S + 1)(L - J - S - 1)}{(J + 1)}$$

For $\Delta L = -1$, $\Delta J = +1$, 0, -1: The formulas for $\Delta L = -1$ can be obtained from those for $\Delta L = +1$ by reversing the sign of ΔJ and using the L, J, S values of the *initial* rather than the final state. A factor involving the frequencies of the multiplet lines and the temperature of the source has been omitted from the sum rules and relative-intensity formulas.   Usually the relative values of this factor for the different lines are not far from unity.

As an example of the application of these rules, there may be cited the studies of Harrison and collaborators.[2]

---

[2] G. R. Harrison and H. Engwicht, *Jour. Opt. Soc. Am.*, **18**, 287 (1929).

10.7. The Effect of External Influences on Atomic Spectra. The energy-level scheme of an atom determines the radiation frequencies which the atom can emit, and the selection rules control the transitions between these levels. Before one can say, however, what the spectrum of an assemblage of atoms will look like, the number of atoms populating each energy level must be known. The populations of the energy levels are quite sensitive to the environment of the assemblage, and therefore this environment is important for the appearance of the spectrum.

Among the most important factors in the environment are temperature and pressure. When thermal equilibrium prevails in an assemblage of atoms, the populations of the various energy levels decrease exponentially with the height of the levels above the ground level and increase exponentially with the temperature [see Eq. (10.20)]. This statement means that as temperature goes higher, the populations of other energy levels than the ground level increase, and therefore the number of atoms that can make transitions to lower levels increases. Consequently, the intensities of the spectral lines emitted by an assemblage of atoms such as those in a star or in a vapor heated by a furnace are strongly dependent on temperature and in turn are a clue to the temperature of the emitter.

When the excitation to upper levels is accomplished by thermal means, the populations of the higher levels are in general much smaller than those of the lower ones. Therefore the intensities of spectral lines of short wavelength, which must come from high levels, are also small. This statement does not mean, however, that all lines of long wavelength are more intensely emitted than lines of short wavelength, because a line of long wavelength can result from a transition between two closely spaced high levels. This is an example of the general rule that the temperature dependence of the intensity of a spectral line is given by the temperature dependence of the population of the energy level from which the radiating transition starts. It should be noted that while the intensities of lines that arise from high starting levels are small, the temperature variation of this intensity, percentagewise, is very large [see Eq. (10.20)].

An interesting situation arises when radiation is emitted by an assemblage of atoms that is divided into two regions, one at a higher and the other at a lower temperature. Such a situation may exist under proper circumstances in a gas discharge tube, in which the atoms at the center of the tube are at high temperatures while the ones on the periphery (near the walls) are at lower temperatures. Those spectral lines which originate at the higher energy levels will be emitted by the high-temperature part of the assemblage with relatively higher intensities than by the low-temperature part; but before this radiation can leave the tube, it must pass through the region of the low-temperature atoms. Here the lower energy levels, which are the final levels of the transitions giving rise to radiation from the high-temperature atoms, act as starting levels in the low-temperature atoms, and the radiation is absorbed. The ground level is particularly important in this process, since its population is always large.

The net result of the absorption of some of the radiation before it leaves the discharge tube is that certain lines, especially those involving the ground level, are markedly diminished in intensity. The diminution may be so great that the lines actually are weaker than the continuous background present in every high-temperature spectrum and hence appear as dark lines against a bright background. Such lines are said to be *reversed.** The outstanding examples are the famous Fraunhofer lines in the sun's spectrum, which arise from the absorption by atoms in the relatively low-temperature outer envelope of the sun's atmosphere. An example frequently met in the laboratory is the reversal of the 2537 A line in the high-pressure mercury arc. Sometimes a bright line is seen with a dark line at its center; this is called *self-reversal.* If the line is merely changed in shape on passing through the assemblage, it is said to be *self-absorbed.*

Another, but minor, influence of temperature on line spectra is the broadening of lines because of the Doppler effect. An atom moving away from the slit of a spectrograph along its optic axis emits radiation of frequency $\nu - \Delta\nu$, whereas an atom moving toward the slit with like velocity emits radiation of frequency $\nu + \Delta\nu$. These frequencies are measured with respect to the frequency ν emitted by a stationary atom, and the value of $\Delta\nu$ is

$$\Delta\nu = \nu \frac{v}{c},$$

where v is the velocity of the moving atom and c that of light. Since the average velocity of the atoms will increase with temperature, the

---

* This kind of reversal of spectral lines is to be distinguished from the "reversal" of very intense lines on the photographic plate. The latter, a purely photographic phenomenon associated with overexposure, is independent of the source of radiation (Compare § 7.2, page 145).

average $\Delta\nu$ will also increase; that is, the observed spectral line will broaden. The magnitude of the effect is indicated by the increase in the half width* of one of the sodium D lines at 5890 A that results from a temperature change from 300 to 3000°K. The half width changes from 6.5×10^8 sec^{-1}, or 0.0075 A, to 20.5×10^8 sec^{-1}, or 0.024 A.

The influence of pressure on spectral lines arises from the increase in the number of atoms per unit volume which occurs when pressure is increased. The intensity of both line and continuous spectra may increase with elevation of pressure simply from the increase in the number of radiating atoms. If self-absorption occurs, the elevation of pressure may reduce the intensity of certain lines. The chief effect of more atoms per unit volume, however, is a higher number of collisions per second between atoms. The exact frequency of a spectral line depends on the energy difference between the initial and final levels. Since these levels are shifted slightly during a collision, the frequency of the line shifts. The effect of increased collisions is twofold—a widening of the spectral line, called *pressure broadening*, and a shift to lower frequencies. Pressure broadening is of the greater practical importance, because the line width limits the accuracy with which its wavelength can be measured, as well as the resolution of closely spaced lines. The order of magnitude of pressure broadening in atomic spectra is about one-third of a wave number per atmosphere.

10.8.   The Stark and Zeeman Effects.   The most fruitful kind of external influence that can be exerted on an atomic spectrum is that of an electric or magnetic field. An electric field affects the spectrum because it adds an additional electric force to that already existing between the atomic nucleus and the electrons. The result is a "splitting" of those atomic energy levels which are degenerate, and a consequent splitting of spectral lines. This splitting, called the *Stark effect*, was not discovered until 1913 because of the tremendously strong electric fields required to produce it to an observable extent. Field strengths in excess of 100,000 volts per centimeter are required. Field strengths of this order, however, are quite weak compared to the fields existing in atoms and molecules. For example, the field of

---

* The term *half width* means the width of a spectral line measured from a point on one side of the line where the intensity is half that of the peak to the corresponding point on the other side of the line (compare Fig. 6.1).

the proton acting on the electron in the deepest energy state of the
hydrogen atom is 100,000 times larger still, or approximately 10 bil-
lion volts per centimeter.

The theory of the Stark effect is of prime importance in the theory
of spectra, but the effect itself is not of much practical use in the
analysis of spectra. The corresponding effect of a magnetic field,
however, is of great practical as well as theoretical importance, chiefly
because of the larger magnitude of the splitting of spectral lines produced by magnetic fields that can be created without great difficulty
in the laboratory. This larger splitting was also responsible for the
earlier discovery (1897) of the effect by Zeeman. One of the reasons
for the practical importance of the effect is Preston's rule, which
states that all the members of a spectral series have the same Zeeman

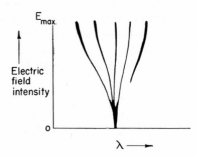

Fig. 10.5a. The Stark effect in the spectrum of helium, according to J. S.
Foster.[3] The electric field producing the effect is inhomogeneous, so that the
magnitude of the effect varies from one point in the source to another.

pattern, that is, exhibit the same splitting in a magnetic field. The
rule has been verified by a vast amount of experimental work and in
turn has contributed powerfully to the understanding of complex
spectra by providing a clear-cut method of classification of lines into
series. Examples of the Stark and Zeeman effects are shown in
Fig. 10.5.

ATOMIC SPECTRA AND ATOMIC STRUCTURE

The elucidation of atomic energy levels and quantum numbers by
the interpretation of atomic spectra has furnished a thorough explanation of the periodic table of the atoms. This explanation has been
as valuable to the chemist as to the physicist, for it has cleared up

---

[3] J. S. Foster, *Proc. Roy. Soc.*, **A 117**, 137 (1927).

mystifying features such as the 14 rare earths, and has enabled the chemist to understand the electronic basis of chemical valence.   The keystone to this explanation is the Pauli exclusion principle, which will be discussed briefly in terms of its application to the periodic table.

10.9. The Pauli Exclusion Principle and the Periodic Table.   The Pauli principle was foreshadowed by Bohr's building-up principle[4] in 1921.   It was announced by Pauli[5] on empirical grounds in 1925 and

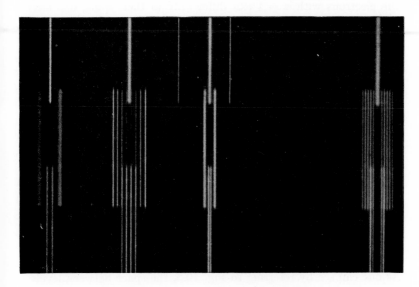

Fig. 10.5b. The Zeeman effect in rhodium, after Molnar and Hitchcock.[6] The top spectrum shows near ultraviolet lines in the normal spectrum of rhodium in the absence of a magnetic field.   The middle gives the perpendicularly polarized and the bottom the parallel-polarized Zeeman effect produced by a magnetic field of 90,500 oersteds.

has since been demonstrated theoretically to be a consequence of the fundamentals of quantum mechanics.   It states that no two electrons in the same atom can have the same four quantum numbers.   Since the quantum numbers themselves are subject to severe restrictions (n = integer, l = integer smaller than n, m = positive or negative in-

[4] N. Bohr, *Zeitschr. f. Physik*, **9**, 1 (1922).
[5] W. Pauli, *Zeitschr. f. Physik*, **31**, 765 (1925).
[6] J. P. Molnar and W. J. Hitchcock, *Jour. Opt. Soc. Am.* **30**, 523 (1940).

teger equal to or smaller than l, and $s = \pm\frac{1}{2}$), the Pauli principle and the energy rules pretty definitely dictate the electronic structure of an atom or ion.

The electrons, in arranging themselves around the atomic nucleus, will try to occupy those energy levels which are lowest; that is, all electrons seek to have a principal quantum number $n = 1$. The Pauli principle, however, excludes all but *two* electrons from the level $n = 1$, since of necessity $l = 0$ and $m = 0$ when $n = 1$. Thus the electrons with $n = 1$ can differ only in their spins, one having $s = +\frac{1}{2}$ and the other $s = -\frac{1}{2}$. The other electrons in the atom must have $n = 2$ or larger. A collection of electrons with the same principal quantum number, such as the pair of electrons with $n = 1$, is called a *shell*.* A shell is said to be *filled* or *completed* if the number of electrons therein is the maximum permitted by the Pauli principle. When $n = 1$, this maximum is 2, but for larger n values the maxima are larger. When $n = 2$, $l = 0$ or 1, and therefore $m = 0$ or $-1, 0, +1$. Consequently, the shell for $n = 2$ can have eight electrons, one pair each for $l = 0$, $m = 0$; $l = 1$, $m = -1$; $l = 1$, $m = 0$; $l = 1$, $m = +1$.

In shells where several values of l are possible, the question of which l value has lowest energy arises. The answer, as we have seen in the case of sodium atom (Fig. 10.4), is that lower l values (eccentric orbits) correspond to lower energies. Therefore in an unfilled shell, the electrons will prefer the levels of lowest l.

Another important energy question arises when n is larger than 3. As one can see by referring to Fig. 10.3, the space between levels of different n is very small when n is more than 3. For these levels, the value of l is of comparable importance to that of n in determining the energy, and one cannot say offhand whether the level $n = 4$, $l = 0$, will have lower or higher energy than the level $n = 3$, $l = 2$. For the sodium atom, the energy-level diagram indicates clearly that the level $n = 4$, $l = 0$ is the lower. As a result, electrons will enter this level in preference to the level $n = 3$, $l = 2$; in other words, electrons will enter the shell $n = 4$ before the shell $n = 3$ has been completed.

---

* Shells are frequently denoted by capital letters:

n	1	2	3	4	5	6	7
Symbol	K	L	M	N	O	P	Q

This preference is illustrated in the periodic table by potassium, the atom with 19 electrons. Of these 19, two are in the shell $n = 1$, eight in shell $n = 2$, and eight in the shell $n = 3$ (2 with $n = 3$, $l = 0$, and 6 with $n = 3$, $l = 1$). There is still room for 10 electrons in the shell $n = 3$ ($n = 3$, $l = 2$), but because the energy of the level $n = 4$, $l = 0$ is lower, the nineteenth electron enters this level. As a result, potassium has an electronic structure similar to sodium, with a single outermost s electron. Likewise, in the atom with 20 electrons (calcium), the nineteenth and twentieth electrons both enter the level $n = 4$, $l = 0$. However, in the atom with 21 electrons (scandium), the twenty-first electron must choose between $n = 4$, $l = 1$ and $n = 3$, $l = 2$, because the level $n = 4$, $l = 0$ will hold only two electrons. As one can see from Fig. 10.4, the level $n = 4$, $l = 1$ is *higher* than $n = 3$, $l = 2$. Hence the twenty-first (and the next nine electrons thereafter) enters the levels $n = 3$, $l = 2$.

Thus from a combination of the Pauli principle with the energy characteristics of electrons as determined by their quantum numbers, the ground-state (lowest-energy) configuration of an atom or ion of any number of electrons can be understood. For chemists this is of great importance because of the relationship between the electronic structure of atoms and their chemical properties. The periodic table of the elements, for example, which was first determined from chemical properties, is completely explained on the basis of the periodicity in electronic configurations of the atoms. In Table 10.3 are summarized the electronic structures of the chemical elements. For detailed discussion of these structures, one should refer to any standard text on atomic spectra, of which several are listed in General References 10.1 to 10.6.

For the spectroscopist, who is interested in *all* the electronic energy levels, an understanding of the structure of polyelectronic atoms is likewise of paramount importance. Spectroscopic principles that follow from the previous reasoning are given herewith:

Similarity of spectra of isoelectronic atoms and ions. The operation of the Pauli principle is not dependent on the size of the positive charge on the nucleus of an atom. The primary effect of a change in this charge is a change in the scale of the atomic-energy levels. We indicated this in our discussion (§ 10.1) of the spectrum of the helium ion He^+, the energy levels of which were those of the hydrogen atom, except for a scale factor of 4 associated with the double charge on the helium nucleus. As a result of the Pauli principle, one can

TABLE 10.3

ELECTRONIC STRUCTURES OF THE ATOMS*

Element	Number of electrons	Inner electrons	Outermost electrons	Ground term symbol
H	1	. . . .	$1s$	$^2S_{1/2}$
He	2	. . . .	$(1s)^2$	$^1S_0$
Li	3		$2s$	$^2S_{1/2}$
Be	4		$(2s)^2$	$^1S_0$
B	5		$(2s)^2 2p$	$^2P_{1/2}$
C	6	He shell	$(2s)^2(2p)^2$	$^3P_0$
N	7		$(2s)^2(2p)^3$	$^4S_{3/2}$
O	8		$(2s)^2(2p)^4$	$^3P_2$
F	9		$(2s)^2(2p)^5$	$^2P_{3/2}$
Ne	10		$(2s)^2(2p)^6$	$^1S_0$
Na	11		$3s$	$^2S_{1/2}$
Mg	12		$(3s)^2$	$^1S_0$
Al	13		$(3s)^2 3p$	$^2P_{1/2}$
Si	14	Neon shells	$(3s)^2(3p)^2$	$^3P_0$
P	15		$(3s)^2(3p)^3$	$^4S_{3/2}$
S	16		$(3s)^2(3p)^4$	$^3P_2$
Cl	17		$(3s)^2(3p)^5$	$^2P_{3/2}$
A	18		$(3s)^2(3p)^6$	$^1S_0$
K	19		$4s$	$^2S_{1/2}$
Ca	20		$(4s)^2$	$^1S_0$
Sc	21		$3d(4s)^2$	$^2D_{3/2}$
Ti	22	Argon shells	$(3d)^2(4s)^2$	$^3F_2$
V	23		$(3d)^3(4s)^2$	$^4F_{3/2}$
Cr	24		$(3d)^5 4s$	$^7S_3$
Mn	25		$(3d)^5(4s)^2$	$^6S_{5/2}$

* Column 1 gives the chemical symbol. Column 2 gives the number of electrons surrounding the nucleus (that is, the *atomic number*) of each chemical element. Column 3 shows the number and distribution of inner electrons, which are those electrons unchanged during chemical reaction. For brevity, these are expressed in terms of the electronic configuration of the rare-gas atoms. The inner electrons in Li, for example, are the two $1s$ electrons, which have the same arrangement that one finds in the He atom. In Na, the inner electrons are the two $1s$, the two $2s$ and the six $2p$ electrons, which is just the arrangement in Ne, and so on. Column 4 lists the remainder of the electrons. The "exponent" of the bracketed symbols indicates the number of electrons of the type within the brackets. For example, $(1s)^2$ means "two $1s$ electrons." The ground term symbols in column 5 are explained in the text (§ 10.4). Although these symbols can be worked out from the electronic configuration in column 4, it must be remembered that the reverse procedure is the one actually followed. The ground term symbol is determined by an analysis of the spectrum, and from it the electronic configuration is inferred. When the spectroscopic evidence for the ground term symbol is not clear-cut, the symbol is marked "?".

TABLE 10.3—*Continued*

ELECTRONIC STRUCTURES OF THE ATOMS

Element	Number of electrons	Inner electrons	Outermost electrons	Ground term symbol
Fe	26		$(3d)^6(4s)^2$	$^5D_4$
Co	27		$(3d)^7(4s)^2$	$^4F_{9/2}$
Ni	28		$(3d)^8(4s)^2$	$^3F_4$
Cu	29		$(3d)^{10}4s$	$^2S_{1/2}$
Zn	30	Argon shells	$(3d)^{10}(4s)^2$	$^1S_0$
Ga	31		$(3d)^{10}(4s)^24p$	$^2P_{1/2}$
Ge	32		$(3d)^{10}(4s)^2(4p)^2$	$^3P_0$
As	33		$(3d)^{10}(4s)^2(4p)^3$	$^4S_{3/2}$
Se	34		$(3d)^{10}(4s)^2(4p)^4$	$^3P_2$
Br	35		$(3d)^{10}(4s)^2(4p)^5$	$^2P_{3/2}$
Kr	36		$(3d)^{10}(4s)^2(4p)^6$	$^1S_0$
Rb	37		$5s$	$^2S_{1/2}$
Sr	38		$(5s)^2$	$^1S_0$
Y	39		$4d(5s)^2$	$^2D_{3/2}$
Zr	40		$(4d)^2(5s)^2$	$^3F_2$
Cb	41		$(4d)^45s$	$^6D_{1/2}$
Mo	42		$(4d)^55s$	$^7S_3$
Tc	43	Krypton shells	$(4d)^65s$	$^6D_{9/2}$?
Ru	44		$(4d)^75s$	$^5F_5$
Rh	45		$(4d)^85s$	$^4F_{9/2}$
Pd	46		$(4d)^{10}$	$^1S_0$
Ag	47		$(4d)^{10}5s$	$^2S_{1/2}$
Cd	48		$(4d)^{10}(5s)^2$	$^1S_0$
In	49		$(4d)^{10}(5s)^25p$	$^2P_{1/2}$
Sn	50		$(4d)^{10}(5s)^2(5p)^2$	$^3P_0$
Sb	51		$(4d)^{10}(5s)^2(5p)^3$	$^4S_{3/2}$
Te	52		$(4d)^{10}(5s)^2(5p)^4$	$^3P_2$
I	53		$(4d)^{10}(5s)^2(5p)^5$	$^2P_{3/2}$
Xe	54		$(4d)^{10}(5s)^2(5p)^6$	$^1S_0$
Cs	55		$6s$	$^2S_{1/2}$
Ba	56	Xenon shells	$(6s)^2$	$^1S_0$
La	57		$5d(6s)^2$	$^2D_{3/2}$
Ce	58		$(4f)^2(6s)^2$	$^3H_4$?
Pr	59		$(4f)^3(6s)^2$	$^4I_{9/2}$?
Nd	60		$(4f)^4(6s)^2$	$^5I_4$
...	61		$(4f)^5(6s)^2$	$^6H_{5/2}$?
Sm	62		$(4f)^6(6s)^2$	$^7F_0$
Eu	63	Xenon shells	$(4f)^7(6s)^2$	$^8S_{7/2}$
Gd	64		$(4f)^75d(6s)^2$	$^9D_2$
Tb	65		$(4f)^9(6s)^2$	$^6H_{15/2}$?
Dy	66		$(4f)^{10}(6s)^2$	$^5I_8$?
Ho	67		$(4f)^{11}(6s)^2$	$^4I_{15/2}$?

TABLE 10.3—*Continued*

ELECTRONIC STRUCTURES OF THE ATOMS

Element	Number of electrons	Inner electrons	Outermost electrons	Ground term symbol
Er	68	*Xenon shells*	$(4f)^{12}(6s)^2$	$^3H_6$?
Tm	69		$(4f)^{13}(6s)^2$	$^2F_{7/2}$
Yb	70		$(4f)^{14}(6s)^2$	$^1S_0$
Lu	71		$(4f)^{14}5d(6s)^2$	$^2D_{3/2}$
Hf	72	*Xenon shells*	$(4f)^{14}(5d)^2(6s)^2$	$^3F_2$
Ta	73		$(4f)^{14}(5d)^3(6s)^2$	$^4F_{3/2}$
W	74		$(4f)^{14}(5d)^4(6s)^2$	$^5D_0$
Re	75		$(4f)^{14}(5d)^5(6s)^2$	$^6S_{5/2}$
Os	76		$(4f)^{14}(5d)^6(6s)^2$	$^5D_4$
Ir	77		$(4f)^{14}(5d)^7(6s)^2$	$^4F_{9/2}$
Pt	78		$(4f)^{14}(5d)^96s$	$^3D_3$
Au	79		$(4f)^{14}(5d)^{10}6s$	$^2S_{1/2}$
Hg	80		$(4f)^{14}(5d)^{10}(6s)^2$	$^1S_0$
Tl	81		$(4f)^{14}(5d)^{10}(6s)^26p$	$^2P_{1/2}$
Pb	82		$(4f)^{14}(5d)^{10}(6s)^2(6p)^2$	$^3P_0$
Bi	83		$(4f)^{14}(5d)^{10}(6s)^2(6p)^3$	$^4S_{3/2}$
Po	84		$(4f)^{14}(5d)^{10}(6s)^2(6p)^4$	$^3P_2$
At	85		$(4f)^{14}(5d)^{10}(6s)^2(6p)^5$	$^2P_{3/2}$
Rn	86		$(4f)^{14}(5d)^{10}(6s)^2(6p)^6$	$^1S_0$
Fr	87	*Radon shells*	$7s$	$^2S_{1/2}$
Ra	88		$(7s)^2$	$^1S_0$
Ac	89		$6d(7s)^2$	$^2D_{3/2}$
Th	90		$(6d)^2(7s)^2$	$^3F_2$
Pa	91		$(5f)^26d(7s)^2$	$^4K_{11/2}$?
U	92		$(5f)^36d(7s)^2$	$^5L_6$
Np	93		$(5f)^46d(7s)^2$	$^6M_{13/2}$?
Pu	94		$(5f)^56d(7s)^2$	$^7K_4$?
Am	95		$(5f)^66d(7s)^2$	$^8H_{3/2}$?
Cm	96		$(5f)^76d(7s)^2$	$^9D_2$?

make the general statement that *the energy levels of two atoms or ions with the same number of electrons* (which are called *isoelectronic* with one another) *are closely similar except for a scale factor.* The closer the two nuclear charges, of course, the closer the similarity and the smaller the scale factor.

This similarity of isoelectronic spectra was first recognized empirically and was enunciated as the *displacement law* by Kossel and Sommerfeld[7]: The spectrum of an ionized atom of net positive charge

---

[7] W. Kossel and A. Sommerfeld, *Verh. der deutsch. phys. Ges.*, **21**, 240 (1919).

TABLE 10.4

MULTIPLICITIES IN THE SPECTRA OF ELEMENTS IN THE FIRST LONG ROW OF THE PERIODIC TABLE

	Neutral — K / Singly ionized — Ca^+ / Doubly ionized — Sc^{++}	Ca / Sc^+ / Ti^{++}	Sc / Ti^+ / V^{++}	Ti / V^+ / Cr^{++}	V / Cr^+ / Mn^{++}	Cr / Mn^+ / Fe^{++}	Mn / Fe^+ / Co^{++}	Fe / Co^+ / Ni^{++}	Co / Ni^+ / Cu^{++}	Ni / Cu^+ / Zn^{++}	Cu / Zn^+ / Ga^{++}	Zn / Ga^+ / …	Ga / … / …
Multiplicities	2	1	2	1	2	1	2	1	2	1	2	1	2
		3	4	3	4	3	4	3	4	3	4	3	
				5	6	5	6	5	6	5			
						7	8	7					

c has a structure closely analogous to that of the neutral atom c places ahead of the ionized atom in the periodic table.

The alternation of multiplicities. According to the displacement law, a neutral atom and the singly ionized atom just following it in the periodic table should show the same kind of spectrum, *including the same multiplicities.* As was mentioned in § 10.4, atoms and ions with even numbers of electrons show odd multiplicities, and vice versa, and so isoelectronic atoms and ions should be expected to show the same multiplicities. *Two neutral atoms adjacent in the periodic table* differ by one electron, and accordingly *show respectively even and odd, or odd and even, multiplicities.* This pattern is illustrated in Table 10.4, which combines the displacement law and the law of alternation of multiplicities for the first long row in the periodic table. The maximum multiplicity of 8 in Mn, Fe^+, and Co^{++} is calculable from the Pauli principle: as the shell with $n = 3$ fills up beyond the halfway point, more and more electrons have to pair up their spins, with consequent decrease in the possibilities for multiplicity.

GENERAL REFERENCES

10.1.   R. F. Bacher and S. Goudsmit, *Atomic Energy States.* New York: McGraw-Hill Book Company, Inc., 1932.

10.2.   E. U. Condon and G. H. Shortley, *Theory of Atomic Spectra.* New York: The Macmillan Company, 1935.

10.3.   G. Herzberg, *Atomic Spectra and Atomic Structure.* New York: Dover Publications, Inc., 1944.

10.4.   F. K. Richtmyer and E. H. Kennard, *Introduction to Modern Physics.* New York: McGraw-Hill Book Company, Inc., 1947.

10.5.   V. Rojansky, *Introductory Quantum Mechanics.* New York: Prentice-Hall, Inc., 1938.

10.6.   H. White, *Introduction to Atomic Spectra.* New York: McGraw-Hill Book Company, Inc., 1934.

CHAPTER 11

Molecular Spectra and Molecular Structure

ATOMIC SPECTRA ARISE FROM ELECTRONS IN MOTION about a single heavy positively charged nucleus. The motion of the atom as a whole, which is essentially unaccelerated straight-line motion, influences atomic spectra only in a relatively minor way through the Doppler effect. In a molecule, on the other hand, the electrons move about two or more heavy positively charged nuclei, and the nuclei themselves not only move together in a straight-line translation but also rotate and vibrate periodically about their center of gravity. These latter motions, being periodic, exhibit spectroscopic activity on their own account, and in addition influence the electronic spectra of the molecule. This influence, which is missing from atomic spectra, results in a highly complicated fine structure. The details of the electronic spectra of molecules, as well as those spectra concerned only with molecular vibration and rotation, will be considered briefly.

ENERGY LEVELS IN MOLECULES

A fundamental statement about energy levels in molecules is that the molecular energy, W_{mol}, is the sum of its translational, rotational, vibrational, and electronic energies:

$$W_{mol} = W_{trans} + W_{rot} + W_{vib} + W_{el} \qquad (11.1)$$

The translational energy, W_{trans}, has no significant effect on molecular spectra and will henceforth be disregarded.

11.1. Rotational Energy Levels in Molecules. The rotational energy, W_{rot}, of a molecule is directly related to the angular velocity with which the molecule rotates. It is a result of quantum mechanics that a molecule may not rotate with any arbitrary velocity but only with certain restricted velocities, and therefore that only certain restricted values of W_{rot} are possible. The set of possible W_{rot} values

261

may be schematically represented by an energy-level diagram analogous to the diagrams previously given for atomic energy levels. The appearance of the rotational energy-level diagram is strongly dependent on the geometrical form of the molecule, because the rotational energy depends on the *moments of inertia* of the molecule, which in turn depend on the molecular geometry. Every molecule except those whose atoms all lie on a straight line has three intersecting, mutually perpendicular axes, passing through the molecular center of gravity, about which the molecule can rotate and with respect to which the three moments of inertia are calculated (see

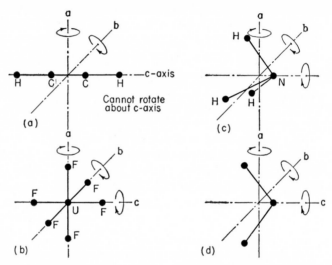

Fig. 11.1. How molecules rotate. (a) Linear molecule (acetylene). (b) Spherical top (uranium hexafluoride). (c) Symmetrical top (ammonia). (d) Asymmetrical top (water).

Fig. 11.1). Each moment is associated with one of the three axes and is determined numerically by multiplying the mass of each atom by the square of its distance from the axis, and adding up these products for all the atoms in the molecule. Symbolically,

$$I_a = \sum_{i=1}^{N} m_i r_{ia}^2 \tag{11.2}$$

Here I_a is the moment of inertia about axis a, and m_i and r_{ia} are, respectively, the mass and the distance from a of atom i. The sum includes all N atoms in the molecule. Equations identical with Eq. (11.2) except for the different values of r_i give the moments I_b and I_c about the two other axes b and c. Ordinarily, the three moments of inertia have different numerical values, but sometimes the molecule has a symmetrical geometry that leads to two or even three equal values. In the former instance, the molecule is known as an *asymmetrical-top rotator** and in the latter two as a *symmetrical-top rotator* and a *spherical-top rotator*, respectively.

When all the atoms in a molecule lie on a straight line, the moment of inertia of the molecule about that straight line as an axis is zero, because all the r_i values are zero. In such a case, the molecule cannot rotate about the straight line determined by the atoms, but only about intersecting axes perpendicular to it. The moments of inertia about these intersecting axes are equal. Such a molecule is a *linear rotator*.

The rotational energy, W_{rot}, is entirely kinetic. It depends on the rotational quantum numbers of the molecule in different ways for the different kinds of rotators. For the linear and spherical-top rotators, only one quantum number, J, is involved,† and the equation is

$$W_{rot} = J(J + 1)Bhc \tag{11.3}$$

where $B = \dfrac{h}{8\pi^2 c I_b}$. The values of J are 0, 1, 2, 3, . . . , ∞.

In the symmetrical top, the equation is

$$W_{rot} = J(J + 1)Bhc + K^2(C - B)hc \tag{11.4}$$

where $C = \dfrac{h}{8\pi^2 c I_c}$. The quantum number K can have both positive and negative values but can never exceed J numerically.

There is no general expression for the energy levels of the asymmetrical top, which depend in detail on the relative values of I_a, I_b,

---

* The word *top* is used here in the sense of the child's toy, which, incidentally, is usually a symmetrical-top rotator.

†This quantum number is not to be confused with the atomic quantum number J of § 10.4. In the atomic case, J depicts the total electronic angular momentum, whereas J in the molecule usually is the index to the total angular momentum of rotation of the nuclei about the molecular axes. In both cases, however, the relation between J and the angular momentum is the same, namely,

$$\text{Angular momentum} = \sqrt{J(J + 1)}\,\frac{h}{2\pi}$$

and I_c.   However, the energy-level scheme can be inferred qualitatively from the fact that it approaches that of the symmetrical top
when two of the values of the moments of inertia approach one
another.

It will be noted that the rotational energies go up as the square
of J; that is, as J gets larger, the spacing between levels gets larger.
This result is in contrast to the electronic levels in atoms, which get
closer together as the principal quantum number gets larger.   Moreover, the energies of rotation are *inversely* proportional to the moment

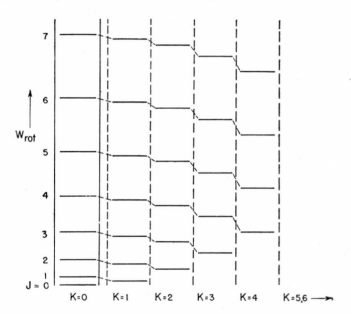

Fig. 11.2.   Rotational energy levels for molecules.

of inertia, so that for *heavier* molecules, both the energy levels and
their spacings are smaller than for *lighter* molecules.   Figure 11.2
shows the lowest energy levels of a symmetrical top in which $I_a = I_b$
$= \frac{1}{2}I_c$.   The energy levels in the column $K = 0$ are also those of a
linear or spherical-top rotator whose moment of inertia is I_b, since
Eq. (11.4) reduces to Eq. (11.3) when $K = 0$.   The rotational
energies of various kinds of molecules are summarized with examples
in Table 11.1.

The preceding discussion is valid only for molecules that can rotate freely; therefore the rotational energy-level diagrams are valid only for molecules in the vapor state.   In liquids and solids, rotation is usually hindered or stopped entirely by intermolecular forces and, with rare exceptions, the rotational energy levels are "smeared out"

TABLE 11.1

ROTATIONAL ENERGIES IN MOLECULES

Type of rotator	Moments of inertia	Rotational energies, W_{rot}	Geometrical forms	Examples
Linear	$I_a = I_b$; $I_c = 0$	$J(J + 1)Bhc$	Straight line	All diatomic molecules; carbon dioxide; acetylene
Spherical top	$I_a = I_b = I_c$	$J(J + 1)Bhc$	Tetrahedron	Methane; phosphorus (P_4)
			Octahedron	Uranium hexafluoride
			Cube	None known
Symmetrical top	$I_a = I_b \neq I_c$	$J(J + 1)Bhc$ $+ K^2(C - B)hc$	Any symmetry with only one threefold or higher symmetry axis, such as:	
			Trigonal pyramid	Ammonia
			Trigonal prism	Cyclopropane
			Plane hexagon	Benzene
Asymmetrical top	$I_a \neq I_b \neq I_c$	No general expression	Any symmetry lacking a threefold or higher symmetry axis	Most polyatomic molecules

into a continuum of levels.   Accordingly, the study of rotational spectra is almost entirely confined to those molecules which can be obtained in satisfactory concentrations in the vapor state.

11.2.   Vibrational Energy Levels.   A molecule containing N atoms has $3N$ kinds of motion.   Three of these are simple translation, and three, as we have just seen, are rotations about the three axes of inertia (two if the molecule is linear).   There are therefore $3N - 6$ additional kinds of motion ($3N - 5$ if the molecule is linear).   These are all vibrational, and associated with each kind is a vibrational frequency.   As long as the vibrations are not violent, that is, are restricted to amplitudes less than about one-tenth the average distance between atoms, the vibrations are essentially *harmonic*.   The actual form of the vibrational pattern may be quite complicated, but it is always possible to regard any harmonic vibration whatever as the superposition of two or more simple vibrations called the *normal* vibrations of the molecule.

In a normal vibration, the atoms all move with the same frequency, which is independent of the amplitude of vibration, and their displacements from the positions they occupy in the nonvibrating molecule vary with time in pure sine-wave fashion.   There are $3N - 6$ normal vibrations, and the $3N - 6$ frequencies associated with them are called the *fundamental frequencies* of the molecule.   These frequencies may all be different, or there may be several pairs or triples of vibrations with the same frequency.   Because the forms of the normal vibrations are strongly dependent on the symmetry of the molecule, symmetry is of great help in the determination of the vibrational amplitudes and frequencies.   For example, it can be shown that any molecule containing a threefold or higher axis of symmetry will have a certain number of its frequencies occurring in pairs, and a molecule with two or more threefold or higher axes will have a certain number of frequencies occurring in triples.   Symmetry is also definitive for selection rules in vibrational spectra.   The normal vibrations of several simple molecules are shown qualitatively in Fig. 11.3, in which the displacements of the atoms are depicted by arrows and by $+$ and $-$ symbols. The latter indicate respectively displacements above and below the plane of the page.

The vibrational energy levels of a molecule form a simple pattern as long as the vibrations are harmonic, since in this case each vibration contributes a set of energy levels to the pattern that is independent of the energy levels of the other vibrations.   The relation between the energies W_{vib} of one vibration whose frequency is ν_1 and the vibrational quantum number v_1 for that frequency is

$$W_{vib} = (v_1 + \tfrac{1}{2})h\nu_1 \tag{11.5}$$

where $v_1 = 0, 1, 2, 3, \ldots$. There is a separate quantum number, v, for each vibration, and the energy-level scheme is obtained by adding up the equations like Eq. (11.5) for all the $3N - 6$ vibrations:

$$W_{vib} = \sum_{i=1}^{3N-6} (v_i + \tfrac{1}{2})h\nu_i \tag{11.6}$$

The following characteristics of the energy levels of a single frequency may be noted:

1. The energy levels are equally spaced, the spacing being $h\nu$;

2. The lowest energy level ($v = 0$) is not at zero energy but at $\tfrac{1}{2}h\nu$. This minimum energy, which remains with the vibrator even at the absolute zero of temperature, is called the *zero-point energy*.

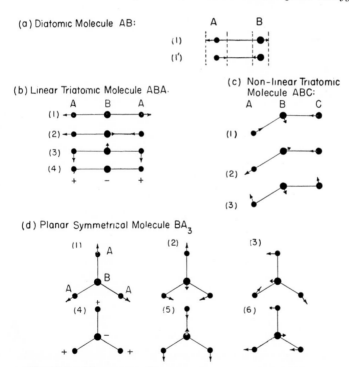

Fig. 11.3. The normal vibrations of some small molecules.

Figure 11.4 shows a few of the energy levels of a single vibrational degree of freedom. Such levels would constitute the entire vibrational energy pattern for a given electronic state in a diatomic molecule, or a small part of the pattern for a polyatomic molecule. The lower levels have been drawn with approximately equal spacing, in accordance with Eq. (11.5), but the higher ones are crowded together somewhat to illustrate the effect of *anharmonicity*. This effect is always present and is a consequence of the fact that the forces between atoms cannot

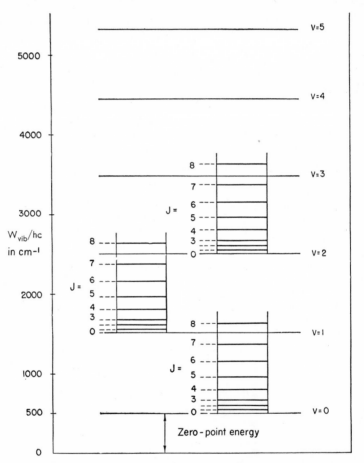

Fig. 11.4. The vibrational energy levels of a diatomic molecule.

be described accurately by simple force constants but vary with interatomic separation in a more complicated fashion.

In order to indicate the relative magnitudes of vibrational and rotational energy levels, a few rotational levels are superimposed on the lower vibrational levels. The levels are those for a diatomic molecule whose vibrational frequency is 1000 cm^{-1} and whose rotational

TABLE 11.2

CHARACTERISTIC VIBRATION FREQUENCIES OF GROUPS OF ATOMS

Group	Frequency, cm^{-1}	Wavelength, microns	Group	Frequency, cm^{-1}	Wavelength, microns
Single bonds:			Double bonds:		
C—C	1000	10.	C=C$_{et}$	1640	6.10
C—N	1100	9.	C=C$_{cnj}$	1590	6.30
C—O	1150	8.5	C=C$_{ar}$	1595	6.27
C—F	1200	8.3	C=N	1640	6.10
C—S	650	15.4	C=O$_{anh}$ {	1775	5.63
C—Cl	750	13.3		1825	5.48
H—C$_{ac}$	3350	3.0	C=O$_{est}$	1745	5.73
H—C$_{et}$	3020	3.30	C=O$_{aci}$	1710	5.85
H—C$_{ar}$	3080	3.25	C=O$_{ket}$	1695	5.90
H—C$_{al}$	2890	3.46	C=S	1530	6.54
H—N$_{am}$	3400	2.9	Triple bonds:		
H—N$_{im}$	3375	2.95	C≡C	2220	4.50
H—O	3600	2.78	C≡N	2250	4.45
H—F	3959	2.59	C≡N$_{iso}$	2150	4.65
H—Si	2260	4.42	C≡O	2165	4.62
H—P	2350	4.26	Some larger groups:		
H—S	2585	3.87	Methyl(CH$_3$)	1385	7.22
H—Cl	2886	3.46	Ether(C — O — C)	565	17.70
H—Se	2230	4.48	Terminal C =CH$_2$ {	985	10.15
H—Br	2559	3.91		1410	7.09
H—I	2231	4.48	Trifluoro (CF$_3$)	1380	7.25
			Nitro(—NO$_2$)	1565	6.39

The above frequencies in cm^{-1} and wavelengths in microns are approximate because group frequencies vary somewhat from molecule to molecule. In general, a frequency value ending in two zeros means the group frequency varies as much as ± 100 cm^{-1} from the value given. A single final zero means ±50 cm^{-1}, and a final 5 means ±10 – 20 cm^{-1}. H—O and H—N frequencies are reduced from the listed values by 200 cm^{-1} and are broadened to a width of 100 cm^{-1} or more by hydrogen bonding such as exists in liquid H$_2$O and NH$_3$.

Abbreviations: *ac*, acetylenic; *aci*, acid; *al*, aliphatic; *am*, amine and amide; *anh*, acid anhydride; *ar*, aromatic; *cnj*, conjugated; *est*, ester; *et*, ethylenic; *im*, imide; *iso*, isocyanide; *ket*, ketone and aldehyde.

constant B [Eq. (11.3)] is 15 cm^{-1}. Each of these levels corresponds to a particular value of v, the vibrational quantum number, and to a particular value of J, the rotational quantum number.

An interesting result of the study of the vibrational spectra of thousands of molecules is that many of the vibrational frequencies of a molecule are essentially those of very small groups of atoms within the molecule, and that these frequencies are characteristic of the groups of atoms regardless of the composition of the rest of the molecule. This fact is of great usefulness in the applications of spectroscopy to the study of molecules containing more than three or four atoms. It serves as a basis for qualitative analysis of molecules and for the elucidation of molecular structure. Not all molecular frequencies, however, are group frequencies, since each molecule also contains vibrations which are characteristic of the molecule as a whole and which are strongly dependent on its over-all structure and composition. A list of characteristic group frequencies is given in Table 11.2.

11.3. Electronic Energy Levels. Electrons in molecules have four quantum numbers, as do electrons in atoms, and moreoever are subject to the restriction of the Pauli principle. They may be classified into three kinds: those which belong to a single atom, those which are shared by two adjacent atoms, and those which are shared by more than two atoms.

The first kind of molecular electron consists of those electrons in the inner shells of the atoms in the molecule. They differ little from the corresponding electrons in the atom when it is not part of a molecule, and they do not contribute to the binding forces that hold the molecule together. Their contribution to the molecular electronic levels may be disregarded.

The second kind occurs in all molecules, and necessarily all electrons in diatomic molecules are either of this or of the preceding kind. An electron that is shared by two atoms has a set of quantum numbers which is similar to the set of atomic quantum numbers. The difference lies in the replacement of the quantum number m by a new number (usually called λ), which is simply the index to the orientation of the electronic orbit with respect to the interatomic axis. The restrictions on the four quantum numbers, n, l, λ, and s are the same as those in atoms. Specifically, λ can be either positive or negative but never larger numerically than l. In diatomic molecules, the λ's and spins couple in a manner quite analogous to the coupling of l's and spins in atoms. The algebraic total of the λ's (called Λ) represents the projection of the total orbital angular momen-

tum of the electrons on the interatomic axis.   This total is denoted
by capital Greek letters $\Sigma, \Pi, \Delta, \Phi, \Gamma, \ldots$, where $\Lambda = 0, 1, 2, 3, 4 \ldots$.
Term symbols, by analogy to atomic symbols, are written

$$^M \Lambda$$

For example, the lowest electronic state in H_2, N_2, and HCl is $^1\Sigma$;
in O_2, $^3\Sigma$; and in NO (nitric oxide), $^2\Pi$.   Most chemically stable
diatomic molecules have $^1\Sigma$ ground states.   There is usually no sub-
script analogous to the atomic quantity J, because the total angular
momentum of the molecule changes from one rotational state to
another, and therefore the total angular momentum is not determined by the electrons alone, as it is in atoms.   However, other
symbols are often added to $^M\Lambda$ to give additional information about
the electrical structure of the molecule.   These are discussed in detail
by Herzberg in General Reference 11.2.

The close analogy between electronic quantum numbers in atoms
and those in diatomic molecules enables one to trace the ancestry of
diatomic quantum numbers to the atomic quantum numbers of the
outer electrons in the two atoms of which the molecule is composed.
There are well-defined rules for this correlation, which lead not only
to an understanding of the electronic quantum numbers in the molecule but also to at least a semiquantitative estimate of the locations
of the various electronic energy levels.

An important feature of the electronic energy levels in molecules
is the dependence of the electronic energy on the distance between
atoms.   Figure 11.5 shows this dependence for two different electronic states in a diatomic molecule.   The curve for each state,
called a *potential curve* or *Morse curve*, shows the interatomic distance
at which the electronic energy is a minimum (that is, the equilibrium
distance r_e) as well as the energy difference between this minimum
and the limiting value reached by the electronic energy as the interatomic distance gets very large.   This energy difference is the dissociation energy D_e of the molecule.   In addition, vibrational energy
levels of the two electronic states are drawn roughly to scale on the
curves.   The two intersections of each vibrational level with the
potential curve give the maximum and minimum values of r during
the course of the vibration corresponding to that level.

The two electronic energy levels shown in Fig. 11.5 are low-lying
levels that would correspond to small values of n.   The levels for
higher values of n converge as n gets larger, just as do the levels in

atoms. This convergence appears experimentally in the form of Rydberg series in the vacuum ultraviolet absorption spectra of many molecules. The limit to these series is an ionization potential of the molecule, just as it is in atoms.

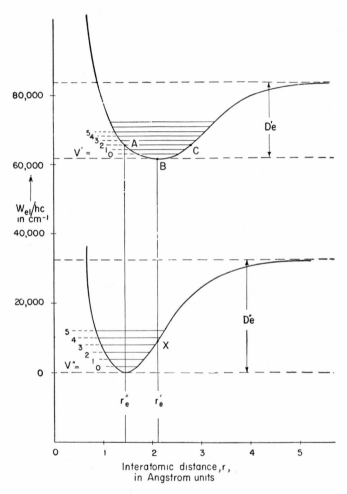

Fig. 11.5. Variation of electronic energy with interatomic distance in a diatomic molecule.

The third kind of electrons in molecules consists of those which cannot be localized on a single atom or a pair of atoms. It is difficult to assign quantum numbers (except for spin) to this kind of electron, since the meaning of the quantum numbers varies from one molecule to another as the geometrical form and number of atoms in the molecule change.   A common practice of molecular spectroscopists[1, 2] is therefore to assign a term symbol to each energy level arising from a collection of such electrons in a molecule without attempting to evaluate the quantum numbers for the individual electrons.   These term symbols are useful in the evaluation of selection rules for transitions between the various levels and serve as a description of the distribution of electrons of this kind in the molecule on the basis of the molecular geometry.   Unfortunately, it is not feasible to interpret these term symbols by means of the conventional structural formulas of the organic chemist, or by means of Lewis[3] "dot structures," and we must refer the interested reader to the articles just cited for further information.   It can be stated in general, however, that electrons of this kind have much smaller energies than the other two kinds and therefore give rise to spectra in the near ultraviolet, the visible and even the near infrared.

The best examples of the third type of electrons are found in molecules possessing what the organic chemist terms *conjugated double bonds*.   Each atom in the conjugated chain of atoms contributes one such electron to the molecule's collection, but these electrons may be regarded as belonging collectively to all the atoms in the chain rather than to a particular atom.   The energy levels associated with such electrons are characterized by relatively low energy and by small and rather regular separations from each other.   It has long been recognized that these levels are of great importance with respect to both the chemical properties and the visible and ultraviolet absorption spectra of the molecule.   They are highly characteristic of the geometrical configuration of the molecule, and of the number and kind of double bonds in the conjugated chain.

An important empirical statement concerning electronic energy levels in molecules is that the energies of electrons in small groups of atoms are often influenced very little by the attachment of neighboring groups of atoms of varying kinds.   This concept was first advanced by dye chemists, who noted that certain groups of atoms

---

[1] R. S. Mulliken, *Jour. Chem. Phys.*, **7**, 121 (1939).

[2] See General Reference 11.6, page 77 *ff*.

[3] See, for example, L. Pauling, *Nature of the Chemical Bond*, **page 5** of 2d ed., Cornell Press, Ithaca, 1944.

in an organic compound cause characteristic absorption of visible light irrespective of the nature of the rest of the compound. Such groups are called *chromophores*, that is, color carriers, but they are not by any means limited to groups absorbing in the visible region of the spectrum.

As an example of a chromophore, one may consider the benzene ring. The first excited electronic level in benzene lies some 38,000 cm^{-1} above the ground state, giving rise to absorption at about 2650 A in the ultraviolet. Many compounds containing the benzene ring, such as alkyl benzenes and the halobenzenes, show absorption very close to this wavelength. Certain other derivatives show the absorption but at somewhat altered wavelengths (about 2950 A in the case of aniline). When a substituent group, such as the amino group in aniline, has a noteworthy effect on the wavelength at which absorption occurs, it is called an *auxochrome*. In the special case that the change in wavelength is to longer wavelengths, that is, to lower frequencies, the group is called *bathochromic* or color-lowering, the lowering referring of course to the frequency and not to the intensity of the color. The distinction between a chromophore and an auxochrome begins to lose significance when the effect of the auxochrome is so large that the characteristics of the chromophore are altered greatly, as when an auxochromic group can conjugate with a chromophore to lengthen a conjugated chain. In such a case the lengthened conjugated system is more properly regarded as a new chromophore in its own right.

A chromophore can absorb light by virtue of transitions between electronic levels either of the two-atom kind or the many-atom kind. An example of the two-atom kind is the carbonyl group as found in aliphatic ketones and aldehydes. This chromophore has a characteristic absorption at approximately 2800 A which is associated with a transition between two electronic levels associated with the carbonyl group alone, as is shown by comparison of the spectra of formaldehyde, higher aldehydes, and aliphatic ketones. The benzene nucleus cited above is an example of a many-atom chromophore. A more striking example is the porphyrin ring system found, with assorted auxochromic substituents, in many natural pigments such as hemin and chlorophyll.

In Table 11.3 are listed some chromophoric groups whose absorption lies between 1700 and 6000 A. The columns marked λ_{max} and log ϵ give, respectively, the longest wavelength at which an absorption maximum occurs in the spectrum of the chromophore and the common logarithm of the molar extinction coefficient ϵ at that maximum (ϵ is defined in § 14.2).   The values of λ_{max} and log ϵ are approximate. They vary somewhat from compound to compound having the same chromophore and change also with state of aggregation, temperature, solvent, molecular geometry, and other factors.

TABLE 11.3

CHROMOPHORIC GROUPS

Chromophore	λ_{max}	log ϵ	Chromophore	λ_{max}	log ϵ
C=C	1900	3.5	—ON=O	3700	1.7
$(C=C)_2$	2200	4.2	—ONO_2	2700	1.2
$(C=C)_3$	2600	4.6	Rings:		
$(C=C)_4$	2900	4.8	Phenyl-	2700	2.4
C≡C	1800	<2	Pyridyl-	2600	3.2
—COOH	2100	1.6	Naphthyl-	3100	2.4
—$CONH_2$	2100	2.2	Cyclopenta-		
			diene	2440	3.4
C=N	1900	3.7	Pyrrole	2400	2.4
C≡N	1700	<2	Pyrimidine	2450	3.5
C=O	2800	1.3	Quinoline	3100	3.8
C=S	3300	1.0	Anthracene	3800	2.8
N=N	3700	1.2			
N=O	6600	1.3			
—NO_2	2700	1.2			

For each chromophore only those atoms are listed which share the electrons responsible for the absorption.   Other atoms or groups such as hydrogen atoms and methyl groups are omitted because of their small effect on λ_{max} and log ϵ.   These omitted groups do not themselves absorb at wavelengths above 2000 A.   Certain generalizations of approximate validity can be used to extend the usefulness of Table 11.3:

1. When two chromophores are joined by an aliphatic link (for example, —CH_2—) their absorptions are additive; for example, log ϵ for two identical chromophores is 0.3 larger than log ϵ for one. When two chromophores are attached directly, they form a new chromophore whose absorption does not usually resemble that of either.

2. The addition of a C=C link to a conjugated chain increases λ_{max} by roughly 300 A and log ϵ by about 0.3; the replacement of

C=C in a chromophore by C≡C does not greatly affect either $\lambda_{\max}$ or log ϵ.

The reader will find extensive tables of chromophores and auxochromes, together with a comprehensive bibliography, in General Reference 11.1. More detailed discussion of electronic energy levels in diatomic molecules is given by General Reference 11.2, and in polyatomic molecules by General Reference 11.6.

MOLECULAR SELECTION RULES AND THE APPEARANCE OF MOLECULAR SPECTRA

In even the simplest molecules, the rich collection of energy levels associated with the electronic, vibrational and rotational degrees of freedom leads to a highly complicated spectrum. Fortunately, the levels can be disentangled to a considerable extent, and the interpretation of molecular spectra is facilitated by the consequent possibility of considering electronic, vibrational, and rotational transitions more or less separately. This division does not mean that the three types of transitions do not occur simultaneously but only that transitions of one kind have *relatively* small effects on the energy levels of the other kinds. The spectra associated with the three types are considered briefly.

11.4. Pure Rotational Spectra. Equation (11.3) shows that the rotational energy of linear (including diatomic) and spherical-top molecules depends only on a single quantum number J, which can have any integral value. The selection rules for this quantum number in pure rotational spectra, that is, spectra in which *no vibrational or electronic energy changes* occur, are as follows:

$\Delta J = 0$ for molecules that do not have a permanent electric dipole moment.*

$\Delta J = \pm 1$ for molecules that have a permanent electric dipole moment.

These rules mean that molecules which have no permanent dipole moment cannot have a pure rotational spectrum. Examples of such molecules are *all* symmetrical linear molecules (H_2, O_2, N_2, CO_2, C_2H_2, and so on) and *all* spherical-top molecules (CH_4, UF_6, and the

---

* A molecule has a permanent electric dipole moment if on the average its center of negative charge does not coincide with its center of positive charge.

like).   Unsymmetrical linear molecules (CO, HCl, HCN, N_2O), on the other hand, show a pure rotational spectrum, the appearance of which is determined by the energy levels (Fig. 11.2), the selection rule $\Delta J = \pm 1$, and the number of molecules populating each level. The last factor depends on the temperature of the molecules; the higher the temperature, the greater the relative populations of the higher levels [compare Eq. (10.20)].   The combination of Eq. (11.3) with the selection rule $\Delta J = \pm 1$ leads to the relationship

$$\sigma = 2JB \qquad (11.7)$$

where σ is the wave number in cm^{-1} of a line in the pure rotational spectrum for which the *upper* energy level has the quantum number J. Since this J can have only integral values from 1 to ∞, the rotational lines occur at equal frequency intervals.   The appearance of the

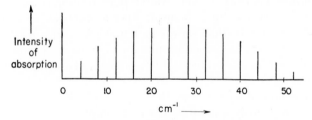

Fig. 11.6.   The pure rotational absorption spectrum of a linear molecule.

resulting spectrum is shown schematically in Fig. 11.6, in which the height of the lines represents their relative intensity.   The maximum in intensity occurs at the J value that corresponds to the most highly populated *initial* level and thus depends on external conditions (the temperature) as well as on the rotational energy levels of the molecule itself.

The rotational line spectrum shown in Fig. 11.6 can in principle be either an emission or an absorption spectrum.   However, such spectra are usually observed in absorption because of the wavelength region in which they occur.*   Since the constant B is *inversely* proportional to the moment of inertia, the larger the molecule, the lower the wave number at which the absorption takes place.   In practice, the absorption maximum seldom occurs above 100 cm^{-1}, which

---

* The pure rotational Raman effect of a few molecules has been studied.   The selection rules are different in this case; in particular, a permanent electric dipole moment is not necessary for the effect.

means that the wavelength region is usually *longer* than 100 μ. Pure rotational spectra thus lie very far in the infrared—so far, in fact, that few have been observed. Recently, however, the pure rotational absorption of numerous molecules has been measured in the "microwave" region of the spectrum, for which λ is approximately 10,000 μ, or 1 cm, and σ is 1 cm^{-1}. The technique of microwave spectroscopy is outside the scope of this book, but certainly the spectroscopist can expect much from this field of research. Because of its development, the importance of pure rotational spectra has been greatly increased.

The energy-level scheme for a symmetrical-top rotator is more complicated (Fig. 11.2) than that of a linear rotator, but the nature of the selection rules simplifies the actual spectrum considerably. The rules for ΔJ are the same as before, and in addition $\Delta K = 0$. Hence symmetrical top molecules that do not have a permanent electric dipole moment do not exhibit pure rotational absorption, whereas those with a dipole moment have a spectrum as given by Eq. (11.7), similar to that shown in Fig. 11.6. Since neither the energy-level pattern nor selection rules for asymmetrical top rotators can be expressed in general terms, little can be said about the appearance of the spectrum of such molecules without explicit knowledge of the moments of inertia and the electric dipole moment. The spectrum is ordinarily quite irregular and complex. For details the reader may consult Chapter I of General Reference 11.3.

Finally, it should be recalled that the foregoing discussion is valid only for molecules in the vapor state, and that ordinarily molecules in solids and liquids cannot rotate freely; that is, they have no simple set of rotational energy levels such as those summarized in Table 11.1.

11.5. Vibrational Spectra. The wave-number range covered by molecular vibrations is approximately 100 to 5000 cm^{-1}, which means that the wavelength range is 2 to 100 μ. The experimental study of vibrational spectra is carried out by means of infrared absorption spectra in this spectral region, and in the visible region of the spectrum by means of the Raman effect (Chapter 18). Most infrared studies are made with prism spectrometers, on which type of instrument the practical upper wavelength limit is 25 μ, or low wave-number limit of 400 cm^{-1}. By means of the Raman effect, however, much lower wave numbers—50 cm^{-1} or even less—are observable.

Although the vibrational energy-level pattern given by Eq. (11.6) is very complex, the equal spacings of the levels associated with each frequency, and the selection rules, combine to simplify the vibrational spectrum. The selection rules restrict the changes in the $3N - 6$ quantum numbers v_i as follows:

1. Only one of the quantum numbers v_i can change during a transition between vibrational levels caused by the emission or absorption of radiation.

2. This change, Δv, is $+1$ or -1.

3. For certain vibrations, Δv must always be zero.

These rules lead to the result that each frequency observed in the spectrum is identical with the frequency of one of the molecular vibrations. However, the complete set of molecular frequencies will not necessarily appear in the spectrum, because those vibrations to which the selection rule $\Delta v = 0$ always applies will not be observed. The geometrical form of the molecule determines the number of vibrations of this kind. In the infrared spectrum, Δv is always zero for vibrations during which the electric dipole moment remains unchanged. For example, in b and d of Fig. 11.3 the vibrations marked (1) have $\Delta v = 0$ and therefore do not appear in infrared absorption. In the Raman effect, the vibrations that do not change the molecular refractivity have $\Delta v = 0$. Examples in Fig. 11.3 are (b) 2, 3, and 4, and (d), 4.

Since the geometrical form—often called the *symmetry*—of a molecule is definitive for the vibrational selection rules, the classification of the vibrations of a molecule according to their symmetry is a necessary preliminary to a determination of their occurrence in their spectrum, or *spectroscopic activity*. Once this classification has been made, it is possible solely on the basis of symmetry to say how many of the $3N - 6$ vibrations will appear in both the infrared and the Raman spectra, how many will appear in one and not the other, and how many will be forbidden to appear in either. Conversely, if the infrared and Raman spectra are known and the molecular symmetry is not, the latter may be inferred from the spectra with the help of the selection rules.

Tables by means of which the vibrations of molecules may be classified and their spectroscopic activity determined have been worked out for all the various likely symmetries (see, for example, General Reference 11.3, Tables 35, 36, and 55). Two examples of the sort of conclusions which can be drawn from such Tables are as follows:

1. A molecule that contains a center of symmetry (for example, the linear molecule ABA in Fig. 11.3b) will never have the same vibration

active in both infrared and Raman spectra. A corollary of this rule says that symmetrical diatomic molecules (H_2, O_2, and the like) cannot absorb infrared radiation by vibrational transitions; that is, they will have no vibrational spectrum, just as they have no pure rotational spectrum.

2. A fundamental frequency in the Raman effect which is found to be polarized arises from a vibration which is totally symmetrical, that is, during the course of which the symmetry of the molecule does not change (examples: all the vibrations (1) in Fig. 11.3).

The vibrational selection rules on which the above discussion is based are ample to explain the chief features of vibrational spectra, but they must be modified if the spectra are to be interpreted in detail. The rules are derived on the assumption that the vibrations are harmonic and that the molecules are in the vapor state, that is, free from the disturbing effects of close neighboring molecules. If these assumptions are not strictly justified, the selection rules must be altered. The chief effects are to allow more than one quantum number v to change during a transition between vibrational levels, and to permit Δv to be 2 or even more. These alterations permit the appearance of so-called *overtones* and *combination tones* in the spectrum. Such overtones in general are of feeble intensity in comparison with the *fundamentals*, the frequencies permitted by the simple selection rules. The Raman effect and infrared absorption differ markedly in this respect, however, the Raman effect showing stricter adherence to the simple rules. Overtones in the infrared spectra of gases in turn are weaker than those in the spectra of liquids. Fortunately, the third selection rule, which excludes certain vibrations from infrared absorption or the Raman effect or both, is less affected by these disturbing influences. Again the Raman effect adheres closely to the rules, as does infrared absorption in the vapor. Only in the infrared spectrum of liquids does one find significant deviation.

11.6. Rotational Fine Structure in Vibrational Spectra. We have already noted that vibrational frequencies are from hundreds to many thousands of times larger than those of rotation. One result is that the frequency of a pure vibrational transition, in which only a vibrational quantum number changes, differs very little percentage-wise from that of the corresponding transition in which both vibrational and rotational quantum numbers change. In consequence, every pure vibrational transition is observed spectroscopically in the immediate neighborhood of a collection of vibrational-rotational transitions. The various members of the collection differ only in the rotational quantum numbers involved, and the collection is called a *vibration-rotation band*.

The positions of the rotational lines in such a band for a diatomic molecule are given to a fair approximation by an expression similar to Eq. (11.7):

$$\sigma = \sigma_{\text{vib}} \pm 2JB \qquad (11.8)$$

in which σ_{vib} is the wave number in cm^{-1} corresponding to the pure vibrational transition, and J takes the values 1, 2, 3, ... The near infrared vibration-rotation absorption band of hydrogen chloride gas, Fig. 11.7a, illustrates the structure of such a band. The left-hand side of this band, called the *P*-branch, is given by Eq. (11.8) with the *minus* sign, corresponding to the selection rule $\Delta J = -1$; and the right-hand side, the *R*-branch, by the *plus* sign ($\Delta J = +1$). Each numerical value of J in Eq. (11.8) refers to the *higher* of the two rotational quantum numbers involved in the transition, as it does in Eq. (11.7). This statement means, however, that the J value is that of the *initial* rotational energy level for the *P* branch, and that of the *final* rotational energy level for the *R* branch.

It will be noted that Eq. (11.8), with J restricted to integers higher than zero, gives no wave number corresponding to the pure σ_{vib}. This limitation, a consequence of the selection rule $\Delta J = \pm 1$, results in a gap in the center of the vibration-rotation band. The center of this gap is the wave number σ_{vib} [compare (a) in Fig. 11.7]. Such a gap always appears in the infrared vibration-rotation absorption bands of diatomic molecules and in certain of the bands of linear polyatomic molecules. It always appears when the dipole moment of the molecule vibrates parallel to the molecular line, which is the only way the moment can vibrate in a diatomic molecule. Bands with the central gap are called *parallel bands*.

In certain of the vibrations of linear polyatomic molecules, such as No. 3 in Fig. 11.3b, the dipole moment vibrates in a direction perpendicular to the molecular line. The rotational selection rule is then $\Delta J = 0, \pm 1$. As a result, the *P* and *R* branches are joined by a third, the *Q* branch, for which $\Delta J = 0$. Since there is no change in rotational energy when J does not change, the various members of the *Q* branch all have the same frequency, which is that of the pure vibration. Hence the *Q* branch occurs in the center of the band.

Such a band, with P, Q, and R branches, is termed a *perpendicular band* and is illustrated in Fig. 11.7b.

Although few molecules have such simple vibration-rotation band structures as those shown in Figs. 11.7a and 11.7b, these can serve

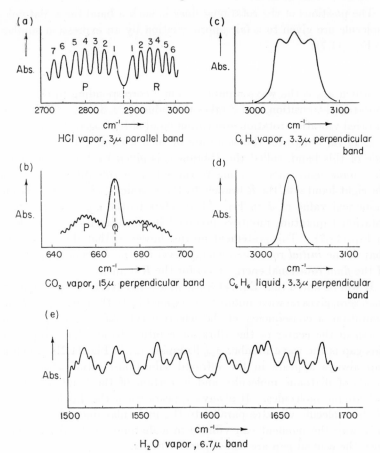

(a) HCl vapor, 3μ parallel band

(b) CO₂ vapor, 15μ perpendicular band

(c) C₆H₆ vapor, 3.3μ perpendicular band

(d) C₆H₆ liquid, 3.3μ perpendicular band

(e) H₂O vapor, 6.7μ band

Fig. 11.7.   Typical vibration-rotation bands in infrared absorption.

as a basis for a consideration of what happens to the appearance of the band structures when various complications are introduced. Some of the complications are

(a) Complex energy-level systems of symmetrical and asymmetrical tops.

(b) Large moments of inertia that lead to unresolvable continuous bands.

(c) Smearing out of rotational levels in liquid and solid phases.

(d) Changes in the energy-level system produced by the mechanical interactions between rotation and vibration and by centrifugal distortion of the molecule.

In Fig. 11.7 the gross effects of these various complications are illustrated. Figure 11.7e shows a complex band in the spectrum of water vapor, whose molecule is an asymmetric top. It will be noted that the regularities present in the bands of the linear molecules have disappeared. Figure 11.7c shows a band for a molecule (benzene) whose moments of inertia are all so large that resolution of the lines associated with individual rotational transitions is impossible. This limitation results, as we have seen in Eq. (11.3), from the fact that the spacing of the rotational levels is *inversely* proportional to the moments of inertia. The rotational band in such a case is simply the "envelope" of unresolved lines. Even this envelope is smeared out, however, if the molecular rotation is hampered or eliminated by condensation of the vapor to a liquid or solid. The same vibrational band as observed in the liquid state is shown in Fig. 11.7d. The complications introduced into the rotational energy-level scheme by centrifugal distortion of the molecule or by vibration-rotation interaction are important for the precise interpretation of the spectra but are beyond the scope of this brief account.*

Finally, it should be mentioned that the Raman effect could, in principle, be used as well as infrared absorption for the study of the rotational structure of vibration-rotation bands. In practice, it is almost never so used because of the difficulty, discussed in Chapter 18, of obtaining the Raman spectra of gases. The rotational structure of Raman lines in the liquid state is suppressed to about the same extent as that of the infrared absorption band for liquid benzene shown in Fig. 11.7d.

11.7. Electronic Spectra of Diatomic Molecules. These spectra arise from transitions during which quantum numbers associated with electronic, vibrational, and rotational energy levels all change. The region where such spectra are found, which may be anywhere from the vacuum ultraviolet to the near infrared, is determined by the electronic levels. The changes in vibrational and rotational quantum

---

* See, for example, Chapter IV of General Reference 11.3.

numbers introduce a fine structure (analogous to the rotational fine structure of vibrational bands) from which the name *band spectra* is derived.

The electronic quantum numbers described in § 11.3 are subject to selection rules similar to atomic selection rules [Eqs. (10.19)]: the total electron spin S does not change during a transition ($\Delta S = 0$), and the angular momentum projection Λ may change by only one unit or not at all ($\Delta\Lambda = 0, \pm 1$). Complications are introduced, however, because the angular momentum of molecular rotation can couple with the electronic spin and orbital angular momenta (compare Russell-Saunders coupling in atoms—§ 10.6, footnote). This coupling can take place in various ways which are beyond the scope of our discussion but which give rise to various additional selection rules. Regardless of these additional rules, however, the general statement can be made that the total molecular angular momentum—spin, orbit and rotation—must change by one unit or not at all.

11.8. Vibrational Structure of Diatomic Spectra. The vibrational selection rules are much more diverse than those for vibration-rotation spectra (§ 11.6) because of the entirely different basis on which they are determined. This diversity stems from the relative sluggishness with which atomic nuclei move in a molecular vibration compared to the speed of electrons in their orbits. The latter speed is of the order of 10^8 cm/sec, whereas the velocity that vibrating nuclei reach is at most one-hundredth of this value and usually is much smaller still. In making a transition from one orbit to another, an electron travels a distance of approximately 10^{-8} cm and therefore will require only about 10^{-16} sec for the switch. During so short an interval, the vibrating nuclei will travel less than 10^{-10} cm, that is, less than one-hundredth of the internuclear distance.

Since the internuclear distance changes by less than 1 per cent, for all practical purposes it remains fixed during the electronic transition. Hence the molecule will go from one electronic level to another without variation of r in Fig. 11.5. If the value of r initially is r_e'', the molecule being in the ground electronic state and not vibrating ($v'' = 0$), absorption of radiation will carry the molecule to an upper level (point A on the upper curve in Fig. 11.5) without change in r.* In the upper state, however, the internuclear separation r_e'' no longer is an equilibrium separation. To restore equilibrium, the molecule

---

* It is standard usage to designate upper state quantities with a single prime and lower state quantities with a double prime.

in the upper level moves from r_e'' (point A) to r_e' (point B), picking up linear momentum as it does so. This momentum, however, carries it past r_e' to a point of potential energy equal to that at point A, that is, to point C. Point C is not a position of equilibrium, so that the molecule moves toward r_e' again, and again picks up momentum, which carries it back to r_e'' (point A). The whole cycle is then repeated; that is, the molecule vibrates between points A and C. This amplitude of vibration corresponds to $v' = 2$. Hence the change, Δv, on going from the lower curve ($v'' = 0$) to the upper ($v' = 2$) is $+2$.

If the vertical ordinate through r_e'' had intersected the upper curve at some other level, say $v'' = 5$, Δv would have been $+5$. In actual molecules, the value of Δv is not restricted sharply to any one value but can have a range of values, a few of which are much more likely than others. The most probable values correspond to the most

Fig. 11.8. Band progression in the electronic spectrum of the nitrogen molecule N_2.

intense bands in the spectrum. This method of determining Δv in diatomic electronic spectra is called the *Franck-Condon principle*.[4, 5]

The collection of vibrational bands associated with a given electronic transition is called a *band system*. In the analysis of such a collection with respect to the values of v' and v'' for each band, it is frequently possible to assign a regular series of bands to a single value of v' and to successive values of v'', or vice versa. Such a regular series, called a *progression*, is illustrated in Fig. 11.8 for the molecule N_2. Another kind of regularity occurs when two Morse curves (Fig. 11.5) are related in such a way that Δv is a constant regardless of the values of v' and v''. Groups of bands with the same value of Δv then occur together and are called *sequences*.

With the help of Fig. 11.5 it can be seen that the value of Δv may be quite different for transitions beginning on the upper curve from its value for those beginning on the lower. If we assume a non-

[4] J. Franck, *Trans. Farad. Soc.*, **21**, 536 (1926).
[5] E. U. Condon, *Phys. Rev.*, **28**, 1182 (1926); **32**, 858 (1928).

vibrating molecule in the upper state ($v' = 0$), the internuclear separation before transition will be r_e', and therefore the transition will take the molecule from point B to the intersection of the ordinate r_e' with the lower curve, or to point X. This transition has $\Delta v = -3$ (or -4) rather than $+2$ as before.* Hence the energy change associated with the transition is quite different, and the emitted band will occur in the spectrum at some considerable distance from the absorption band $\Delta v = +2$. This is simply another way of saying that the emission-band spectrum of a molecule and its absorption-band spectrum can be, and experimentally often are, quite different in appearance. Part of the difference, it should be added, comes from the diversity of vibrational excitation imparted by the electrical discharge or high-temperature flame required to excite the emission spectrum.

A valuable by-product of the vibrational analysis of diatomic spectra is the possibility of tracing the vibrational levels of the ground state to such large quantum numbers that the amplitude of vibration corresponds almost to dissociation of the molecule. When this tracing can be done, as is often the case, the energy of dissociation (D_e'' in Fig. 11.5) can be measured directly and accurately. Indeed, the most accurately known heats of dissociation, such as H_2 and the halogens, have been determined in this way. However, when the dissociation energy is very large, as in N_2 and CO, it may prove difficult to follow the usual procedures because of the tremendous spectral range involved. This difficulty has given rise to considerable controversy over the interpretation of the spectra of N_2 and CO.

11.9. Rotational Fine Structure of an Electronic-Vibrational Band. Each electronic-vibrational transition of the sort just described gives rise to a single band of which numerous examples can be seen in Fig. 11.8. Accompanying the transition is a set of rotational energy changes that give the band its fine structure just as in the case of the vibrational-rotational bands depicted in Fig. 11.7. The rotational selection rules in the two cases are quite similar: $\Delta J = 0, \pm 1$ except when the electronic transition takes place between two $^1\Sigma$ levels, for which case $\Delta J = \pm 1$. These two rules result in perpendicular and parallel bands, respectively.

The basic difference between the rotational structure of electronic bands and that of vibrational bands arises from the fact that the

---

* By definition, $\Delta v = v' - v''$.

moment of inertia of a diatomic molecule changes little in passing from one vibrational level to another in the same electronic state but changes considerably (sometimes as much as a factor of 2) when the electronic state changes. Therefore the spacing of the rotational levels differs markedly in the two electronic states. It is usually, though not always, smaller in the upper electronic level, corresponding to a larger moment of inertia, because a higher electronic state usually has weaker binding between the two atoms, and hence a larger internuclear distance.

An expression for the P, Q, and R branches of an electronic-vibrational band analogous to Eq. (11.8) can be derived from the above selection rules and Eq. (11.3) applied to the two electronic-vibrational levels:

$$\sigma = \sigma_{\text{el-vib}} \pm (B' \pm B'')J + (B' - B'')J^2 \qquad (11.9)$$

This expression gives the wave numbers in cm^{-1} of the rotational lines in the P branch if the first minus sign and the second plus sign are taken. The Q-branch formula results if the first plus sign and the second minus are used, whereas the R branch is given by the first and second plus signs. J takes the values 1, 2, 3, . . . , but as before (§ 11.6) the significance of J differs for each branch. In the P branch the J value is that in the lower electronic level; in the R branch it is that in the upper electronic level; and in the Q branch the two are of course the same, since $\Delta J = 0$. The reason for starting J at one instead of zero for the Q branch lies in the coupling between rotation and electronic angular momentum which is always present in molecules giving rise to perpendicular bands. It will be noted that Eq. (11.9) reduces to the form of Eq. (11.8) when $B' = B''$, that is, when the moments of inertia are the same in both upper and lower states.

The presence of the J^2 term in Eq. (11.9) has the result that, for high enough J values, all three branches lie on the same side of $\sigma_{\text{el-vib}}$. Since B' is usually smaller than B'' (that is, $I_b' > I_b''$), this side is the low-frequency side. The lines of highest J are always very weak, which means that the three branches ordinarily fade out towards the red end of the spectrum from $\sigma_{\text{el-vib}}$. Such bands are said to degrade toward the red. On the violet side of $\sigma_{\text{el-vib}}$ there is a frequency of maximum value that occurs in the R branch shortly before the J^2 term overtakes the J term of opposite sign. This maximum frequency, which depends on the magnitude of the *differ-*

ence between B' and B'', is called the *band head* and is clearly to be distinguished from σ_{el-vib}, which is called the *band origin*. Experimentally, the band head is more prominent and can be measured directly. The band origin, on the other hand, has to be determined by analysis of the rotational branches.

The foregoing discussion is illustrated in Fig. 11.9, which shows the structure of two bands degraded toward the red. When B' is

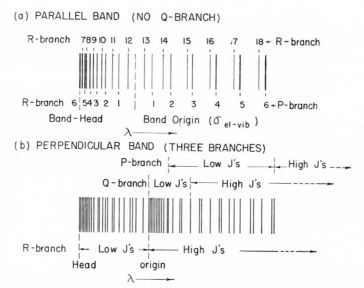

Fig. 11.9.   The rotational fine structure of diatomic bands.

larger than B'', the above discussion needs to be changed by replacing "low-frequency" by "high-frequency," "red" by "violet" and vice versa, "maximum" by "minimum," and "R branch" by "P branch."

The several members of the P, Q, and R branches vary in intensity in much the same way as they do in vibration-rotation bands (Fig. 11.7), the most intense lines corresponding to those originating from the most highly populated rotational levels. Since the population factor is given by an expression of the form of Eq. (10.20), in which all quantities except the temperature T are either known or obtainable from the spectrum, a measurement of intensity distribution among the various branches can be used to determine T. In this way the effective temperatures of molecules in flames and electrical discharges, which might be difficult to measure by other means, can be determined with reasonable accuracy.

The rotational fine structure can be made to yield information about the moments of inertia of the molecule in the upper and lower electronic states, and hence, if the identity of the molecule is known, about the internuclear distances in the two states. There are two ways in which this information can be obtained, to both of which an assignment of the various rotational lines to their initial and final levels is prerequisite. Once this assignment has been accomplished, the first method proceeds by working out an empirical quadratic formula relating the observed frequencies of various lines to their J numbers. The coefficient of the J term is numerically equal to $B' + B''$, and the coefficient of the J^2-term is equal to $B' - B''$, in accordance with Eq. (11.9) for the P and R branches. Hence B' and B'' can be evaluated from these coefficients.

The other and more commonly followed procedure consists of finding the energy difference between the individual rotational levels by taking the difference between appropriate lines in the band. For example, the difference between the eighth and ninth rotational levels in the ground state is the difference between the Q-branch transition $J' = 9 \rightarrow J'' = 9$ and the R-branch transition $J' = 9 \rightarrow J'' = 8$. From such energy differences the constants B' and B'' can be obtained, along with additional information such as the effect of centrifugal force on the internuclear distance.

The foregoing discussion applies to diatomic molecules in the vapor phase. As soon as most molecules are condensed to liquids or solids, the previously mentioned complications ensue. The rotational energy levels are "smeared out" by the collisions and by the strong electric fields of closely packed molecules. Accordingly, diatomic spectra are studied almost exclusively in the vapor state. For a comprehensive discussion of the manifold details of diatomic spectra, the reader is referred to General Reference 11.2.

11.10. Electronic Spectra of Polyatomic Molecules. It can readily be seen from the foregoing simplified account of the main features of the electronic spectra of diatomic molecules that even the simplest polyatomic molecule should have a still richer electronic spectrum. The electronic energy levels can be much more complicated (especially in molecules with conjugated double bonds), there are $3N - 6$ vibrational degrees of freedom, and there are three moments of inertia, usually all different. It is not surprising, then, that few polyatomic spectra have been thoroughly analyzed. There is much active work in this field, however, and extensive experimental as well as theoretical progress is being made.

There is, to be sure, a vast literature (see Chapter 14) of visible and ultraviolet absorption spectra of polyatomic molecules of all kinds. Most of this material, however, was obtained on molecules dissolved in some relatively transparent solvent, and by means of spectrographs of low resolving power. In consequence, even the coarsest features of the spectra are usually "washed out," and only rather broad generalizations, of the sort incorporated in Table 11.3, have been possible from the data. It seems probable that this state of affairs will improve markedly by progress along these lines:

1. Investigation of more and more molecules in the vapor state, at low pressures but with long optical paths, with spectrographs of high dispersion.

2. Study of spectra over wide temperature ranges, and especially at very low temperatures.

3. Extension of the study of spectra to shorter wavelengths.

4. Improvement of means of excitation of polyatomic spectra, so that emission spectra as well as absorption and fluorescence spectra can be used in the study of the upper electronic levels.

It was indicated in § 11.3 that it is difficult to assign quantum numbers to individual electrons in most polyatomic molecules, and that instead the over-all distribution of the electrons with respect to the various atomic nuclei is described by a term symbol. These term symbols carry the multiplicity $(2S + 1)$ as a superscript, just as in atomic and diatomic term symbols, but the remainder of the symbol indicates simply the geometry of the over-all electron distribution in the molecule. The usefulness of such symbols lies in the fact that selection rules can be expressed in terms of them, and, in turn, observed spectra can be interpreted with the help of the selection rules to give the symbols for the various observed states. A complete discussion of these symbols and the associated selection rules can be found in General Reference 11.6. The only one of these rules we will mention is the one already given for atoms and diatomic molecules: $\Delta S = 0$.

11.11. Vibrational Structure of Electronic Spectra in Polyatomic Molecules. The vibrational selection rules in polyatomic electronic spectra are based on an extension of the Franck-Condon principle.

To a first approximation the result of this extension is the rule that *the only vibrations for which Δv differs from zero are the totally symmetrical vibrations* [compare §§ 11.2 and 11.5 and vibrations marked (1) in Fig. 11.3]. For these vibrations the most likely values of Δv are determined, as for diatomic molecules, by the relative interatomic distances in the upper and lower electronic states. This rule is of first importance for the interpretation of the spectra of highly symmetrical molecules, in which the number of totally symmetrical vibrations is small, because it sweepingly simplifies the vibrational pattern in the spectrum.

In the benzene molecule, for example, there are 30 vibrational degrees of freedom, with 20 distinct frequencies. Only two of these are totally symmetrical, one of which is a pulsation or "breathing" of the ring and the other a vibration of the hydrogens. In the first excited electronic state of benzene, the ring size is slightly larger than in the ground state, but the carbon-hydrogen distance is practically the same. As a result, the most probable Δv's for the totally symmetrical ring vibration are 2 and 3, whereas $\Delta v = 0$, 1 and 4, 5, 6, . . . are less probable but still permitted. The Δv for the hydrogen vibration, on the other hand, is zero. In consequence, the most prominent feature of the absorption spectrum of benzene is a simple progression of evenly spaced bands that resembles roughly a progression of diatomic bands because only one vibration is involved. The ultraviolet absorption spectrum of benzene *in solution* is given in Fig. 11.10a, along with the more complicated vapor spectrum of Fig. 11.10b. The absorption spectrum of permanganate ion in aqueous solution is also shown in Fig. 11.10c. Presumably, this ion has only one totally symmetrical vibration, and therefore its electronic absorption shows a simplified vibrational structure because of the action of the Franck-Condon principle.

It is apparent from the foregoing that the more complete our knowledge of the vibrational energy levels of a polyatomic molecule, the better our chance of making a satisfactory interpretation of the vibrational fine structure of its electronic spectrum. For this reason the results of infrared and Raman spectra are frequently an indispensable adjunct to the understanding of the data obtained in the visible and ultraviolet regions.

11.12. Rotational Fine Structure in Electronic Spectra. The rotational fine structure of polyatomic electronic bands provides less information, generally speaking, than does that of diatomic bands, because of the much larger moments of inertia, the usually smaller fractional difference between the moments in one electronic state and another, and the complex patterns associated with the band struc-

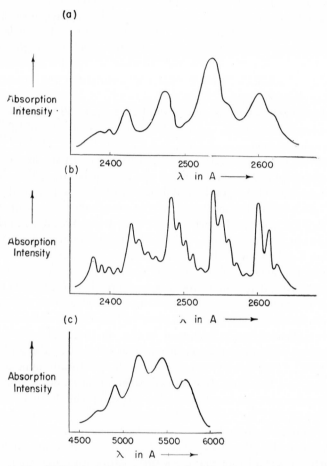

Fig. 11.10. Vibrational fine structure of electronic spectra in polyatomic molecules. (a) The absorption spectrum of benzene in cyclohexane solution in the 2600 A region. (b) The absorption spectrum of benzene vapor in the 2600 A region. (c) The absorption spectrum of permanganate ion in the green region of the visible spectrum.

tures for symmetrical and asymmetrical tops. These characteristics render the resolution of the rotational fine structure exceedingly difficult for any but the smallest and lightest molecules. Naturally, even for such molecules it is necessary to study the spectra in the vapor state and to keep the pressures as low as possible. Some progress has been made in the analysis of rotational fine structure in the ultraviolet spectra of carbon disulfide (linear rotator), formaldehyde (quasi-symmetrical top), and nitrogen dioxide and sulfur dioxide (asymmetrical tops).

The selection rules for the rotational fine structure are similar to those for the infrared, but several new features enter that make the transition possibilities more diverse. As for diatomic molecules, the moments of inertia may differ in the upper and lower electronic states, leading to fine-structure expressions like Eq. (11.9). In addition, however, all polyatomic rotators except asymmetrical tops have degenerate vibrations, such as (3) and (4) of Fig. 11.3b, which can give rise to vibrational angular momentum. This angular momentum can couple with the angular momentum of rotation in various ways, and it increases the complexity both of the energy level scheme and of the transitions between levels. The possibility also exists that the actual geometrical structure of the molecule may be different in two electronic states; for instance, it may be a symmetrical top in the ground state and an asymmetrical top in an upper state.

From the preceding statements it can be seen that for both theoretical and experimental reasons the rotational structure will be difficult to observe and to analyze. For further details, the reader is referred to General Reference 11.6.

11.13.   The Effects of External Influences on Molecular Spectra. The external variables that affect molecular spectra are much the same as those which affect atomic spectra (§ 10.7), but their relative importance is quite different. One reason is the difference in methods of excitation of atomic and of molecular spectra. The latter are studied more frequently in absorption than in emission, and are not often excited by arc and spark discharges. The high-voltage, high-frequency discharge, with or without electrodes in direct contact with the vapor being studied, is used for excitation of emission spectra, especially for small molecules.

Fluorescence is of importance in the analysis of many molecular spectra. It is studied with a technique not greatly different from that used for the Raman effect (see Chapter 18). The chief requirement is an intense source of sharply monochromatic radiation of a wavelength that corresponds to the energy difference between two electronic levels whose band systems are under investigation. The correspondence need not be exact so long as the minimum energy required is available, and it is usually better to have the exciting radiation correspond to a combined electronic-vibrational transition for which the transition probability is high. The spectrum obtained in fluorescence depends not only on the exciting wavelength but also on temperature and pressure, as indicated below. One limitation of fluorescence spectra (shared also by absorption spectra) exists because of the selection rule $\Delta S = 0$. Since most molecules are in the ground state before excitation of fluorescence and since this state is usually a singlet, in general only singlet levels in the upper state can be studied by this means.

Temperature. The effect of temperature on molecular spectra is of great importance. As we have already seen, the distribution of intensity among the rotational lines is strongly temperature-dependent. The same statement can be made for vibrational bands in electronic spectra. In ultraviolet absorption spectra, a temperature effect is noticed for both totally symmetrical and nontotally symmetrical vibrations. The intensities of the former change as v'' changes (see Fig. 11.5), because, for example, a totally symmetrical band for which $v'' = 1 \rightarrow v' = 5$ will grow in intensity if the number of molecules in the level $v'' = 1$ increases. Nontotally symmetrical bands, for which $\Delta v = 0$, will be affected similarly. The change in the appearance of the spectrum is even more striking here because of the fact that in general v'' and v' for a given vibration are different, and therefore the bands due to transitions $v'' = 0 \rightarrow v' = 0$, $v'' = 1 \rightarrow v' = 1$, $v'' = 2 \rightarrow v' = 2$, and so on, occur at different places in the spectrum. The fine structure in between the tall peaks of the benzene vapor spectrum (Fig. 11.10b) is largely associated with different v'' values for nontotally symmetrical vibrations and shows a strong temperature variation in intensity.

Conversely, the quantitative variation of intensity with temperature can frequently be the means for confirmation or rejection of the analysis of a band system. If an interpretation of the spectrum asserts that a given band or progression of bands arises from a vibration in the ground state with $v'' = 2$ for a frequency of v'', the assertion can be checked by comparison of the observed effect of temperature on band intensity with that calculated from Eq. (10.20). Moreover, it can be seen that the absorption spectrum will be considerably simplified if it is obtained from molecules with T near $0°K$, because then all vibrations in the ground state have $v'' = 0$, and *only* totally symmetrical vibrations can give rise to transitions to upper vibrational levels with v' different from zero.*

Pressure. The effects of pressure on molecular spectra are also somewhat more complex than those on atomic spectra (see § 10.7). The broadening of atomic lines by collisions, which of course increase in number with increase in pressure, has a molecular analogue. Atoms, however, can only exchange electronic and translational energy upon collision, whereas molecules in addition trade vibrational and rotational energies. It has been found, moreover, that it takes very many collisions (of the order of 10^4 or more for each molecule) to establish a new balance among the various degrees of freedom once the old balance has been upset in some way. Hence the spectrum emitted by an assembly of molecules whose equilibrium has been disturbed during excitation will depend on the extent to which equilibrium has been restored prior to the emission of radiation.

In the fluorescence of vapors, for example, the equilibrium among molecules may be upset by the exciting radiation, because the molecules are transferred to an upper state in which the molecules have higher vibrational energy than their temperature warrants. If this extra vibrational energy can be given up to other degrees of freedom (vibrational as well as rotational and translational) before the molecule radiates (a time lag of about 10^{-8} sec exists between excitation and reradiation), the emitted spectrum will correspond roughly to one in which all the v' values are zero or at most very small. This situation obtains when the molecules are under relatively high pressure (say 1 to 10 atmospheres at room temperature), so that the requisite number of collisions can take place in 10^{-8} sec. If the pressure is low (say 10^{-4} atmosphere at room temperature), an insufficient number of collisions occurs before reradiation,† and the resulting spectrum contains bands for which the v' values are high (values given by the Franck-Condon principle for transitions from the vibrationless ground state) as well as low (in those molecules which have made sufficient collisions). The general result is that "high-pressure" fluorescence spectra are somewhat simpler, involving primarily the upper vibrational state in which all v' values are equal to zero, and show vibrational spacings corresponding to different v'' values. Low-pressure

---

* To a more refined approximation, vibrations that are not totally symmetrical can have $\Delta v = 2$ as well as $\Delta v = 0$, but these transitions are extremely weak.

† If the lifetime of the excited state is longer than 10^{-8} sec for some reason, the pressure values must be revised downward.

fluorescence (sometimes called *resonance fluorescence*) may be more complex, since it involves both upper state and ground state vibrations.

Because the probabilities for allowed transitions between various levels in the same molecule may vary over a wide range, it is always valuable in the study of absorption spectra, both infrared and ultraviolet, to vary the number of molecules in the absorbing path as much as possible. There is no difficulty in making this number indefinitely small, but frequently vapor pressure furnishes an upper limit. Even when no limit is set by vapor pressure, increase in the number of molecules per unit volume by increasing pressure is not always desirable because of collision broadening. A solution to this problem can sometimes be made by simple increase in the path length of the radiation through the vapor. On occasion, to be sure, the broadening produced by pressure may be useful, as for example when one wishes to measure directly the integrated intensity of an entire band,[6] or even band system, without resorting to the difficult and usually inaccurate procedure of measuring the intensity of each resolvable line and summing.

Electric and Magnetic Fields. The effects of electric and magnetic fields are relatively unimportant in molecular spectra. The Stark effect is extremely small and cannot be observed in molecules with the usual spectrographic techniques. In the microwave region, however, the Stark effect on the pure rotational spectrum (§ 11.4) is readily observable and is frequently of use in the detection of weak lines, in the assignment of rotational quantum numbers, and in the measurement of permanent electric dipole moments. The Zeeman effect is usually small or missing altogether. Singlet electronic levels predominate in molecules, and there is no need for the Zeeman effect as a means of series identification. Magnetic rotation spectra are sometimes useful in the analysis of diatomic spectra.[7] It also appears likely that the Zeeman effect on nuclear spins will be of value in the determination of such spins by means of molecular microwave spectra.

Condensed Phases. One influence of first importance is that of the state of aggregation. It has been indicated several times in the foregoing discussion that change from the vapor to a condensed state— liquid, solid, or solution—results in considerable change both in the

---

[6] E. B. Wilson, Jr., and A. J. Wells, *Jour. Chem. Phys.*, **14,** 578 (1946).

[7] See General Reference 11.8, page 729.

energy-level scheme and in the selection rules.   The rotational levels are most drastically affected, since the close approach of neighboring molecules in condensed phases hinders or halts entirely molecular rotation.   The vibrational levels are usually affected only slightly, but in certain vibrations—mainly those involving the binding of hydrogen to strongly negative atoms like fluorine, oxygen and nitrogen—the difference in frequency between gas and liquid phases may be as much as 10 per cent.   The effect on vibrational selection rules is more pronounced.   Since the rules are based on molecular symmetry and since the random intermolecular forces can never increase the symmetry and usually destroy it, it may be expected that the rules are invalidated to a greater or lesser extent.   This expectation is realized for infrared vibrational spectra (§ 11.5) but very slightly for Raman spectra.   It is difficult to generalize concerning the effect on vibrational selection rules in electronic spectra. Certainly in many instances the rules do not seem to be drastically altered.

The question of the effect of the condensed phases on electronic levels is a serious one because of the immense amount of ultraviolet and visible spectroscopic data obtained on molecules in solution.   The extent of the effect on the levels themselves of collisions and electric fields due to near neighbors must be clearly differentiated from solvent effects that actually alter the structure or composition of the molecule and are not properly considered as "condensation" effects at all. True condensation effects seem to vary considerably with the nature of the molecule and its solvent but not so drastically as to prevent identification of levels in the vapor phase with those in the liquid. Hydrocarbon molecules dissolved in hydrocarbon solvents show the least effect on energy levels, selection rules, and transition probabilities, whereas polar molecules dissolved in water or other highly polar solvents show the largest.   On the other hand, a familiar but striking example of *structural* alteration of molecules in solution is provided by chemical indicators, whose color (related to the electronic energy scheme) changes drastically with change in concentration of hydrogen ion or other chemical substance.   The subject of solvent effects on absorption spectra does not lend itself to sweeping generalization, however, and it is impossible to summarize briefly and justly the results of the large amount of investigation in this field.

11.14. Summary of Molecular Spectra.   In order to summarize the results of the foregoing sections, the energy levels and transitions

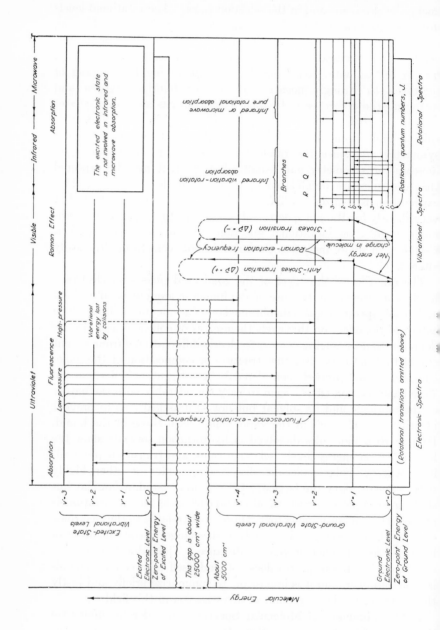

esponsible for the various kinds of molecular spectra are presented
n one comparative diagram in Fig. 11.11.

GENERAL REFERENCES

11.1. E. A. Braude, "Ultraviolet Light Absorption and the Structure of Organic Compounds," *Ann. Reports of Chem. Society* (London), XLII, 105 (1945).

11.2. G. Herzberg, *Molecular Spectra and Molecular Structure:* I: *Diatomic Molecules*. New York: Prentice-Hall, Inc., 1939.

11.3. G. Herzberg, *Infrared and Raman Spectra*. New York: D. Van Nostrand Company, Inc., 1945.

11.4. R. deL. Kronig, *The Optical Basis of the Theory of Valency*. London: Cambridge University Press, 1935.

11.5. L. Pauling and E. B. Wilson, Jr., *Introduction to Quantum Mechanics*. New York: McGraw-Hill Book Company, Inc., 1935.

11.6. H. Sponer and E. Teller, "Electronic Spectra of Polyatomic Molecules," *Rev. Mod. Phys.*, **13**, 75 (1941).

11.7. G. B. B. M. Sutherland, *Infrared and Raman Spectra*. London: Methuen & Co., Ltd., 1935.

11.8. R. W. Wood, *Physical Optics*. New York: The Macmillan Company, 1934.

Additional references on ultraviolet, infrared, and Raman spectra will be found in the General References for Chapters 14, 17, and 18, respectively.

CHAPTER 12

The Measurement of Spectral Intensities

FOUR PRINCIPAL MEANS ARE AVAILABLE for the determination of intensities in spectra:

1. The radiation may be absorbed on the blackened surface of a radiometric device, which uses the heating effect of the radiant energy to obtain an electrical or other readily measured signal.

2. The radiation may actuate a photoelectric device of some sort. In such a device the electrical signal is produced by the direct conversion of the energy in the radiation rather than through its heating effect.

3. The radiation may be permitted to fall on a photographic emulsion for a controlled period of time. The density of the silver deposit produced in the emulsion on development can be made a measure of the total radiation.

4. The radiation can be determined by the human eye. So severe are the limitations of the eye as a light-measuring device, however, that it is useful only for special types of photometry, some of which will be discussed in Chapter 14.

These four methods are compared in Table 12.1. The significance of the columns in the table is as follows: *Wavelength range* means the spectral region over which the method can be used. *Sensitivity* (sometimes called *responsivity*) is the slope of the curve relating the response of the receiving device in each method to the radiant energy required to produce that response, whereas *linearity* refers to the closeness with which such a curve approaches a straight line. For many receivers this curve for radiation of one wavelength will differ from that for another wavelength. If the differences are negligibly small, the receiver has high *neutrality;* that is, it responds as well to one wavelength as to another. The *cumulative property* and the *panoramic property* are possessed to a significant extent only by the photographic emulsion. The former is the ability of the emulsion to respond to light of exceedingly low intensity by prolongation of the time of exposure. The *panoramic property* means that the photographic emulsion can simultaneously register different beams of radiation on different parts of the plate or film.

TABLE 12.1

PROPERTIES OF VARIOUS METHODS
FOR THE MEASUREMENT OF SPECTRAL INTENSITIES

Method	Wavelength range	Sensitivity	Linearity
Radiometric	All wavelengths	Low	Excellent
Photoelectric	10–30,000 A	High	Good
Photographic	10–12,000 A	High	Poor
Visual	4000–7500 A	High	Very poor

Method	Neutrality	Cumulative property	Panoramic property
Radiometric	Excellent	None	None
Photoelectric	Poor	Fair	None
Photographic	Poor	Good	Excellent
Visual	Poor	None	Limited

It is apparent from a glance at Table 12.1 that no single method of radiation measurement is superior to the others. The most suitable one for a given purpose depends on the details of the spectroscopic procedure, the speed with which results must be obtained, and other factors. In this and the following chapter, the various methods are described, and the circumstances to which each is best suited are discussed.

RADIOMETRY

A *radiometer* is any device for the detection and measurement of radiant energy by means of its heating effect. Since the heating effect is strictly proportional to the amount of the radiant energy which does the heating, accurate measurement of the heating gives

an accurate indication of the incident radiant energy if none i
allowed to go astray by reflection or otherwise. Therefore the
radiometric method is usable for the measurement of radiation of any
wavelength that can be effectively absorbed. Absorbing surfaces can
be made that are more or less uniformly black to radiation from the
vacuum ultraviolet through the far infrared, and in consequence the
radiometric method can be used throughout the entire optical range
At wavelengths below 1 μ, however, the sensitivity of radiometric
devices is markedly inferior to that of photoelectric and photographic
detectors. Radiometric methods are therefore seldom used in this
part of the spectrum except for calibration purposes or other circum
stances under which linearity and spectral neutrality of response are
essential.

On the other hand, only radiometric devices can be used at wavelengths longer than about 3 μ because no other kind of detector is sensi
tive in this region. This statement means that all infrared spectrometers except those operating in the photoelectric infrared use thermal
detectors. Because of the importance of thermal detectors for this
purpose, they will be considered in some detail, along with the
auxiliary equipment needed for amplification and recording of the
detected radiation.

Of the many physical properties of substances that are dependent
on temperature, the change of electrical resistance with temperature
and the thermoelectric effect lend themselves most readily to the
detection of minute temperature changes. Devices which use
these effects are known, respectively, as *bolometers* and *thermocouples*.

12.1. Bolometers. The bolometer is a device, usually in the form
of a short, narrow strip, for the detection of radiation by the change of
electrical resistance that accompanies the temperature rise produced
in the device by radiation. Since the temperature rise produced by
a given amount of radiant energy will be greater as the heat loss and
specific heat of the bolometer are smaller, it is desirable to keep the
mass of the bolometer to a minimum. In a small bolometer the rate
of the temperature rise will also be faster than in a large one, which
may be useful if a greater speed of response is desired. For a given
temperature rise, the change in electrical resistance will depend on the
temperature coefficient of resistance, which suggests the use of materials with high temperature coefficients.

The bolometer is ordinarily used in some modification of the

Wheatstone bridge circuit, in which one of the other arms of the bridge is another bolometer strip. Radiation to be measured does not strike his latter strip, which otherwise is subject to the same environmental influences, including bridge current, as those operating on the active strip. The constant bridge current flowing through the two strips is called the *heating current*, because it results in a bolometer temperature hat may be 50°C above the ambient temperature. The unbalance n the bridge caused by radiation produces a voltage linearly proportional to the radiation and also proportional to the heating current. The optimum measurement of this voltage demands a careful matching of the electrical characteristics of the bridge circuit to those of the amplifying and recording system, which adds another factor to be considered in the choice of bolometer material and design.

Because of the number and variety of the factors involved, no single bolometer design has a clear-cut superiority over all others. This situation is reflected in the number of different materials and designs that have been used successfully and in the lively controversies over their respective merits.

12.2. Metal Bolometers. Metal strips can be produced and handled which are as thin as 0.1 μ. It is hardly convenient to make them smaller than a few millimeters in length, however, and since in the measurement of spectral intensity their length and width are related to the size of the exit slit of the spectrometer, metal bolometers usually have dimensions of the order of 0.5 cm $\times$ 0.5 mm $\times$ 1 μ. In this size their electrical resistance will be a few ohms for such metals as nickel and platinum.

In operation the strip may be suspended from wire leads or supported on some kind of nonconducting backing. In the latter case the thermal contact between the strip and its support will be extensive and the temperature rise of the strip when exposed to radiation will be smaller because of heat transfer to the mounting. This heat transfer will increase the minimum amount of detectable radiation but will speed up the rate at which equilibrium temperatures are reached, a result that may be desirable. If the strip is mounted in a gas-filled container, it will also lose heat by gaseous conduction. Evacuation of the container increases the temperature rise produced by a given amount of radiation, but the time required to reach temperature equilibrium will be simultaneously increased.

Whether the advantage of increased sensitivity obtained by vacuum operation is offset by the increased time of response depends on the amplifying and recording system. In general, evacuation of the bolometer housing is desirable. However, the strip can be operated with higher bridge currents when gas conduction is available to remove the electrical heating. For this reason metal bolometers have been operated on occasion under a few millimeters pressure of hydrogen gas.

Most metals are good reflectors in the infrared, and therefore metal bolometers must be blackened by evaporated metallic blacks to absorb the radiation.[1] The amount of blackening is rather critical, since too much of it will both impede the flow of heat from the black to the strip and increase the heat capacity of the bolometer.

At room temperature, the temperature coefficients of resistance of metals used as bolometers are about 0.3 to 0.5 per cent per degree centigrade. By way of illustration of the orders of magnitude involved, the following figures are given for a nickel bolometer of about 20 ohms resistance. In a certain electrical setup, a minimum change in resistance of about 10^{-6} ohm can be detected, corresponding to a temperature rise of the order of 10^{-5}°C. The amount of radiant power required to produce this temperature rise depends on the structure of the bolometer and, for a given bolometer, on the way in which the radiant power is supplied. If no heat were lost by any mechanism, however, such a temperature rise would be produced by an amount of radiant energy equal to the specific heat of the bolometer material (nickel) times its mass. For a bolometer of 10^{-6} gram, the product will be 4 ergs per degree or 4×10^{-5} erg for 10^{-5}°C. If radiant power is supplied to the bolometer at the rate of 1 microwatt, none of which is lost by reradiation and other processes, 4×10^{-6} sec would be a sufficient time to raise the temperature 10^{-5}°C; 0.04 sec would be required if the power is 10^{-4} μw. This latter figure is somewhat smaller than the minimum detectable power realized in practice with metal bolometers used in infrared spectrometers.

Details of the construction and use of metal bolometers will be found in many articles and books (see General Reference 12.5).

12.3. Semiconductor Bolometers. The large (negative) temperature coefficient of semiconductors (for example, -15 per cent per °C for cuprous oxide, as compared with $+0.3$ per cent for nickel) makes

---

[1] A. H. Pfund, *Rev. Sci. Inst.*, **1**, 397 (1930); *Jour. Opt. Soc. Am.*, **23**, 270, 375 (1933).

them potentially valuable as bolometer materials, but until recently practical difficulties such as their very high resistance prevented their use.   Becker[2, 3] and coworkers have described briefly a "thermistor" type of semiconductor suitable for use as a bolometer material in infrared spectrometers.   The temperature coefficient of the thermistor material is about -5 per cent per °C, and the resistance of a strip $3 \times 0.2 \times 0.01$ mm is some 4 megohms.   According to the references cited, such a bolometer, mounted in thermal contact with a quartz backing, will respond with a temperature rise of 2×10^{-6} °C when irradiated at the rate of 2×10^{-8} watt for 3 milliseconds.   This rise corresponds to a resistance change of about 0.3 ohm and, under operation in a particular Wheatstone bridge circuit that includes a 400-volt drop across the bolometer, results in a bridge output of 3×10^{-6} volt.

One shortcoming of the thermistor bolometer is its appreciable transmission of radiation in the neighborhood of 6 μ.   This is not too serious a matter, however, and can be minimized by coating the bolometer with blackening or with some other material that absorbs uniformly in the 6 μ region.

12.4.   A Superconductor Bolometer.   The tremendous resistance change associated with the transition from the normal to the superconducting state of certain metals and semiconductors at very low temperatures suggests the possibility of a superconductor bolometer. This possibility has been realized by Andrews and coworkers,[4] who utilized the semiconductor columbium nitride, found by Horn[5] to become superconducting at about -257°C.   The temperature coefficient of this substance in the transition range is as much as 5000 per cent per °C.   It is evident that the difficulties of bolometer operation at these very low temperatures are considerable, but certainly the utility of the superconductor bolometer for spectrometric purposes deserves study.

12.5.   Thermocouples and Thermopiles.   The thermoelectric effect, in which two similar bimetallic junctions kept at two different temperatures generate an electromotive force, may be used to detect

[2] J. A. Becker and H. R. Moore, *Jour. Opt. Soc. Am.*, **36**, 354 (1946).
[3] W. A. Brattain and J. A. Becker, *Jour. Opt. Soc. Am.*, **36**, 354 (1946).
[4] D. H. Andrews, R. M. Milton, and W. DeSorbo, *Jour. Opt. Soc. Am.*, **36**, 518 (1946).
[5] See F. H. Horn, W. F. Brucksch, Jr., W. T. Ziegler, and D. H. Andrews, *Phys. Rev.*, **61**, 738 (1942).

radiant energy by the temperature rise the radiation produces in one junction. If the two junctions are constructed as nearly alike as possible and are subjected in use to the same conditions, the temperature difference between the two junctions can be restricted essentially to that produced by the irradiation of one junction. The junction receiving the radiation is known as the *active junction* and the other as the *compensating junction*, and the thermocouple is said to be *compensated*.

The voltage developed by a small temperature difference between a pair of junctions depends linearly on this difference and on the thermoelectric powers of the two metals. A given quantity of radiation will produce a larger temperature rise in a system of lower heat capacity; and therefore the heat capacity, and hence the mass, of the junction should be kept as small as possible. The selection of the metals for the junction, however, cannot be made simply on the basis of thermoelectric powers alone. The thermal and electrical conductivities are also involved, as is shown in detail in the theory as developed by Cartwright.[6] From a consideration of the various factors involved, Cartwright has reached the conclusion that a junction of pure bismuth with an alloy of 5 per cent tin and 95 per cent bismuth represents a satisfactory compromise among the several conflicting factors involved. However, various other materials have been used with equally good or better results[7] (see also General Reference 12.5).

The construction of a compensated vacuum thermocouple using the above metal-alloy junction is described in great detail by Strong and Cartwright.[8] To keep the heat capacity of the couple small, wires of pure bismuth and bismuth-tin alloy are made about 3 mm long and 0.025 mm in diameter. The soldered junction of these fine wires is scarcely larger than their diameters and is thus much too small for use with a spectrometer, the exit slit of which is many times greater. The transfer of radiant energy to the junction is made with the help of a thin metal strip called a *receiver*, which is about the same shape and size as a conveniently formed image of the widened exit slit. The receiver is cemented or soldered to the junction to give good

[6] C. H. Cartwright, *Zeitschr. f. Physik*, 92, 153 (1934).

[7] D. F. Hornig and B. J. O'Keefe, *Rev. Sci. Inst.*, 18, 479 (1947).

[8] J. Strong and C. H. Cartwright in Chapter VIII, General Reference 12.3.

thermal contact and is blackened to increase its absorption. In physical characteristics the receiver differs little from a bolometer strip, but its function is simply to collect radiation and transfer it to the thermocouple. In order to simulate the active junction as closely as possible, the compensation junction is also equipped with a receiver, which, however, is not subjected to the radiation to be measured.

The thermocouple is mounted in a case which is evacuated to 10^{-4} mm or better. The use of a vacuum reduces the loss of heat by gas conduction from the couple and may increase the sensitivity of the couple to radiation as much as twentyfold. However, there is an attendant decrease in the speed of response, which may have certain disadvantages discussed below in connection with amplifiers.

One way of increasing the electromotive force generated by thermo-electric means is to use several thermocouples in series, an arrangement called a *thermopile*. The many factors that must be considered[9] make it impossible to say dogmatically that the improved performance of a thermopile over a single couple will warrant the trouble of making the extra junctions. Actual practice indicates a widespread conviction to the contrary on the part of infrared-research workers who make their own detectors as well as by commercial concerns producing infrared spectrometers. There is a technique for the production of thermopiles, however, by which multiple junctions are just as readily produced as single junctions. The procedure[10] consists of making the metallic junctions by successive deposition of the two metals in a vacuum evaporator. A separate pattern or mask is used during the evaporation of each metal to form the strips of that metal, and the junctions occur at areas where the two masks have open areas in common. The metals, usually bismuth and antimony, are deposited on a thin supporting film of plastic such as cellulose acetate or Formvar. The evaporation technique has also been used for the fabrication of fast thermocouples[11] and bolometers.[12]

---

[9] See Cartwright, footnote 6, page 306.

[10] L. Harris and coworkers, *Rev. Sci. Inst.*, **4**, 454 (1933); **5**, 153 (1934); *Jour. Opt. Soc. Am.*, **30**, 519 (1940).

[11] See, for example, L. C. Roess and E. N. Dacus, *Rev. Sci. Inst.*, **16**, 164 (1945).

[12] See, for example, B. H. Billings *et al.*, *Jour. Opt. Soc. Am.*, **36**, 354 (1946).

Other thermopile design and construction details will be found in articles by Hornig and O'Keefe[7], Pfund[13] and Coblentz (General Reference 12.1, page 191).

12.6.   Other Thermal Detectors. Various detecting devices in addition to bolometers, thermocouples, and thermopiles have been used extensively at one time or another for the measurement of infrared radiation. For sundry reasons they find little application today. The vane radiometer, most familiar in the form of the simple Crookes radiometer, has been refined by Nichols and others[14] to a point where it is at least as sensitive, if not more so, than the detectors considered above. However, the construction of these instruments is so difficult, their maintenance and operation demand such elaborate precautions, and they require so much time for a single reading that they are rarely used today for spectroscopic purposes.

Another detecting device that has interesting possibilities is the pneumatic radiometer known as the *Golay cell*. This device, a predecessor of which is the *Hayes cell*,[15] measures radiation by the pressure increase in a gas chamber accompanying the temperature rise caused by absorption of the radiation.[16] The radiation is not absorbed by the gas itself but by a thin metal film in contact with the gas, as shown in Fig. 12.1. The temperature of the gas is raised then by gaseous conduction of heat away from the film. The small pressure increase is observed by the deflection of one of the walls of the gas chamber, which is made very thin and flexible. Measurement of the deflection can be made optically or electrically. In the Golay cell, shown in Fig. 12.1, the deflectable wall is used as a mirror, and the amount of light reflected from it through a matched gridwork is measured photoelectrically. It has a time constant of about 3×10^{-4} sec and in comparison with other types of infrared receivers is reported to show a sensitivity[17] several times better than those of conventional bolometers and thermocouples. The Golay cell is made commercially by the Eppley Laboratories of Newport, R. I.

---

[13] A. H. Pfund, *Rev. Sci. Inst.*, **8**, 417 (1937).

[14] E. F. Nichols, *Phys. Rev.*, **4**, 297 (1897).

[15] H. V. Hayes, *Rev. Sci. Inst.*, **7**, 202 (1936).

[16] H. A. Zahl and Marcel Golay, *Rev. Sci. Inst.*, **17**, 511 (1946). See also R. A. Weiss, *Jour. Opt. Soc. Am.*, **36**, 356 (1946).

[17] See, for example, H. H. Nielsen *et al.*, *Jour. Opt. Soc. Am.*, **36**, 358 (1946).

12.7. Amplification and Recording Methods in Radiometry. The electrical output of bolometers and thermocouples under steady radiation is a small DC voltage that may be measured directly with a sensitive galvanometer of appropriate characteristics. When the galvanometer is pushed to the limit of its sensitivity, however, in the measurement of voltages near 10^{-9}, serious difficulties are encountered. A sensitive galvanometer is sensitive to other things besides the e.m.f. the experimenter wants to measure, particularly to mechanical vibrations and stray electrical interference. These can be reduced respectively by supports such as the Julius suspension[18] and by

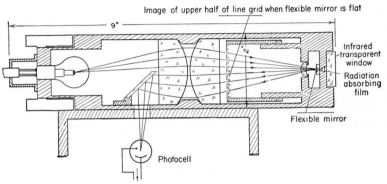

Fig. 12.1. The pneumatic radiometer or Golay cell.
(Courtesy the Eppley Laboratory.)

careful shielding, but often cannot be eliminated. A galvanometer suspension also indulges in erratic torsional fluctuations associated with Brownian motion, which ultimately set a limit to the voltage which can be measured. Moreover, the relatively long time required by a sensitive galvanometer to come to full deflection is a decided inconvenience when thousands of readings have to be taken.

In addition to these troublesome features, a more serious difficulty arises from the imperfect compensation of thermocouples and bolometers. As a result, the "zero reading" of the detector output in the absence of radiation does not stay at zero but slowly changes in one direction or the other. This phenomenon, called *drift*, is troublesome

---

[18] Vibrationless mountings for galvanometers are discussed in Chapter XIV of General Reference 12.3.

to correct and adds much labor in the form of extra zero readings to the process of obtaining an infrared absorption spectrum with a galvanometer and scale. Drift can also introduce inaccuracy in galvanometer readings when the drift during one reading is an appreciable fraction of the deflection.

It has proved possible to eliminate drift by virtue of the fact that its rate of change with time is slow. The method (see below, §§ 12.8 and 12.9) is to "chop" the radiation from the infrared source with a shutter several times a second and then to amplify the output of the thermal detector with an AC amplifier tuned to the chopping frequency. To eliminate drift by this kind of procedure, as well as to minimize the other difficulties mentioned above and to reduce the labor of obtaining an infrared spectrum, various kinds of amplifiers and automatic recorders have been introduced.

12.8. Photorelays. The photorelay is a device for amplifying the deflections of a primary galvanometer by means of a photocell and a second galvanometer. The first photorelay, that of Moll and Burger,[19] actually used a thermopile rather than a photocell, but the principle of later devices is the same. Light reflected from the mirror of the first galvanometer falls on the surface of a sensitive photocell of some kind. The photocurrent thereby generated is sent to a second galvanometer but is balanced potentiometrically so that at the zero reading of the first galvanometer the second galvanometer also reads zero. When the mirror of the first galvanometer suffers a slight deflection, the amount of light falling on the photocell changes and a current flows through the second galvanometer. The optical system can be arranged to give a linear relationship between the two galvanometer deflections. Since the magnitude of the photocurrent can be made quite large by use of an appropriate optical arrangement and intense light source, tremendous amplification of the primary galvanometer deflection is possible. It is relatively easy by means of the photorelay to amplify the primary galvanometer deflections to such an extent that the Brownian fluctuations therein are readily observable.

Of the several modifications of the photorelay,[20] that made by

---

[19] W. J. H. Moll and H. C. Burger, *Phil. Mag.* (6), **50**, 621 (1925).

[20] A. H. Pfund, *Science*, **69**, 71 (1929); R. B. Barnes and R. Matossi, *Zeitschr. f. Physik*, **76**, 24 (1932); C. H. Cartwright, *Rev. Sci. Inst.*, **3**, 221 (1932).

Pfund and called by him the "resonance radiometer" is the most significant. The photorelay described in the preceding paragraph unfortunately does not eliminate zero drift. Pfund pointed out that by tuning the primary and secondary galvanometers to the same period, one can make the photorelay particularly sensitive to electrical impulses of that period and much less sensitive to other impulses, especially those of drastically differing period,* such as a slow zero drift. The response of the thermocouple or bolometer to radiation is made to vary with the period to which the galvanometers are tuned by "chopping" the radiation at that period. A rotating sector or pendulum-controlled shutter may be used for this purpose.

In actual practice, the resonance radiometer is somewhat complicated to use and has a relatively slow response time, but the fundamental idea of eliminating drift by periodic interruption of the radiation and sharp tuning of the photorelay to that period is very sound. The replacement of the photorelay by a tuned AC amplifier results in a simpler over-all system, in widespread use.

12.9. Alternating-Current Amplifiers. In recent years great advances have been made in the design of vacuum-tube amplifiers, particularly in the development of low-frequency, sharply tuned amplifiers. One of the most significant of these advances, due to Scott,[21] is the so-called "Twin-T" negative feedback circuit. In this circuit, sharp tuning of the amplifier to a narrow band of frequencies is achieved by negative feedback from the late stages of the amplifier to the first stage. The negative feedback cancels the gain of the amplifier, but by the insertion of sharply tuned filters in the feedback line, a narrow range of frequencies can be eliminated from the feedback. For this frequency range, the gain of the amplifier is not nullified. With such an arrangement it is possible to construct amplifiers of low frequency (10 cycles per second or less) and very narrow pass band (1 to 2 per cent of the tuned frequency is attainable). Several such amplifiers for use with bolometers or thermocouples in infrared spectrometers have been described.[3, 22, 23]

---

* The resonance radiometer does not eliminate the effect of Brownian motion, since the random fluctuations of the primary galvanometer are superimposed on its harmonic oscillations.

[21] H. H. Scott, *Proc. Inst. Radio Eng.*, **26**, 226 (1938).
[22] L. C. Roess, *Rev. Sci. Inst.*, **16**, 172 (1945).
[23] N. Wright and L. W. Herscher, *Jour. Opt. Soc. Am.*, **37**, 211 (1947).

The specifications of the AC amplifier of course depend on the radiation detector and the measuring and recording system with which it is used. Clearly, the frequency at which the radiation beam is interrupted must not be so high that the detector is unable to respond to the interruptions. It was remarked above in the discussion of bolometers and thermocouples that those features of a detector which make it very sensitive, such as vacuum housing, also decrease the speed with which maximum response is attained; and in general it may be said that high speed of response is gained only at a price of decreased sensitivity, and vice versa. The chopping frequency must therefore be a compromise that is not too high for the speed of the detector and not too low for good amplifier design and recording speed. Chopping speeds as low as 1 cycle per second [22] have been used with vacuum thermocouples,* and as high as 40 cycles per second with bolometers. A compromise of 15 cycles per second has been reported for a thermistor bolometer mounted on a glass backing.[3]

In addition to the great advantage of the tuned AC amplifier for the elimination of drift, good amplifier design will also eliminate sensitivity to mechanical vibration and to stray electrical interference. The electrical analogue of the Brownian motion of the galvanometer suspension, however, is still present in the form of random voltage fluctuations (the so-called Johnson noise[24]) in the thermocouple or bolometer. The effect of Johnson noise may be reduced by sharpening the tuning of the amplifier, since the noise is proportional to the square root of the pass-band width. This kind of reduction is limited, however, by considerations of speed. The response time of the amplifier is essentially the reciprocal of the band width; and halving the band width, which will reduce the noise by only $1/\sqrt{2}$, doubles the response time. Thus the optimum band width is a compromise between low noise and speed. There is obviously no point to making the amplifier response time materially faster than that of the indicating device to which the amplifier output is fed. Since this latter is usually not much faster than 1 sec, band widths are rarely narrower than 1 cycle per second. Many amplifier-recording systems permit control of both noise level and recorder

---

* Vacuum thermocouples need not be this slow. They have been made faster by a factor of 10 or more.

[24] J. B. Johnson, *Phys. Rev.* **32**, 97 (1938).

speed so that the optimum combination of the two factors may be selected.

12.10.   A Direct-Current Amplifier.   Despite the advantage of the AC amplifier in the elimination of zero drift, there is a DC amplifier* that has been widely adopted for use in conjunction with a vacuum thermocouple.   This amplifier[25] is a DC amplifier in the sense that a small DC voltage fed into the input terminals appears as a highly amplified DC voltage at the output terminals. As far as the circuit is concerned, it is an AC amplifier not drastically different from those described in the references cited in the previous section.   The conversion of the DC input to low-frequency alternating current (75 cycles per second) is accomplished by a motor-driven commutator.   The same motor simultaneously drives a second commutator that rectifies the amplified 75-cycle output to direct current. Used in conjunction with a commercial pen recorder, the amplifier permits measurement of voltages as low as 10^{-9}, which is approaching the Brownian motion limit of a sensitive galvanometer.

12.11.   Recorders.   The wearisome task of taking thousands of galvanometer scale readings in the course of charting a single spectrum makes highly desirable some method for automatic registration of these readings.   For rapid industrial work this is imperative. Automatic recording was, in fact, the first of the automatic techniques to be used and was introduced as long ago as 1895 by Langley and Ångström.   The recording method consisted, in principle, of replacing the galvanometer scale by photographic paper wrapped on a cylinder, the axis of the cylinder being parallel to the long dimension of the scale.   Rotation of the cylinder at a fixed rate with respect to the traversal of the spectrum causes the galvanometer spot to trace out a permanent record of its displacements and establishes a definite relationship between angular position of the cylinder and the spectrometer setting.

The great advantage of recording on photographic paper is its ready addition to the standard galvanometer setup, and the principal disadvantage is the delay involved in the photographic processing. It has been used widely, and numerous special photographic arrange-

---

* This amplifier may be purchased from the Perkin-Elmer Corporation, Glenbrook, Conn.

[25] M. D. Liston, C. E. Quinn, W. E. Sargeant, and G. G. Scott, *Rev. Sci. Inst.*, **17**, 194 (1946).

ments have been described. Reproductions of photographic records have often appeared in the literature.[11, 26, 27, 28]

A simple device which makes possible the substitution of pen-and ink for photographic recording has been described by Pompeo and Penther.[29] The light beam from the final galvanometer falls on a split-cathode photocell mounted on a carriage holding a pen. The photocell output controls a motor that drives the carriage in such fashion that the galvanometer beam is always centered on the photocell. The carriage track is mounted parallel to the axis of a revolving cylinder, and the moving pen records on paper wrapped about the cylinder.

The development of high-gain amplifiers like those described in the preceding section occurred simultaneously with the commercial availability of fast, low-voltage pen-and-ink recorders suitable for use with them. Many of these recorders are well suited for use with radiometric devices, and accordingly most of the infrared spectrometers now on the market are equipped with standard commercial recorders. The Electronik high-speed strip recorder of the Brown Instrument Company, shown in Fig. 12.2, is a representative example.

PHOTOELECTRIC MEASUREMENT OF INTENSITY

Many of the electrical properties of matter are affected by light, so there are various kinds of "photoelectric effects." Three kinds of photoelectric phenomena have been adapted to the measurement of spectral intensity: the *photoemissive* effect, which is the ejection of electric charge from matter through the agency of radiation; the *photoconductive* effect, which is the change of electrical conductivity produced by radiation; and the *photovoltaic* effect, which is the generation of a potential difference between two electrodes as a result of the irradiation of one of them.

Since about 1930 the characteristics of photocells of these three types have been improved so much that photoelectric methods are now used to an extent comparable with photography in the detection and measurement of spectra. Especially striking advances have been made in (a) the reduction of the threshold of radiant power that is

---

[26] F. A. Firestone, *Rev. Sci. Inst.*, **3**, 163 (1933).

[27] N. Wright and H. M. Randall, *Phys. Rev.*, **44**, 39 (1933).

[28] N. Wright, *Ind. Eng. Chem., Anal. ed.*, **13**, 1 (1941).

[29] D. J. Pompeo and C. J. Penther, *Rev. Sci. Inst.*, **13**, 218 (1942).

needed to produce a recognizable response from the photocell;
(b) development of techniques for the manufacture of stable, reproducible photosensitive surfaces; (c) extension of the spectral range
of sensitivity well into the infrared and ultraviolet regions; and
(d) development of new means for amplification of the photocurrent.
These improvements are still in progress, and the procedures described below for the photoelectric measurement of spectra will
unquestionably undergo important changes in the future.

In the evaluation of a photocell as a measuring device for spectral
radiation, the properties of primary importance are its sensitivity,

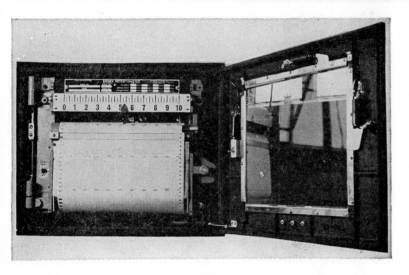

Fig. 12.2.   The "Electronik" high-speed strip recorder.
(Courtesy Brown Instrument Company.)

linearity, wavelength range, neutrality, and threshold of detection.
These properties have been defined, with the exception of *threshold*,
which may be taken as the radiant power needed by the cell to produce
an electrical signal that is at least as large as the electrical noise generated in the cell. Unfortunately, it is difficult to determine an
absolute value of the noise, because a measured value depends not
only on the cell itself but also on the characteristics of the amplifying
and indicating systems.   For this reason comparisons of the thresh-
olds of detection in photocells of different types must be made with
care and with due allowance for any differences in circuits.

12.12. Photoemissive Cells and Electron-Multiplier Tubes. For the measurement of spectral intensity, the photoemissive cell is probably the best all-round photocell with respect to all the above characteristics except wavelength range. It is linear over widely different intensities of illumination. Its threshold of detection is low at room temperature and can be made still lower by refrigeration, if necessary. The sensitivity is high and the working stability of the cell is satisfactory. A typical cell is shown in Fig. 12.3, and a convenient circuit for the measurement of low light levels in Fig. 12.4.

In the form of the *electron multiplier*, the photoemissive cell promises to be more widely used in spectrophotometers than any other kind of photocell. This is a combined photoemissive cell and electronic DC amplifier in a single envelope. Its operation is illustrated in Fig. 12.5. The basic principle is the phenomenon of secondary electron emission from a treated metal surface under bombardment by primary electrons. The importance of the phenomenon lies in the fact that a single primary electron may give rise to four or five secondary electrons. In the electron multiplier the first primary electrons are those ejected by radiation falling on the photocathode C. These electrons are accelerated to the first anode (electrode No. 1) by an electrical potential of, say, $+100$ volts applied to it. The photoelectrons impinge on the first anode with sufficient velocity to eject four or five secondary electrons each. The newly released secondaries are then accelerated to electrode No. 2 by a higher potential (for example, $+200$ volts above the photocathode), where each in turn gives rise to several secondary electrons. The process continues in this fashion through a number of stages (six in Fig. 12.5), the number of electrons being multiplied at each stage by a constant factor of approximately 4.5. The electrons from the final electrode

Fig. 12.3. A typical photoemissive cell.
(Courtesy RCA Laboratories.)

are collected at the anode A, whence they are conducted away and measured as photocurrent.

The photoelectric properties of the electron multiplier are determined by the photocathode. The over-all amplification may range

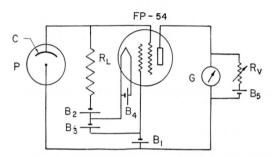

Fig. 12.4. A simple photocell circuit for the measurement of low light levels (order of microlumens). Representative values of the electrical components would be: $B_1 = 2$ volts; $B_2 = B_3 = B_4 = B_5 = 4$ volts; $R_L = 1000$ megohms; R_v is a balancing resistor; P = photocell (*e.g.*, RCA-929); C = photocathode; G = galvanometer.

from one thousand for a six-stage tube to as much as a million for an 11-stage tube. For precise spectrophotometry, the potentials supplied to the several stages must be carefully controlled (to ± 0.1 per cent approximately), because a voltage fluctuation of x per cent in an n-stage multiplier changes the amplification factor by about nx per cent. Suitably stable power supplies have been designed,[30, 31] or

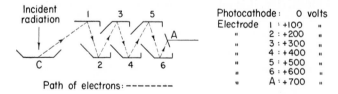

Fig. 12.5.   Diagram of a six-stage electron multiplier tube.

B batteries may be used. The spectral sensitivity curves of two types of photocathodes are shown in Fig. 12.6.

12.13. Photoconductive cells. When photoelectric detection of spectra beyond 1 μ is desired, it is necessary to use photoconductive

[30] F. V. Hunt and R. W. Hickman, *Rev. Sci. Inst.*, **10**, 6 (1939); W. R. Hill, *Proc. Inst. Radio Eng.*, **33**, 38 (1945).
[31] G. H. Dieke and H. M. Crosswhite, *Jour. Opt. Soc. Am.*, **35**, 471 (1945).

cells; these can be constructed with workable sensitivity to wavelengths as great as 3 μ or even longer. In the past the most practical photoconductive cells used a thin film of elemental selenium as the material whose electrical conductivity increased markedly upon illumination, although many other substances with this property were known. Cells of superior qualities are now available whose photosensitive element consists chiefly of the sulfide of lead or of thallium.[32]

The thallous oxysulfide or "thalofide" cell shows optimum response to radiation of about 0.95 μ, and has a useful sensitivity to about 1.4 μ. It is easy to use and has quite a low threshold of detection. Its chief shortcoming is a nonlinear sensitivity curve. The lead sulfide cell is usable out to 3 μ or even beyond. Despite the wide

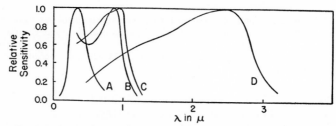

Fig. 12.6. Spectral sensitivities of photocells. Each curve is relative to its own maximum sensitivity. (A) Cesium-antimony photoemissive cell; (B) cesium oxide-silver photoemissive cell; (C) thalofide photoconductive cell; (D) lead sulfide photoconductive cell.

range of sensitivity, it is relatively neutral over most of this range, in contrast to the thalofide cell, which has a very steep sensitivity-vs.-wavelength curve in the range 0.95 to 1.5 μ. The threshold of detection of the lead sulfide cell is higher than that of the thalofide cell, but refrigeration of the lead sulfide surface with "dry ice" both lowers the threshold and extends the usable range to longer wavelengths. Like the thalofide cell, the lead sulfide cell is nonlinear.

The spectral sensitivity curves of thalofide and lead sulfide cells are shown in Fig. 12.6. Other kinds of photoconductive materials, for example lead selenide, show promise of workable sensitivity at even longer wavelengths.

12.14. Photovoltaic Cells. In the form of the "barrier-layer" cell, the photovoltaic cell is probably the most convenient kind of photocell

---

[32] R. J. Cashman, *Jour. Opt. Soc. Am.*, **36**, 356(A), (1946).

obtainable.   It requires no auxiliary voltage supply, since it utilizes the incident radiation to generate rather than to modulate a voltage. Under proper circumstances its linearity is good, and for any photometric purpose where plenty of light is available, the photovoltaic cell is simple and easy to use.   Unfortunately, most spectrophotometers run short of light at one end or the other of their operating spectral range, and the low sensitivity of the photovoltaic cell in these regions is a great handicap under such circumstances.   In addition, the amplification of the response presents special problems due to the low impedance of the cell.   For these reasons photovoltaic cells are little used in spectrophotometers.   The spectral sensitivity curve of a typical photovoltaic cell does not differ much from curve A of Fig. 12.6.   The peak of sensitivity is at slightly longer wavelength, say 0.56 μ.

12.15.   The Incorporation of the Photocell in the Spectrograph. Because the photocell does not discriminate between two different wavelengths, it is necessary to isolate each wavelength at which intensity measurement is to be made.   The spectrograph in which photoelectric detection is used must therefore function as a monochromator.   A monochromator is provided with an exit slit, and the first requirement to be met in photoelectric detection is the arrangement of the photocell to utilize the maximum amount of monochromatic radiation emergent from the exit slit.   This arrangement is ordinarily a simple one.   The size of the exit slit and the angle at which the monochromatic beam emerges are often such that the photocathode area in the photocell can intercept the entire beam if the photocell is placed at the proper orientation and within the proper distance from the slit.

If it is desired to place other devices in the region between the exit slit and the photocell (for example, an absorption cell for absorption spectrophotometry as in Chapter 14), an optical system is needed to carry the beam through this region and then to project it upon the photocathode.   The nature of this system depends on the function it is required to perform.   Usually it consists of a collimating lens to render parallel the beam from the slit, and a focusing lens to project the beam on the photocathode.   A sketch of this optical arrangement is shown in Fig. 12.7.

A second requirement to be met concerns the method of scanning the spectrum, that is, the method of bringing the various wavelengths successively to the exit slit.   In most monochromators the spectrum is scanned by rotation of the dispersing element, whether it be prismatic or diffractive. Under this arrangement the exit slit is usually fixed in position, and therefore the entire optical system from the exit slit to the photocell may also be fixed. No addition is required to the optical system mentioned in the previous paragraph, apart from some method of making changes in lens positions and other corrections required by the change in wavelength of the emergent beam.

Sometimes the optical or mechanical arrangement of the monochromator precludes scanning of the spectrum in this way. An alternative procedure is to keep the dispersing element in a fixed position and to move the exit slit along the surface in space on which the spectrum is focused. Necessarily, the emergent beam will move with the slit, and this motion must be compensated in some way to keep the beam properly directed onto the photocathode. Such compensation can sometimes be effected by optical means, but it is

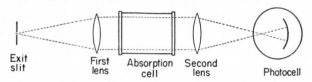

Exit slit   First lens   Absorption cell   Second lens   Photocell

Fig. 12.7. Simple optical system for photocell.

usually found preferable to keep the photocell in fixed relationship to the exit slit. This requires moving the entire slit-photocell system during the scanning of the spectrum, which is somewhat awkward. However, with grating spectrographs whose mountings prevent scanning of the spectrum by rotation of the grating, such as the Paschen or Wadsworth mountings, this procedure is always followed.

The construction and use of various types of photoelectric spectrophotometers are considered in Chapter 14.

12.16. Amplification and Recording of Photocurrents. Because of the high impedance of both photoemissive and photoconductive cells, electronic amplification of their photocurrents is readily achieved. The problem of amplification has two aspects, however, one concerned with the sensitivity of the photocell and the other with its threshold of detection.

As defined at the start of the chapter, sensitivity is the slope of the curve relating the photocurrent to the radiant power which produces it. Amplification of the photocurrent by a given factor multiplies the slope of this curve by this same factor and therefore increases the sensitivity by this factor.   Inasmuch as the currents produced in a photocell by the light intensities available in spectrometers are usually so weak as to require a sensitive galvanometer for measurement, amplification of the photocurrent is essential if it is to be recorded, for example, on a commercial recording milliammeter. One purpose of amplification, then, is to elevate the photocurrent to a usefully high level.

The threshold of detection of a photocell, on the other hand, is a property that cannot be altered (except for the worse) by mere amplification of the photocurrent.   It was defined previously as the radiant power required to produce an electrical signal equal to the electrical noise present for various reasons in the current output of the photocell.   An important point to be remembered is that in amplification of all components of the photocurrent the noise is amplified along with the signal, so that such amplification does not alter the signal-to-noise ratio (except for the worse, in case the amplifier introduces appreciable noise).   Therefore mere amplification of all photocurrent components does not lower the threshold of detection.

The electron-multiplier tube furnishes a simple example of these two aspects of amplification.   A certain amount of radiant power incident upon the photocathode (C in Fig. 12.5) will produce a photocurrent between C and anode 1.   The sensitivity of the first stage of the photocell is the ratio of this photocurrent to the radiant power which produces it.   Now the photoelectrons incident upon anode 1 liberate a larger number of electrons, which in turn impinge upon anode 2.   This larger number constitutes an amplified photocurrent, and a correspondingly increased sensitivity.   The sensitivity increases with each stage in this way, the over-all amplification amounting to several powers of ten.   This increase in sensitivity, achieved so neatly within the confines of a single vacuum tube, is the great virtue of the electron multiplier.

On the other hand, the threshold of detection of a multiplier tube is no lower than that of the first stage, because the photocathode is constantly emitting electrons by virtue of the thermionic effect.   The thermionic current forms the chief part of what is usually called the *dark current* because it is best measured in the absence of light, which would of course give rise to a photocurrent.   The dark current depends on the temperature of the cathode, on the potential of the first anode with respect to the cathode, and on other factors, but *on the average* is constant when all these factors are constant. If the dark current were absolutely constant, it could be subtracted out of the total current and would not limit the least detectable signal. However, the real dark current fluctuates slightly in random fashion about its average value. These current fluctuations fix a threshold for the least detectable signal that is about equal to the mean value of the fluctuations themselves; that is, the ratio of least detectable signal to the noise is about unity. Any smaller signal tends to get buried in the noise.

The amplification stages of the multiplier amplify the dark current with its fluctuations indiscriminately along with the photocurrent. The ratio of photocurrent to noise is therefore not altered* during the amplification, and the size of the least detectable signal is not lowered.

In most photoelectric spectrometers the optical system feeds the photocell sufficient light (except perhaps at the long and short wavelength limits of the instrument), so that the prime objective of the amplifying system is the elevation of the photocurrent to levels suitable for recording. Discussion of the many types of amplifying systems is outside the scope of this book, and the reader is referred to treatises and journal articles on electronic amplification for information on this subject (General Reference 12.4). However, it is worth while to consider briefly the possible steps by which the threshold of detection might be lowered with the help of selective amplification.

We have seen in § 12.9 that amplification by a tuned AC amplifier of the alternating output of a bolometer or thermocouple can eliminate long-period drifts in thermoelectric recording. There the objective is the amplification of a signal alternating with much higher frequency than that of the drift. The fluctuations in dark current from a photocathode, on the other hand, are not confined to a particular period but are spread out over a "noise spectrum." This means that a tuned AC amplifier will amplify some of the noise but only that part of it which falls in the frequency band to which the amplifier is tuned. The narrower this band, the smaller the total fraction of the noise amplified. Hence the threshold of detection can be lowered if the light to be measured is interrupted by a shutter or

---

* The amplification stages may introduce noise of their own, thereby raising the minimum detectable signal. This effect is usually small compared to the one under discussion.

"chopper" so that the resultant photocurrent alternates at the frequency to which the amplifier is tuned.

A practical advantage for the tuned amplification of alternating photocurrents stems from the fact that photocells have in general a high speed of response. Because of this high speed, the chopping rate can be fast; that is, the alternating current from the photocell has a high frequency. It is easier to construct stable high-gain AC amplifiers for which the frequency is above, say, 100 cycles per second than for lower frequencies. Hence the difficulty encountered in the AC operation of thermocouples and bolometers, where chopping frequencies well below 100 cycles per second must be used, is not met with in the amplification of photocurrents.

It might be supposed that the threshold of detection can be reduced to indefinitely low values by reduction in the band width of the tuned amplifier. Such a reduction would reduce the fraction of the noise amplified, to be sure, but would be attended by a complication mentioned in § 12.9: an AC amplifier with a band width of $\frac{1}{2}$ cycle has $1/\sqrt{2}$ as much noise as a similar one with a band width of 1 cycle, but it exhibits twice as large a time lag (roughly two seconds compared with one). For this reason, the threshold of detection of radiant power can be reduced by selective amplification only at the expense of a much larger increase in the time required to detect a change in the radiant power.

Since the thermionic current is a function of the temperature of the photocathode, another possibility for reducing the dark current and the random fluctuations thereof lies in refrigeration of the photocathode. The anticipated reduction is very great, because of the exponential factor in the thermionic current-temperature relationship. In actual practice,[33] the reduction in thermionic current that accompanies a temperature drop from room temperature ($300°K$) to that of liquid air ($90°K$) may be as much as ten-thousandfold, which corresponds to a reduction in thermionic fluctuations of a factor of 100. The radiant power level which will produce an electrical signal equal to the noise at $90°K$ is phenomenally low—of the order of 10^{-13} lumens under certain circumstances. Usually it is neither necessary nor expedient to operate at so low a threshold, but for certain applications, notably the study of the Raman effect (Chapter 18), light levels of this low value are typical.

---

[33] R. W. Engstrom, *Jour. Opt. Soc. Am.*, **37**, 420 (1947), and references there cited.

The output of an AC amplifier is an alternating current. This current has to be rectified, either electronically or by some other means, to be recorded or otherwise registered. Discussion of rectification methods is outside the scope of this book. It is of interest to note, however, that when the rectified output is fed to a galvanometer or other output meter, such as a recording potentiometer, the time lag inherent in such a meter in effect imposes a narrow band width even on a broad-band amplifier: fluctuations of any kind, whether noise or signal, which have a period of, say, 0.001 sec, will not be registered by a galvanometer of a period of a second or larger. In consequence, if a slow galvanometer is used with a DC or broad-band AC amplifier, the sluggishness of the galvanometer "filters out" all noise with appreciably shorter period than that of the galvanometer itself. This kind of filter will not eliminate drift from thermocouples, because the period of thermocouple drift is so long, but it can be highly useful in improving the ratio of DC signal to noise from a photocell.

12.17. Photoelectric Spectrometers. Spectrometers using photoelectric detection are manufactured by various firms and are in widespread use. Several of these, with attachments making them useful for special purposes, are described in Chapters 14 and 16. Among the first descriptions of the adaptation of a large-grating spectrograph to photomultiplier detection and measurement of emission spectra was that of Dieke and Crosswhite.[31] One condition to be fulfilled in their adaptation was that of easy change of the instrument, in which the grating was in a Wadsworth mounting, from photoelectric to photographic use. For this reason, a scanning method had to be devised which interfered with the photographic procedure as little as possible. The photographic plateholder was therefore altered so that a small carriage could be mounted on it, and could be moved smoothly along the focal plane in the direction perpendicular to that of the exit slit. Upon the carriage were mounted the exit slit (in such a way that the slit always moved in the focal plane) and the electron-multiplier tube. The divergent beam from the slit fell directly on the multiplier's photocathode, which was at a distance no larger than 3 or 4 cm.

The spectrum was scanned by motion of the carriage along a track in the plateholder. Since the effective length of the plateholder was only 50 cm, the coverage of a wider spectral range involved a resetting of the entire plateholder in the usual fashion for the Wadsworth mounting. The fact that the plateholder could be used interchangeably for photographic and photoelectric detection enabled the optimum focus for a new plateholder setting to be determined photographically. The spectral region covered by the new setting could then be scanned photoelectrically with the assurance that no further focusing was needed.

The output of the photomultiplier was fed to a Leeds and Northrup recording microammeter, usually without intervening amplification. Figure 1.4 shows photographic and photoelectric records of the same emission spectrum taken with this instrument. A sketch of the optical arrangement of the spectrograph is given in Fig. 12.8.

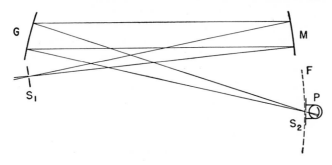

Fig. 12.8. Photoelectric detection of spectra with a Wadsworth mounting. S_1, entrance slit; M, collimating mirror; G, concave grating; S_2, exit slit; P, photocell mounted on carriage; F, focal curve along which exit slit and photocell move.

GENERAL REFERENCES

12.1. W. E. Forsythe (Ed.), *Measurement of Radiant Energy*. New York: McGraw-Hill Book Company, Inc., 1937.

12.2. H. J. Reich, *Theory and Application of Electron Tubes*. New York: McGraw-Hill Book Company, Inc., 1939.

12.3. J. Strong, *Procedures in Experimental Physics*. New York: Prentice-Hall, Inc., 1938.

12.4. F. E. Terman, *Radio Engineering*. New York: McGraw-Hill Book Company, Inc., 1937.

12.5. V. Z. Williams, "Infrared Instrumentation and Techniques," *Rev. Sci. Inst.*, **19**, 135 (1948).

12.6. V. K. Zworykin and E. Wilson, *Photocells and Their Applications*, 2d ed. New York: John Wiley & Sons, Inc., 1934.

CHAPTER 13

Photographic Photometry

Outstanding advantages of photographic photometry for spectroscopic purposes are its high sensitivity, its feature of integrating the light which falls on the emulsion over the entire period of an exposure, the possibility it gives of recording the intensities of a large number of beams of light (spectrum lines) simultaneously, and the fact that it gives a permanent record in simple form. Its disadvantages are extreme variation of sensitivity with wavelength, non-linearity of response, its requirement of careful control of a number of variable factors whose importance is easily overlooked, and the delay introduced by photographic processing. The advantages outweigh these disadvantages, however, and photographic photometry is used widely for determining the relative intensities of spectrum lines in the visible and ultraviolet regions, and hence for quantitative spectrochemical analysis.

The properties of the principal photometric methods were compared in Table 12.1. Comparison of beams of different wavelengths, called *heterochromatic photometry*, requires a "neutral" or "non-selective" photometric method, in which sensitivity does not vary with wavelength. Unfortunately, only the radiometric methods are neutral, and these are often insufficiently sensitive to be used directly. They can, however, be used to standardize more sensitive non-neutral methods, which can then be made to serve for heterochromatic photometry. The photographic emulsion is also nonlinear in response and therefore must be calibrated at each wavelength in terms of beams of light of known relative intensity.

Many problems, such as those involving measurements of the attenuation of a beam of light by absorption, scattering, reflection, or interference, require that comparisons be made only between an original beam and a weakened beam of the same wavelength; these involve *homochromatic photometry*. Plate standardization is then not required, but calibration or its equivalent is still needed. Special methods of homochromatic photometry have been developed which use the photographic emulsion merely as a null indicator or which introduce other short cuts that avoid the necessity of direct calibration; these come under the heading "spectrophotometry" and are discussed in detail in Chapters 14 and 16.

Although photographic photometry and the sensitometry of photographic emulsions (discussed in Chapter 7) are superficially similar, a fundamental difference exists between them. As most plates and films are used for camera photography, commercial sensitometry is usually only semiquantitative and is mainly concerned with the qualitative response of an emulsion to fairly intense white or colored light. Photographic photometry is usually applied to the precise quantitative comparison of faint monochromatic beams of light, which may be visible or invisible. The proper use of a photographic emulsion for intensity measurements requires control of so many variable factors that for years the method was believed incapable of yielding precise results. However, it is now possible to obtain without difficulty photographic results self-consistent to within ±2 per cent.

13.1. Photometric Characteristics of the Emulsion. The general characteristics of the photographic emulsion were discussed in Chapter 7. There it was pointed out that the response of an emulsion to a beam of light depends on at least seven factors: the intensity i of the light, its wavelength λ, the time of exposure t, the nature of the emulsion, and the time, type, and temperature of the development it undergoes. In addition, various minor factors must be controlled, such as the effect on any developable patch of the conditions in the surrounding emulsion. Because of the difficulty of controlling all these factors accurately, photographic photometry cannot be used for absolute photometric measurements. It is best used as a null method, but if a plate or film is carefully calibrated when this method is used, it can be made to function as the equivalent of a direct-reading instrument.

Variable factors can best be controlled by keeping constant those which need not vary. In each measurement using homochromatic photometry, only the intensity i of the light beam being measured and the density d, which is a measure of this intensity, are essentially involved, and all other factors can be kept constant. In heterochromatic photometry the wavelength λ of the light also is varied.

Three methods of determining plate response have come into common use: (1) measurement of density with a densitometer, which is the most direct and precise; (2) estimation of the least visible density that can be seen by eye and correlation of this density with intensity—a quick and convenient method but only semiquantitative; and (3) visual search for adjacent areas of equal density. This last is a quick method but usually can be applied only with the special null methods of absorption spectrophotometry discussed in Chapter 14.

The fundamental law of monochromatic photographic photometry was first enunciated by Hartmann in 1899 approximately as follows: *If two light beams of the same wavelength produce equal densities on a given plate in the same time of exposure, they are equal in intensity.* That is, if all the auxiliary variables are kept constant and $d_1 = d_2$, then $i_1 = i_2$. When two beams of unequal intensity are to be compared, one need only determine the ratio by which the stronger beam must be reduced in intensity to make its density equal to that produced by the weaker beam. With this equality of intensity, the emulsion is being used as a null indicator.

In practice, it is not necessary to make d_2 exactly equal to d_1, though the highest precision is attained when this is done, and when the two exposed areas are close together and similarly isolated on the

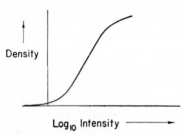

Density

Log$_{10}$ Intensity ————————▶

Fig. 13.1. Calibration curve relating photographic density to the logarithm of light intensity.

photographic plate. It is possible under controlled conditions to determine how d varies with i. Then an unknown intensity can be interpolated between two known values of i, by interpolating the density that this intensity produces on the curve expressing the d-$\log i$ relation as in Fig. 13.1, where a typical *calibration curve* is shown, similar to the characteristic curve of § 7.2.

It is customary to plot density against the common logarithm of the intensity producing it, on account of the relatively simple shape of the curve which results and for convenience in covering a wide range of intensities. Other functions of the blackening of the plate and the light intensity could be plotted against one another and could be used satisfactorily for interpolation purposes if a smooth and reproducible curve resulted. Sometimes d is plotted directly against i

when work is being done in the underexposure region or with X rays. A few workers prefer to use blackening (§ 13.15) instead of density. Since the variable that is usually read directly is the galvanometer or microammeter deflection of a densitometer, which is inversely proportional to the opacity of the emulsion being measured, it is convenient to plot this deflection directly on double logarithmic paper so that a curve of d against $\log_{10} i$ results. This inverted curve, of the form shown in Fig. 13.2, is more convenient than Fig. 13.1 for calibration purposes (see § 13.2).

If the calibration curve is determined over an intensity range sufficiently wide that all desired i values can be interpolated, more accurate results can be obtained than when extrapolation is required. Each individual plate or film used must be calibrated, preferably at wavelengths within 25 A of all wavelengths reduced. It is not satisfactory to expose two plates or films simultaneously, develop and fix them together, and then measure one in terms of a calibration curve determined on the other.

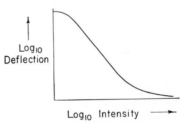

Fig. 13.2. Calibration curve relating densitometer deflection to light intensity.

Because every emulsion varies somewhat in sensitivity over its surface, it is wise to keep calibration and unknown exposures as close together as possible. It is also desirable, because of the Eberhard effect (§ 7.13). to surround known and unknown spectral regions to be measured by areas of similar density. Thus it is unwise to calibrate a plate by means of a continuous spectrum if individual spectrum lines are to be measured on it; artificial spectrum lines should be produced by using a diaphragm to cut off parts of the continuous spectrum, care being taken to avoid errors due to diffraction.

Since film is coated in large areas that are cut up subsequently, films are likely to be more uniform than plates, which are coated on the concave side of sheets of glass of only moderate size and later are cut into several pieces over which the thickness of the emulsion may vary somewhat.

To fulfill the condition that the wavelengths of the unknown and calibration exposures should be the same, a plate should be calibrated not merely with another spectrum line of the same wavelength but preferably with one of the same shape, size, and other characteristics,

to reduce errors due to the Eberhard effect. This recommendation
suggests the desirability of actually using the line under measurement
to produce its own calibration curve, as is done in the single-exposure
automatic calibration methods discussed below. Keeping the time,
temperature, and character of the development the same for both
the known and unknown exposures presents no problem if we put
both on the same piece of plate or film and arrange that the developer
be evenly distributed by one of the special methods discussed later.

Much work has been done on the exact form of the relationship
between the different variables mentioned above. This information
is largely irrelevant to the purposes of photometry, since in practical
work we can achieve the desired results without it. However, knowledge of the qualitative relationships between the variables is convenient as a guide in selecting the best working conditions for photographic photometry. These are discussed in Chapter 7.

The photographic plate as ordinarily used commercially is exposed
to white light for a small fraction of a second. There is a large
literature dealing with the characteristics of emulsions under these
conditions. Much less is known regarding their behavior when
exposed to monochromatic light for minutes and hours. Plates and
films are used on three illumination levels, which have been called,
respectively, the *photographic level*, the *spectrographic level*, and the
astronomical level. These may be taken as involving light-intensity
ratios of approximately 1,000,000 to 1000 to 1, corresponding to times
of exposure of 0.02 sec, 20 sec, and 5 hr. Qualitatively, the responses of an emulsion are similar under these three conditions, but
they differ greatly quantitatively.

HOMOCHROMATIC PHOTOMETRY

Homochromatic photometry can be used whenever a beam of light
is to be compared with itself after being absorbed, scattered, or
attenuated by other means, or when two or more spectrum lines
having wavelengths not more than 25 A apart are to be compared.
It is also the first step in heterochromatic photometry, which can be
thought of as a number of separate problems in homochromatic
photometry that must be correlated. Homochromatic photometry
requires calibration of the response of the emulsion to light of varying
intensity.

13.2. Calibrating the Emulsion. An obvious method of calibrating the emulsion would be to expose various areas on it to a spectrum of constant intensity, for equal times of exposure, through a series of neutral filters that transmitted equal fractions of the light of each wavelength to the plate. The undiminished light intensity at each wavelength could then be called 100, and that passing through each succeeding filter might be 70, 50, 30, 15, 8, 4, and 2 per cent. The densities produced by each intensity at each wavelength in a specified time of exposure could then be measured on a densitometer, and calibration curves could be plotted for important spectrum lines spaced not more than 25 A apart over the spectrum range to be covered. Curves of the type shown in Fig. 13.3 would be obtained.

Unfortunately, truly neutral filters are not available, and filters called neutral show variations in transmission with wavelength that may amount to 10 per cent or more in the visible region alone. In recent years, however, it has been demonstrated that the rotating-sector disk, if operated under carefully controlled conditions, can be made the equivalent of a neutral filter, and this is the most commonly used method of varying light intensity.

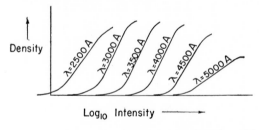

Fig. 13.3. Calibration curves for different wavelengths. (Each curve is plotted to the same scale but with different origin to prevent overlap.)

Various methods that have been used for imposing intensity calibration marks on photometric plates are listed in Table 13.1, where they are grouped as single-exposure methods and multiple-exposure methods. If various parts of a single beam can be sent simultaneously through different weakeners, it is unnecessary to use a steady source; but if multiple-exposure methods are used, the light intensity must not vary between one exposure and the next. The single-exposure methods are in turn divided into those in which the light being measured can be used to produce its own calibration marks and those which require an auxiliary source, which need not, however, be steady. In general, Table 13.1 is laid out with the most convenient methods of

TABLE 18.1

Methods of Imposing Intensity Calibration Marks on Photometric Plates*

Selective; Neutral	Requirements for use	Remarks
Auto-calibration — Step-sector disk / Logarithmic sector	At slit, rapid rotation, stigmatic spectrograph	Convenient and accurate if made and used properly
Step weakener / Wedge weakener	At slit, calibrate, stigmatic spectrograph	Convenient and accurate once calibrated at proper wavelengths
Step diaphragm / Wedge diaphragm	Astigmatic optical system, careful adjustment	Convenient but unsuitable for accurate work if neutrality is assumed
Step diaphragm / Wedge diaphragm	Rowland-type grating mounting	Convenient for large gratings but covers only short range at a setting
Step weakener / Wedge weakener	At plate, astigmatic spectrograph or long even lines	Very accurate and simple, once suitable weakeners have been obtained and calibrated
Theoretical astigmatism	Paschen or other fixed grating mount	Not yet thoroughly tested
Theoretical line shapes	Large instrumental broadening	Seldom used except for interpreting old spectrograms without intensity marks
Single-exposure methods — Coarse crossed grating	Calibrate grating orders for intensity	Useful in astronomical work or qualitative estimates
Geometrical shadow	Special cases only	Seldom used

	Method	Condition	Remarks
Auxiliary source	Step slit / Wedge slit	Continuous spectrum, stigmatic spectrograph	Easy but questionable unless Eberhard effect avoided
	Theoretical line ratios	Avoid self-reversal and excitation errors	Useful when all else fails
	Variable diaphragms	Uniform beam section	Careful tests for uniformity needed; usually less convenient than others
	Wire gauze screens	Wide optical beam	Avoid diffraction errors
	Semineutral filters	Calibrate filters for transmission vs. wavelength	Avoid refraction errors
	Inverse-square law	Long optical path	Suitable scatterer needed; avoid atmospheric absorption
	Variable slit length	Astigmatic spectrograph	Simple if illumination carefully controlled
	Variable slit width	Continuous spectrum	Avoid diffraction errors and Eberhard effect
Multiple-exposure methods; steady auxiliary source	Diffuse reflection	Calibrate reflector	Seldom used
	Variable exposure time	Compensate reciprocity failure	Often easiest method for qualitative work; to be used with discrimination
	Variable-sector disk	At slit, rapid rotation	Avoid errors from extreme conditions
	Control of source	Suitable calibrated source	Seldom convenient
	Polarizers	Transparent polarizers	Seldom convenient for photography

* After G. R. Harrison, *Jour. Opt. Soc. Am.*, **24**, 60 (1934).

calibration at the top, so that in selecting a method it is necessary only to run down the column until a method that will fit the circumstances is reached.

It is desirable to use the spectrum being studied as its own calibration spectrum whenever possible, since this method reduces errors due to the Eberhard effect (§ 7.13), results in a great saving of plate space and time (since only one exposure is needed to produce all the calibration marks), and ensures constancy of exposure time. Also, a number of determinations of each intensity ratio desired can be obtained from each pair of lines, since each appears at several densities.

When two lines being compared have the same wavelength, their two calibration curves should be identical but displaced owing to the different intensity scales, and the amount of this displacement gives the intensity ratio of the two lines. This method enables one to determine the intensity ratio from the whole course of a curve, as in Fig. 13.4, rather than from a single point on it. When available, this method is usually more convenient and precise than any other, and always more rapid. It is listed in Table 13.1 as a single-exposure autocalibration method.

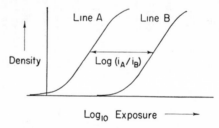

Fig. 13.4. Determination of intensity ratio for two spectral lines of same wavelength. The two curves are plotted to the same scale, and their separation gives $\log i_A - \log i_B = \log (i_A/i_B)$.

When this method cannot be used, a number of separate exposures of equal duration must be made, requiring use of an auxiliary source unless the source of light being measured is steady during the time required to take all necessary exposures.

Although the nonneutral or selective methods given in Table 13 1 are capable of giving results as accurate as the neutral methods, they are less convenient because different transmission values must be plotted at each wavelength. Under several of the methods listed in Table 13.1 will be found two alternatives which differ only in that one produces step spectra as shown in Fig. 13.5a and the other wedge-spectra,* shown in Fig. 13.5b.   The step spectra are more convenient for densitometer use since positions along the line can be determined more readily.   The wedge spectra are designed primarily for use with the limiting density methods discussed below, which are somewhat less precise than densitometer methods, though simpler.

13.3. Methods of Varying Light Intensity.

1. *Step sector or logarithm sector disk at spectrograph slit.* This method is widely used on account of its convenience. It has been the subject of much controversy because the *average* intensity of light falling on the plate is varied, rather than the actual intensity. The investigations of Twyman,[1] of O'Brien,[2] and especially of Webb,[3] have

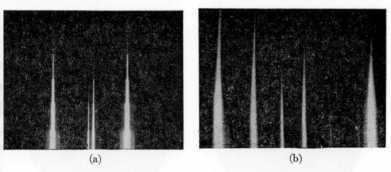

(a)   (b)

Fig. 13.5.   (a) Short portion of a step spectrum.   (b) Short portion of a wedge spectrum.

justified its use under controlled circumstances. Webb's results indicate that an intermittent exposure is equivalent photographically to a continuous exposure when the rate of flash is so great that each grain of the emulsion receives on the average not more than one quantum of light per flash.   It is now realized that frequency of flash was the critical variable that caused such lack of correlation among the results of many earlier workers.   Webb showed that for each intensity, emulsion, and wavelength a critical frequency of flash exists above which it is safe to use intermittent exposures as equivalent to continuous.   The critical frequency for ordinary conditions is of the

* A term derived from the use of wedge-shaped cells or filters varying in density from top to bottom.

[1] F. Twyman and A. Harvey, *Trans. Opt. Soc.* (London), **33**, 1 (1931–32).

[2] B. O'Brien, *Phys. Rev.*, **33**, 640 (1929); B. O'Brien and E. D. O'Brien, *Phys. Rev.*, **37**, 471 (1931).

[3] J. H. Webb, *Jour. Opt. Soc. Am.*, **23**, 157 and 316 (1933).

order of ten flashes per second; to be safe, however, a rotating-sector disk should be run as rapidly as possible, preferably at a speed greater than 1200 rpm. The greatest reciprocity and intermittency failures occur when the quanta are small (infrared region), the emulsion grain small (slow plates, films, or papers), or the intensity high; but even under such conditions O'Brien and Parks[4] showed that sufficiently high sector speeds could be used to give accurate results. Strobo-scopic effects must of course be avoided if AC-operated sources are used.

Convenient forms of step and wedge sectors are shown in Fig. 13.6. These disks can be obtained commercially, or may readily be filed out of thin disks of aluminum, appropriate counterweights being added to balance any asymmetry. They may be mounted on the spindle of a small motor and placed directly in front of the slit of a stigmatic

(a)   (b)

Fig. 13.6. (a) Step-sector disk (logarithmic). (b) Wedge-sector disk (logarithmic).

spectrograph. The motor should be so fastened that any vibration which it may produce will not affect the spectrograph.

Errors to be guarded against arise from running the disk too slowly or from using it in such a way that all parts of the spectrograph col-limator are not simultaneously filled with light during a flash. Under these conditions the resolving power of the spectrograph and the shape of the spectrum lines may be changed, and the intensity steps may not be truly neutral. The cutoff edge of the disk should be mounted accurately parallel to the spectrograph slit.

2. *Step weakener or wedge at slit.* To avoid any possibility of errors due to reciprocity or intermittency failures, a step weakener or an

⁴ B. O'Brien and V. L. Parks, *Phys. Rev.,* **41,** 387 (1932).

optical wedge can be used at the slit.   Unfortunately, no substance
has been discovered that reduces light uniformly throughout the
spectrum, so a truly neutral wedge does not exist.   It is, however,
possible to measure the transmission of each step of such a weakener
by means of a thermoelectric or photoelectric photometer, used in
conjunction with a quartz-mercury arc and monochromator.   Figure
13.7 shows typical calibration curves for the various steps of a
platinum-on-quartz step weakener.   In making such a calibration it
is not safe to assume linearity of density with thickness.   Monel or
aluminum evaporated on quartz gives weakeners that are approximately neutral throughout the visible and ultraviolet.

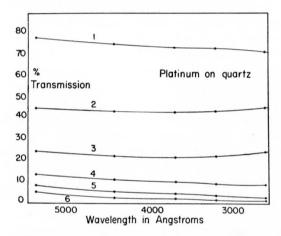

Fig. 13.7.   Calibration curves for a platinum-on-quartz step weakener.   The
steps are numbered in order of increasing density.

For the visible and photographic infrared regions, a weakener can
be produced by exposing a photographic plate, preferably one of fine
grain such as a contrast or positive plate.   Absorption and scattering
produce the desired reduction of intensity, but both vary rather
rapidly with wavelength.

A step or wedge reducer must be uniformly illuminated along its
length, and obtaining this uniformity may present difficulties.   Accepted methods are discussed in § 6.6.   In selecting a method of slit
illumination, it should be borne in mind that the resolving power of
the spectrograph may be lowered if an image of the source is focused
on its collimator so that it is not illuminated with coherent radiation.
In order to make sure that uneven illumination of the slit has not

affected the intensity ratios, it is desirable to invert the step weakener, wedge, or sector frequently so that such effects will tend to cancel out.

3. *Step diaphragm before the slit.* Diaphragms in which steps equivalent to those of a step weakener are produced by geometrical means have been described by several workers.[5] Diaphragms having steps of various lengths are introduced into the beam, and by means of astigmatic focusing the illumination on each part of the slit is made proportional to the length of one of the steps. Wide departures from spectral neutrality can sometimes occur with such diaphragms because of changes in the illumination of the spectrograph from one step to the next. Though this method is suited only to use with a stigmatic mounting, Frerichs[6] has used step diaphragms with a Rowland mounting by placing the diaphragm at the position of the vertical astigmatic focus outside the slit, as in Fig. 13.8. Only a limited spectral region can be photographed at one time by this means, however, since the position of the step diaphragm must be shifted for each new wavelength setting. This method is frequently used with spectrographs using the Eagle mounting.

4. *Step weakener or wedge at the plate.* Concave grating mountings and certain types of prism spectrographs are frequently so astigmatic that the methods listed above cannot be used, since any point on the slit is drawn out into a vertical line in the spectrum. In the Paschen-Runge and Eagle mountings, for example, long astigmatic lines are produced with central portions that may be uniform in intensity and hence ideally suited for superposition of intensity-reducing devices. This condition suggests placing a reducing wedge or weakener directly in front of the plate and photographing the lines through it. This method is practicable when narrow multiplets or Zeeman or Stark patterns are to be measured, but a reducer that will cover more than a few inches of plate is seldom available.

5. *Step slit or wedge slit.* With a stigmatic spectrograph having a fairly long slit, one can use a slit having varying widths along its length. In this method, when calibrations are made by means of a source with a continuous spectrum, a spectrogram consisting of several bands having known relative intensities is obtained, just as in the case of the step-weakener or step-diaphragm methods. The

---

[5] G. Hansen, *Zeitschr. f. Phys.*, **29**, 356 (1924); A. von Hippel, *Ann. d. Physik*, **80**, 672 (1926).

[6] R. Frerichs, *Zeitschr. f. Phys.*, **36**, 524 (1926).

method has been successfully used by Ornstein and his collaborators[i] (see General Reference 13.1) in the visible region and in the near ultraviolet, where an incandescent lamp can be used to give the continuous spectrum, and by Thompson and Duffendack[8] in the ultra-

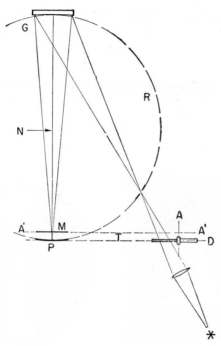

Fig. 13.8. Step diaphragm as used with a Rowland mounting by Frerichs. The rotating diaphragm, D, is located on the tangent, T, to the Rowland circle, R, at point P. The line A is the axis of rotation of the diaphragm, and as the diaphragm rotates, a mask M rotates synchronously about axis A' in front of the plate, P. This mask contains slits that cause a fixed part of the spectral line image to be photographed through a given step in the rotating diaphragm.

violet, using a hydrogen discharge tube as a continuous source. It can be used also with lines which are broader than the slit.

The method has limited application, because the slit must never be so narrow that diffraction produces errors or so broad that overlapping of wavelengths becomes important. Also, the fact that a

[7] L. S. Ornstein, *Phys. Zeitschr.*, **28**, 688 (1927); *Proc. Roy. Soc.* (London), **37**, 337 (1925).

[8] K. B. Thompson and O. S. Duffendack, *Jour. Opt. Soc. Am.*, **23**, 101 (1933).

continuous spectrum is being used to calibrate a plate on which line spectra are being measured may cause large errors due to the Eberhard effect. The form of wedge slit illustrated in Fig. 13.9 will be found useful, the width of the slit varying logarithmically along its length.

6. *Multiple-exposure methods.* If it is necessary to use a multiple-exposure method, a steady source must be provided. An incandescent lamp is usually satisfactory for the region 10,000 to 3800 A (or to 2800 A if a quartz window is provided), a quartz-mercury arc for the region 5800 to 2300 A, and a hydrogen discharge tube for 7000 to 900 A. Steady sparks between rotating electrodes also can be used for calibration.

One of the simplest methods of intensity variation is that in which the cross section of a collimated beam of light is altered by means of

Fig. 13.9. A wedge slit whose width varies logarithmically along its length. (Magnified horizontally.)

Fig. 13.10. A rotating-sector diaphragm. The open sectors are made variable so that average intensity can be varied.

a diaphragm of variable aperture. This change may be made readily when the beam in which the aperture is placed is of uniform cross section for all wavelengths used and when all wavelengths are treated alike by the spectrograph. These conditions are difficult to fulfill, however, since most lenses have zonal variations of focus and transmission. A diaphragm of the shape shown in Fig. 13.10 may serve with a spectrograph, but it may cut the resolving power in half if placed so as to reduce the apparent width of the dispersing unit, and such a system should be calibrated at selected wavelengths.

Wire-gauze screens[9] are effective multiple-aperture diaphragms that avoid the difficulties outlined in the preceding paragraph, but they may introduce diffraction errors unless handled carefully as described in the references. They should have their transmission factors calibrated under the conditions of use, whereupon they are usually found to be sensibly neutral. They should be kept in continuous relative oscillating motion when used in multiple.

If the transmission factors of a series of (approximately) neutral filters are known at various wavelengths over the spectral range desired, a method is available that is useful for revealing hidden errors in other methods of calibration. The filters are introduced into the beam, preferably where it has a large cross section, one at a time or in groups, since they are additive in density. Care must be taken to see that all filters are plane, because any prismatic effect may cause some light to be thrown off the slit and thus introduce refraction errors. Interreflection effects between slit jaws and filters should also be avoided.

The inverse-square law gives a fundamental method of varying light intensity. This method is very useful for testing the accuracy of other methods directly, since it can be used with a sufficiently intense source that approximates a point. A mat surface, such as a quartz disk with both sides rough-ground, is placed at the normal position of the light source being studied and is illuminated by an intense source, such as a short section of mercury arc or an incandescent lamp, placed on an optical bench at an adjustable distance from the scattering surface. The intensities at the mat surface are accurately proportional to the inverse square of the distance between source and scatterer if the distance is large in comparison with the effective source size (say $20\times$). It is particularly necessary to keep out stray light and to avoid atmospheric refraction and absorption in long paths.

Variation of exposure time, so commonly resorted to because of its simplicity, should be used only as a check on the other methods, or when the reciprocity failure of the plate is determined directly, as in the fluorescence method of Harrison and Leighton.[10] Under no circumstances should it be trusted for use with a given type of emulsion

---

[9] L. B. Ham, D. H. Fehr, and C. Bitner, *Jour. Franklin Inst.*, **178**, 299 (1914); G. R Harrison, *Jour. Opt. Soc. Am.*, **18**, 492 (1929).

[10] G. R. Harrison and P. A. Leighton, *Jour. Opt. Soc. Am.*, **20**, 313 (1930); *Phys. Rev.*, **36**, 779 (1930).

just because someone else found that this emulsion obeyed the reciprocity law. Reduction of intensity by varying the excitation of the source or by using polarizing apparatus, though of value in other methods of photometry, has little application in photography.

Calibration exposures may be made with a spectrograph different from that used for photographing the spectrum to be measured, but great care must be taken to control scattered and false light and to ensure that the Eberhard effect associated with differences in line shape will not affect the results.

HETEROCHROMATIC PHOTOMETRY

13.4. Uses of Heterochromatic Photometry. When we wish to compare two beams of light having different wavelengths or to measure the relative intensities of two spectrum lines more than 25 A

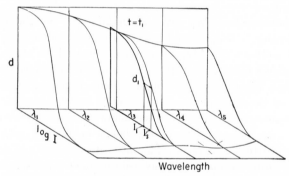

Fig. 13.11. Three-dimensional plot of the relation between density, log intensity, and wavelength.

apart, a new step must be added that is not involved in homochromatic photometry. This step is designed to take account of the variation in sensitivity of the emulsion with wavelength, whereas in homochromatic photometry throughout a range of spectrum we need take account only of the variation of contrast with wavelength.

In homochromatic photometry each calibration curve is determined by producing known variations in the unknown but fixed intensity of a light beam. The additional step in heterochromatic photometry involves determining the intensities used for the different calibration curves. It is usually not convenient to take this step by determining the intensity variation with wavelength of the source used for calibration.   Instead, additional exposures are made to a source whose intensity distribution is known throughout that part of the spectrum being studied.   This process is called *plate standardization*.

The basis for heterochromatic photometry is illustrated in Fig. 13.11.   The three-dimensional plot in the figure gives the relation between density, log intensity, and wavelength for a typical emulsion. Calibration curves at the various wavelengths appear as plane sections cut through the surface of this plot perpendicular to the wavelength axis, and the process of standardization consists in determining the relative intensity values that will put the calibration curves in their proper positions along the log i axis (see General References 13.2 and 13.3).

13.5.   Light Sources for Standardization.   Commonly used standard sources are the blackbody (§ 8.5), whose spectral energy distribution is known theoretically, sources of continuous radiation (§§ 8.6 and 8.7) having known emissivity, and sources which have

Fig. 13.12.   The quartz mercury-arc spectrum.

such steadiness that their spectral-energy distribution can be measured directly with a monochromator or thermopile or other nonselective radiometer.

A convenient source for use in standardizing plates in the visible and ultraviolet regions is the quartz-mercury arc, operated at constant current and temperature so that the voltage drop across it and the pressure within it remain constant throughout the exposure series, as discussed in § 8.14.   A quartz monochromator can be used to separate the various mercury lines, which are intense and well separated in groups that can be identified readily.   The mercury spectrum contains strong lines well spaced in the range 5800 to 2300 A, as shown in Fig. 13.12 and listed in Table 9.1.

The transmission of the monochromator for various wavelengths is first measured, preferably with another monochromator and a photoelectric cell or thermopile.   It is important to ensure that all diaphragms and other stops in the second monochromator be adjusted exactly in the manner in which they will be used later in making

the intensity-distribution measurements. The slit of the first monochromator is made sufficiently wide that all mercury lines or line
groups are flat-topped, and the light passing from this slit through the
entrance slit of the second monochromator is then measured at some
convenient wavelength. A similar reading for the same setting is
then made by moving the radiometer so as to intercept all the light
passing through the exit slit of the second monochromator. The
ratio of the two deflections gives the transmission of the second
monochromator at that wavelength, if the radiometer has a linear
response. These readings are then repeated throughout the spectrum. Transmission factors for a typical quartz-prism monochromator are given in Table 13.2.

TABLE 13.2

MEASURED TRANSMISSION FACTORS FOR A TYPICAL QUARTZ-
PRISM MONOCHROMATOR

Wavelength	Per Cent Transmission
2000 A	14
3000	26
4000	34
5000	38
6000	41

Once such a transmission curve has been determined for a given
monochromator, it can be used with thermoelectric or other spectrally
neutral radiometric equipment to measure the actual amounts of
energy in the spectrum of a mercury arc or other steady source run
under constant conditions. This spectrum can then be impressed
on the photographic plate that is to be standardized.

It may be necessary to reduce the intensity of the light from the
mercury arc by some method approaching neutrality as closely as
possible, to the point where it will produce densities in the range 0.3
to 1.5 during the exposure time used on the plate being standardized.
The principal errors of heterochromatic photometry arise from the
difficulty of bridging this gap between the lowest intensities that can
be measured precisely with a neutral radiometer and the highest
intensities that can be recorded in a suitable time of exposure on the
photographic plate. This gap may in some cases exceed 1000 to 1
and can probably best be bridged by a combination of a rapidly
rotating sector disk and a specially calibrated screen.

A somewhat more direct method of standardization, especially useful in the visible region, involves use of a blackbody operated at a known temperature as measured by an optical or other pyrometer. The energy distribution can be determined from Wien's law cast in the following form:

$\log_{10} I$

$= 28.532 - 5 \log_{10} \lambda - \text{antilog} (7.7939 - \log_{10} \lambda - \log_{10} T)$ (13.1)*

or from tables (§ 8.4). To ensure the blackbody character of the radiation used, simply take the radiation from the inside of a V-shaped hollow in the side of a graphite rod. A convenient blackbody is described by Harrison,[11] and other forms are discussed in General References 13.3 and 13.4.

The principal limitation of the use of the blackbody is that at all practicable temperatures the intensity falls rapidly in passing from the near infrared to the ultraviolet, and the radiation is usually not of sufficient intensity to be used for standardizing plates at wavelengths shorter than 3000 A. Also, a continuous spectrum is produced, so that the Eberhard effect is likely to cause error unless the spectrum is artificially broken up into "spectrum lines" of the approximate size and shape of those being measured.

A tungsten filament can be used as a standard source, especially if it is of the ribbon type made for radiometric purposes. The coiled filament is not so useful, because the temperature varies greatly over the surface of an individual coil. Since tungsten is not a true blackbody, its color temperature must be used instead of its true temperature. The brightness temperature of the filament can be determined by means of an optical pyrometer. Tables giving the conversion from brightness temperature to color temperature or from brightness temperature to true temperature to color temperature are given in Chapter 8 and in the International Critical Tables. The actual temperature of the filament is likely to vary considerably along its length, and its brightness temperature should be determined on the actual area which is used to produce the standard spectrum.

When a continuous spectrum is used for standardization, it is necessary to correct the actual emissivity values for the dispersion of the spectrograph, since the radiation is spread thinner where the disper-

---

* In this expression, I is in watts per cm² of blackbody surface per angstrom of spectral range, λ is in angstroms, and T is in °K.

[11] G. R. Harrison, *Jour. Opt. Soc. Am.*, **19**, 290 (1929); H. B. Dorgelo, *Phys. Zeitschr.*, **26**, 767 (1925).

sion increases. With line spectra this correction is not necessary, since all of the energy of a spectrum line usually goes into the radiometer regardless of effective slit width.

APPARATUS AND METHODS FOR PHOTOGRAPHIC PHOTOMETRY

13.6. Selection of the Spectrograph. For photographic photometry a spectrograph should be selected which will permit a fairly large number of exposures to be taken on a single plate and which is as free as possible from scattered light. The latter consideration makes the Littrow mounting and those mountings in which light traverses a prism more than once less satisfactory than other spectrographs. A spectrograph having dispersion as great as is consistent with other requirements should be selected, inasmuch as higher dispersion yields higher precision in wavelength measurements on continuous spectra and allows wider slits to be used with line spectra. Increased dispersion also reduces the intensity of the continuous background relative to the lines, and diffraction errors of the type discussed below are decreased as the dispersion and slit width are increased. In photographic photometry the slit is often made as much as 10 times as wide as is suitable for wavelength measurements, to obtain flat-topped lines. In general, concave grating spectrographs are somewhat more convenient and flexible for photographic photometry of line spectra than are prism instruments.

For measuring relative spectrum line intensities, it is not necessary to know the transmission of the spectrograph, since under proper conditions of illumination, transmission losses affect unknown and standard beams alike.

13.7. Selection of the Emulsion. From among those types of emulsion which are sensitive in the spectral regions desired, one having good photometric characteristics should be chosen. Usually an emulsion of medium contrast and speed will be found most useful. Fast emulsions, which usually have low contrast, are undesirable for photometry because large variations in intensity produce only small variations in density. Also, large errors may result from the tendency of a fast emulsion to fog, and from its high sensitivity to pressure, temperature, and humidity effects. On the other hand, plates having very high contrast can be used over only a narrow intensity range, and one is likely to find it necessary to work on the under- and overexposed portions of the curve where the rapidly changing slope increases the error of interpolation. Though it is not at all necessary to restrict measurements to the straight-line portion of a calibration curve, a fairly long straight-line portion with a slope of 45 deg is likely to be found most convenient.

Certain types of emulsion have multiple coatings of different speeds. Such emulsions should be avoided for photometric purposes, since they often show a change in contrast in the middle of the calibration curve. The advantage of having a number of points lying in a straight line is then lost.

Although it is, of course, necessary to use dyed and coated emulsions in certain regions of the spectrum, each additional treatment of an emulsion increases the possibility of variation over its surface, so "clear-working" plates, showing little residual dye, should be used when possible. Schumann plates are so nonuniform as to be undesirable for photographic photometry, and special methods must be used in the extreme ultraviolet (§ 19.7).

Plates to be used for photographic photometry should always be stored on edge in a cool place to reduce pressure marks and fogging. No intensity marks or other important exposures should be made within $\frac{1}{2}$ in. of the edge of a plate.

13.8. Timing the Exposure. Usually it is not necessary to know the exact duration of an exposure, but merely to ensure that all exposures to be compared are of the same duration. There is a certain amount of choice in the time of exposure to be employed unless the light source is very weak, since it is always possible to reduce the intensity of a strong source by changing the mode of illumination of the spectrograph. If such a change is necessary, it should be made to give a time of exposure of at least 1 min., (a) because the response of the emulsion is somewhat more uniform to a moderate rate of illumination, (b) because the effect of short-time fluctuations in the intensity of the light source will then be averaged out, and (c) because timing of the exposure can be more precise. The most satisfactory exposure time is usually from 1 to 3 min.

When exposures of 5 min or longer are used, a hand-operated shutter, or a card held in front of the slit, can be timed with an ordinary watch. For exposure times between 1 sec and 5 min, a magnetically operated shutter run by impulses from a clock beating seconds, or from an electric clock, is useful. For exposures that must be less than 1 sec in duration, a double-sector disk is effective. This disk consists of two coaxial disks arranged to rotate at a known speed ratio with a single sector cut out of each. One disk moves so slowly that the spectrograph shutter can be opened or closed conveniently during a single revolution. The operator opens the shutter while the light beam is cut off by both disks. The slow disk then allows the beam to strike the fast sector, which shortly thereafter permits the light to fall on the slit for a brief exposure. Before it can repeat this operation, the slow sector has again cut off the light; and before the slow sector opens again, the spectrograph shutter has been closed.

13.9. The Brush Effect. It is probably desirable in photometry to let a longer time elapse between the last exposure on the plate and the beginning of development than has elapsed between the first and last exposures, because of a phenomenon known as the *Brush effect*.[12] Although the existence of this effect has been the subject of much controversy, the evidence seems to indicate that something of the sort occurs. The effect involves a progressive change in the latent image during the time between its production and its development. To avoid possible errors from this cause, exposures that are to be compared should theoretically be allowed equal times to change. It would be undesirable, for example, to expose a plate to an unknown spectrum one day and to the calibration and standardization exposures the next morning just before development, not only because of possible Brush effect but also because the humidity and temperature of the plate may affect its sensitivity to a slight extent.

13.10. Processing the Spectrogram. Photographic photometry requires close control of development. A developer should be chosen which will not stain the emulsion and which will keep chemical fog and Eberhard effect (§ 7.13) to a minimum. It has been claimed that Rodinal produces less Eberhard effect than other developers. The most effective method of reducing the Eberhard effect is that suggested by Clark,[13] in which the plate is brushed continuously throughout development. The intimate contact of the brush removes the developer from the regions where it has been depleted and mixes it thoroughly. Rocking the trays is insufficient because it does not remove the thin adhering layer of developer next to the emulsion. Various workers[14] have described devices for mechanical agitation

---

[12] C. F. Brush, *Phys. Rev.*, **3**, 241 (1910).

[13] W. Clark, *Phot. Jour.*, **65**, 76 (1925).

[14] G. M. B. Dobson, I. O. Griffith, and D. N. Harrison, *Photographic Photometry*. London: Oxford University Press, 1926, page 121.

during development, but the brush method is simpler and more effective.

To obtain the greatest uniformity over the emulsion surface, development should not be unusually rapid, because high speed may result in uneven penetration of developer. On the other hand, development should not be unduly slow because of tediousness in carrying out the development process. Development should be allowed to proceed fairly well toward completion, or so that it will give, with a plate of moderate contrast, a characteristic curve whose straight-line portion has a slope of about 45 deg.

Development should be carried out in the dark in developer of carefully controlled temperature and for a time accurately measured with a stop clock. After development, the plate should be processed as outlined in § 7.10.

Fig. 13.13. Point of density match determined by eye.

It is often desirable to reduce the time required for processing plates when high-speed quantitative spectroscopic analysis is involved, and many of the procedures outlined can be simplified. Eastman spectroscopic plates have been produced to permit development in a much shorter time than is required by the ordinary emulsion.

To test whether a photometric method is satisfactory, a sample plate of the type to be used may be exposed in a darkroom to a light placed as far away as possible, so as to get uniformity of illumination, and then developed and fixed under the standard conditions chosen. Test areas measured on a densitometer will then reveal the uniformity of response over the surface of the emulsion. When the spectrum being measured, the calibration spectrum, and the standardization spectrum are taken on the same plate under conditions which give uniform response over the entire plate in such a test, photometric errors should be small.

13.11. Short-cut Methods of Photographic Photometry. Simple methods of photographic photometry that use the emulsion as a null indicator have been developed. It is easy to locate by eye two contiguous areas of equal density in two photometric strips varying in density in opposite directions, as in Fig. 13.13. Since other variables are kept identical in the two exposures, equality of density indicates equality of intensity. The minimum density at which a line fades into the background can also be used as an indication of intensity. These methods when carefully controlled can be used to give precision to within 5 to 10 per cent and make possible rapid determination of the course of an absorption curve, for example, over a long spectral range. Such methods are discussed in Chapter 14 under Absorption Spectrophotometry.

By means of optical comparators it is possible to bring into apparent juxtaposition the lines of two spectra as in Fig. 13.14 (§ 16.13) and to adjust one of them until points of equal density are matched. This method is considerably superior to that involved in determining the end point of a line, since the minimum observable density has low sensitivity because of the very low contrast of the emulsion at this point in the characteristic curve. When two lines varying logarithmically in intensity along their lengths are brought into juxtaposition, they can be compared along their entire lengths.

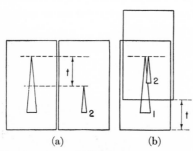

(a)   (b)

Fig. 13.14.   Matching of two spectra by means of an optical comparator. In (a) are shown two spectrum lines photographed through a logarithmic sector. The two rectangles represent two different fields of view of the comparator that can be translated horizontally and vertically so that any part of line 2 can be brought into coincidence with any part of line 1. In (b), t shows the distance through which line 2 has to be translated to match the density of line 1. t may be read directly from the comparator.

DENSITOMETRY

The density of the silver deposit in any portion of a photographic emulsion is most readily measured with a *densitometer*, a photometric device designed to determine the reduction in intensity of a beam of light when sent through a restricted area of the emulsion. When the area is small, as in the case of a spectrum line, the instrument may be called a *microdensitometer;* it is sometimes incorrectly referred to as a "microphotometer" (General References 13.2–13.5).

Fundamental features of a densitometer are a source of light that provides a beam to measure the plate, provision for ensuring that this beam passes through only that part of the emulsion which is to be measured, and a device to compare the intensity of the beam of light after passing through the exposed emulsion to that of the same beam passed through an unexposed area of emulsion. Most densitometers utilize thermoelectric or photoelectric devices for measurement of the beam, though a few less precise instruments use eye-match methods.

13.12. Densitometers. Densitometers may be classified as *direct-reading*, in which the deflection is a function of the density of the plate, and *null* instruments, which permit matching of an unknown density by an equivalent known density. Direct-reading densitometers are of the *recording* type, in which the deflection of the indicating device is recorded on paper or on a photographic plate or film, and the *spotting* or nonrecording type, in which deflections are read only at selected locations, as for example on the flat tops of certain spectrum lines. Many densitometers are of the *projection* type, in which an area of the emulsion immediately surrounding the part being measured can be observed visually immediately before or during measurement.

A densitometer may determine either diffuse or specular densities. In measuring diffuse density, all the light passing through the emulsion up to a considerable angle is included in the emergent beam, which is then compared to the incident beam. Specular density, on the other hand, is determined by including only that part of the light which continues in the direction of the original beam. Specular density is thus always greater than diffuse density for a given silver deposit. Most microdensitometers used in spectroscopic work measure specular densities.

The density of a silver deposit varies considerably with the color of the light used to measure it. A densitometer that uses blue light, for example, will give entirely different density readings for a given deposit from one using red light. This effect makes it necessary to keep as constant as possible, during the measurement of a given plate or film, the temperature of the densitometer lamp filament and the arrangement of all optical parts used. In photometric work, only densities on a given plate are compared, so that this requirement offers no difficulty, and changes made between plates are of no consequence.

Figure 13.15 shows the optical system of a typical microdensitometer. Two beams may be supplied, one with which to inspect the plate to aid in locating the exact spot to be measured and a second to carry out the measurement. Often the first beam is converted into the second at the moment of measurement by insertion or removal of a lens, and sometimes of a filter. Unless care is taken, light scattered in the optical system of the densitometer will produce errors in reading.[15]   It is necessary not only to take into account the error in reading produced by the scattered light but also that produced by variations in the amount of scattered light which result when different parts of the plate are brought into the beam.   The effect is to reduce the apparent density of areas surrounded by less dense areas, and is one of the most common sources of error in densitometry.   Every densitometer when first set up should be tested for scattered light. The test should be repeated whenever optical surfaces may have become dusty, by setting on a very dense line and then seeing if the deflection changes when most of the light passing through the surrounding plate is shielded.

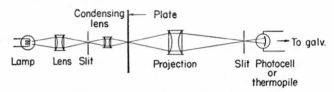

Fig. 13.15.   The optical system of a typical microdensitometer.

This effect is especially serious in instruments having mirrors or large numbers of lens components in their optical systems.   It is possible to reduce the effect by cutting off any viewing beam during actual measurement, or in a photoelectric instrument by using for viewing light of a color which, though visible, does not affect the photometer.   It can also be minimized by using an extremely narrow shutter to simulate a spectrum line of infinite density and taking a zero reading with this over every area being measured, thus permitting the scattered light to enter the photometer while the zero is being taken.

13.13.   Photoelectric Densitometers.   The original photoelectric microdensitometer was designed by Koch.[16]   His optical design is shown in Fig. 13.16.   Light from the Nernst lamp L (in modern instruments replaced by an automobile headlight lamp) passed through the plate P to be measured and was focused on photocell C_1.   An electrometer E was used to measure the voltage across this cell, this voltage depending not only on the amount of light passing through the plate but also on that falling on cells C_2 and C_3,

[15] K. Schwarzschild and W. Villiger, *Astrophys. Jour.*, **23**, 287 (1906).
[16] P. P. Koch, *Ann. d. Physik*, **39**, 705 (1912).

which were connected so as to form a variable compensating leak across C_1. Two cells were used in parallel so that the electrometer could work on either side of ground potential. A projection system was used to throw an image of the electrometer thread on a recording plate.

The Koch microdensitometer as improved by Goos[17] was manufactured commercially for many years by Krüss of Hamburg. A projection system for viewing the plate during measurement was added, and to eliminate errors due to scattered light a red filter was put in the viewing beam and a photocell insensitive to red light was used. This recording instrument, in which various ratios of record

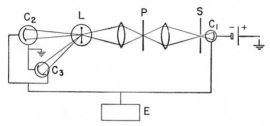

Fig. 13.16. The optical and electrical arrangement of the original photoelectric microdensitometer of Koch (1912).

motion to plate motion were provided, was in effect a recording comparator.

In recent years photronic and other barrier-layer photocells have come into wide use in microdensitometers, since they require no batteries and can be connected directly to a galvanometer. The Hilger densitometer shown in Fig. 13.17 uses such a cell. When barrier-layer cells are used, it is important to put a suitable resistance in series or in parallel with them so that the galvanometer will be made approximately dead-beat when the cell is exposed to light corresponding to a medium-density reading. It is desirable to choose cells of a type showing low fatigue effects and to remember that photoconducting cells give linear current vs. light flux for low load resistance.

The advantages of photoelectric densitometers are high sensitivity, which permits use of short-period galvanometers; freedom from thermal disturbances; limited spectral sensitivity, so that few errors

[17] F. Goos, *Zeitschr. f. Inst.*, **41**, 313 (1921); *Phys. Zeitschr.*, **22**, 468 (1921); F Goos and P. P. Koch, *Zeitschr. f. Physik*, **44**, 855 (1927).

are introduced if the focusing lenses are not completely achromatic; and output that can readily be fed into amplifiers. The characteristics of photoelectric photometers have been discussed in Chapter 12.

The photoelectric cell responds more quickly than any thermoelectric device yet developed; and since ordinarily it has a higher output impedance, its response can be amplified more effectively. It

Fig. 13.17. The Hilger microdensitometer, Model H451 with H534 reader unit attached. (Courtesy Jarrell-Ash Company, Boston.)

can be used as a sensitive null indicator. In this form it provides the basis for the most accurate type of densitometer yet devised, since almost every factor producing irregularities can be balanced out. Two beams of light may be used, one passing through the plate to be measured and the other through a comparison wedge of graded density, which should be as similar as possible to the plate and hence may well be made of an exposed photographic emulsion. A single beam can also be used, made to pass alternately through the plate to be measured and the wedge.

In a well-designed densitometer every variable should be kept as constant as possible. For example, the same photocell should be used to measure both beams, if possible. Although two cells may be balanced at one light intensity, they are likely to get out of balance at other intensity levels. If great care is taken to match them in this respect, it will usually be found that the sensitivity of one will change with time more than that of the other. Cells are likely to vary in sensitivity over different portions of their sensitive surfaces and to have different wavelength responses, so that if the color of one measuring beam changes, they will be thrown out of balance. An ideal photometer of this sort would be one in which a single light source, light beam, and measuring device were used, the plate to be measured and a similar plate whose density characteristics were known being put alternately into the beam. Such a design has the advantage that the precision would be about the same for high as for low densities, readings being reproducible to 0.2 per cent or better.

A photomultiplier cell has been used in the microdensitometer that is a part of the automatic comparator designed by Harrison (§ 9.11), in which ten inches of plate can be scanned per minute, the opacity curve being photographed on motion-picture film. The photomultiplier tube is to be considered as being a phototube plus a very simple and convenient form of DC amplifier.

13.14. Thermoelectric Densitometers. Thermoelectric devices of the sort discussed in Chapter 12 lend themselves to use in simple and rugged densitometers. They are more suited to use in direct deflection than in null instruments. On account of the low impedance of most thermoelectric devices, their output currents are difficult to amplify electrically and are ordinarily fed to low-impedance galvanometers, though the so-called G–M amplifier (§ 12.10) has been highly successful. The prototype of thermoelectric densitometers is that of Moll,[18] which has for many years been manufactured commercially by Kipp and Zonen in Delft. It was in the early years cheaper and simpler than its photoelectric competitors, though not so rapid in action.

The advantages of using simple thermocouple-galvanometer combinations have been offset to a considerable extent in recent years by

---

[18] W. H. J. Moll, *Proc. Phys. Soc.* (London), **33**, 207 (1921).

the introduction of the photronic cell, which is an equally simple and more sensitive photometric device and is, moreover, free from thermal disturbances. Thermoelectric photometers must be very carefully shielded from air currents if they are to be kept free of drift. They are sensitive to all wavelengths and so must be shielded from stray light and heat rays. Focusing lenses used with them must be carefully achromatized, since most of the light received from an incandescent lamp lies in the near infrared region. Neglect of this fact may greatly reduce the resolving power of a microdensitometer where an image of the slit is thrown on the plate by an incompletely achromatized lens.

Densitometers have been constructed using the Boys radiomicrometer and the Nichols radiometer, and various types of thermocouples, bolometers, and thermopiles. These densitometers, though formerly the simplest to use, are in general giving way to the newer types of photocells for densitometric purposes.

13.15. Operation of the Densitometer. Although the operator of a densitometer may feel that he need make only one measurement for each spot measured on the photographic emulsion, actually each determination of the density d involves measuring four quantities.

$$d = \log_{10} \frac{I_0}{I} = \log_{10} \frac{G - G_0}{G' - G_0} \tag{13.2}$$

where I_0 is the incident light being used to measure the plate, I is that transmitted by the portion of the plate being measured, and G, G', and G_0 are the readings of the galvanometer corresponding to intensities I_0, I, and no light, respectively. It cannot always be taken for granted that G_0 will remain constant from one reading to the next. The difference in deflection $G - G_0$, called the *clear reading*, should be taken through a developed but unexposed portion of the plate having any fog and stray light exposures on it that may be present in the spectrum but having no exposure to the spectral radiation being measured. $G - G_0$ is also sometimes called the "100 reading," since it is convenient to adjust the intensity of the densitometer beam so that the galvanometer scale reading is exactly 100 for a clear portion of the plate near the exposed portion to be measured. The difference $G' - G_0$ is the deflection on the exposed line. In a good densitometer the light source remains constant and the detector does not drift, so that the 100 reading and the zero reading remain constant. To justify these two assumptions, it is necessary to use a very constant light source, operated from a storage battery, a stabilized transformer, or an electronic voltage regulator, and to use a recorder and amplifier system with little drift.

G depends not only on the brightness of the densitometer beam but also on the transmission of the unexposed portion of the plate, which is likely to vary considerably over the plate surface. In consequence, one of the principal problems in photographic photometry is to determine where to measure the clear plate readings G. Best results are obtained when chemical and other controllable fog is kept to a minimum so that the plate surface is as uniform as possible in

Fig. 13.18.   The Baird Associates' nonrecording densitometer.

transmission.   Neglect of this factor is probably responsible for more of the errors of photographic photometry than any other cause.

If zero drift is low, the number of determinations of G_0 can be kept small.   When G_0 and G are kept constant, G' is the only quantity that need specifically be determined for points on the plate which are to be measured, and it is the continuous curve of G' values which is given by a recording microdensitometer.

Some operators prefer to use *blackening* rather than density as an indicator of plate response.   Blackening is the difference between the clear plate reading and the line reading, or $G - G'$, when the clear plate reading is set at 100, and G_0 is zero.

13.16. Recording Densitometers. The recording devices discussed in Chapter 12 can be used for densitometry. Ordinarily a record is useful only when line contours or some similar features are to be measured. For routine work in quantitative spectrochemical analysis or for making intensity measurements on spectrum lines, it is usually more convenient to make spot measurements than to spend the time required for taking a complete record and then selecting from each record the lines to be measured.

Fig. 13.19. The Leeds and Northrup recording microdensitometer.

In densitometers of the older type, the galvanometer deflections were recorded by a light beam on photographic paper. This paper was wrapped on a drum which was driven by clockwork or, in later models, by synchronous motors provided with reduction gears. In some of the higher-priced commercial instruments, which are now less in fashion than formerly, complicated gear arrangements were provided to move a long photographic plate on which the opacity curve was recorded. This recording method is of importance only when the comparator features are necessary so that intensities and distances along the plate can be exactly determined simultaneously. Modern practice tends more in the direction of rapid records on paper, as in the Leeds and Northrup densitometer shown in Fig. 13.19.

13.17. Precision of Densitometers. The precision available in well-designed densitometers is usually greater than that required for photographic photometry. Instrumental errors can readily be kept below 0.5 per cent for the direct-reading type and below 0.2 per cent for the null type. Failure to reproduce readings to this precision is usually caused by the difficulty of repeat setting on the same portion of the plate. An advantage of the recording method is that no uncertainty is introduced as to whether the exact peak of a narrow line is set upon. To obviate this uncertainty, many spotting instruments are provided with a transverse screw motion that can be quickly locked in when the line is nearly in position. The line is then slowly moved across the measuring light beam and the minimum deflection of the galvanometer is read.

The Zeiss firm at one time manufactured a spotting microphotometer in which a given spectrum line would appear in position at the slit when the proper key was pressed. Thus when the same four or five lines were to be measured in a number of different spectra on the same plate, it was easy to set on one line after another, then to rack up the next spectrum and measure the same lines. The Applied Research Laboratories manufacture a projection instrument with a similar feature, shown in Fig. 13.20. This uses a contact slit.

When very short and narrow slits are used in the densitometer, variations in deflection may be encountered due to graininess of the emulsion. These effects can be reduced by lengthening the slit, providing an oscillating motion of the plate parallel to the spectrum line, using an astigmatic optical system, or by various other means.

13.18. Special Computing Densitometers. Since it sometimes takes longer to determine with the aid of calibration curves the intensity of the light which has fallen on a plate than to measure the plate with a densitometer, it is desirable to have this translating done automatically. Wouda[19] has described an instrument for the rapid reduction of data from a calibration curve. The image of a long straight-filament lamp is moved across a plot of the calibration curve by the deflection of the galvanometer mirror of the densitometer. By adjustment of the size of the plot or the optics of the projection system, line intensities can be read off directly from the intersection

---

[19] J. Wouda, *Zeitschr. f. Physik*, **79**, 511 (1932).

of the filament image and this curve. However, the calibration curve for each portion of the plate must be determined by the operator and set into the machine; and since from 2 to 20 calibration curves may be required for reduction of a single plate, the region which can be reduced from a single curve is likely to be limited.

Fig. 13.20.   The Applied Research Laboratories' projection microdensitometer.

A similar automatic device is that of Thompson,[20] which sends a long line of light from the galvanometer mirror of the densitometer through a slit cut to the predetermined shape of the calibration curve for a portion of the plate. That section of this line which is transmitted through the slit lies in a position that indicates the intensity of the line directly. This method suffers from the same limitations

---

[20] N. Thompson, *Proc. Phys. Soc.* (London), **45**, 441 (1933); see also G. O. Langstroth and D. R. McRae, *Jour. Opt. Soc. Am.*, **28**, 440 (1938).

as Wouda's device.   The utility of these devices lies in the fact that the intensity curves obtained with them from a continuous record can be integrated directly by means of a planimeter to obtain total intensities of lines that are not flat-topped.

GENERAL REFERENCES

13.1.   L. S. Ornstein, W. J. H. Moll, and H. C. Burger, *Objektive Spektral-photometrie.*   Braunschweig: Vieweg, 1932.
13.2.   G. R. Harrison, "Instruments and Methods Used for Measuring Spectral Light Intensity by Photometry," *Jour. Opt. Soc. Am.*, **19**, 267 (1929).
13.3.   G. R. Harrison, "Current Advances in Photographic Photometry," *Jour. Opt. Soc. Am.*, **24**, 59 (1934).
13.4.   W. E. Forsythe (Ed.), *Measurement of Radiant Energy.*   New York: McGraw-Hill Book Company, Inc., 1937, Chapters VIII and IX.
13.5.   K. Henney and B. Dudley (Eds.), *Handbook of Photography.*   New York: McGraw-Hill Book Company, Inc., 1939.
13.6.   G. M. B. Dobson, I. O. Griffith, and D. N. Harrison, *Photographic Photometry.*   London: Oxford University Press, 1926.

CHAPTER 14

Absorption Spectrophotometry

ABSORPTION SPECTROPHOTOMETRY IS THE TECHNIQUE of determining the relationship between the wavelength, or frequency, of radiation and its attenuation by absorption upon passage through a particular medium. The following discussion will be limited to absorption spectrophotometry in the region from approximately 2000 to 10,000 A. These wavelengths correspond to the nominal limits within which measurements can be made satisfactorily with usual equipment for the visible and ultraviolet. Spectrophotometric measurements at wavelengths longer than about 10,000 A (in the infrared) and shorter than about 2000 A (in the vacuum ultraviolet) require special techniques that are discussed respectively in Chapters 17 and 19.

Spectrophotometry in the range 2000 to 10,000 A is normally applied to the study of substances in the solid or liquid state or in solution. The observable absorption may be continuous and fairly uniform throughout the region in question, in which case it is called *general absorption*, or it may exhibit one or more broad maxima and minima, in which case it is called *selective absorption*.

The techniques to be described have wide application in organic chemistry in the characterization of compounds, in the control of isolation and purification procedures, in the determination of molecular structure, and in qualitative and quantitative analysis. Other applications include the determination of the transmission characteristics of dyestuffs and filters, the study of cytochemical and histochemical problems by microspectrophotometry, and the investigation of photochemical reactions.

LAWS OF ABSORPTION AND THEIR APPLICATION TO ABSORPTION SPECTROPHOTOMETRY

14.1. Lambert's Law. The simplest case of absorption is that in which a parallel beam of monochromatic radiation passes rectilinearly through a homogenous absorbing medium. Under such circumstances, the intensity of the radiation is reduced by the same fractional amount in equal succeeding portions of its path. Thus, if the intensity is reduced by half in the first centimeter, it will be reduced by half again in the second centimeter (that is, to one-fourth of the original intensity), and so on. The medium may be considered to be made up of layers of infinitesimal thickness, dl, perpendicular to the path of the radiation. Let I represent the intensity at any point of the path, and α the fraction by which absorption reduces the intensity in unit length of path.* Then

$$-\frac{dI}{dl} = \alpha I \tag{14.1}$$

The constant α is known as the *absorption coefficient*. It is characteristic of the absorbing medium and is a function of the wavelength of the radiation.

When Eq. (14.1) is integrated between the thickness limits 0 and x, an expression known as Lambert's law results. It gives the ratio, I_0/I_x, of intensity of radiation before, to that after, passing through the thickness x:

$$\log_e \frac{I_0}{I_x} = \alpha x, \qquad \text{or} \qquad I_x = I_0 e^{-\alpha x} \tag{14.2}$$

Using base 10 instead of base e, Eqs. (14.2) become, respectively,

$$\log_{10} \frac{I_0}{I_x} = Kx, \qquad \text{or} \qquad I_x = I_0\, 10^{-Kx} \tag{14.3}$$

where $K = 0.4343\alpha$ and $\alpha = 2.303K$. The constant K is known as the *extinction coefficient;*[1] $1/K$ is the thickness of absorbing layer necessary to reduce I_x to $(1/10)I_0$.

Only in the rare case of a neutral absorbing substance, which exhibits the same absorbing power throughout the entire wavelength region under consideration, are α and K independent of wavelength.

---

* There is considerable variation in the letter symbols used by various authors to designate quantities of interest in absorption spectroscopy, and the symbols used here should, therefore, not be regarded as representing a universally accepted standard nomenclature. Insofar as practicable, the symbols used have been chosen to correspond with those employed widely in the literature, including scientific papers in German and French as well as in English. Where confusion might arise from the use of one symbol for two different quantities, a separate letter symbol has been used for each quantity.

[1] R. Bunsen and H. E. Roscoe, *Pogg. Ann. Physik*, **101**, 235 (1857).

In all other instances, the preceding expressions are valid only for strictly monochromatic radiation. Apparent deviations from Lambert's law may, therefore, occur in practical measurements if the radiation employed is insufficiently monochromatic. Other causes of apparent deviation from Lambert's law are geometric factors, such as obliquity or lack of parallelism of the beam of radiation, which may introduce errors in the assumed path length x; lack of homogeneity in the absorbing medium; and losses by reflection from surfaces in the path of the beam of radiation.

14.2. Beer's Law. If the absorbing medium is a substance in solution, the attenuation of radiation on traversing a given path length depends on the concentration of the solution. Under suitable conditions, the absorption by dissolved substances is closely proportional to the number of molecules of solute per unit volume of solution, whence

$$\alpha = \mu c \qquad (14.4)$$

and
$$K = kc \qquad (14.5)$$

where α and K are, respectively, the absorption and extinction coefficients as previously defined, c is the concentration of the absorbing substance, expressed in suitable units, and μ and k are, respectively the absorption and extinction coefficients per unit of concentration. The above expressions are known as *Beer's Law*.[2]

Beer's law is based on the assumption that the specific absorption per molecule of the absorbing substance does not vary with the concentration of the substance in solution. This condition is often satisfied within the limits of experimental error (particularly for highly dilute solutions), but it is by no means universally applicable. Changes in concentration may lead to changes in the nature of the molecular species in solution. Such changes include, on the one hand, polymer formation and the formation of other kinds of molecular associations (including complexes with the solvent), and, on the other hand, dissociation. If such changes take place and if the specific molecular absorption is influenced thereby, μ and k become functions of c instead of constants, and apparent deviations from Beer's law are observed.

Lambert's and Beer's laws may be combined in single expressions

---

[2] A. Beer, *Pogg. Ann. Physik*, **86**, 78 (1852).

for the attenuation of the monochromatic radiation that traverses a solution of absorbing material, thus:

$$\log_e \frac{I_0}{I_x} = \mu cx; \quad \text{or} \quad I_x = I_0 e^{-\mu cx} \tag{14.6}$$

$$\log_{10} \frac{I_0}{I_x} = kcx; \quad \text{or} \quad I_x = I_0 10^{-kcx} \tag{14.7}$$

If the concentration c in the Lambert-Beer equations is expressed in gram-molecular weights per liter (moles), the corresponding coefficients of specific absorption may be represented by E and ϵ; the latter is known as the *molecular extinction coefficient*.

14.3. Variables Measured in Absorption Spectrophotometry. Spectrophotometric measurements of the absorbing characteristics of substances lead to the evaluation, at one or more wavelengths, of the *transmissivity T*, where

$$T = \frac{I_x}{I_0} \tag{14.8}$$

the *per cent transmission t*, where

$$t = 100 \frac{I_x}{I_0} \tag{14.9}$$

the *opacity O*, where

$$O = \frac{I_0}{I_x} \tag{14.10}$$

or the *optical density D*, where

$$D = \log_{10} \frac{I_0}{I_x} \tag{14.11}$$

Such evaluation may be accomplished either by direct determination of the ratios I_x/I_0 or $\log_{10}(I_0/I_x)$ or by separate determinations of the two light intensities or the logarithms thereof.

To determine the attenuation of the radiation that traverses a medium, a suitable specimen is placed in the path of the radiation. If the substance is a solid, the specimen may be a slab or block of material with polished, plane-parallel faces, so placed that a parallel beam of the radiation enters and leaves the specimen perpendicularly to the faces. If the substance is a liquid or is in solution, it may be contained in a cell with polished, plane-parallel end plates that are substantially transparent to radiation in the region of interest. The cell and its contents may then be placed in the path of the radiation in the same manner as a solid specimen.

14.4. Elimination of Effects Due to Reflections and Absorption by Cell Windows and by Solvents. In order for the foregoing equations to be applicable to absorbing specimens, I_0 must be the intensity of radiation that enters the absorbing medium and I_x the intensity incident upon the exit face. I_0 is not usually the same as the intensity I incident on the entrance face of a solid specimen or cell, nor is I_x the same as the intensity i of radiation leaving the exit face, since the intensity is reduced at all faces by reflection whenever changes in refractive index occur at these points. The intensity may be reduced further by absorption in the cell windows in the case of a cell containing a liquid or solution. In absorption spectrophotometry, I and i are the intensities that are readily measurable. One is confronted, therefore, with the problem of how to determine I_0 and I_x (or I_0/I_x) from measurements of I and i (or I/i).

In the case of solids, I_0/I_x may be determined by measuring i_1 and i_2 for two specimens of unequal lengths x_1 and x_2. If x_1 is greater than x_2, i_2/i_1 is equivalent to $I_0/I_{x'}$ where x' corresponds to the difference in path length $x_1 - x_2$, provided that the entrance faces and the exit faces of the two specimens reflect the same fractions γ and δ of the radiation incident upon them.

$$\frac{i_2}{i_1} = \frac{e^{-\alpha x_2}}{e^{-\alpha x_1}} = e^{\alpha x'} = \frac{I_0}{I_{x'}} \tag{14.12}$$

The same method may be employed for absorbing liquids. The intensities i_1 and i_2 of the transmitted radiation are determined with cells of different lengths x_1 and x_2 but otherwise identical. The ratio i_2/i_1 is then equivalent to $I_0/I_{x'}$, where $x' = x_1 - x_2$.

With substances in solution, it is also essential to eliminate effects due to absorption by the solvent. If the method outlined for liquids is employed, the resultant measurement of i_2/i_1 yields a value of $I_0/I_{x'}$ representing the attenuation of intensity by both solute and solvent in a path length x'. To eliminate absorption by the solvent, it is customary to employ two cells that are identical in every respect, including length, one containing the solution and the other the solvent. If the solvent has the same absorbing effect in the presence or absence of the solute and if the reflection coefficients at the cell faces are the same in both instances, the ratio I_0/I_x can be measured directly. The first condition holds except for instances in which interaction between solute and solvent modifies the absorbing characteristics of both. The second condition is not true insofar as the inner faces of the cells are concerned when the index of refraction of the solution is different from that of the solvent. However, the reflection error introduced by differences in refractive index at the inner faces is not usually as great as other experimental errors and is commonly neglected.

Additional sources of error in the determination of I_0/I_x may arise from fluorescent radiation emitted by the absorbing medium, scattering of radiation by suspended particles in a liquid medium, multiple reflections between the faces of a solid specimen or a cell, and reflections from the sidewalls of a cell or the sides of a solid specimen when the beam of radiant energy is not strictly parallel. The conditions of measurement should be so chosen as to reduce such effects to a minimum.

14.5. Presentation of Data. All spectrophotometric data are expressed in terms of two variables which it is convenient to call the *intensity variable* and the *wavelength variable*. The intensity variable indicates, directly or indirectly, the power of the absorbing substance to attenuate radiation at a particular wavelength. It may be expressed as transmissivity, per cent transmission, opacity, absorption coefficient, extinction coefficient, and so on, as these terms have been defined previously. The wavelength parameter designates the wavelength, or frequency, of radiation to which a particular attenuation factor applies. It may be expressed as wavelength in angstroms or millimicrons, as frequency in oscillations per second, or as wave number in cm^{-1}. The choice of the most appropriate terms in which to express these two variables depends on the application to be made of the data.

In the case of optical filters, the information usually desired is the fraction of the incident intensity transmitted at various wavelengths by a filter of definite thickness and composition. The intensity variable may therefore be expressed in transmissivity or per cent transmission.

In the use of spectrophotometric data to characterize chemical compounds, it is desirable, for purposes of comparison, to express the intensity variable in terms that are independent of the specific conditions of measurement (such as length x of optical path or concentration c of a solution). For solids or liquids, the intensity variable is therefore conveniently expressed in terms of the absorption coefficient α or extinction coefficient K. For solutions, the corresponding specific absorption and extinction coefficients μ and k per unit concentration may be employed. Molecular extinction coefficients are convenient for comparing the absorption of solutions on the basis of molecular concentration or for computing the absorption of a complex molecule in terms of its constituent chemical groups. Occasionally, the logarithm of the extinction coefficient or of the molecular extinction coefficient is employed in order to permit presentation of curves with widely different values on a single graph sheet or presentation of curves having specific shapes characteristic of the substances regardless of the units of concentration and path length employed. The wavelength variable for chemical compounds is usually expressed in angstroms or millimicrons. Frequency or wave-number units have some advantages for theoretical studies but are less generally used.

Table 14.1 summarizes the various expressions employed for the intensity variable in absorption spectrophotometry.

SELECTION OF APPARATUS FOR ABSORPTION SPECTROPHOTOMETRY

14.6. Choice of Source of Radiation. For absorption spectrophotometry in the visible region, incandescent lamps are generally used. An ordinary 60 to 100 watt lamp with flashed opal bulb placed close to the slit of the dispersing system will give sufficient intensity for the direct qualitative observation of spectra (without a photometer) and has the advantage of giving uniform slit illumination without the necessity of critical alignment. Where greater intensities are required for quantitative observations, a lamp with clear bulb may be employed in conjunction with a condensing lens for forming an image of the filament on the slit. The shape, size, and brightness of the filament should be such that the working portion of the slit can be filled with uniform radiation of sufficient intensity for convenient observation. The image of a ribbon filament most closely approximates the geometry of the usual slit, but concentrated coil filaments of the type used in projection lamps give sufficiently good images for many purposes. Ribbon-filament lamps are used in lieu of slits in the collimating systems of certain simple photoelectric spectrophotometers. Suitable sources for use with polarizing and other types of photometers for the visible region are described in Chapter 8.

For abbreviated absorption spectrophotometry in the visible region, using filters instead of a dispersing system, mercury arcs have the

TABLE 14.1

SUMMARY OF EXPRESSIONS USED FOR TRANSMISSION AND ABSORPTION OF RADIATION

Expression	Units usually employed	Nomenclature	Principal applications
$T = \dfrac{I_x}{I_0} = \beta^x$		T = transmissivity	
		β = coefficient of transmission	Transmission characteristics of filters and dyestuffs
$t = 100\dfrac{I_x}{I_0}$	x in cm	t = per cent transmission	
$O = \dfrac{I_0}{I_x}$		O = opacity	Photographic blackening measurements
$D = \log_{10}\dfrac{I_0}{I_x}$		D = density	Photographic blackening measurements. Indication of absorption of solutions
$a = \dfrac{1}{x}\log_e\dfrac{I_0}{I_x}$	x in cm or mm	a = absorption coefficient	Absorption of solids or liquids (Continental usage)
$\mu = \dfrac{1}{cx}\log_e\dfrac{I_0}{I_x}$	x in cm or mm, c in grams per liter, mg per ml, per cent, or grams per ml	μ = absorption coefficient	Absorption of solutions (Continental usage)
$K = \dfrac{1}{x}\log_{10}\dfrac{I_0}{I_x}$	x in cm or mm	K = extinction coefficient	Absorption of solids or liquids (British and American usage)
$k = \dfrac{1}{cx}\log_{10}\dfrac{I_0}{I_x}$	x in cm or mm, c in grams per liter, mg per ml, per cent, or grams per ml	k = extinction coefficient	Absorption of solutions (British and American usage)
$\epsilon = \dfrac{1}{cx}\log_{10}\dfrac{I_0}{I_x}$	x in cm, c in moles per liter	ϵ = molecular extinction coefficient = Mk	Useful in computing the combined absorption of substances present in known molar ratios
$\log_{10} k$ or $\log_e k$			Used in compressing data so that curves occupy less space, etc.
$\gamma = \dfrac{\lambda}{4\pi x}\log_e\dfrac{I_0}{I_x}$	λ in cm in medium under consideration; $\lambda = \dfrac{\lambda_0}{n}$ where λ_0 is for vacuum and n is refractive index; x in cm	γ = absorption index	Used in discussion of absorption as derived from classical electromagnetic theory

advantage of providing several widely spaced emission lines, permitting isolation of more nearly monochromatic radiation than is possible by the use of filters with continuous sources. This advantage is, however, somewhat offset by the resulting restriction to a limited number of wavelengths; hence incandescent sources are ordinarily employed. There is usually no slit or stop in such a system to act as a secondary source. Therefore, if the optical system is to provide a nearly parallel beam of radiation, a lamp with concentrated filament or emitter, such as a projection lamp, an automobile headlight lamp, or a Western Union concentrated arc, must be used.

For photographic absorption spectrophotometry in the ultraviolet region, a condensed spark between tungsten-steel electrodes is convenient and often adequate. The spectrum of this source is rich in strong lines, but there are troublesome gaps (for example, at about 2650 A), and the intensity falls off abruptly below about 2350 A. Aluminum electrodes give several strong groups of lines in the region below 2000 A, in which tungsten is particularly deficient. They may be used as a supplementary source when it is desired to measure absorption in this region. Uranium electrodes give a spectrum very rich in lines of almost uniform intensity and have been recommended as a substitute for continuous sources. They are costly, however, and their spectrum is quite weak below 2200 A. With suitably cored carbons, such as National Carbon Co. 6 mm C, carbon arcs can be used satisfactorily as a substitute for the condensed tungsten spark. They may require somewhat more frequent adjustment than sparks, even when provided with automatic feeding mechanisms, and they do not approximate point sources so closely.

Continuous sources have a definite advantage in ultraviolet spectrophotometry when it is desired to study the finest details of complex absorption spectra. Of such sources, the underwater spark is adequate, but hydrogen discharge tubes in quartz are more convenient and more readily available. Both of these sources permit observation to the short-wave limit of transmission of usual ultraviolet spectrophotometric equipment. The General Electric type H–4 high-pressure mercury arc with outer glass envelope removed yields a spectrum with a strong continuous background, in addition to the mercury lines, down to about 2100 A.*

---

* Some lamps of this type will not operate satisfactorily without the outer glass envelope unless they are placed in an enclosure that will maintain them at a comparatively high operating temperature.

For photoelectric absorption spectrophotometry, it is usually essential that the radiant output of the source be free from fluctuations. It is also desirable that the spectrum of the source be continuous, since the presence of strong emission lines may cause such characteristics as nonuniform wavelength response of the photocell, scattered radiation, and limited resolving power of the dispersing system, to result in appreciable errors in the measurements. The usual choices are, therefore, incandescent lamps for the visible region and well-regulated hydrogen discharge tubes in quartz for the ultraviolet.

For a more detailed discussion of sources, Chapter 8 should be consulted.

14.7. Choice of Absorption Cells. The general characteristics to be considered in the choice of absorption cells for the spectrophotometry of liquids or solutions are as follows: transmission characteristics of cell windows, path length through absorbing medium (*inside cell length*), precision and uniformity of inside cell length, flatness and parallelism of window faces, perpendicularity of faces to the path of radiation, and convenience in manipulation.

Glass windows are sufficiently transparent for use in the region 10,000 to 3400 A. Below about 3400 A, quartz, fluorite, or lithium fluoride must be used. Fused quartz is the usual window material for cells for ultraviolet spectrophotometry. If it is desired to eliminate effects due to fluorescence of the windows and to obtain the greatest possible transparency below 2200 A, crystal quartz* is somewhat better.

The inside cell length should usually be chosen so that it is possible to obtain a density, $\log_{10}(I_0/I_x)$, of about 0.4 to 0.5 for photoelectric spectrophotometry and of about 1.5 to 2.0 for photographic spectrophotometry, at the absorption maxima for which precise data are required. The possibility of diluting the absorbing material so as to change its density per unit path length within wide limits usually permits considerable latitude in choice of cell length. For general use, therefore, it suffices to have available cells of a few convenient inside path lengths, say 1, 2, and 4 cm. For some samples, shorter or longer path lengths may be required.

The precision and uniformity of the inside cell length should be such that the over-all errors of the measurements are not increased

---

* Crystal-quartz windows must be cut perpendicular to the optic axis to avoid effects caused by double refraction.

appreciably by path-length errors.   Cells are available commercially in which the inside-length tolerance is kept below ±0.15 per cent of the total path, corresponding to a maximum density error of about ±0.0023 at a density of 1.5 or of about ±0.00075 at a density of 0.5.

The cell-window faces should be flat to within a few wavelengths, at most, of the radiation used, and all faces should be parallel to within a few minutes of arc.

The dimensions of cells perpendicular to the path of the radiation should be sufficient to ensure that radiation will not strike the cell walls and be reflected from them.   This condition having been fulfilled, it is desirable to keep these dimensions to a minimum in order that minimum volumes of material will be required.

For convenience in manipulation, cells with removable windows have the advantage of being easy to clean.   Certain designs may

Fig. 14.1.   Typical types of cells for visible and ultraviolet absorption spectrophotometry.

have disadvantages, such as variation in path length upon reassembly, leakage, and contamination of cell contents by absorbing substances from the gaskets.   When gaskets are used, troublesome contamination can often be avoided by washing the gaskets repeatedly, before use, with the solvent or liquid absorbing medium to be used in the measurements.   Spacer tubes of metal are sometimes used in demountable cells; glass or silica must be employed if there is danger that metal may be attacked by the cell contents.   Permanently assembled cells with cemented-on windows can be used only with fluids in which the cement is insoluble.   Hence one-piece cells with fused-on windows are preferable for general applications.   Permanently assembled cells with open tops or with two filler tubes are somewhat easier to clean than those with a single filler tube, but the single-tube type with a ground-glass stopper is useful when it is desired to prevent evaporation of the cell contents during long periods of use.   Typical absorption cells are shown in Fig. 14.1.

A cell of variable length, such as a *Baly tube* (Fig. 14.2), is a convenience in preliminary explorations to determine the most convenient concentration of a solution to employ with a particular cell of fixed length.   Baly cells are obtainable with micrometer adjustment whereby the path length may be set to within about ±0.005 mm. Other cells of special design, such as the *notched echelon cell*, are described in later sections dealing with special spectrophotometric methods.

14.8.   Choice of Spectrophotometric Method.   It is convenient to classify spectrophotometric methods according to the radiation detector employed.   If one uses this basis of classification, there are three principal spectrophotometric methods from which to choose: (1) visual, (2) photographic, and (3) photoelectric.   Although

(a)   (b)

Fig. 14.2.   Baly cells.   (a) Sliding tube type.   (b) Micrometer type.

thermoelectric methods are used in the infrared where no others are available, their comparative insensitivity makes them undesirable for regions where one of the three more responsive methods can be employed.

The visual method is of use only in the region from about 4000 to 7500 A.   For this region it has the advantage of simplicity and the disadvantage of yielding results that may vary considerably from observer to observer even under the best of operating conditions. Particularly in those spectral regions in which the eye is least sensitive, some workers find it difficult to obtain satisfactory results by this method.

The photographic method has the advantage of providing a permanent record which, at sufficiently high dispersion, may be made to record the minutest details of complex absorption spectra.   If the photographic record is photometered visually, this method has some of the disadvantages inherent in visual spectrophotometry, though the situation is improved by the fact that the photometric procedure can be carried out with light of high intensity and uniform spectral quality. The pitfalls of visual photometry may be avoided by the use of objective photometric devices (for example, photoelectric densitometers; see Chapter 13). The time required to process the emulsion is a further disadvantage of the photographic method.

Photoelectric methods may be subdivided into those which involve point-by-point measurements at selected wavelengths and those which permit automatic recording at all wavelengths within the range to be investigated. A special case of the former is the *absorptiometer* or *colorimeter*. The colorimeter is a device equipped with a simple dispersing system, or with filters, that permits determination of the concentration of substances by their absorption of approximately monochromatic radiation at a selected wave band. Such devices are useful in analytical chemical procedures. Point-by-point photoelectric spectrophotometers are convenient for routine measurements in applications to analytical chemistry, organic chemistry, and biochemistry, but the data obtained with them may not show all the important details of the absorption spectrum because of the missing data between the observed points. Automatic-recording photoelectric spectrophotometers have the advantage of covering, continuously, the entire range of wavelengths under investigation. They present, however, maintenance and adjustment problems somewhat in proportion to their complexity. Photoelectric methods, in general, share the advantage of yielding objective measurements that can be reproduced consistently with less skill and care than are usually required for similarly consistent results with visual or photographic methods.

Table 14.2 summarizes the bases of choice among the various methods of spectrophotometry (compare Table 12.1).

VISUAL ABSORPTION SPECTROPHOTOMETRY

14.9. General Considerations. Apparatus for visual absorption spectrophotometry requires the following principal components: (1) a suitable light source; (2) a means for separating the light from the source into two parallel beams (one traversing the absorbing medium and the other serving as a comparison beam) and for bringing these beams into juxtaposition so that they may be viewed ultimately as parts of the same photometric field; (3) a means of

TABLE 14.2

CHOICE OF SPECTROPHOTOMETRIC METHOD

Method		Range to which applicable	Advantages	Disadvantages	Principal application
Visual		4000–7500 A	Simplicity	Accuracy of data depends on vision and skill of observer	Absorption spectra of dyes and filters; reflection spectra
Photographic		2000–10,000 A	Yields permanent record of entire spectrum; capable of showing details of spectra	Requires time-consuming manipulations; data depend on vision and skill of observer if plates are photometered visually	Absorption spectra of organic compounds; determination of fine structure in spectra; spectrophotometric research
Photoelectric	Absorptiometers	3400–10,000 A	Simplicity; provides objective measurements	Employs broad spectral bands; not suited to precise determination of absorption spectra	Quantitative chemical analysis by colorimetric procedures
	Point-by-point spectrophotometers	2000–10,000 A	Simplicity; convenience and speed; provides objective measurements	Yields data at selected wavelengths only; not well adapted to fine structure investigations	Routine spectrophotometry of organic compounds
	Automatic recording spectrophotometers	2000–10,000 A	Yields permanent record of entire spectrum; capable of showing details of spectra; convenience and speed	Requires elaborate equipment	Routine spectrophotometry where work load warrants cost; spectrophotometric research

changing, by known amounts, the intensity ratio of the two beams; (4) suitable absorption cells (if liquids or solutions are used); and (5) a spectrometer that permits isolation of a narrow spectral band in both beams and presentation of this spectral region of the two beams in a photometric field for visual comparison.

Any variation in the brightness of the different portions of the light source from which the radiant flux is collected into the two parallel beams may cause irregularities in the brightness of the different portions of the final photometric field. Consequently, directly illuminated diffusing screens or indirectly illuminated diffuse reflecting surfaces are often used as light sources in order to ensure that the entire area contributing flux to the photometer will be essentially uniform. This method of illumination is wasteful of light and is likely to result in low brightness of the photometric field, especially when highly absorbing materials are to be measured. When the highest intensity of effective illumination of the field is desired for transmission measurements of specimens of high density, a nearly uniform concentrated source, such as a Pointolite, Western Union concentrated arc, or ribbon-filament lamp, may be used (§ 8.7).

The two light beams are separated, recombined, rendered parallel, and brought to focus by suitable reflecting and refracting surfaces. The design of this portion of the optical system is governed by the applications to which the instrument is to be put as well as by mechanical and optical considerations. Control of the intensity of one or both light beams is most commonly accomplished by the use of polarizing prisms in tandem. The analyzer is mounted so that it may be rotated with respect to the polarizer (or polarizers) by known amounts indicated by a circular scale. Alternatively, fixed diaphragms of variable aperture or rotating sectors may be employed for attenuating the beams.

The photometer may be an integral part of the spectrometer, as in the original König-Martens instrument (§ 14.11), or it may be separate from it. In the latter case, it is customary to use a constant-deviation type of spectrometer employing a Pellin-Broca prism (Chapter 3). The light source, beam-splitting and focusing optics, cell holders, and intensity-controlling device are, in this latter case, usually mounted as a single unit which is called the *photometer* or (somewhat incorrectly) the *spectrophotometer*.

Various forms of absorption cells may be used in studying the transmission of liquids and solutions. Inside path lengths of 2 to 4 cm may be required for specimens that have low absorption coefficients. Commercial visual spectrophotometers are usually designed so that they may be used for reflectance as well as transmission measurements, and for measuring absorption by relatively opaque materials.

Since visual spectrophotometers are intended for use in the visible region of the spectrum only, all transmitting optical components, except polarizing prisms, are of glass.

14.10. Advantages and Limitations of the Visual Method. The visual spectrophotometer is easily set up and is free from the complications of photographic manipulation or of the operation and maintenance of electrical measuring devices. As a consequence, it has been used widely and is still employed considerably in industrial control and research laboratories for measurements of transmission, reflectance, and absorption by opaque samples within the range of the visible spectrum.

The limitations of the visual method arise from certain characteristics of vision, among which the following are most important: the matching of intensities by the eye involves subjective as well as objective factors; under the same conditions of observation, different eyes vary considerably in the precision with which they make it possible for the observer to perceive differences in contrast; the sensitivity of an observer to differences in contrast varies markedly with the average brightness level of the visual field; and the visual stimulus is a complex function of the wavelength of the exciting radiation.

As shown in Fig. 14.3, the average observer is able to perceive intensity differences of about 1 per cent (corresponding to density differences of about 0.0043) at a brightness of 10 mL.* However, at a brightness of 0.001 mL, an intensity difference of about 20 per cent (corresponding to a density difference of 0.079) is required for discrimination. In order for the percentage density error to be small in measurements of absorbing substances in the region of maximum absorption, it is essential that the measurements be made with samples having high density values (say 1.5 to 2.0). Such values correspond to low transmissions and may result in reduction of brightness of the field to the point at which sensitivity to contrast is

---

* The *lambert*, abbreviated L, is a unit of brightness equal to the average brightness of a surface emitting or reflecting 1 lumen per square centimeter. The *millilambert*, abbreviated mL, which equals 0.001 L, is generally used as the unit of brightness except for very bright surfaces.

materially reduced (Fig. 14.3).   This reduction is especially apt to occur at the two ends of the visible spectrum, where the luminosity per unit of radiant energy is quite low.

In general, it may be concluded that (a) the visual method is useful in some routine work, (b) more objective methods should be employed if the greatest precision is required, and (c) special caution needs to be used when the visual method is applied to transmission measurements of specimens having absorption bands at the extreme red and blue ends of the visible spectrum.   In the following four sections, several typical visual spectrophotometers are discussed.

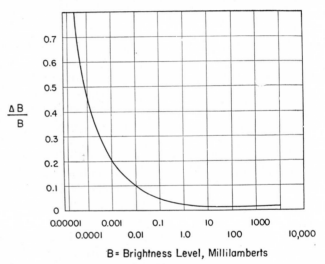

Fig. 14.3.   Variation in discrimination of the eye for change in brightness, ΔB, at different brightness levels, B.

14.11.   Instruments Using the Martens Type of Polarizing Photometer.

The Martens type of polarizing photometer (Fig. 14.4) employs a Wollaston prism as a polarizer.   When the two beams of light to be photometered are passed through such a prism, each beam is split into two beams which diverge from each other and which are plane-polarized in directions perpendicular to each other.   Thus four beams emerge from the Wollaston prism.

Of these beams, only two, polarized perpendicularly to each other and corresponding to the two original beams of light to be photometered, are to be observed in the final photometric field.   It is necessary, therefore, to discard the undesired beams and to direct the desired ones in such a manner that they will be brought together side by side in the field of view. This result is accomplished by a bi-prism, which splits the four beams into eight but directs only the two desired ones toward the photometric field, and by appropriate stops

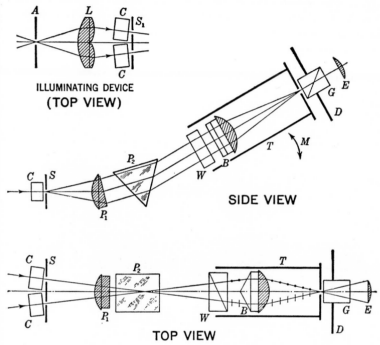

Fig. 14.4. Schematic diagram of König-Martens Spectrophotometer. *A*, light source; *L*, condensing lenses; *C*, absorption cells; *S*, entrance slits; P_1, collimating lens and refracting prism; P_2, dispersing prism; *W*, Wollaston polarizing prism; *B*, biprism and telescope lens; *G*, analyzing prism; *D*, divided circle; *E*, eyepiece lens. (By permission from *Optical Methods of Chemical Analysis* by T. R. P. Gibb, Jr. Copyrighted 1942 by McGraw-Hill Book Co., Inc.)

which minimize the possibility that scattered light from the discarded beams will traverse the system. The observer, looking into the eye-piece at the end of the optical train, sees a field of view divided in the middle. One half is illuminated by plane-polarized light from one of the original beams; the other half is illuminated by perpendicularly plane-polarized light from the second of the original beams. A Glan-

Thompson or Nicol prism, placed at a suitable position between the biprism and the eye of the observer, is used as an analyzer.

As the analyzer is rotated continuously in one direction, the two halves of the photometric field are extinguished alternately at 90-deg intervals.   These positions of the analyzer are known as the *extinction points*.   The two halves of the photometric field are matched in intensity at intermediate positions between the extinction points, known as the *zero points*.   If the original beams are of the same intensity and if the optical system is symmetrical, zero points occur halfway between extinction points;   otherwise, this may not be precisely true.

Fig. 14.5.   Polarizing spectrophotometer manufactured by the Gaertner Scientific Corp., Chicago.

In the König-Martens spectrophotometer,[3] the Wollaston prism and biprism are mounted at the position of the telescope lens of the spectrometer.   The analyzer prism is mounted in the eyepiece, behind a slit that gives a photometric field in which each half is illuminated uniformly throughout with a mixture of colors corresponding to the spectral range under examination.

Many commercial instruments, such as those of Bausch & Lomb and Gaertner (Fig. 14.5), employ an alternative arrangement in which the photometer (together with accessories for illumination, holding the cells, and other purposes) is a unit separate from the spectrometer, the latter being of the constant-deviation type.   With this arrangement, the photometer field is focused on the entrance slit

---

[3] H. J. McNicholas, *Bur. Standards J. Research*, **1**, 793 (1928).

of the spectrometer. The field viewed through the eye lens of the spectrometer consists of two spectra, one immediately above the other. The spectral range in view at any one time is limited by laterally adjustable stops in the spectrometer eyepiece.

For transmission measurements, the Bausch & Lomb and Gaertner instruments use a back-illuminated diffusing screen as a source. For measuring the transmission of liquids, the Bausch & Lomb photometer may be obtained in a modified form with cells of continuously adjustable depth similar to those used in Duboscq colorimeters. For reflection measurements, both the Bausch & Lomb and Gaertner instruments use sphere illuminators.

14.12. Hilger-Nutting Polarizing Spectrophotometer. The Hilger-Nutting polarizing spectrophotometer employs a photometer and constant-deviation spectrometer arranged in tandem as in the Bausch & Lomb and Gaertner instruments. The original Hilger-Nutting photometer had one fixed polarizing prism system followed by a rotatable analyzer. An improved model, described in two papers by Dowell,[4] utilizes a second, fixed analyzer-prism system following the rotatable analyzer, which results in a more extended, or open, density scale at the higher density values (§ 14.13), in the elimination of a certain amount of stray light, and in the emergence from the photometer of a beam with a constant plane of polarization instead of one that rotates with changes in the setting of the rotatable analyzer as in the case of instruments with a single analyzer. The constant plane of polarization obviates the possibility that changes in the photometer adjustments might cause changes in the transmission characteristics of the spectrometer as a result of reflections at optical surfaces.

For transmission measurements, the Hilger-Nutting spectrophotometer ordinarily uses a Pointolite-lamp source, which gives a comparatively bright photometric field. It may also be fitted with a sphere illuminator, which gives a somewhat more uniform field but one of much less brightness, not so well adapted to transmission measurements at high densities. For reflectance measurements, the sphere illuminator should be used. An attachment is provided whereby opaque objects and standard reflecting surfaces may be illuminated by a 500-watt Pointolite lamp, the angles between the specimens and the light source on the one hand and between the

---

[4] J. H. Dowell, *Jour. Sci. Inst.*, **8**, 382–384 (1931); **10**, 153–156 (1933).

specimens and the photometer beams on the other being adjustable. To measure absorption by polished opaque specimens with high surface reflectance, a Pointolite illuminator is provided in which the light from the source is reflected back and forth several times between two samples of the specimen before entering the photometer.

14.13. Manipulation of Polarizing Spectrophotometers. For transmission measurements, the specimen is placed in the path of one of the photometer beams. If the absorbing specimen is a substance in solution, a duplicate cell containing the solvent is placed in the path of the other beam (§ 14.4). For reflectance measurements and for measurements of the absorption of opaque substances, the light entering one of the photometer beams is reflected from the specimen and the light entering the other photometer beam is reflected from a comparison surface (*reference standard*) having a nearly uniform reflection coefficient in the range of the visible spectrum. Magnesium oxide is, aside from its fragility, an excellent material for a reference standard. Its reflection coefficient is about 0.97 throughout the visible region, it is a good diffuser, and its reflection characteristics do not vary appreciably with time. If a less fragile surface is desired, white glass or porcelain may be used and calibrated with respect to MgO. Further details regarding methods of illumination and manipulation in reflectance measurements are given in the references at the end of this chapter.

Several commercial photometers are provided with scales from which opacity, reflectance, and density may be read directly.

To determine a complete spectral curve of transmission or reflectance, readings are taken at intervals throughout the spectrum, the wavelength being adjusted by means of the spectrometer drum for each new set of readings. The most appropriate wavelength interval between readings depends on the accuracy with which it is desired to determine the characteristics of the specimen and the nature of the spectral transmission or reflectance curve. For specimens with pronounced selective absorption, determinations must be made at more frequent intervals than for those having general absorption only. Intervals of 50 to 500 A are commonly used. The width of the entrance and exit slits should be adjusted for the maximum purity of spectrum consistent with sufficient brightness of field for accurate matching. Measurements should be carried out in a darkened room after the eyes have become accommodated to the low light level of the room.

14.14. Other Visual Spectrophotometers and Their Manipulation.
The Keuffel and Esser color analyzer[5] (Fig. 14.6) employs a rotating
sector of fixed angle in the specimen beam and one of variable angle
in the comparison beam, both being mounted on the same shaft. A
motor rotates the sectors at sufficient speed to eliminate noticeable
flicker. The two photometer beams illuminate the entrance slit of
a constant-deviation spectrometer. The division in the photometric
field is produced by a biprism placed between the dispersing prism

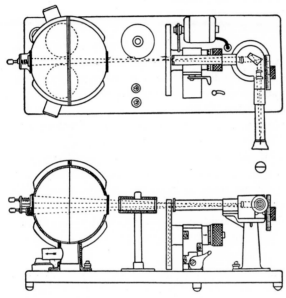

Fig. 14.6. Keuffel and Esser color analyzer. (By permission from *Measurement of Radiant Energy*, edited by W. E. Forsythe. Copyrighted 1937 by McGraw-Hill Book Co., Inc.)

and the spectrometer telescope lens, resulting in a field similar to that
viewed in the König-Martens spectrophotometer (§ 14.11) except
that the dividing line is horizontal instead of vertical. The variable
sector is adjusted by a special mechanical arrangement, while the
sectors are in motion, until the two halves of the photometric field
match. The value of I_x/I_0 or R/R_0 corresponding to this adjustment
is read directly from a suitable scale. A sphere illuminator is used
for both transmission and reflectance measurements.

[5] C. W. Keuffel, *Jour. Opt. Soc. Am.* and *Rev. Sci. Inst.*, **11**, 403 (1925).

For comparison of the intensities of light sources, it is advantageous to be able to introduce two widely separated light beams into the spectrometer. The Lummer-Brodhun[6] and Guild[7] photometers accomplish this by the use of two collimating systems in conjunction with a suitable optical system for causing the two collimated beams to illuminate different portions of the final photometric field. The Buckley and Brookes photometer[8] uses a Lummer-Brodhun cube to bring together two light beams before focusing them on the slit of a constant-deviation spectrometer.

Several means of varying the light intensities other than those previously described have been used. Variation of collimator slit width has been employed with the Lummer-Brodhun instrument. Adjustment of a rotating sector while in motion can be accomplished by the use of a cylinder instead of a disk and by cutting away the cylinder in such a way that moving it along its axis perpendicular to the light beam changes the effective aperture.[9] The Guild instrument [7] employs a series of interchangeable fixed sectors in combination with movable neutral absorption wedges placed close to the collimator slit.   In the Buckley and Brookes photometer,[8] the brightness of the source is varied by controlling the voltage at which it is operated. With small concentrated sources, use may be made of the inverse-square law as a means of varying the intensity.*   Finally, a variable aperture may be placed at a suitable point in the optical train at which there is a uniform parallel beam of radiation (§ 14.22).

PHOTOGRAPHIC ABSORPTION SPECTROPHOTOMETRY

14.15. General Considerations. Photographic absorption spectrophotometry involves the use of homochromatic photographic photometry, which was discussed in detail in Chapter 13 and is considered here only in relation to certain special aspects concerned with absorption measurement.

Photographic materials may be applied to the study of absorption (a) as qualitative or semiquantitative recorders for indicating the

---

[5] O. Lummer and E. Brodhun, *Zeitschr. Instrumentenk.*, **12**, 132 (1892).

[7] J. Guild, *Trans. Opt. Soc.*, **26**, 74–94 (1925).

[8] H. Buckley and F. L. C. Brookes, *Jour. Sci. Inst.* **7**, 305–317 (1930).

[9] F. L. Dunn, *Rev. Sci. Inst.*, **2**, 807–809 (1931).

* The inverse-square law holds strictly only for point sources.   As a general working rule, it may be assumed that deviation from the inverse-square law is less than 0.1 per cent if the minimum distance from the source is 15 times its diameter.

positions and relative magnitudes of absorption maxima and minima, (b) as calibrated responders to radiant energy for determining the relative intensities, I_0 and I_x, of the radiation incident upon and transmitted by an absorbing specimen at particular wavelengths, and (c) as null indicators for determining the wavelengths at which the spectra of radiation transmitted by an absorbing specimen match comparison spectra photographed with predetermined reductions in intensity level or time of exposure.   One or the other of these applications is the basis of every method of photographic absorption spectrophotometry.

All the above applications make use of: (a) a suitable light source (§ 14.6), (b) a means of introducing the specimen into the beam of radiation between the source and the spectrograph slit (for example, absorption cells, as discussed in § 14.7, if liquids or solutions are to be examined), (c) a spectrograph, and (d) photographic plates or films and appropriate means of processing them.   In addition, the second and third applications require a means of changing the intensity of the radiation or the time of exposure by known amounts.   This requirement is most often met by a split-beam photometric device, placed between the source and the spectrograph.

The determination of absorption spectra photographically with a split-beam photometer is somewhat similar to the techniques described in the section on visual spectrophotometry.   In visual spectrophotometry, however, one normally selects a particular wavelength region and adjusts the photometer until the two halves of the photometric field are matched in that region.   With photographic methods, it is customary to photograph a series of pairs of spectra, each with a different setting of the photometer, and then to determine the wavelengths, if any, at which match points occur for each spectrum pair (see Fig. 14.7).   This procedure is an example of the *null method*.   The same plate, with its several pairs of spectra, may be examined also at specific wavelengths, the photometric settings that correspond most closely to match points being determined for each wavelength, and the corresponding values of I_x/I_0 being estimated by interpolation.   This procedure is an example of the *calibration method*.

14.16. Advantages and Limitations of the Photographic Method. Photographic spectrophotometry is not so well adapted to use by semiskilled technicians as is photoelectric spectrophotometry with standard commercial instruments.   In addition to the manipulation of the photometer and spectrograph, photographic processing and examination and interpretation of the plates are involved. These

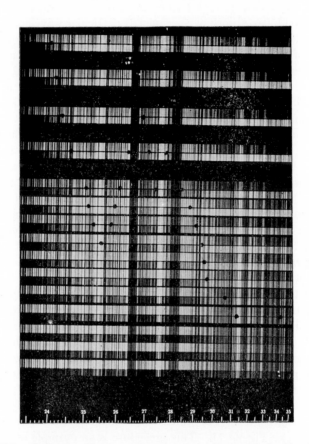

Fig. 14.7.   Absorption Spectra of human serum photographed with a Spekker split-beam photometer (§ 14.20).   The dots indicate match points between adjacent spectra (comparison and absorption) as determined visually.   The general shape of the absorption curve (corresponding to the presence of proteins and nucleic acids in the serum) is indicated by the positions of the dots, but for a more quantitative presentation these data would be plotted as an absorption curve.

require considerable skill and care if reliable results are to be obtained, so that commercial photoelectric spectrophotometers will probably be preferred in many laboratories.

On the other hand, the photographic method offers certain advantages. A simple test plate, taken and processed in less time than is required for a point-by-point photoelectric determination of an absorption curve, often yields information of considerable value. The fact that the entire spectrum is recorded on the plate often makes it possible to observe details of absorption that might be overlooked with point-by-point methods. Furthermore, spectrum details that are unresolvable with simple photoelectric instruments may sometimes be observed in photographic spectrograms. Because of these advantages, research laboratories find it useful to have available both photographic and photoelectric absorption spectrophotometers, using each for the particular applications to which it is best suited.

14.17. Spectrographs for Photographic Absorption Spectrophotometry. Prisms have been employed much more extensively than gratings in spectrographs for photographic absorption spectrophotometry, partly as a result of the greater availability of prisms. This situation may change as improvements take place in the production of gratings and grating replicas. Gratings have several advantages, including approximately constant dispersion as a function of wavelength. They also have disadvantages, of which the most important for many spectrophotometric applications are (a) the astigmatic images of the slit formed on the spectrum plate, except when the Wadsworth type of mounting or special methods of illumination are used, and (b) the necessity for removing overlapping orders, except in the first order of wavelengths (Chapters 2 and 4).

Prism spectrographs for absorption spectrophotometry usually have quartz optics, since the photographic method is largely employed for the ultraviolet region from 2000 to 4000 A. Glass optics are, of course, better for work in the visible region, where the dispersion of quartz is low, and many suitable spectrographs with glass optics are available (Chapter 3). Constant-deviation wavelength spectrometers of the type used in certain visual absorption spectrophotometers (see §§ 14.11 to 14.14) may usually be fitted with a camera in place of the viewing eyepiece, thus converting them to spectrographs suitable for photographic spectrophotometry in the visible region. Finally, some spectrographs may be obtained with interchangeable optics of various materials, including glass and quartz. Typical commercial quartz spectrographs for absorption work are listed in Table 14.3.

The choice between a small or a medium quartz spectrograph depends largely on whether measurements are to be made with it only in the ultraviolet or are to include the visible region. The so-called "medium" size usually has about three times the theoretical resolving power and linear dispersion of the "small" size. This higher resolving power and dispersion are of distinct advantage in the range above 4000 A because of the low dispersion of quartz in this region. In the ultraviolet, however, the situation is different. With a slit width of 0.02 mm, the effective resolution obtainable with a typical small

TABLE 14.3

SPECIFICATIONS OF TYPICAL COMMERCIAL QUARTZ SPECTROGRAPHS USEFUL IN
ABSORPTION SPECTROPHOTOMETRY

(All dimensions in centimeters)

Manufacturer and type No.	Prism	Collimator lens	Telescope lens	Length of spectrum 2000 to 8000 A
Small instruments				
Adam Hilger	Cornu 1.7 × 2.2	Diam 1.9 f_D 20.8	Diam 2.6 f_D 19.7	7.3
Gaertner	Cornu 2.0 × 3.0	Diam 2.5 f_D 18.5	Diam 2.5 f_D 16.5	7.2
Medium or intermediate instruments				
Adam Hilger	Cornu 4.1 × 6.5	Diam 5.1 f_D 61.0	Diam 5.1 f_D 61.0	22.5
Bausch & Lomb	Cornu 4.0 × 6.5	Diam 5.0 f_D 67.5	Diam 5.0 f_D 67.5	24.9
Gaertner	Cornu 4.0 × 6.5	Diam 5.0 f_D 70.0	Diam 5.0 f_D 70.0	37.5

quartz spectrograph is about 1.2 A at 2500 A and 3.0 A at 3000 A; these values are entirely acceptable for routine absorption spectrophotometry, and the dispersion from 1850 to 3000 A is satisfactory for most needs. For work in the region below 2300 A, where quartz absorbs appreciably, small spectrographs are sometimes to be preferred because of shorter path length through their optical components, and the greater feasibility of selecting small quartz specimens of high transmission in this region. Spectrography to 1850 A may be accomplished readily with small instruments having specially selected quartz optics.

The greater dispersion of medium instruments may be useful even in the ultraviolet when techniques involving direct visual examination of the plates are employed. Usually one may accomplish this equally well by enlarging the plates or examining them by projection. If, however, spectra are to be matched or densitometered by objective devices such as photoelectric densitometers, which are unable to distinguish between true photographic effects and defects in the plate, a large spectrum size on the negative is of advantage in reducing errors that arise from grain size, dust specks, and scratches in the emulsion.

14.18. Photographic Materials and Processing. Photographic emulsions of moderate speed, high contrast, and small grain size, such as process plates or film, are best adapted to routine absorption work. Contrast lantern-slide plates are quite satisfactory for use with small spectrographs. For wavelengths longer than about 5000 A, especially sensitized emulsions must be used. Panchromatic process plates are entirely suitable. So also are the various fine-grain, high-contrast spectroscopic plates sensitized for this spectral range (see Chapter 7).

Below about 2300 A in the ultraviolet it becomes necessary either to use special emulsions in which the ultraviolet absorption due to gelatin is negligible or to sensitize the plates with a surface coating of a suitable fluorescent substance. A thin coating of almost any light machine oil,[10] swabbed on the emulsion with a piece of chamois or a tuft of lint-free cloth, gives satisfactory sensitization for absorption work below 2500 A. Before development of the plate, the oil must be washed off carefully with a suitable solvent, such as benzene. Special ultraviolet-sensitized spectrographic plates may also be obtained (see Chapter 19).

The precautions outlined in Chapter 7 as to uniformity of conditions of development, fixing, and washing should be observed. In order to minimize sources of error in density comparisons, it is particularly important to avoid the presence of air bubbles on the emulsion during development and fixing, and to carry out all processing, including drying, in an atmosphere as free from dust as practicable.

For further details regarding photographic techniques, see Chapter 7.

14.19. Semiquantitative and Plate-calibration Methods. Semiquantitative indications of relative absorption may be obtained by photographing a series of absorption spectra with different exposure times and constant intensity, different intensities and constant ex-

---

[10] G. R. Harrison, *Jour. Opt. Soc. Am. and Rev. Sci. Inst.*, **11**, 113, 341 (1925).

posure time, or different thicknesses of the absorbing specimen (using, for example, a Baly tube, as described in § 14.9). Such groups of spectra can be made to blacken the plate in such a way that the outline of the less dense areas traces out an approximate absorption curve of the specimen (Fig. 14.8). Much early work in absorption spectrophotometry was done by such means.

Instead of photographing a series of separate absorption spectra, one may take a single spectrogram through a wedge-shaped or multi-step specimen so placed that the light arriving at different portions of the spectrograph slit (and thence proceeding to different positions on the photographic plate) traverses different thicknesses of the specimen.[11, 12] Alternatively, the plate may be caused to move at varying

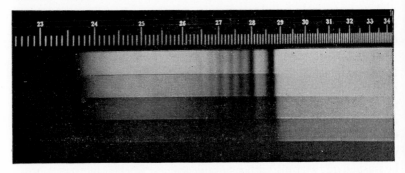

Fig. 14.8. Absorption spectra of tyrosine at liquid-hydrogen temperatures, photographed with different exposure times.

rates of speed, by means of a motor-driven cam, during the period of exposure, so that the time of exposure is a function of the position of the spectrum on the plate,[13] or the plate may be caused to move at constant speed while the intensity of the light incident on the specimen or the thickness of the absorbing specimen is changed.

From these semiquantitative methods, it is but a step to the calibration of the plate (see Chapter 13) and the quantitative determination of I_x/I_0. If a series of comparison spectra is photographed at different intensities or exposure times, the blackening of the plate

---

[11] H. S. Uhler and R. W. Wood, *Atlas of Absorption Spectra*. Washington, D. C.: Carnegie Institute, 1907.

[12] C. E. K. Mees, *Atlas of Absorption Spectra*. London: Longmans, Green and Co., 1909.

[13] E. R. Holiday, *Jour. Sci. Inst.*, **11**, 166 (1937).

at particular wavelengths by the comparison spectra may be compared with the blackening produced by the absorbing spectrum, and the values of I_x/I_0 may be determined at these wavelengths by interpolation. The density comparison may be made with a densitometer (Chapter 13) or by visual means. In one of the earliest methods of quantitative absorption spectrophotometry, Henri[14] took alternate spectrograms through equal path lengths of solution and solvent, varying the time of exposure through the solvent. He then determined the wavelengths at which adjacent pairs of spectra matched each other in blackening and computed the ratios of I_x/I_0 from the relative times of exposure. Corrections were made for reciprocity law failure by application of an expression due to Schwarzschild (Chapter 7).

A simple method of quantitative absorption spectrophotometry, similar to that of Henri and based on a simplified method of plate calibration, is the following: A series of exposures of say 10, 20, 50, and 100 sec duration is photographed through the specimen and a series of comparison exposures is photographed on the same plate in steps of 1 sec from 1 to 10 sec, inclusive. After development of the plate, an enlargement is made. The absorption spectra are cut out and brought into juxtaposition with the various comparison spectra to determine approximate match points visually at various wavelengths. The ratios I_x/I_0 at each wavelength are determined by interpolation between the adjacent comparison spectra most closely matching the absorption spectra, on the assumption that the reciprocity law holds. Uncertainties regarding the reciprocity law may be eliminated by varying the intensity by one of the methods of Chapter 13.

14.20. Split-beam Photometers. Split-beam photometers are devices for splitting a beam of light from the source into two beams, one of which traverses the specimen and the other a comparison cell (if one is used), for bringing the two beams into juxtaposition on the spectrograph slit and for reducing the intensity, or time of exposure, of the comparison beam by known amounts. Such devices permit the simultaneous photography of pairs of absorption and comparison spectra under circumstances in which the relative exposures of the two spectra may be controlled.

For photographic spectrophotometry in the spectral regions which

---

[14] V. Henri, *Phys. Zeitschr.*, **14**, 515-516 (1913).

Fig. 14.9.   Rotating sector photometer manufactured by the Gaertner Scientific Corp., Chicago.

they transmit (roughly 3400 to 10,000 A), combinations of polarizing split-beam photometers and wavelength spectrometers of the type described in §§ 14.13 and 14.14 may be used. The eyepiece of the spectrometer is replaced by a camera, and a series of pairs of spectra is photographed with different photometer settings corresponding to the values of I_x/I_0 for which spectral match points are to be determined. While polarization photometry is possible down to 2300 A with appropriate polarizing prisms,[15] modern split-beam photometers for the ultraviolet employ adjustable rotating sectors or variable apertures rather than polarization optics.

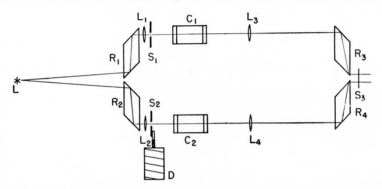

Fig. 14.10.   **Diagram of Spekker photometer.** L, light source; R_1, R_2, R_3, R_4, reflecting rhombs; L_1, L_2, L_3, L_4, collimating and focussing lenses; S_1, fixed slit; S_2, variable slit, adjusted by drum D; C_1, absorption cell; C_2, comparison cell; S_3, spectrograph slit.

The rotating-sector photometer, first employed by Henri[14] and later developed by Twyman,[16] has been used extensively for photographic spectrophotometry, particularly in combination with quartz spectrographs for studies in the ultraviolet region. A rotating sector of fixed angular aperture (usually 180 deg) interrupts the light beam passing through the absorbing specimen, and one of variable angular aperture (usually 0 to 180 deg) interrupts the comparison beam. These sectors may be mounted on separate shafts, as in the Hilger photometer, or may be parts of a single sector disk mounted on one shaft, as in the Bausch & Lomb and Gaertner photometers (Fig. 14.9). The Judd-Lewis[17] and Spekker[18] photometers (Figs. 14.10, 14.11)

[15] R. W. Wood, *Physical Optics.* New York: The Macmillan Company, 1934.
[16] See H. E. Howe, *Phys. Rev.*, **8**, 674 (1916).
[17] S. Judd-Lewis, *Trans. Chem. Soc.* (London), **115**, 312-319 (1919).
[18] F. Twyman, *Trans. Opt. Soc.* (London), **33**, 9-19 (1931-32).

are adjustable-aperture devices that are similar in principle though somewhat different in optical design. Both control intensity by varying the sizes of apertures in parallel beams of radiation that are uniform in intensity throughout their cross section. For this purpose, the Judd-Lewis uses mechanical vanes that may be adjusted by rotation so as to pass more or less of the beam, whereas the Spekker uses a rectangular aperture adjustable by a micrometer screw. The Spekker photometer has been employed extensively in photographic absorption spectrophotometry. It has a sufficiently open scale at the higher densities to permit settings up to a density of 2.0 with errors of probably less than 1 per cent.

Fig. 14.11.   Spekker photometer, manufactured by Adam Hilger, Ltd., London.
(Courtesy Jarrell-Ash Company, Boston.)

The instruments described represent the principal types of split-beam photometers used in photographic absorption spectrophotometry. Other methods may, of course, be used both for accomplishing separation and juxtaposition of the beams and for varying the intensity or time of exposure of one or both beams.

14.21. Multiple-beam Photometers. Split-beam photometers require a separate exposure for each pair of absorption and comparison spectra. Several ingenious methods have been devised to permit the photography of several pairs of spectra at the same time, thus reducing the total exposure time.

The notched-echelon-cell photometer[19] (Fig. 14.12) employs a pair of cells in which the path length through the cell contents varies as a function of the height in a series of 10 steps.   The ratio of the length of each new step to that of the one immediately preceding it is a constant.   The edges of the cells are cut at 45 deg to the faces so as to act as totally reflecting prisms.   One edge of the absorption cell has a series of rectangular notches cut in it, each of which overlaps

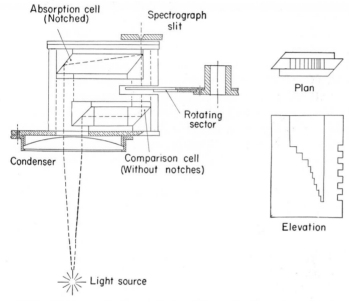

Fig. 14.12.   Diagram of the notched echelon cell photometer developed by Adam Hilger, Ltd., London.

half of two adjacent steps.   When the cells are mounted and illuminated, light from the comparison cell and from the specimen cell alternately impinges on the spectrograph slit, because of the action of the notches in alternately blocking and transmitting each beam. As a result, there appears on the photographic plate, after one exposure, a series of 10 pairs of spectra corresponding to the 10 different path lengths through the specimen and the solvent.   An adjustable rotating sector is used to reduce the intensity of the comparison

[19] F. Twyman, *Proc. Phys. Soc.* (London), **45**, 1-19 (1933).

beams by a known amount. The cells used are difficult to make and to maintain, and the instrument has not come into wide use.

O'Brien[20] made use of a multiple cube to bring into juxtaposition on a spectrograph slit 10 or 12 alternate beams of light from an absorption cell and a comparison cell. The comparison beams were reduced in exposure time by a rotating step sector with steps corresponding to the various beams. A multiple spectrograph slit, consisting of a series of apertures of different widths to provide variation in light intensity of the comparison beam and a single aperture of the maximum width for the specimen beam, is used by Kipp and Zonen in a simple apparatus for photographic absorption spectrophotometry. Other methods include the use of multiple-aperture diaphragms of fixed aperture in combination with wedge or step cells, multiple-aperture diaphragms of variable aperture, and so on.[21, 22, 23]

14.22. Considerations Governing Alignment and Illumination. Critical attention to optical alignment is important (see Chapter 5). Some spectrographs and photometers are equipped with optical benches to simplify alignment procedures. If the fittings that support absorption cells are adjustable, care should be exercised to see that the cells are centered in, and parallel to, the beams in which they are placed.

Condensed spark sources, frequently used in photographic spectrophotometry, may deposit evaporated metal on near-by areas. This debris must be cleaned, at regular intervals, from any optical surfaces on which it accumulates. Spark and open-arc sources should be retrimmed and realigned before the electrodes show appreciable wear. If a shutter is used to control exposures, it should be placed between the source and the specimen so as to minimize the possibility of photochemical effects on the absorbing material.

The possibility of errors resulting from synchronization between an intermittent source and a rotating sector may be eliminated by using a discharge tube or arc source operated on direct current. In a circuit with comparatively high capacitance operated from a 60-cycle AC transformer, trains of sparks may occur only once in each half cycle (that is, 120 times per second, corresponding to sector rotations

[20] B. O'Brien, *Phys. Rev.*, **37**, 471 (1931).

[21] F. Twyman, L. J. Spencer, and A. Harvey, *Trans. Opt. Soc.* (London), **33**, 37 (1932).

[22] A. Harvey, *Science Progress*, **27**, 650 (1933).

[23] O. E. Miller, *Rev. Sci. Inst.*, **3**, 30 (1932).

of about 9 to 30 deg).   Under such circumstances, the illumination of the different aspects of the sector throughout a single revolution may be quite different.   An averaging out to yield approximately uniform integrated illumination of the sector openings during the exposure may be assumed only if the sector rotation is not synchronized with the alternations of the AC supply and if many revolutions of the sector take place during an exposure.   Similar considerations apply if an AC-operated discharge tube or arc is used (or any other source operated from alternating current or low-frequency interrupted direct current).

Dirt on the spectrograph slit is especially troublesome in methods of photographic photometry in which spectrograms arising from different portions of the slit are to be compared.   Lack of parallelism of the slit jaws may also introduce errors in such instances.

14.23. Choice of Density in Specimens; Determination of Match Points.   The greatest accuracy in matching or measuring the plates is attainable if the specimen has comparatively high density values.   On the other hand, the accuracy of some photometers (for example, sector photometers) is somewhat decreased at the highest density values for which they are calibrated.   Good results are generally obtained with specimens that have a maximum density, within the spectral range to be measured, of about 1.5 for sector photometry and of about 1.8 to 1.9 for photometry with the Spekker instrument.   Samples of higher density may be measured with the notched echelon cell, the simple method described in § 14.19, and certain other photometric methods.

The appropriate concentration and cell length to yield the optimum maximum density may be computed in advance for solutions of substances whose concentration and absorption characteristics are known.   If either the concentration or the absorption characteristics of the solute are unknown, one or more test plates must be taken to determine the concentration and cell length to use.   After some experience, a rapid visual examination of the plate will suffice to indicate, very closely, what changes in concentration or cell length are required.   Alternatively, test plates may be taken with several different cell lengths.

The final plate in split-beam photometry is usually taken with a considerable range of density settings, at density intervals of about 0.1.   For greatest precision in density determinations, intervals of 0.05 may be used; closer settings are of little assistance.

The determination of the positions of match points on adjacent pairs of absorption and comparison spectra may be accomplished by observing the plate directly or under a magnifying glass, the match points being marked with ink spots. This procedure is tedious and difficult for many persons, even when appropriate viewing stands and illumination systems are provided. Some workers prefer to use paper positives, at $4\times$ to $5\times$ enlargement, for the visual determination of match points. Others prefer to project the plates upon screens, at many times enlargement, determining the match points on the projected images. If the plates are projected through tracing cloth or paper, the match points may be spotted on the reverse side, so as to yield a permanent record.

Better accuracies in visual matching may sometimes be attained by determining, through interpolation, the densities at particular wavelengths that correspond to match values, rather than by determining the wavelengths that correspond to match points for each particular pair of spectra. Photoelectric densitometry may also be employed (see Chapter 13).

14.24. Precision of Determination of Wavelengths and Densities. Spectrographs for photographic absorption spectrophotometry are usually equipped with built-in transparencies by means of which scales of wavelengths (or frequencies) may be printed directly on the plate while it is in the spectrograph. Ordinarily, a scale is printed at the top of the plate, and again at the bottom, and the wavelengths of positions on the intervening spectra are determined by placing a straight-edge across the spectra and corresponding marks on the two scales. This method involves errors of the positioning of the individual spectra on the plate, as well as errors in the scale and its positioning, but it is sufficiently accurate for much absorption work. It is well to check the positioning of a built-in scale by comparing it with the known wavelengths of a line source, such as a mercury arc, before relying on it for wavelength determination. When the greatest wavelength accuracy is desired, a line source may be employed and wavelengths may be determined from the lines and from interpolation between them. If a continuous source is used, a line source may be photographed on the same plate for wavelength calibration.

When match points are determined visually, the precision attainable is primarily a function of the ability of the eye to distinguish between different brightness levels. The precision of concentration determinations is about ± 1 per cent at a density of 1.0 or ± 0.5 per cent at a density of 2.0, if a method is used in which densities are determined at particular wavelengths. In general, an error of about ± 1 per cent may be expected if high density values are used. Determination of match points by photoelectric densitometers may decrease the detectable density increment, ΔD, by a factor of 10 or more.[24] With such an increase in the precision of match-point determination, other errors, such as those of photometer calibration and adjustment, usually become limiting.

PHOTOELECTRIC ABSORPTION SPECTROPHOTOMETRY

14.25. General Considerations. Photoelectric and thermoelectric photometry are discussed in detail in Chapter 12. Photoelectric photometry is used extensively in absorption spectrophotometry of the ultraviolet and visible; thermoelectric photometry, in the infrared.

Photoelectric absorption spectrophotometry usually makes use of photocells as radiation receivers either to measure the intensity of radiation in specimen and comparison beams alternately at a succession of wavelengths, or to determine when an equality of intensity has been established, at each of a series of wavelengths, between specimen and comparison beams in optical null methods of photometry. In either of these methods, two important problems arise: that of achieving sufficient freedom from scattered light in the dispersing system so that the photocells (which usually have markedly different sensitivities at different wavelengths) are not unduly influenced by scattered radiation; and that of providing a sufficiently low threshold of response in the photocell-amplifier-indicator system (in terms of radiant power required to produce a signal equal to the background noise level) to permit measurements to be made with a high degree of spectral purity at low light levels.

Scattered light is a particularly troublesome source of error when measurements are made in a spectral region for which the photocell sensitivity is low and in the presence of scattered radiation for which its sensitivity is high. Insofar as practicable, therefore, photocells should be chosen to have at least as high sensitivity in the range to be measured as outside this range. To approximate this condition, it is possible to use two or more photocells of different characteristics to

---

[24] F. Twyman and G. F. Lothian, *Proc. Phys. Soc.* (London), **45,** 643 (1933).

cover the spectral range 10,000 to 2000 A (see Chapter 12) and to supplement them with filters to modify their effective response characteristics within certain regions. Below 2500 A the situation is particularly difficult, since both photocell response and available light intensity are usually low in this range.

Errors resulting from scattered light may be reduced by using a suitably designed double monochromator (Chapters 3 and 4).

Photoelectric absorption spectrophotometry requires a light source, a dispersing system, a specimen holder, and a photocell and accessory electrical components. The possibility of making measurements with narrow bands of comparatively high spectral purity is facilitated by use of sources of high steradiancy, dispersing elements of large area and high angular dispersion, and sensitive photocell-amplifier systems with low noise level. Choice of an appropriate light source was discussed in § 14.6. The dispersing system is usually a monochromator; various suitable monochromators are described in the following discussions of individual types of spectrophotometers as well as at the ends of Chapters 3 and 4. Except in certain optical null methods and automatic recording instruments, the specimen holder is usually a movable mounting by means of which absorption and comparison cells can be shifted alternately into the light beam between the photocell and the monochromator exit slit. Photocells, amplifiers, and measuring instruments are discussed in Chapter 12.

14.26. Point-by-Point Instruments for Relative Intensity Measurements. With instruments of this type, separate determinations of the relative intensities of the specimen and comparison beams are made at each wavelength for which measurements of I_x/I_0 or $\log_{10}(I_0/I_x)$ are desired.

The Beckman spectrophotometer (Fig. 14.13) is an example of a commercial instrument in this category designed to cover the range 10,000 to 2000 A. It employs a quartz prism of the Littrow type with a concave mirror of 50 cm focal length for collimation. The relative aperture of the system is about $f/11$. Two light sources are used: a 32-candle-power, 6-volt automobile headlight bulb, for measurements from 10,000 to 3200 A, and a hydrogen discharge tube, for extension of the short-wave limit to about 2200 A. The wavelength scale is calibrated to 2000 A, but the practical working limit of the instrument with present light sources is somewhat less when substances having considerable absorption in this region are being measured. Filters are used to reduce stray light in various spectral regions.   It is claimed that stray light can be kept below 0.2 per cent throughout most of the 10,000 to 2000 A range.   Two photocells are employed, one for the region above 6250 A and one for that below. The photocell circuit consists of a two-stage direct-coupled amplifier. An output meter indicates when the potential developed by the phototube current has been balanced by an opposing potential from a slide-wire potentiometer in the input circuit.   The potentiometer is calibrated in per cent transmission from 0 to 110 and in densities from 0 to 2.0.

Fig. 14.13.   Beckman photoelectric quartz spectrophotometer, manufactured by National Technical Laboratories, South Pasadena, Calif.   This instrument is also obtainable with glass optics.

To operate the instrument, the wavelength at which transmission is to be determined is first selected by means of a calibrated dial that controls the angle of the prism relative to the collimated beam.   With the slide wire adjusted to correspond to 100 per cent and the beam passing through the comparison cell, the slit widths and the sensitivity are then adjusted until a null reading is obtained on the output meter.   Next, the cell containing the absorbing specimen is shifted into the beam and the potentiometer is adjusted until a null reading is again obtained.   The per cent transmission, or density, at the wavelength in question may then be read directly from the slide-wire scale. In such a reading, it is assumed, of course, that the photocell current is a linear function of the intensity of radiation incident on it and that the slide wire is uniform. The accuracy with which I_x can be determined is about ± 1 per cent of I_0 or better throughout most of the spectrum, provided sufficiently large slit widths are used. To achieve high accuracy in transmission measurements, it is often necessary to use slit widths corresponding to spectral band widths of about 50 to 100 A at half-maximum intensity. In order to measure samples that transmit less than 10 per cent (D greater than 1.0), the sensitivity may be increased tenfold to permit use of the full potentiometer scale for transmission measurements from 0.1 to 10 per cent (D from 3.0 to 1.0).

The Coleman double-monochromator spectrophotometer employs two transmission gratings in tandem as the dispersing system and a storage-battery-operated, 32-watt incandescent lamp as the light source, to cover the spectral range 10,000 to 3500 A. The use of two gratings reduces the stray light to less than 1 per cent on the average. The potential developed by the photocell current in an adjustable decade resistor is balanced against an opposing potential from a potentiometer. Null settings are determined with the aid of an electronic amplifier as in the case of the Beckman instrument. Adjustment (at any particular wavelength) for 100 per cent reading on the slide wire, with the comparison beam incident on the photocell, is accomplished by means of the decade resistor. The slits are of fixed width, corresponding to spectral band widths of 300, 150, 75, or 50 A. The accuracy of determination of I_x is ± 1 per cent of I_0 or better, depending on the slit widths used, except at the extremes of the spectral range. The potentiometer and electronic amplifier are external to the monochromator. It is possible to use a pH meter to supply these components.

The Coleman single monochromator spectrophotometer (Fig. 14.14) is of somewhat simpler design, employing a single transmission grating as the dispersing component and a barrier-layer photocell, connected to a sensitive galvanometer, as the radiation detector. A wider band width must be used than in the case of the double monochromator under similar conditions, but the instrument is considerably simpler and more compact. The photocell response may be read directly on the galvanometer or determined by means of a built-in potentiometric circuit.

The Cenco Spectrophotelometer (Fig. 14.15) makes use of a concave replica grating in a modified Eagle mounting as the dispersing system, an incandescent lamp as the light source, and a barrier-layer photocell and galvanometer as the radiation-sensitive receiver and indicating system.   Fixed exit slits of 200, 100, or 50 A band width are used.

Fig. 14.14.   Photoelectric spectrophotometer for the region 3500 to 10,000 A. Manufactured by Coleman Instruments, Inc., Maywood, Ill.

The value of I_x/I_0 at a particular wavelength is determined from successive readings of the galvanometer with the specimen and comparison beams incident on the photocell.   The spectral range covered is 10,000 to 3500 A.

The commercial instruments described are typical of those used routinely in chemical, biochemical, and biological laboratories.   In order to obtain sufficient transmitted light for accurate transmission measurements, they all require entrance and exit slit widths corresponding to a lower order of magnitude of spectral purity (50 to 300 A band width) than is usually achieved in photographic spectrophotometry (1 to 5 A band width).   Although the use of a wide band eliminates the possibility of observing fine details of absorption or of obtaining true measurements of substances having very narrow absorption bands, the convenience, moderate cost, and ease of operation

Fig. 14.15.   Spectrophotelometer employing a concave replica grating in a modified Eagle mount for photoelectric absorption spectrophotometry in the range 3,500 to 10,000 A.   Manufactured by Central Scientific Company, Chicago.

of such instruments make them extremely useful in routine analytical work.

Many point-by-point photoelectric spectrophotometers have been designed and used by individual research workers.   The German investigators (Pohl, Kuhn, Smakula, and others) were pioneers in the application of this method of spectrophotometry.   A number of interesting designs of instruments, each with certain novel features,

have been described in recent years.[25-35]   The type of spectrophotometer developed by Hogness and his associates,[34] which is capable of
measuring I_x with an accuracy of 0.2 per cent of I_0 with slit widths
limiting the transmission band to 10 A or less, is an example of what
can be done by careful attention to details when low cost, compactness, and simplicity are not essential.

14.27. Photoelectric Null Methods: Nonrecording. Photoelectric cells may be employed in null methods of spectrophotometry to
determine when two beams of radiation or two halves of a photometric
field are matched, using any of the usual optical methods of varying
the intensity or intermittent exposure of one or both beams (polarizing
prisms, rotating sectors, diaphragms).   Several such arrangements
have been suggested and used by individual workers.[36, 37]   The
optical null method has the advantage of involving no assumptions as
to the linearity of photocells, amplifiers, and indicating instruments.
It has the disadvantage of being limited in its precision of determining
I_x/I_0 by the accuracy of the optical device used to balance the two
beams.

The Hilger photoelectric spectrophotometer (Fig. 14.16) employs
two gas-filled photocells connected in opposition to a Lindemann
electrometer.   A collimated beam of light from the monochromator
is partially reflected into one photocell by a quartz plate placed at an
angle to the beam.   The remainder of the light passes through a
rotating sector of the cylindrical type (which may be adjusted while
in motion) to the second photocell.   The value of $\log_{10}(I_0/I_x)$ at a
particular wavelength is determined from the two sector settings required to achieve a null reading of the electrometer with, say, a

[25] D. H. Follett, *Proc. Phys. Soc.* (London), **46,** 490 (1934).

[26] S. Jacobsen, H. E. Bent, and A. J. Harrison, *Rev. Sci. Inst.*, **11,** 220 (1940).

[27] F. P. Zscheile, Jr., *Jour. Phys. Chem.*, **28,** 95 (1934).

[28] E. S. Miller, *Plant Physiology*, **12,** 667 (1937).

[29] W. C. Bosch and K. D. Coleman, *Phys. Rev.*, **57,** 941 (1940).

[30] D. L. Drabkin, *Proc. Seventh Summer Conference on Spectroscopy, 1939.*   New
York: John Wiley & Sons, Inc., 1940.

[31] W. C. Bosch and B. B. Brown, *Jour. Opt. Soc. Am.*, **29,** 466 (1939).

[32] M. Barnard and P. McMichael, *Jour. Opt. Soc. Am.*, **21,** 588 (1931).

[33] S. Schlaer, *Jour. Opt. Soc. Am.*, **28,** 18 (1938).

[34] T. R. Hogness, F. P. Zscheile, Jr., and A. E. Sidwell, *Jour. Phys. Chem.*, **41,** 371
(1937).

[35] W. Deck, *Helvetica Phys. Acta*, **11,** 3 (1938).

[36] H. von Halban and H. Giegel, *Zeitschr. phys. Chem.*, **96,** 214 (1920).

[37] H. von Halban and K. Seidentopf, *Zeitschr. phys. Chem.*, **100,** 208 (1922).

solution cell and a solvent cell in the beam.   The monochromator employed is of large aperture (approximately $f/4$ to $f/6$, depending on the wavelength) and of high dispersion (equivalent to a train of four 60-deg prisms), and has interchangeable optics of quartz, glass, and rock salt for work in different spectral regions.   Because of the large monochromator aperture and the sensitivity of the photocell-electrometer circuit, comparatively narrow spectral band widths may be used.   The precision of density determinations (limited by the accuracy of the sector) is said to be about 0.004 for densities near 0.43. By using suitable photocells for different regions, a spectral range of 12,000 to 1850 A can be covered.

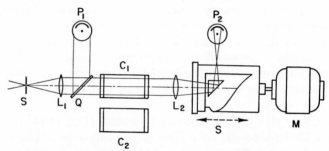

Fig. 14.16.   Optical system of null type of photoelectric photometer developed by Adam Hilger, Ltd., London. S, slit; L_1 and L_2, collimating and focusing lenses; C_1 and C_2, absorption and comparison cells; Q, quartz plate; P_1 and P_2, photocells; S, rotating sector; M, motor.

14.28.   Automatic Recording Photoelectric Spectrophotometers.

The earliest successful automatic recording spectrophotometer is that of Hardy,[38-41] of which a commercial model is manufactured by the General Electric Company (Fig. 14.17).   It is designed for transmission or reflectance measurements in the visible region.   It employs a method developed from that used by Dobson and Prefect,[42] in which the absorption (or reflection) and comparison beams are allowed to illuminate a single photocell alternately in such a manner that a fluctuating current is set up in the photocell circuit unless the two beams are of equal intensity.   Rotating mechanical shutters were

[38] A. C. Hardy, *Jour. Opt. Soc. Am.*, **25**, 305 (1935).

[39] A. C. Hardy, *Jour. Opt. Soc. Am.*, **28**, 360 (1938).

[40] J. L. Michaelson, *Jour. Opt. Soc. Am.*, **28**, 365 (1938).

[41] K. S. Gibson and H. J. Keegan, *Jour. Opt. Soc. Am.*, **28**, 372 (1938).

[42] G. M. B. Dobson and D. S. Prefect, *Photoelectric Cells and Their Applications.* Pages 79, 174, 185.   London: The Physical Society, 1930.

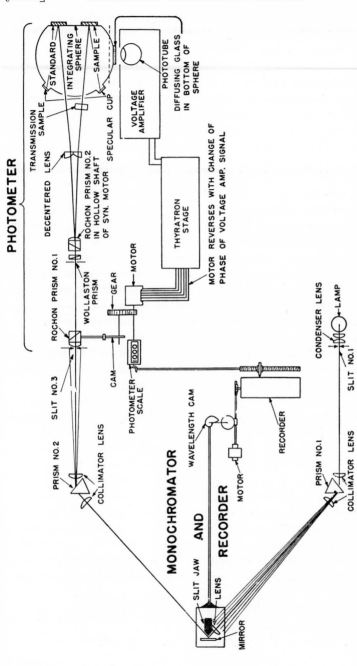

Fig. 14.17. Hardy automatic recording photoelectric spectrophotometer for the visible region. (Courtesy General Electric Company, Schenectady, N. Y.).

used to alternate the beams in early instruments employing this principle. In order to obtain smoother transition from one beam to the other, Hardy's system makes use of a rotating Rochon prism to alternate the beams, these having been polarized perpendicularly to each other by prior passage through a fixed Wollaston prism. When the beams are unbalanced, the alternating current generated in the photocell circuit is applied, through a suitable amplifier, to a control circuit that causes a motor to rotate a second Rochon prism in the beams until they are balanced. The direction of rotation of the light-balancing motor depends on the phase of the alternations of the unbalanced beams and is always such as to compensate the unbalance. The recording pen is coupled to this balancing mechanism.

The principle of this optical null method is the same as that of the König-Martens type of photometer (§ 14.11), except that balancing is achieved and recorded automatically instead of manually. A double-prism glass monochromator is used. The spectrum band is shifted continuously by a motor-driven cam mechanism while the wavelength axis of the record chart is correspondingly shifted with respect to the recording pen. A curve of absorption or transmission throughout the visible range is plotted automatically in from 2 to 5 min. The slit widths of the commercial instrument normally correspond to a spectral band width of 100 A, but special instruments may be obtained for operation at 40 A band width. The precision of determination of I_x is considerably better than ± 1 per cent of I_0.

Brode and Jones[43] have described methods for adapting the Hardy spectrophotometer to measurements in the ultraviolet, using a quartz prism in a Wadsworth mounting as the dispersing system. They have employed both rotating aluminized reflection sectors and rotating polarizing prisms for chopping the beams. In the former case, adjustment of relative intensities was accomplished by a vane photometer; in the latter case, by polarizing prisms.

The automatic recording spectrophotometer designed by Harrison[44] and improved by Harrison and Bentley[45] (Fig. 14.18) will measure, at high speed, transmissions or densities throughout the range, 9700 to 2300 A with spectral band widths of 1 A or less throughout most of this range. Thus an effective resolution is attained which compares

[43] W. R. Brode and C. H. Jones, *Jour. Opt. Soc. Am.*, **31**, 743 (1941).

[44] G. R. Harrison, *Proc. Sixth Summer Conf. on Spectroscopy*, 1938, page 91. New York: John Wiley & Sons, Inc., 1939.

[45] G. R. Harrison and E. P. Bentley, *Jour. Opt. Soc. Am.*, **30**, 290 (1940).

favorably with that achievable under optimum conditions in photographic spectrophotometry. The precision of measurement of I_x,
about ± 1 per cent of I_0, is limited, in all but the extreme ends of the
spectral range, by the precision of the mechanical and optical components of the photometer rather than by the sensitivity of the
photocell-amplifier system.

The 3-meter concave grating employed (which is ruled, 15,000 lines
to the inch, on an aluminized glass blank) gives a plate factor of 5.5 A
per millimeter, almost linear with respect to wavelength. The en-

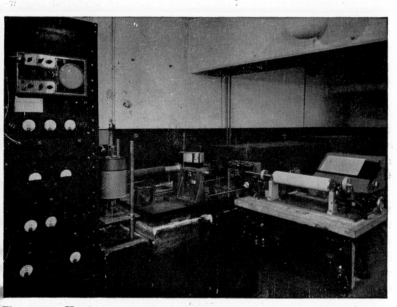

Fig. 14.18. Harrison automatic recording photoelectric spectrometer for the
visible and ultraviolet regions.

trance and exit slits are adjustable in width from 0 to 2 mm. A
110-volt coil-filament incandescent lamp is used from 9700 to 3400
A and a high-pressure mercury arc (G.E. H–6) from 3400 to 2300 A.
The radiation receiver is an 11-stage photomultiplier tube, connected
to a "memory unit" incorporating a 0.01 mf condenser, through an
appropriate amplifier.

In operation, the monochromatic light beam from the exit slit is
passed alternately through the absorption and comparison cells by
an oscillating biprism, while a sector rotates in front of the entrance

slit in synchronism with the rotation of the drum on which the recording chart is wrapped. With the specimen beam incident on the photocell, a potential corresponding to the beam intensity is developed across the condenser in the memory circuit. This potential is stored while the comparison beam is shifted to the photocell and the variable-width portion of the sector is rotated before the entrance slit. As the intensity of the comparison beam increases, the potential developed in the photocell circuit increases also. When it equals the stored potential (that is, when the intensity of the comparison beam has been matched to that of the specimen beam), a thyratron triggering circuit causes a point to be marked on the recording chart at the appropriate density or transmission value. A separate motor drive automatically shifts the wavelength of the transmitted band, and the corresponding position of recording on the chart, at a maximum speed of 100 A per second.

The system is inherently low in scattered radiation. To decrease further the effects of stray light, filters are interposed automatically in the incident beam when measurements are being recorded in the various wavelength regions. The optical null method used involves a time delay, less than 0.05 sec in normal operation, between evaluation of the intensities of the specimen and comparison beams.

H. Cary[46] has developed an automatic recording photoelectric spectrophotometer for the visible and ultraviolet regions which is manufactured by the Applied Physics Corporation (Fig. 14.19). It employs a double-prism monochromator to obtain high dispersion and freedom from scattered radiation. The light beam is chopped at 90 cps, and the radiation receiver is a photomultiplier tube. The output of the photomultiplier is fed through an electronic amplifier to a strip-chart recorder of the type used with infrared spectrophotometers. Except in the extreme ultraviolet, half-intensity band widths as small as 1 A may be used with this instrument.

These examples indicate the trend in instrument design, which is toward both automatic recording and improved effective spectral resolution.

14.29. Abbreviated Absorption Spectrophotometry and Fluorimetry. In many routine analytical chemical procedures, it is desirable to be able to determine the concentration of a single substance in a solution by means of such optical properties as color or fluorescence.

---

[46] *Ind. Eng. Chem.*, **39**, 75A (1947).

Various photoelectric instruments employing principles of spectro-photometry in simplified form are available for such measurements.

In the case of the determination of concentration by application of the property of color, use is made either of the natural color of the substance itself or, if the substance is colorless, it is treated with appropriate reagents with which it forms a color complex. Trans-

Fig. 14.19.   Cary automatic recording photoelectric spectrophotometer for the visible and ultraviolet regions.   Manufactured by Applied Physics Corp., Pasa-dena, Calif.

mission measurements are then made at or near the wavelength of maximum absorption, and the concentration is determined by ap-plication of the Lambert-Beer law or by use of a calibration curve made by determining the transmission values of a series of dilutions of a solution of known concentration.

Though it is entirely feasible to employ spectrophotometers of the types previously described for quantitative analyses by this method, it is often customary to use simpler devices, variously known as *photoelectric colorimeters, abbreviated absorption spectrophotometers*, or *absorptiometers* for this purpose. These employ optical filters (§ 14.30) or simple dispersion systems for isolating the spectral band with which transmission measurements are made. In general, the band width employed is large (from 200 to 400 A or even more); hence it is preferable to base the determination upon a calibration curve rather than to assume that the Lambert-Beer law applies.

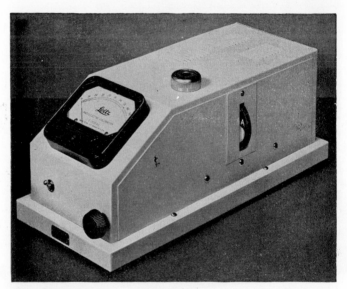

Fig. 14.20. Typical photoelectric absorptiometer (colorimeter) of the filter type. Manufactured by E. Leitz, Inc., New York.

Many designs of absorptiometers are available (Fig. 14.20). Further information regarding the technique of photoelectric absorptiometry will be found in General Reference 14.3.

The concentration of a substance that fluoresces in solution when excited by ultraviolet radiation may be determined by photoelectric measurement of the intensity of the fluorescent light.[47] In comparatively dilute solutions, the concentration is approximately pro-

---

[47] See J. R. Loofbourow and R. S. Harris, *Cereal Chem.*, **19**, 151 (1942) for a discussion of typical commercial fluorimeters.

portional to the intensity of fluorescence for constant intensity of exciting radiation:

$$c = AI_f \tag{14.13}$$

where c is the concentration, in suitable units, A is a constant, and I_f is the intensity of fluorescence. If relative values of I_f are measured with, for example, a barrier-layer photocell and galvanometer, and if the photocell galvanometer response is proportional to I_f, then [provided Eq. (14.13) is valid]:

$$c = (R - R_b) \frac{c_1 - c_2}{r_1 - r_2} \tag{14.14}$$

where c is the concentration in an unknown sample, R and R_b are, respectively, the galvanometer readings with the sample and solvent alone in the cell, and r_1 and r_2 are calibration readings of the galvanometer corresponding to known concentrations c_1 and c_2. In order for Eqs. (14.13) and (14.14) to be approximately valid, it is necessary that the solution concentration be such that only about 10 per cent of the exciting radiation is absorbed in the solution.

Excitation of fluorescence in fluorimeters is usually produced by radiation in a spectral band including the 3650 A mercury line. High-pressure mercury arcs of the type described in Chapter 8 are convenient sources of such radiation, and glass optics transmit it freely. Quartz-mercury arcs and quartz optics are used in certain instruments to extend the range of the exciting radiation below 3400 A. It is necessary to eliminate visible light as effectively as possible from the exciting radiation, since the fluorescence to be measured is primarily in the visible range. This reduction is accomplished by suitable primary filters (§ 14.30). In general, the more effective the primary filter is in eliminating visible radiation, the less effective it is in transmitting exciting radiation.

It is also necessary to eliminate response of the photocell to the exciting radiation insofar as practicable, by the use of secondary filters (§ 14.30) and usually by placing the photocell at right angles to the exciting beam. Secondary filters for absorbing stray exciting radiation may convert an appreciable fraction of the absorbed radiation into fluorescent light in the visible range. It is therefore usual to follow the ultraviolet-absorbing filter by one or more additional filters to absorb the fluorescence excited in the first filter. Even with the best of primary and secondary filter combinations, stray visible and ultraviolet light usually falls on the photocells in sufficient quantities to cause appreciable readings with a "blank" (cell containing solvent only) in the beam.   Hence a correction must be made for the reading with the blank [R_b in Eq. (14.14)].

14.30.   Optical Filters.   As indicated in § 14.29, optical filters are frequently used in absorptiometers and fluorimeters for isolating desired spectral regions.   They are also used extensively to obtain approximately monochromatic radiation for photochemical or photobiological investigations, and to reduce the effects of stray radiation or undesired spectral orders in dispersing systems.

The three principal types of optical filters depend for their operation, respectively, on selective absorption, interference, and selective scattering.   Of these, selectively absorbing filters are most widely used.

Selectively absorbing filters may be solids, liquids, or gases, the first being the most convenient to use.   Many types of colored glasses,

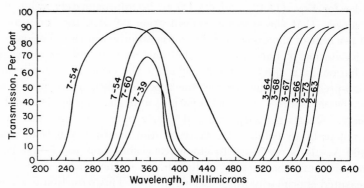

Fig. 14.21.   Transmission curves of typical glass filters.   Manufactured by the Corning Glass Company, Corning, N. Y.

having different selective-absorption characteristics, are available for use as optical filters in the visible region, and to a somewhat lesser extent such filters are also applicable to the isolation of spectral regions in the ultraviolet and near infrared.   Transmission curves of a few typical glass filters are illustrated in Fig. 14.21.   Glass filters manufactured by the Jena Optical Works, Corning Glass Company, Eastman Kodak Company, and others are available in wide variety and detailed data on their transmission characteristics will be found in the catalogues of their respective manufacturers.   Solid filters may also be made by imbibing absorbing materials in gelatin or adsorbing them on cellophane. These are often mounted between protecting covers of glass. Such filters are obtainable from distributors of photographic and stage-lighting equipment.

Liquid filters (including solutions) provide a greater variety of transmission characteristics than do selectively absorbing glasses. They must, of course, be used in suitable cells with windows transparent to the radiation to be transmitted. Gaseous filters are occasionally employed to isolate spectral bands in the ultraviolet but are

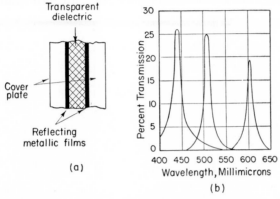

Fig. 14.22. **Interference filters.** (a) Method of construction. (b) Typical transmission curves.

seldom used in the visible region. Again, they require the use of suitable filter cells. Transmission data for liquids, solutions, and gases suitable for use as filters will be found in compilations of absorption spectra, including General References 14.7 and 14.8.

Interference filters depend on the same principle as the Fabry and Perot etalon, described in Chapter 20. They consist of two partially reflecting evaporated metal films, separated by a transparent spacer of evaporated dielectric, together with glass protecting covers (Fig. 14.22a). For a given optical path length through the dielectric, the interference arising from multiple reflections between the metallic films is such as to result in maximum transmission (about 25 to 35 per cent) at particular wavelengths, on each side of which the transmission falls rapidly to nearly zero (Fig. 14.22b). Interference filters are available commercially for maximum transmission at any wavelengths within the range 3700 to 7000 A. Those with transmission maxima near the ends of this range have two transmission bands within this region, the unwanted one of which is removed by the use of auxiliary glass filters. Interference filters must be used with a collimated beam of radiation. The wavelength position of the transmission band may be shifted over a considerable range by varying the angle of incidence of the collimated beam on the filter.

Christiansen filters, based on selective scattering, have long been used for isolating comparatively narrow spectral regions in the infrared, visible, and near ultraviolet (see General Reference 9.1), and their use has been extended recently to the ultraviolet region from 3000 to 2000 A.[48]   In the Christiansen filter, small irregular chips of a solid

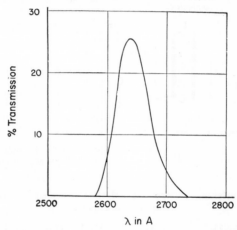

Fig. 14.23.   Transmission curve of a Christiansen filter[48] for the ultraviolet, consisting of quartz chips suspended in a mixture of decahydronapthalene and cyclohexane.

are suspended in a medium of different dispersion but with a refractive index the same as that of the chips at the wavelength for which maximum transmission is desired. This combination results in minimum scattering, and hence maximum transmission, at the specified wavelength. The transmission decreases rapidly upon departure from the optimum wavelength as a result of the increasing difference in the refractive indices of the two media and increased scattering of radiation. Christiansen filters must be used in a collimated light beam, and the position of their transmission maximum is sensitive to temperature, especially if the suspending medium is a liquid. A typical transmission curve of such a filter for the ultraviolet region is shown in Fig. 14.23.

[48] R. L. Sinsheimer and J. R. Loofbourow, *Nature*, **160**, 674 (1947).

ABSORPTION OF SUBSTANCES IN SOLUTION

14.31. General Remarks Regarding Solvents. The properties that must be considered in choosing a solvent are the solubility in it of the material to be investigated, its transmissivity for radiation in the region to be explored, and its volatility.

It is desirable that the material to be investigated be soluble easily in the solvent up to the highest concentration required for spectra. Otherwise, errors may arise from the failure of samples to go entirely into solution. If the maximum extinction coefficient of the substance is known, the required concentration for a given density at the maximum may be computed from the Lambert-Beer law [Eq. (14.6)]. Often this concentration is exceedingly small; hence it sometimes happens that substances listed in the usual handbooks as insoluble in particular solvents may be dissolved in them in sufficient concentrations for absorption spectrophotometry.

The solvents most commonly employed in absorption spectrophotometry are distilled water, methyl alcohol, ethyl alcohol, chloroform, hexane, cyclohexane, carbon tetrachloride, and ethyl ether. Unless specially purified, many of these solvents contain sufficient concentrations of such impurities as ketones, aldehydes, and benzene to cause appreciable absorption in the ultraviolet. The extent to which they must be purified for practical use depends on the spectral region of interest. In general, the greatest care in solvent purification is required for work in the region below 2400 A, where various factors previously discussed combine to make measurements difficult.

Highly volatile solvents, such as ethyl ether, introduce possibilities of error as a result of concentration changes brought about by evaporation. Therefore such solvents should be used only if other solvents will not serve, and then only with special precautions against evaporation.

14.32. Absorption by Solvents; Purification. As indicated in Table 14.4, many commercial solvents of the best grades are satisfactory for measurements to 2450 A. For work at shorter wavelengths than those listed as the useful limit, only especially purified solvents should be used. Some of the solvents listed in the table and purified for chemical work show absorption obviously attributable to traces of impurities. This fact is indicative of the different requirements as to purity for laboratory reagents and for solvents for absorption spectroscopy. Merely because a reagent is ideal for chemical purposes does not necessarily mean, therefore, that the particular impurities which are most troublesome in spectroscopy have been removed to the extent that might be desired.

TABLE 14.4

APPROXIMATE WAVELENGTH LIMIT OF USEFULNESS OF VARIOUS
COMMERCIAL SOLVENTS IN 2-CM CELLS*

Solvent	Shortest useful wavelength
Distilled water (from laboratory supply).......	2000 A
Ethyl ether...............................	2250
Hexane, practical, Eastman Kodak Co.........	2250
Methyl alcohol...........................	2300
Ethyl alcohol, 95%........................	2350
Ethyl alcohol, absolute, U.S.P...............	2350
Hexane, synthetic, Eastman Kodak Co.........	2450
Chloroform...............................	2450
Cyclohexane, pure, Eastman Kodak Co........	2650
Carbon tetrachloride.......................	2700
Cyclohexane, practical, Eastman Kodak Co....	2750

Laboratory-distilled water redistilled twice in all-glass stills is usually sufficiently free from absorbing substances for work to 1850 A. The usual methods for preparing conductivity water may be employed if the greatest purity is desired.

Ethyl alcohol (95 per cent) may be purified by adding 25 cc of 12 N sulfuric acid per liter, refluxing for several hours, and distilling.[49] The distillate is then treated with 20 grams of potassium hydroxide and 10 grams of silver nitrate per liter, refluxed, and distilled. This method yields a solvent sufficiently good for work to 2000 A. If this product is dried over aluminum amalgam, the transmission at shorter wavelengths is somewhat improved.

Ethyl ether distilled once from alkali has sufficiently good transmission characteristics for most work in which this solvent is required.

An outline of useful methods for purifying cyclohexane, hexane, carbon tetrachloride, chloroform, ethyl alcohol, and methyl alcohol is given in General Reference 14.2.

---

* These data, which are based on experience of the authors and on the assumption that the solvent should transmit at least 50 per cent of the radiation at useful wavelengths, agree approximately with those in General Reference 14.1, in which data on a number of additional commercial solvents will be found.

[49] P. A. Leighton, R. W. Cary, and L. T. Schipp, *Jour. Am. Chem. Soc.*, **53**, 3017 (1931).

14.33. Relation of Absorption to Chemical Constitution. As was pointed out in Chapter 11, the electronic spectra of solids, liquids, and substances in solution as ordinarily observed by absorption spectro-photometry in the 10,000 to 2000 A region do not show the fine structure observed in the absorption spectra of substances in the gaseous state. Rotational transition lines are not resolved at all, and the vibrational band structure can only be identified clearly in special instances. The lack of detail in the spectroscopic data, together with the complexity of the substances usually studied by absorption spectrophotometry, has, in general, made it imprac-ticable to work out relationships of structure to absorption in a manner analogous to analyses of the absorption spectra of simple molecules in the gaseous state. Some progress in this direction has been made, however,[50] and advances may be expected to be more rapid as techniques of measurement and analysis improve.

From the empirical point of view, a number of generalizations regarding absorbing groups (designated as "chromophores"; see § 11.3) and their relation to absorption have been worked out, espe-cially insofar as dyestuffs are concerned [51-58] (General Reference 14.5). Certain of these generalizations that are particularly useful to the practical worker in applying absorption spectrophotometry to problems of organic chemistry are summarized below:

1. To a close approximation, electronic absorption spectra asso-ciated with unsaturated linkages occur in the region $\lambda > 2000$ A, whereas those associated with saturated linkages occur in the region $\lambda < 2000$ A.

---

[50] For a summary to about 1940, see G. E. K. Branch and M. Calvin, *The Theory of Organic Chemistry*, Chapter V. New York: Prentice-Hall, Inc., 1941.

[51] R. Nietzki, *Verhandl. des Vereins zum Beförderung des Gemeibefleisses*, **58**, 231 (1879).

[52] J. B. Cohen, *Organic Chemistry for Advanced Students*. Part II, Chapter II. New York: Longmans Green & Co., Inc., 1939.

[53] T. Förster, *Zeitschr. f. Electrochemie*, **45**, 548 (1939).

[54] H. Niimiya, *Chem. Rev. Japan*, **3**, 2240 (1937).

[55] B. Beilenson, N. I. Fisher, and F. M. Hamer, *Proc. Roy. Soc. (London)*, **A163**, 138 (1937).

[56] F. Pruckner and A. Stern, *Zeitschr. f. phys. Chemie*, **A180**, 25 (1937).

[57] G. N. Lewis and M. Calvin, *Chem. Rev.*, **25**, 273 (1939).

[58] G. Scheibe and W. Frömel, *Hand- und Jahrbuch der chem. Physik*, 1936, Vol. 9, page 142.

2. The principal groupings contributing to absorption are the following:[50-58] $>C=C<$, $>C=O$, $>C=S$, $>C=N—$, $—N=N—$, $—N=O, >S=O, —N\diagdown_O^{\diagup O}, —N\diagup^{\diagup O}=N—, >C=C=O,$ and conjugated chains or rings made up of $>C=C<$, $>C=N—$, or $—N=N—$ groups (compare Table 11.3).

3. The absorption maximum associated with a particular group is, in general, shifted toward longer wavelengths (lower frequencies) when a substituent is linked to the group; this effect is increased with increasing atomic weight of the substituents.[57, 58]

4. Separation of unsaturated groups by two or more single-bond linkages usually reduces the influence of such groups on each other to such an extent that the total absorption may be considered as the sum of the absorption bands attributable to each of the structures so isolated.[59, 60]

5. The mutual influence of unsaturated groups on absorption is considerable in structures involving conjugated double bonds. Marked absorption is found in structures with several conjugated double bonds in which there are many possibilities for resonance (as in benzene, for example). In general, increase in the number of conjugated double bonds results in an increase in absorption and a shifting of the absorption bands toward longer wavelengths (lower frequencies).[61-64]

6. The influence of substituents, especially those of higher atomic weight on an absorbing group or a conjugated double bond structure, is usually to increase the absorption.[58, 61-65]

7. Changes in the substituents of, or linkages to, absorbing groups as a result of salt formation,[65-67] association,[68, 69] and so on, may cause

[59] V. Henri, *Etudes de Photochemie*, Paris, 1919.

[60] W. Aumüller, H. Fromherz, and C. O. Strother, *Zeitschr. f. phys. Chemie*, B37, 30 (1937).

[61] L. B. Arnold, Jr. and G. B. Kistiakowsky, *Jour. Am. Chem. Soc.*, 54, 1713 (1932).

[62] K. W. Hausser, R. Kuhn, A. Smakula, and K. H. Krenchen, *Zeitschr. f. phys. Chemie*, B29, 371 (1935).

[63] K. W. Hausser, R. Kuhn, and G. Seitz, *Zeitschr. f. phys. Chemie*, B29, 391 (1935).

[64] R. Kuhn and A. Deutsche, *Ber.* 65, 43 (1932).

[65] R. Kuhn and M. Hoffer, *Ber.* 65, 651 (1932).

[66] K. v. Auwers and R. Hügel, *Zeitschr. f. phys. Chemie*, A178, 315 (1937).

[67] R. K. Callow, *Biochem. Jour.*, 30, 906 (1936).

[68] E. C. C. Baly and E. K. Eubank, *Jour. Chem. Soc.* (London), 87, 1347 (1905).

[69] H. Ley, *Zeitschr. f. phys. Chemie*, 94, 405 (1920).

changes in absorption.   Salt formation may arise as a result of the
presence of acids or bases in solution, as for example when these are
used to adjust pH.   Association may be influenced by the nature
of the solvent and the concentration of the solution.

8. Changes in the kinds or positions of unsaturated groups in
molecules as a result of molecular rearrangements may cause marked
changes in absorption.[70-76]   When such effects arise from changes in

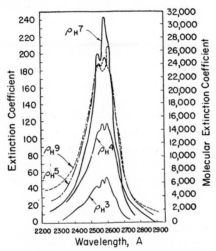

Fig. 14.24.   Effect of pH of the solution on the absorption spectrum of barbituric
acid.[76]

the pH of the solution, they are easily brought about and are useful
in the identification of substances (Fig. 14.24).   The colorimetric
determination of pH is based on this phenomenon.

14.34.   Photochemical Effects; Fluorescence.   The radiation used
to determine the absorption of substances may give rise to photo-

[70] W. L. Lewschin, *Acta Physicochimica U.R.S.S.*, **1**, 685 (1935).

[71] G. Scheibe, *Kolloid Zeitschr.*, **82**, 1 (1938).

[72] W. Stenström and M. Reinhard, *J. Phys. Chem.*, **29**, 1477 (1925).

[73] C. S. Hicks, *Jour. Chem. Soc.* (London), **128**, 643 (1926).

[74] E. R. Holiday, *Biochem. Jour.*, **24**, 619 (1930).

[75] F. F. Heyroth and J. R. Loofbourow, *Jour. Am. Chem. Soc.*, **53**, 3441 (1931);
56, 1728 (1934).

[76] J. R. Loofbourow and M. M. Stimson, *Jour. Chem. Soc.* (London), 844 (1940);
1275 (1940).

chemical effects that have a marked influence on the absorption.   If
such changes take place to an appreciable extent while the absorption
spectrum is being determined, they may lead to errors in the determinations.   There is more likelihood of errors arising from this source
in ultraviolet spectrophotometry than in visible spectrophotometry;
even though some substances, such as riboflavin, are photochemically labile in the visible region, instances are quite rare in
which photochemical changes sufficient to influence the validity of
measurements are encountered in absorption spectrophotometry in
this region.

Those methods of absorption spectrophotometry which involve the
least total irradiation of the specimen with photochemically active
radiation are freest from the possibility of error as a result of photochemical change.   At first sight, it appears that photoelectric
methods, in which the specimen cell follows the exit slit of a monochromator, are superior in this regard to photographic methods, in
which the cell is placed before the entrance slit of a spectrograph.
This superiority is not necessarily actual, however, if a point-by-point
method is used, involving many determinations not carried out at
high speed.

In most instances the amount of radiant energy required to cause
appreciable change in absorption is considerably greater than that to
which the specimen is exposed during measurements with any of the
usual spectrophotometric methods.   Whether errors caused by
photochemical effects are being encountered may be checked by
successive absorption determinations on the same specimen.

Many substances that absorb in the ultraviolet exhibit appreciable
fluorescence when exposed to such radiation.   When the absorption
spectra of such substances are determined by photographic methods,
some of the fluorescent radiation enters the slit of the spectrograph
and causes blackening of the photographic plate in the spectral
regions to which the fluorescence corresponds.   As a result, absorption spectra determined photographically sometimes show what
appears to be negative absorption at wavelengths longer than that of
the absorbing region.   Since the fluorescent light is radiated in all
directions, this effect is unlikely to be noticed unless the specimen cell
is placed close to the slit.

Data regarding the absorption of particular substances are given
in the General References.

GENERAL REFERENCES

Methods and Theory

14.1.   W. R. Brode, *Chemical Spectroscopy*, 2d ed.   New York: John Wiley & Sons, Inc., 1943.
14.2.   F. Twyman and C. B. Allsopp, *The Practice of Absorption Spectrophotometry*, 2d ed.   London: Adam Hilger, Ltd., 1934.
14.3.   Thomas R. P. Gibb, Jr., *Optical Methods of Chemical Analysis*.   New York: McGraw-Hill Book Company, Inc., 1941.
14.4.   W. West in *Physical Methods of Organic Chemistry*, Vol. 2, Ed. by A. Weissberger.   New York: Interscience Publishers, Inc., 1946.
14.5.   E. A. Braude, *Ann. Rep. Chem. Soc. (London)*, **42**, 105 (1945).

Compilations of Data

14.6.   R. A. Morton, *The Applications of Absorption Spectra to the Study of Vitamins, Hormones, and Coenzymes*.   London: Adam Hilger, Ltd., 1942.
14.7.   E. P. Carr, M. L. Sherrill, and V. Henri, in *International Critical Tables*, Vol. 5.   New York: McGraw-Hill Book Company, Inc., 1929; W. C. Holmes, *idem.*, Vol. 7.
14.8.   V. Henri, in *Tables Annuelles de Constantes et Données Numériques*.   New York: McGraw-Hill Book Company, Inc., (1910–1936).
14.9.   F. Ellinger, *Tabulae Biologicae*, **12**, 291 (1937); **16**, 265 (1938), Den Haag: Junk.
14.10. E. S. Miller, *Quantitative Biological Spectroscopy*.   Minneapolis: Burgess Publishing Company, 1934.
14.11. W. R. Brode, "The Absorption Spectra of Vitamins, Hormones and Enzymes," *Advances in Enzymology*, **4**, 269 (1944).
14.12. John R. Loofbourow, "Physical Methods for the Identification and Assay of Vitamins and Hormones," *Vitamins and Hormones*, **1**, 109 (1943).

CHAPTER 15

Qualitative Spectrographic Analysis of Materials

To DETERMINE WHICH METALLIC ELEMENTS ARE PRESENT in a given sample of material, analysis by the emission spectrum gives a method that is usually more direct, more rapid, more specific, more complete, and probably easier to use than any other yet developed. It does not require the analyst to guess in advance which elements are likely to be present, to select methods of procedure that may or may not turn out to be justified, or to separate the constituent materials into chemical groups. All elements that are readily detectable spectrographically can be found in a single operation.

Qualitative spectroscopic analysis as discussed in the present chapter refers to analysis by means of the emission spectrum. Absorption spectrophotometry (Chapter 14) can be used as a method of analysis for certain molecules, atoms, and ions, but it is somewhat less specific, though often more sensitive, than the emission method. Both methods should be considered before any given problem of analysis is undertaken. Emission analysis for qualitative purposes is one of the most widely used fields of spectroscopy, yet its development has been neglected somewhat in recent years. This neglect is due partly to the great amount of attention that has been given to quantitative analysis, a more difficult field, but it also arises from the fact that qualitative emission analysis is relatively so satisfactory that little attention has been given to improving it.

Qualitative analysis with the spectrograph is a relatively simple process. A small sample of the material to be analyzed is placed in an electric arc, spark, or other suitable source of excitation in such a way that the molecules of the sample will be dissociated into their constituent atoms, which are then stimulated to emit light. This light is sent through the spectrograph, which separates the various wavelengths and records these individually as spectrum lines on a photographic plate. Each chemical element emits a well-known group of lines whose wavelengths are recorded in printed tables of the types listed in Tables 9.7 and 15.2 and given in Appendices I and II. Lines in the spectrum can be positively identified, when their positions have been determined, as having come from a specific element. Numerous lines are emitted by each kind of atom, but at most two lines are needed to give positive identification.

Spectrographic analysis gives a permanent record so that results are readily available for future reference. This feature also makes it possible for unskilled personnel to carry out routine parts of an analysis and to prepare spectrograms from which an expert spectrographer can later make an accurate analysis. The method is especially valuable in cases in which the operator does not know what elements to look for. It is also much more specific than most chemical wet methods, for so definite are the wavelengths emitted by the atoms that misidentification of elements is almost impossible.

The spectrograph can be used for qualitative analysis of substances difficult to handle by wet methods, such as glasses and slags. It can also be used to detect in alloys minute impurities that are sufficient in amount to affect crystal structure but are in concentrations too low to be found by wet methods. It can be used to differentiate between two chemically similar substances. For instance, neodymium and praesodymium are so much alike as to defy chemical separation, but they resemble each other as little spectroscopically as silver resembles calcium. The spectrographic method can be used to resolve doubts remaining from wet analyses, as in the case where the brown coloration of a solution produced by hydrogen sulfide may be open to various interpretations. It can also be used effectively to follow the course of a chemical reaction or separation.

The spectrographic method is especially suited for use with samples of which only small amounts are available. In some cases 0.1 mg of sample is sufficient for a complete qualitative analysis, although 10 mg is desirable if available. The sensitivity of the method varies from element to element as discussed below, but amounts of certain elements as small as 10^{-8} gram can be detected, in concentrations of less than 1 part in 100 million.

The spectrographic method cannot be used satisfactorily to determine negative elements or ions such as Cl^- and $SO_4^=$ that may be present in a sample, since these are not stimulated to emit light in ordinary sources unless the radicals contain metallic atoms. Since most molecules are broken down in the source, chemical combinations

cannot usually be determined by emission analysis. Spectrographic
analysis of nonmetallic elements such as gases require special tech
niques which are discussed in § 15.7.

The visual spectroscope can be used for certain types of qualitative
analysis in the manner originated by Kirchhoff and Bunsen,[1] but i
serves merely as a simple approximation of the general spectroscopic
method and is applicable only in special cases.

15.1. Sensitivity of Detection of Various Elements. It is com
monly stated that only some 70 of the known chemical elements can
be detected spectrographically. Actually, any type of atom can be
detected and identified through the radiation it emits under proper
excitation, and therefore any atom can be detected spectrographically
with proper techniques. In general, however, spectrographic meth
ods for nonmetals, particularly for the halogens and gases, are as yet
more complicated and difficult than are the equivalent chemical we
methods. Therefore spectrographic analysis is ordinarily restricted
to the metallic elements and some of the metalloids. The 20 element
commonly not considered susceptible to such analysis are the perma
nent gases, the halogens, sulfur and selenium, and a few of the rare
heavy metals.

If we examine in detail the list of "nonspectroscopic" elements, it i
easy to see why these are difficult to detect: their atoms either are
relatively difficult to excite to emit radiation, especially radiation in a
readily accessible spectral region; or they emit so many spectrum
lines that none are especially intense. These difficulties can some
times be overcome by methods discussed in § 15.7.

Neutral atoms have ionization potentials lying between the 3.1 volts
of cesium and the 25.4 volts of helium, as discussed in Chapter 10
The metals almost all have ionization and excitation potentials lying
between 5 and 10 volts, whereas those of the gases and halogens lie
above this value (see Table 10.1, Column I).

It is desirable to distinguish between the *concentrational sensitivity*
and the *absolute sensitivity* of detection by spectrum lines. Fig
ure 15.1 shows the intensities of two spectrum lines plotted as func
tions of the percentage concentration of the element producing them
in a sample, or matrix, which is otherwise kept uniform. It will be
noted that over the range plotted these lines have different slopes and
therefore produce different concentrational sensitivities. Also, the

[1] G. R. Kirchhoff and R. Bunsen, *Ann. d. Physik*, **110**, 160, (1860); *Phil. Mag.*, **20**, 89 (1860); *ibid.*, **22**, 329 (1861); *Ann. Chim. Physique*, **62**, 452 (1861).

curves intercept the axis of minimum detectable intensity at different points, so that they produce different absolute sensitivities.   In making quantitative analyses, concentrational sensitivity is of great importance, whereas in qualitative analyses, where detection of the minimum possible concentration is desired, the absolute sensitivity is of importance.

The absolute sensitivity of analysis for an element depends on which spectrum line is selected for its detection.   In the following discussion, it is assumed that the most sensitive lines of each element are used.

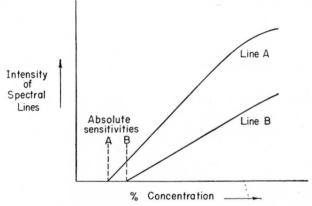

Fig. 15.1.   Line intensity curves as a function of percentage composition, showing the distinction between concentrational sensitivity and absolute sensitivity of detection.

Table 15.1 gives a list of the present approximate limiting concentrations that have been reached for the various elements.   Boron, for example, has been determined spectrographically to below 1 part in 10^7, whereas sulfur has been detected only to one part in 10^5.   These factors are, of course, only very approximate and can be expected to change as further progress is made in developing special methods for improving the sensitivity of analysis for any given element.   Absolute sensitivity can be increased by various methods discussed in § 15.3, which have been tried with some elements and not others.   Chemical preconcentration methods can be used also, reducing the limiting concentration factor by as much as 10^4 in some cases.   In theory, there should be no limit to absolute sensitivity, since a single atom, if kept in the source for a sufficiently long time, could be excited over

TABLE 15.1

APPROXIMATE SENSITIVITY LIMITS OF DIRECT SPECTROGRAPHIC DETECTION
OF THE ELEMENTS*

Element	Least detected ppm by weight	Element	Least detected ppm by weight
Ag	0.5	Mg	1
Al	1	Mn	10
As	100	Mo	10
Au	10		
		Na	0.1
B	0.1	Nb	80
Ba	1	Nd	90
Be	2	Ni	5
Bi	10		
		Os	100
C	. . .		
Ca	0.5	P	10
Cb	80	Pb	0.2
Cd	0.2	Pd	10
Ce	90	Pr	90
Cl	10	Pt	50
Co	40		
Cr	0.2	Ra	. . .
Cs	5	Rb	70
Cu	0.5	Rh	10
		Ru	10
Dy	90		
		S	10
Er	10	Sb	20
Eu	10	Sc	1
		Se	1
F	1	Si	80
Fe	0.1	Sm	300
		Sn	2
Ga	4	Sr	0.5
Gd	90		
Ge	7	Ta	50
		Tb	90
Hg	50	Te	500
Ho	90	Ti	50
		Tl	10
In	5		
Ir	100	V	0.3
K	0.1	W	10
La	10	Y	4
Li	0.5	Yb	3
		Zn	2
		Zr	20

* Many elements listed as having been detected to lower limits than others are less
readily detectable but have been more intensively studied.

and over again to emit light until enough was accumulated to give a detectable spectrum line. In practice, however, most of the atoms wander from the excitation stream before they are excited even once. The limit on absolute sensitivity is set by the background intensity, which overwhelms the weak light produced by the small number of atoms which are excited. Any method that will reduce the relative background intensity can be expected to increase absolute sensitivity.

The minimum amount of material that can be detected spectrographically is known for very few elements. For materials not difficult to detect, it appears to lie between 10^{-8} and 10^{-9} gram. Greatly increased absolute sensitivity of detection usually results whenever sources of excitation are improved specifically with this sensitivity in mind. The main objective is to prevent the atoms of interest from wandering from the excitation stream or from combining into molecules that do not readily dissociate, and to keep other atoms and molecules from emitting radiation.

The statement is sometimes made that 10^{-8} gram of lead is the least that can be detected spectrographically. This figure corresponds to 10^{13} lead atoms. An average spectrograph will project onto the plate only about 1 quantum of radiation of a given wavelength out of every 10,000 such quanta emitted by the source. Simple calculations based on these facts show that only 1 atom out of each 200 put into the source emits even one quantum of the line 4580 A commonly used for lead detection before it is lost from the stream of excitation.

15.2. Sensitive Lines and Ultimate Lines. Since some spectrum lines are stronger than others because of a high probability of occurrence of the appropriate transition in the atom, and since some are more easily excited than others, it is not surprising that certain lines should be found more sensitive for detecting small quantities of material than others. Usually, though not always, the strongest lines of a spectrum are the most sensitive. De Gramont,[2] Hartley,[3] and others have made careful empirical studies to determine the sensitive lines of each element. In particular, de Gramont has published tables of so-called *raies ultimes*, or *ultimate lines* (General Reference 15.5). The *raie ultime* is the last line of an element to disappear as the

---

[2] A. de Gramont, *Compt. Rend.*, **144**, 1101 (1907); *ibid.*, **145**, 1170 (1907); *Rev. Met.*, **19**, 90 (1922).

[3] W. N. Hartley, *Jour. Chem. Soc. (London)*, **41**, 90 (1882); *Phil. Trans.*, **175**, 50 (1884).

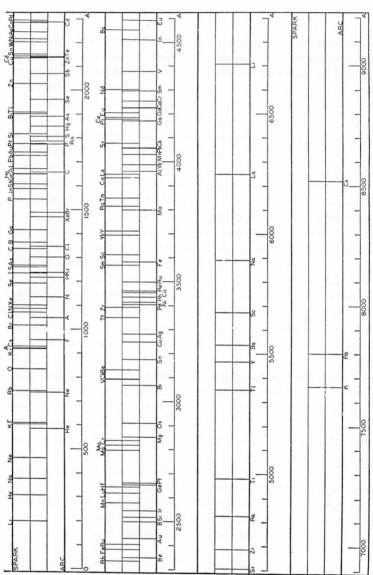

Fig. 15.2. Chart given by Hasler and Kemp,[4] showing the wavelength distribution of the most sensitive arc and spark lines of the elements.

quantity of the element burned in a sample is decreased to the vanishing point.   De Gramont's tables are to some extent out of date, since the ultimate line of an element depends strongly on the spectroscopic techniques used.   Several lines may tend to disappear together as the limit of sensitivity is reached.   These usually are lines belonging to the same multiplet, which differ only slightly in natural intensity (that is, by not more than a factor of 2 or 3).   To be sure of the presence of a specific element in a given sample, it is in any case desirable to identify at least two lines originating from it, so several lines are ordinarily listed as "ultimate."

Tables of sensitive lines are very useful, since if the most sensitive lines of an element do not appear in a spectrum being studied for qualitative analysis, the element can be marked absent.   This absence should be understood as being qualitative, however, and merely means that within the limits of possible detection the element was not found.   Appendices 1 and 2 contain lists of sensitive lines of the elements.   Figure 15.2 shows a chart, due to Hasler and Kemp,[4] of the distribution of sensitive lines according to wavelength. Comprehensive tables of spectral wavelengths are listed in Table 9.7, and abbreviated tables useful for routine spectrochemical analysis are listed in Table 15.2.

TABLE 15.2

ABBREVIATED TABLES FOR SPECTROCHEMICAL ANALYSIS*

1. H. Kayser, "Emission Spectra of Elementary Substances," *International Critical Tables*, Vol. V (New York: McGraw-Hill, 1929), page 276. Contains about 12,000 lines in the range 350 to 31,000 A, in arc and spark, for 86 elements, with precision of from 1 to 0.001 A, and intensity range 1 to 10.   Contains also table of air lines.

2. H. Kayser and R. Ritschl, *Tabelle der Hauptlinien der Linienspektren aller Elemente*, 2d ed. (Berlin: Springer, 1939).   Contains about 27,000 lines in the range 90,850 to 33 A, in arc, spark, and discharge, for 88 elements, given to 0.1 and 0.01 A, with intensity range 0 to 1000.

3. *Handbook of Chemistry and Physics*. Cleveland: Chemical Rubber Publishing Co.

4. W. R. Brode, *Chemical Spectroscopy* (New York: Wiley, 1939).   Contains a number of tables: (1) persistent lines by wavelength, listing 400 lines in the range 7950 to 1850 A, given to 0.1 A; (2) persistent lines by elements, with 400 lines in the range 9000 to 1600 A, given to 0.1 A for 71 elements; (3) principal lines by wavelength, containing about 4300 lines for the more

---

[4] M. F. Hasler and J. W. Kemp, *Jour. Opt. Soc. Am.*, **34**, 21 (1944).
* Reprinted by permission from G. R. Harrison, *Jour. App. Phys.*, **10**, 76 (1936).

TABLE 15.2 (*Continued*)

common elements, with the gases and some other nonmetals omitted, in wavelength range 8000 to 2000 A, given to 0.5 A, with intensity range 2 to 10; (4) principal lines by elements, containing about 6000 lines in the range 8000 to 2000 A, in arc and spark, given to 0.5 A, with intensity range 1 to 10; (5) spark spectrum of air, containing 300 lines in the range 7952 to 2288, given to 0.1 A, with intensity range 1 to 10; (6) principal lines by elements, discharge spectrum, containing about 300 lines in the range 8000 to 2500 A, given to 0.1 A, with intensity range 1 to 10.

5. D. M. Smith, *Visual Lines for Spectrum Analysis* (London: Hilger, 1928).

6. A. Gatterer and J. Junkes, *Atlas der Restlinien* (Castel Gandolfo, Italy: Specola Vaticana, 1937). Contains about 2400 lines in the range 8100 to 2200 A, in arc and spark, for 30 elements, given to 0.01 A; also some band spectra.

7. W. Gerlach and E. Riedl, *Die chemische Emissions-Spektralanalyse*, Part III (Leipzig: Voss, 1936). Contains about 3000 lines in the range 5900 to 2140 A, in arc and spark, for 57 elements, given to 0.1 A. Gives control lines and possible interfering lines.

8. J. A. Hannum, "Wavelength of the Principal Lines in the Emission Spectra of the Elements," *Handbook of Chemistry*, N. A. Lange, ed. (Sandusky, Ohio: Handbook Publishers, Inc., 1937), page 863. Contains about 5600 lines in the range 90,850 to 124 A for 83 elements, with accuracy to 1 A. Sensitive and ultimate lines are indicated.

9. G. R. Harrison, *M.I.T. Wavelength Tables* (New York: Wiley, 1939). Table of 500 sensitive lines of the elements according to elements and again in wavelength order, in range 9237 to 2025 A, in arc, spark, and discharge, for 85 elements, mostly given to 0.001 A, with intensity range 1 to 9000.   (Reproduced in part in Appendices 1 and 2.)

10. W. J. Crook, *Metallurgical Spectrum Analysis* (Stanford University Press, 1935).   Contains 9540 lines in the range 5800 to 2780 A, in the arc, for 64 elements, given to 0.1 A, with intensity range 1 to 10.

11. W. J. Crook, *Table of Arc Spectrum Lines Arranged in Order of Wavelengths* (Stanford University Press, 1933).

12. J. M. Eder and E. Valenta, *Atlas typischer Spektren* (Vienna: Hölder, 1911). Contains about 35,000 lines in the range 7950 to 1850 A, in arc, spark, and flame, for 75 elements, given to 0.01 A, with intensity range 1 to 100.   Contains also some band heads.   Note Rowland scale.

13. F. Exner and E. Hascheck, *Die Spektren der Elementen bei normalem Druck*, Vol. I (Leipzig and Vienna: Deuticke, 1911). Contains about 20,000 lines in several tables (not mutually exclusive), in the range 7070 to 2135 A, in arc and spark for 77 elements, given to 0.01 A, with intensity range 1 to 1000.   Note Rowland scale.

14. F. Twyman and D. M. Smith, *Wavelength Tables for Spectrum Analysis* (London: Hilger, 1931). Contains a number of tables: (1) Sensitive lines in spark spectra of solutions (Hartley; Pollok; Pollok and Leonard; Leonard and Whelan). Contains about 1300 lines, arranged by elements, in the range 6725 to 2200 A, for 42 elements, given to 0.1 A, with intensity range 1 to 10.

TABLE 15.2 (*Concluded*)

(2) Sensitive lines in spark spectra of solids and fused substances (De Gramont). Contains 330 lines, arranged both by elements and by wavelengths, in the range 7948 to 2138 A, for 83 elements, with accuracy to 0.1 A. Most sensitive lines indicated.   (3) Sensitive arc lines of 50 elements (in R.U. powder) arranged by elements. Contains 367 lines in the range 6717 to 2288 A, given to 0.01 A, with intensity range 1 to 10. Most sensitive lines are indicated.   (4) Sensitive lines in flame spectra arranged both by elements and by wavelengths. Contains 98 lines in the range 7699 to 2484 A, for 25 elements, given to 0.1 A.   (5) Sensitive lines in arc and spark spectra, arranged by elements. Contains about 1000 lines in the range 7000 to 2000 A, for 50 elements, given to 0.01 A, with intensity range 1 to 10.

15. F. Löwe, *Atlas der letzen Linien der wichtigsten Elementen* (Leipzig and Dresden: Steinkopf, 1928). Table of persistent spark lines of the more important elements.

16. G. Scheibe, *Physikalische Methoden der analytischen Chemie*, Part I, W. Böttger, ed. (Akademische Verlagsgesellschaft, Leipzig, 1933), p. 67. Contains about 1100 lines in the range 7950 to 1862 A, in arc and spark, for 62 elements, given to 0.01 A, with intensity range 0 to 40. Includes some air lines.

17. J. C. Boyce and J. M. MacInnes, *Wavelengths of the Extreme Ultraviolet Lines from Gas Discharges* (Princeton, N. J.: Palmer Physical Laboratory, 1930). Contains about 2300 lines in the range 2500 to 115 A, in discharge tube, for 10 elements, given to 0.01 and 0.001 A, with intensity range 000 to 10. Contains air lines and some bands.

18. J. C. Boyce and H. A. Robinson, "Wavelength Identification Lists for the Extreme Ultraviolet," *Jour. Opt. Soc. Am.*, **26**, 133 (1936). Contains about 2600 lines in the range 2000 to 38 A, in discharge, for 14 elements, given to 0.001 A, with intensity range 00 to 50.

Meggers and Scribner[5] have formulated a rule for predicting theoretically the ultimate lines of any element: "A *raie ultime* in any spectrum originates with a simple interchange of a single electron between *s* and *p* states, usually preferring configurations in which only one electron occurs in such a state." This rule usually gives the strongest line characteristic of the spectrum, even though it may not involve the normal state of the atom as a lower level, but does not necessarily give the *raies ultimes*. Excitation and other factors can greatly affect the result.

In some elements those lines which would be expected to be most sensitive, or ultimate, lie in relatively inaccessible spectrum regions. This is the case with rubidium and cesium, for example, which from an excitation standpoint should be the most readily detectable of all elements. Their theoretically ultimate lines lie in the infrared, but

[5] W. F. Meggers and B. F. Scribner, *Jour. Res. Nat. Bur. Standards*, **13**, 657 (1934).

in the absence of fast plates for this region, weaker lines in the blue region are usually more sensitive. The improvement in infrared sensitivity of photographic emulsions in recent years makes it possible that the infrared lines will ultimately be found the most sensitive.

The ultimate lines of oxygen, nitrogen, sulfur, and the other gases lie in the vacuum ultraviolet region. Equipment for taking spectrograms in this region is not available in many laboratories, however. Special methods of excitation may be used to produce other sensitive lines in easily accessible regions, as discussed in § 15.7.

Certain elements can be detected with greater sensitivity in the spark than in the arc, whereas others require use of special sources to be detected at all. The data given in most tables of sensitive lines apply when the most suitable source is used in a given case. The final determination of ultimate lines must in the long run be made empirically by the individual investigator using his own apparatus.

15.3. Improvement of Sensitivity Limits. If the ultimate lines of an element do not appear on a spectrogram, the analyst is likely to conclude that the element in question is not present in significant amounts. This absence may be due in part, however, to reduction in the exciting power of the source by prevalence of ions produced from atoms of low ionization potential, such as sodium or other alkalies. As smaller impurity concentrations become significant, it becomes increasingly necessary to introduce factors that will lower detection limits.

It is a common misapprehension to suppose that the absolute sensitivity limit is usually set by the light-gathering power of the spectrograph. Although sensitivity to light is the limiting factor when only a small sample of material is available, most qualitative analyses are made on samples available in considerable amounts. Under such circumstances a spectrograph of high aperture, which often involves low dispersion, and an emulsion of high speed, which almost always has low contrast, are seldom best for reaching the limit of sensitivity. When plenty of material is available, the lower detection limit is set by the ratio of intensity of the line being searched for to that of the background spectrum, a sort of "signal-to-noise ratio." When plate sensitivity or time of exposure are increased, both faint lines and background increase, and no improvement in detection results.

Many spectrographic analyses are carried out with instruments having dispersion too low to give the best results, not only for qualitative sensitivity but also for quantitative precision. If a spectrograph of low resolving power is used, the background intensity is increased relative to the line intensity over what would be obtained with an instrument of higher dispersion. To take an extreme case, it was found that a 35-ft concave grating in a Wadsworth mounting, plate factor 3.2 A per millimeter, could be used to photograph in two minutes 10 tin lines in concentrations too small to be detected with a standard medium quartz spectrograph, having a plate factor of 16.2 A per millimeter, in any exposure time, however long. A good general rule when extreme sensitivity is desired is to use a spectrograph with resolution and dispersion as great as is consistent with obtaining a suitable exposure in a reasonable time with the amount of material available for burning.

It is often possible to increase the intensity of a faint line relative to that of its neighboring background by the use of some of the following procedures:

1. By using a spectrograph of high resolution and dispersion, to decrease continuous background relative to line intensity.

2. By selecting the optimum slit width for the lines being sought.

3. By selecting excitation conditions such that the line intensity is increased relative to the background intensity.

4. By reducing factors in the source that produce continuous background or bands.

5. By reducing scattered light and chemical fog.

6. By using the moving-plate technique discussed in § 15.7 to separate lines that have maximum intensity at different times in the burning life of the arc or spark.

7. By using fractional distillation of the sample in the source (§ 15.6).

8. By treating with pure reagents the material being analyzed, to change the negative radicals to another form in which background intensity will be reduced and line sensitivity increased.

9. By introducing buffer materials in the arc, or by using around the arc an atmosphere that suppresses bands and continuous background more than it reduces line intensity.

10. By using the carrier-distillation method of Scribner and Mullin (§ 15.8) to accelerate fractional distillation in a certain part of the burning cycle and aid in sweeping into the arc stream the atoms to be excited.

By a combination of these means it is often possible to extend the sensitivity limit of analysis for a particular element by a factor of 100,000 or more.

15.4. Identification cf Elements. It is ordinarily not necessary to determine wavelengths accurately for qualitative analysis, since master spectrograms can be prepared with the spectrograph used, to show the locations of all important lines. For certain elements the lines will lie in definite patterns that can be identified at sight. Once a master spectrogram has been prepared, spectrograms taken with the same instrument for other samples can be superposed on this on a viewing box, and lines that coincide on the two can readily be marked. The Judd-Lewis comparator shown in Fig. 9.4 is a device for bringing the master and sample plates to optical coincidence without putting them in mechanical contact.

When master plates taken with the instrument being used are not available, it is still possible to identify lines by comparison of patterns. Standard charts of the type described in § 9.3 will be found useful for this purpose, if proper allowance is made for differences in dispersion, or for variation in dispersion with wavelength, when the master chart is taken with a prism or grating instrument and the sample spectrogram is taken with an instrument of the other type.

The Spekker Steeloscope,[6] shown in Fig. 3.4, is a spectroscope of moderate dispersion with an eyepiece that has been marked for setting on the positions of sensitive lines of several metallic elements. It furnishes a simple and convenient means of making quick optical estimates of such elements as nickel, chromium, and copper, in steel or other samples, and can be used for some quantitative as well as qualitative work.

The R.U. powders and charts discussed in § 9.3 are also of considerable aid in qualitative analysis, since the operator can take spectrograms with his own instrument of samples of R.U. powder and quickly identify from the charts the various lines in which he is interested. On spectrograms he should be able to find the more important sensitive lines of each "spectroscopic" element.

Incorrect identification of an element is unlikely if more than one line is used to establish its presence or absence. Errors due to inhomogeneity of the sample are much more likely, and here it is necessary to have recourse to those established procedures which ensure that the sample is truly representative.

---

[6] F. Twyman, General Reference 15.3, page 275.

15.5. Light Sources and Handling of Material. The original method of qualitative spectroscopic analysis introduced by Bunsen and Kirchhoff [1] in 1859 involved spraying liquids or powders into the gas fed to a Bunsen burner. Although flame excitation is often used, particularly for analysis by the method of Lundegårdh,[7] the flame does not supply the excitation needed to make more than about 30 metallic atoms detectable. Properly designed flame photometers are extremely simple to use. Photography of a flame spectrum offers little advantage over visual observation, however, since the excitation is so low that many of the lines are confined to the visible. The excitation can be increased somewhat by using an oxyhydrogen or oxy-acetylene flame.

Except in the case of modern flame photometers, emission spectroscopic analysis is ordinarily accomplished with the arc or spark as source. The arc gives greater sensitivity in most cases, burns more of the sample, involves a simpler electric circuit than the spark, and requires no dangerously high potential. The spark requires somewhat less attention than the arc and may be used when very small samples are to be consumed and extreme sensitivity is not required, as for example in determining constituents in the metallic coating of a watch case. Circuits for arcs, sparks, and other sources are discussed in Chapter 8.

Certain parts of an arc or spark provide greater sensitivity than others for the detection of various elements.[8] Lines arising from molecules that may readily be dissociated appear most strongly in the outer layers of an arc, whereas lines arising from un-ionized atoms may appear near the positive electrode, and from ionized atoms near the negative.

If the material to be analyzed can be obtained in rods or chunks, "self-electrodes" should be used. These may be roughly shaped and held in an arc holder such as that shown in Fig. 8.5. Alternatively, the sample may be placed in a hollowed-out electrode of pure graphite, as shown in Fig. 15.3. The sample electrode is usually made positive because the positive becomes hotter than the negative, this difference in temperature assisting in vaporizing the material. However, increased sensitivity of detection may result from making the sample electrode negative.

To avoid contamination, the sample to be analyzed should be

---

[7] H. Lundegårdh, *Zeitschr. f. Physik,* **66,** 109 (1930).
[8] See L. Strock, General Reference 15.7, page 49.

handled as little as possible. So sensitive is the spectrographic method that an arc operated in a room in which a commutator-equipped electric motor is running may show copper lines even though no copper is present in the sample. It is usually desirable to use a sample of 10 mg or larger both for convenience in handling and so that it may truly be representative of the master sample.

Very pure graphite electrodes, wrapped in cellophane until used and handled only with scrupulously clean tongs, are useful for holding

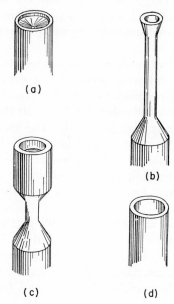

Fig. 15.3.   Several forms of hollowed-out graphite electrodes.

samples to be analyzed. Such "spectrographic carbons" can be obtained from several companies or may be prepared in the laboratory.[9] Carbons of $\frac{3}{16}$-in. diameter are most convenient for the lower electrode, and may be bored out with a $\frac{1}{4}$-in. drill kept clean for the purpose. The upper electrode may well be $\frac{1}{4}$ in. in diameter or less and somewhat pointed. A 5-amp arc is suitable for this size of electrode.

A disadvantage of the graphite electrode is the prevalence of cyanogen bands, which are due to the molecule CN, when it is used,

---

[9] See J. S. Owens, General Reference 15.13, page 17.

These bands, some of which are shown in Fig. 15.4, are likely to interfere with sensitive lines in various parts of the spectrum, especially in low-dispersion spectrograms. The bands are especially strong when the sample material has been burned out of the electrode. This condition can readily be detected by the appearance of strong violet light in the arc. Provision should be made to turn off the arc whenever this condition appears or to bar the light from the spectrograph while the arc is being reloaded.

Copper or silver electrodes are sometimes used instead of graphite in exciting samples, but their use, which largely eliminates the cyanogen bands, greatly reduces sensitivity. This reduction results both because graphite electrodes become hotter than metallic ones and because the carbon arc stream reaches a higher level of excitation than that of a metallic arc.

To reduce the likelihood of contamination, electrodes may be preburned for a few seconds before the sample is introduced. Merely

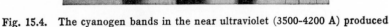

Fig. 15.4. The cyanogen bands in the near ultraviolet (3500-4200 A) produced by graphite electrodes burning in air.

because a given element is not found in the spectrum of the empty electrode, however, one is not justified in assuming that it is not present in the electrode material, since sensitivity of detection is likely to be increased in such circumstances by the addition of metallic ions to the arc stream, as when the sample is added. Thus, certain highly purified graphite electrodes show no vanadium when burned in the arc, but when a small amount of pure metallic salt, known to contain no vanadium, is added, vanadium lines may appear. Electrodes should always be cut or shaped with tools which have been carefully cleaned with alcohol or ether and wiped with clean filter paper.

Any material can be made to support an electric arc if it can be heated to the point of volatilization into the arc stream. When a nonconducting powder is to be studied, it can be mixed with a conducting material that gives few spectrum lines. Powdered graphite is useful for this purpose. Ammonium sulfate can also be used, since its component atoms do not give lines in the visible or ultraviolet regions under arc excitation. Slags, refractories, and inorganic materials can be ground up with pestle and mortar, preferably of agate or other hard substance, and mixed with the conducting material, which may be moistened with pure dilute HCl. Biological materials may be ashed in a furnace or by digestion in pure acids, and the ash introduced into the arc for analysis.

Strock[8] has described the cathode glow method of analysis of Mannkopf and Peters,[10] in which use is made of the very high sensitivity of excitation that exists in the small region of the electric arc near the negative electrode when this is used to hold the sample. This so-called "Glimmschicht method" is widely used. High ab-

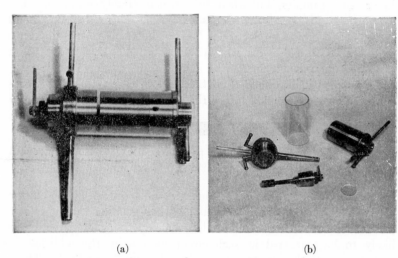

(a)   (b)

Fig. 15.5. Hollow-cathode source of McNally, Harrison, and Rowe[12] for spectrochemical analysis. (a) Assembled. (b) Parts.

solute sensitivity is also obtainable with the high-voltage AC arc, as described by Duffendack[11] and his coworkers. A transformer giving about 1200 volts is connected to the electrodes, and 1 amp or more is sent through the spark, so it becomes an incipient arc. This source must be handled very carefully on account of the danger of shock.

The hollow-cathode tube, discussed in §§ 8.19 and 15.7, probably gives the most sensitive means of detecting small quantities of mate-

---

[10] R. Mannkopf and C. Peters, *Zeitschr. f. Physik*, **70,** 444 (1931).

[11] O. S. Duffendack and K. B. Thompson, *Proc. Am. Soc. Testing Materials*, **36,** 310 (1936).

[12] J. R. McNally, Jr., G. R. Harrison, and E. Rowe, *Jour. Opt. Soc. Am.*, **37,** 93 (1947).

rial. Since the sample can be evaporated into the excitation column over and over again, it does not escape excitation so readily as in other sources. McNally, Harrison, and Rowe[12] found that with the hollow cathode they could go down to extreme limits of concentration even in detecting the halogens and sulfur. Their source is shown in Fig. 15.5.

A very convenient form of spark electrode for qualitative analysis is shown in Fig. 8.10. This is applicable when electrodes can be formed of the sample to be analyzed. It is desirable that the spark should wander somewhat in order to prevent overheating of a portion of the electrode, but this wandering should be held in a line parallel to that connecting the spark with the slit so as not to get off the spectrograph line-of-sight. Very small electrodes can be used with a spark, especially if the amount of current flowing is kept small; for example a satisfactory spark can be formed between two pieces of the hair spring of a watch.

The spark is likely to be less satisfactory than the arc in reaching a high sensitivity because continuous background is usually more intense in the spark. Another disadvantage is the likelihood of excitation of "air lines," which do not appear in sources having lower excitation. These may be partially suppressed by the addition of inductance to the spark circuit, shown in Fig. 8.11. The inductance shown in that figure should be adjusted to suppress air lines as much as possible without reducing excitation below the needed level.

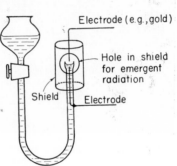

Fig. 15.6. Arrangement for sparking from metal to liquid surface.

Liquids can be handled directly by using them to wet graphite powder placed on the graphite holder in an electric arc or spark, or they can be used with one of the various methods for sparking from metal to liquid surfaces[11, 13] (Fig. 15.6). Also, as in the Lundegårdh[7] method, liquids can be introduced into a flame that can then be excited electrically, if necessary.

15.6. Moving-Plate and Fractional Distillation Methods. It was shown by Mannkopf and Peters[10] that when a sample is held in a

[13] F. Twyman and C. S. Hitchen, *Proc. Roy. Soc.* (London), **A133**, 72 (1931).

deep hole drilled in the lower terminal of a graphite arc, the various constituents are distilled into the arc at different times. They used this fractional distillation method to increase the sensitivity of quantitative analysis, but it is also extremely useful for qualitative analysis, especially when combined with the moving plate technique. Preuss,[14] who took several successive exposures during the burning time of the arc, mentions that fractional distillation was useful for separating lines which happened to lie close together. The plate can be moved continuously parallel to the spectrum lines during the exposure,[15] by hand or with a small motor provided with a suitable reducing gear, and in this way resolution in time is effected even more conveniently. Figure 15.7 shows such a plate, taken with a medium

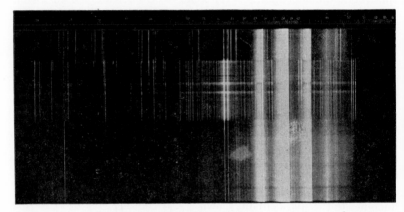

Fig. 15.7. Moving plate spectrogram of a brass sample in a carbon arc.
The elapsed time was 4 min.

quartz spectrograph. The plate was moved uniformly at such a speed that 4 min was required to cover the distance from the wavelength scale at the top to the bottom of the photograph. At the top, just after the arc was started, lines of zinc, cadmium, lead, and copper predominate. After about half a minute, zinc, cadmium, and lead disappear, the copper spectrum is greatly enhanced, and iron lines appear. These last for another minute or more, there is a flash of calcium and aluminum lines, and finally there is nothing left except weak copper lines, a carbon line, and the cyanogen bands.

[14] E. Preuss, *Chem. Erde*, **9**, 365 (1935); *Zeitschr. angew. Min.*, **1**, 93 (1937).
[15] See D. Richardson, General Reference 15.13, page 64.

The advantages of using the moving plate are again apparent on inspection of Fig. 15.8, in which the intensities of lines from elements having different ionization and excitation potentials are plotted against time as 50 mg of brass turnings is burned in pure graphite electrodes.   If the spectrogram from which these data were taken had been obtained from a single 10 sec exposure, the lines of both elements would have been lost at concentrations 100 times greater than those reached by spreading the light from the arc out on a time scale. Similar sensitivity could have been attained, of course, by photo-

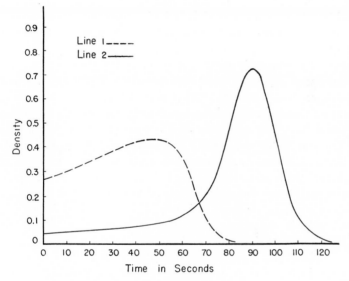

Fig. 15.8. Intensity-time curves for different elements in the same sample.

graphing the arc for 10 sec at just the proper time, but the best time to take this exposure varies from element to element and from sample to sample, and the moving-plate technique gives the opportunity to select the optimum portion of the exposure for each element.

The moving-plate method is especially valuable for biological material, in which the character of the matrix is often somewhat indeterminate.   The conditions of excitation at any instant are the complex result of a number of different boiling points, diffusion rates, and excitation and ionization potentials.   If fairly high concentrations of a material having a low ionization potential and a low boiling point are present, the excitation conditions in the arc are depressed.

Scribner and Mullin[16] have added a further development to the use of fractional distillation in the arc, known as the *carrier-distillation* method. To the sample they add a material that is found empirically to speed up the "washing" into the arc stream of the impurities being detected. They first convert the sample chemically to a form having high volatility, so that the rate of distillation in the arc will be increased. They then mix a carrier material of intermediate volatility to the amount of about 2 per cent with the powdered sample. This carrier may be gallium oxide, as they recommend, silver chloride, as used by Kent,[17] or some other material found empirically to be suitable. Use of such material results in a speeding up and spreading out of the fractional distillation process, which is very effective in extending sensitivity limits when the moving-plate method or an equivalent technique is used.

High-speed plates are sometimes recommended for high sensitivity of detection, because it is thought that weak lines can be detected most readily in this way. Weak background intensity is correspondingly increased, however; and since what is wanted is increased density of the line over that of the rapidly increasing background, high contrast or, better still, rapidly increasing contrast is a more desirable plate property. This observation suggests that slow plates, such as process plates, are desirable for qualitative work when limiting sensitivities are to be reached, and such plates are indeed found to give a real gain in detection sensitivity. The use of a high contrast developer such as Eastman D–11 is also helpful.

15.7. Analysis for Elements Difficult to Detect. The 20 elements considered least susceptible to spectrographic analysis, either qualitative or quantitative, are the permanent gases, the four halogens, sulfur and selenium, polonium, actinium, protoactinium, thorium, and uranium. In recent years it has been found possible to analyze for thorium, uranium, and the other heavy elements by using spectrographs of high resolution and by using various innovations of excitation and handling.

The gases are difficult to detect spectrographically, not only because they are hard to excite but also because their principal lines lie below 2000 A.[18] This vacuum ultraviolet region has been studied

---

[16] B. F. Scribner and H. R. Mullin, *Jour. Res. Nat. Bur. Standards.*, **37**, 369 (1946).

[17] R. Kent III, unpublished report.

[18] But see R. A. Wolfe and O. S. Duffendack, General Reference 15.14, page 66; also footnote 19.

extensively in scientific laboratories, and it is usual to find lines of nitrogen, oxygen, and other gases appearing on almost all vacuum spectrograms. These elements can readily be detected by the methods of vacuum spectroscopy, especially in hot spark and other sources having high excitation (Chapter 19). Gatterer and Frodl [19] have investigated their excitation with high-frequency sources and have developed methods for their detection down to low concentrations.

Sulfur and selenium show no ultimate lines in most tables because their sensitive lines lie at wavelengths shorter than 2000 A. Harrison and Merrill [20] developed three different ways of analyzing for these two elements. For sulfur the three lines that theoretically should be the most sensitive lie between 1807 and 1826 A, while for selenium they lie between 1960 and 2062 A. The standard type of quartz spectrograph does not quite reach them, because of absorption by its quartz optical train and because of the absorption of light of these wavelengths by oxygen in the air and by the gelatin in the photographic emulsion. It is also necessary to overcome the effect of the high excitation potentials of sulfur and selenium, which are above the ionization potentials of the metals forming the usual matrix. The latter difficulty can be overcome by using arcs of high current density or sparks with high average excitation. The former difficulty was overcome by flushing an ordinary spectrograph continuously with a stream of commercial tank nitrogen, allowing this to leak out the slit against the arc or spark placed directly in front of it, and by using specially sensitized plates. When a lithium fluoride optical train or a diffraction grating was used instead of a quartz prism, an increase of sensitivity resulted. By this means, nickel was successfully analyzed for sulfur down to concentrations below 1 in 10^5.

Harrison and Merrill carried out similar analyses by using infrared lines of sulfur which, though not the ultimate lines, were found very sensitive when used with modern infrared plates. Sulfur was also analyzed in the ordinary spectrum range by using the hot spark and detecting the stronger lines of SII and SIII. The first of these three methods was found most convenient and practical, but the hollow-cathode method was found later to detect S and Se at still lower concentrations.

[19] A. Gatterer and V. Frodl, *Ric. Spettroscop.*, **1**, 201 (1946).
[20] See G. R. Harrison and D. P. Merrill, General Reference 15.16.

Konovalov and Frisch[21] used the hollow cathode to detect nitrogen and argon to a few tenths of 1 per cent. McNally, Harrison, and Rowe[12] have developed a method of spectroscopic analysis of the non-metals with emphasis on analysis for fluorine, and their paper gives references to previous papers on the analysis of gases spectroscopically. They studied the relative sensitivities of fluorine lines in the vacuum ultraviolet region and in the visible, and found that certain visible lines appeared more sensitive than the theoretical ultimate lines of fluorine. By using a specially designed hollow-cathode source, they were able to detect as little as 10^{-8} gram of fluorine at a concentrational sensitivity of less than 1 in 10^6. Chlorine and sulfur were readily detected in amounts as small as 0.2 μg, and 1.0 μg respectively, in samples weighing 20 mg.

Fluorine can be determined spectrographically by adding calcium salts to the sample, if necessary, and using the band head of calcium fluoride at 5291 A, since the CaF molecule resists dissociation in the arc. Papish, Hoag, and Schnee[22] obtained an absolute sensitivity limit of 10 μg of fluorine by this method.

15.8. The Qualitative Analysis. Figure 15.9 shows a typical master plate marked with the sensitive lines of the principal elements obtained with R.U. powder (§ 9.3). The extra trouble of preparing such master plates is worth while for any spectrograph that is to be used extensively for analytical work.

It is convenient in making a qualitative analysis to put the elements sought into four categories: major constituent, minor constituent, trace, and absent, corresponding roughly to the ranges 100 to 1 per cent, 1 to 0.01 per cent, 0.01 per cent to the minimum detectable, and less than this. Such categories and limits are only approximate and will vary greatly from element to element. Often a great deal of semiquantitative information can be obtained from the relative intensities of the lines, particularly when several similar samples are being compared in which the amount of one element relative to another is changing. The temptation to estimate amounts without some sort of control should be resisted, even if the estimate is no closer than a factor of 10, since the intensity of a line depends on many factors in addition to the concentration of the element being studied. A typical qualitative analysis report is given in Table 15.3.

---

[21] V. A. Konovalov and S. E. Frisch, *Jour. Tech. Phys.* (*U.S.S.R.*), **4**, 523 (1934).

[22] J. Papish, L. E. Hoag, and W. E. Snee, *Ind. Eng. Chem.*, *Anal. ed.*, **2**, 263 (1930).

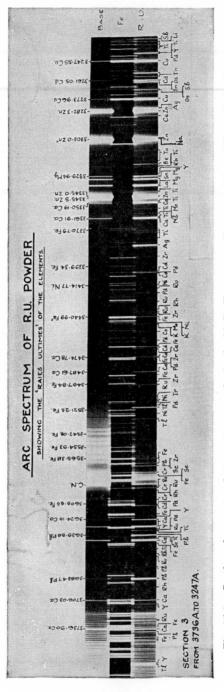

Fig. 15.9. Section of a master plate spectrogram obtained with R. U. powder. (Courtesy Adam Hilger, Ltd., London.)

TABLE 15.3

Report of Spectrochemical Qualitative Analyses

For: *Tissue Analysis Lab.* Date: *March 28*

Element	Sample					Element	Sample				
	1	2	3	4	5		1	2	3	4	5
Ag	m-	m-	m+	m	m-	Na	M	M	M	M	M
Al	M	M	M	M	M	Nd					
As		tr		tr		Ni		tr			m
Au						Os					
B						P	m	m	m	m	m
Ba	m	m	m	m	m	Pb	tr	tr			
Be						Pd					
Bi						Pr			tr	tr	
Ca	M	M	m	M	M	Pt					
Cb						Ra					
Cd	tr	m	tr			Rb					
Ce						Re					
Co						Rh					
Cr						Ru					
Cs	tr				tr	Sb	tr				
Cu	M	M	M	M	m	Sc					
Dy						Si	m	m	m	M	M
Er						Sm					
Eu						Sn		tr	m		
Fe	m	m	m-	m	m-	Sr	m	m	tr	tr	m
Ga						Ta					
Gd						Tb					
Ge						Te					
Hf						Th					
Hg						Ti		m	tr		m
Ho						Tl					
In	tr		tr			Tm					
Ir						U					
K	M	M	M	m	M	V	tr	tr			
La		tr				W					
Li	m	m		m	m	Yb					
Lu						Yt					
Mg	m	m	m	m	m	Zn	m	m	m	tr	tr
Mn						Zr		tr		tr	
Mo											

M = constituent probably major
m = constituent probably minor
tr = constituent probably trace

GENERAL REFERENCES

15.1. W. R. Brode, *Chemical Spectroscopy*, 2d ed. New York: John Wiley & Sons, Inc., 1942.

15.2. R. A. Sawyer, *Experimental Spectroscopy*. New York: Prentice-Hall, Inc., 1944.

15.3. F. Twyman, *The Spectrochemical Analysis of Metals and Alloys*. Brooklyn: Chemical Publishing Company, Inc., 1941.

15.4. D. M. Smith, *Bibliography of Spectrochemical Analysis*, 2d ed. London: British Non-Ferrous Metals Research Association, 1940.

15.5. F. Twyman and D. M. Smith, *Wavelength Tables for Spectrum Analysis*, 2d ed. London: Adam Hilger, Ltd., 1931.

15.6. T. R. P. Gibb, Jr., *Optical Methods of Chemical Analysis*. New York: McGraw-Hill Book Company, Inc., 1942.

15.7. L. W. Strock, *Spectrum Analysis with the Carbon Arc Cathode Layer*. London: Adam Hilger, Ltd., 1936.

15.8. W. Gerlach and E. Schweitzer, *Die chemische Emissions-spektralanalyse*, I. Leipzig: Voss, 1930.

15.9. W. Gerlach and E. Schweitzer, *Foundations and Methods of Chemical Analysis by the Emission Spectrum*. London: Adam Hilger, Ltd., 1931. (Translation of 15.8.)

15.10. W. Gerlach and W. Gerlach, *Die chemische Emissions-spektralanalyse*, II. Leipzig: Voss, 1933.

15.11. W. Gerlach and W. Gerlach, *Clinical and Pathological Applications of Spectrum Analysis*. London: Adam Hilger, Ltd., 1934. (Translation of 15.10.)

15.12. W. Gerlach and E. Riedl, *Die chemische Emissions-spektralanalyse*. Leipzig: Voss, 1936.

15.13. Proc. Fifth Summer Conf. on Spectroscopy, 1937. New York: John Wiley & Sons, Inc., 1938.

15.14. Proc. Sixth Summer Conf. on Spectroscopy, 1938. New York: John Wiley & Sons, Inc., 1939.

15.15. Proc. Seventh Summer Conf. on Spectroscopy, 1939. New York: John Wiley & Sons, Inc., 1940.

15.16. G. R. Harrison, "Practical Possibilities in Spectrographic Analysis," *Metals and Alloys*, Nov. 1936.

15.17. W. F. Meggers, "Principals and Principles of Spectrochemical Analysis," *Spectrochimica Acta*, **3**, 5 (1947).

15.18. W. F. Meggers and B. F. Scribner, *Index to the Literature in Spectrochemical Analysis*. Philadelphia: American Society Testing Materials, 1939.

15.19. *Jour. Applied Physics*, Nov. 1939, Vol. 10.

CHAPTER 16

Quantitative Spectrochemical Analysis

QUANTITATIVE ANALYSIS OF MATERIALS BY EMISSION SPECTROSCOPY is frequently referred to as *spectrochemical analysis*, less frequently as *spectrum analysis*, the latter term being likely to be confused with the analysis of spectra. Since 1930 the development of spectrochemical methods has been rapid, and they can now be made so precise, can be carried out so rapidly and simply, and are used in so many routine industrial applications that they must be considered as well tested and established.

Spectrographic emission methods of quantitative analysis can be readily used whenever the elements to be determined are metallic or metalloidal, when the chemical combinations in which they are present in the sample need not be determined, and when the combined concentrations of the elements of interest are less than about 5 per cent of the entire sample. Outstanding advantages of the method are its rapidity, the smallness of the sample that can be analyzed, the simplicity of the operations needed, the sensitivity available for determining very low concentrations of material, and the precision obtainable. Precision to within 2 per cent of the amount of element being determined is no longer unusual, and this precision is to a considerable degree independent of the actual concentration. Thus it is usually as easy to determine spectrographically the difference between 0.0010 and 0.0011 per cent of lead in gold, for example, as that between 0.10 and 0.11 per cent. Ten milligrams of sample may suffice for the quantitative determination of from 1 to 30 elements, and if necessary as little as 0.01 mg may serve.

Probably the greatest usefulness of spectrochemical methods arises in carrying out routine procedures where similar analyses are to be made on hundreds or thousands of samples, as in production composition control. Here the time and effort consumed in preparing standard samples and in setting up special procedures are soon repaid in savings of time in individual tests, and in consequent reductions of operating costs in plants and laboratories.   In most of the metals industries and in many chemical laboratories, spectrochemical analysis is now a routine control process.

As chemical wet methods grow less precise at lower concentrations owing to the small quantities of material available, spectroscopic methods gain in advantage.   Quantitative analyses can be made spectrographically under almost all conditions in which qualitative spectrographic analyses can be made, the difference being largely the control of the conditions of spectrography.   The situations in which quantitative spectrographic analysis is most useful are similar to those discussed in Chapter 15 for qualitative analysis.

Simple quantitative spectrographic methods serve for determination of some 70 of the chemical elements, including all metallic and metalloidal elements.   Special methods, somewhat less convenient than those sufficing for metallic elements, have been developed for sulfur, selenium, and some of the halogens (§§ 15.7 and 16.14).   Satisfactory spectrographic methods have not yet been developed for the analysis of gases in gross quantities, but tentative steps in this direction were discussed in § 15.7.

Quantitative determination of molecular constituents in a sample can sometimes be carried out with high sensitivity and excellent precision by the methods of absorption spectrophotometry and Raman spectroscopy.   These are discussed in Chapters 14, 17 and 18. Many points of importance in quantitative analysis were examined in Chapter 15, and the contents of that chapter should be carefully kept in mind in connection with the problems now to be discussed.

THE BASIC PROCEDURE OF QUANTITATIVE ANALYSIS

Though many procedures of quantitative analysis are discussed in the literature and are given the names of their proposers, practically all are variations of one basic procedure.   Since the relative numbers of atoms present in a sample are to be determined by means of the radiation which they are caused to emit and since the quantity of this radiation can depend on many factors besides the number of atoms emitting it, a null method is required.   Elimination of the influence of factors that need not be determined can most readily be done by keeping as many of them constant as possible.

16.1. Basic Procedure. The sample to be analyzed may be regarded as consisting of the following: (a) one or more major constituents, which together constitute the matrix. These influence the excitation conditions in the source, such as the equivalent temperature of burning, by the number and character of the ions they provide. (b) From 1 to 70-odd atomic constituents, the elements which are to be quantitatively determined, present in such small quantities that variations in their concentrations will not significantly affect the excitation conditions.

Suppose that we have a sample of palladium in which we wish to determine quantitatively the amount of platinum. This can be done

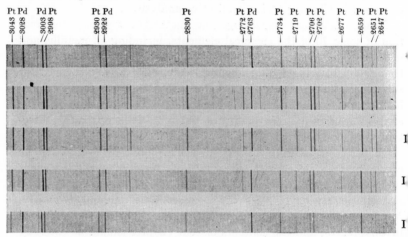

Fig. 16.1. Determination of platinum in palladium sample. The Pt lines (λ 2650) shown in the spectrum *a* (the unknown) are seen to have an intensity between that of standard sample III and standard sample IV.

by preparing a series of otherwise identical palladium samples in which the amount of platinum present is controlled. These standard samples are then burned in a uniform manner in an electric arc or other source of excitation, and the unknown sample is burned in as closely the same manner as possible. From the resulting spectrogram that standard sample is selected which has produced Pt lines of most nearly the same density as those produced from the sample being analyzed, the "unknown." This situation is shown in Fig. 16.1. Here the two standards III and IV are seen to bracket the unknown sample *a*. A new series of standards intermediate in Pt content between III and IV can then be made up and burned, until one is found whose Pt lines duplicate in intensity those of a. The unknown can then be assumed to have the same concentration of Pt as this standard sample.

In practice it is not necessary to match the density of the line in a standard sample exactly to that of the unknown. A working curve of concentration against intensity of light emitted under controlled conditions can be plotted, on which the unknown concentration can then be interpolated from measured densities. It is essential, however, that standard and unknown samples be treated as nearly as possible alike. The precision of an analysis will usually depend on how closely this duplication can be controlled.

16.2. Sources of Excitation. Arc, spark, and flame excitation, as discussed in Chapters 8 and 15, can all be used for quantitative analysis, and any one of these may serve best for a particular type of sample. In the electric arc more of the sample is likely to be consumed, and hence the sample can more easily be made truly representative of the material being analyzed. The arc produces very bright spectrum lines, involves simple electrical circuits, and produces no confusing air lines that sometimes interfere with spark analysis. Somewhat higher excitation, which is sometimes needed, can be obtained with the spark than with the arc in air. The spark requires less attention than the arc, consumes a smaller amount of material, may produce less continuous background and fewer interfering bands, and vaporizes volatile material less rapidly. With special methods, such as those of Ramage[1] and of Lundegårdh,[2] flames of various types have certain advantages, especially when biological samples are to be consumed. The flame photometer has been referred to in Chapter 15.

For certain types of samples the AC arc method [3] developed by Duffendack and his collaborators gives very high sensitivity, and the *Glimmschicht* or cathode-layer method described in § 15.5 gives equally high sensitivity under other conditions. The hollow cathode (§§ 8.19 and 15.7) forms an extension of the cathode-layer method and probably gives the highest sensitivity of all sources when an extremely small amount of material is available for excitation. The reason for this sensitivity is that when the cathode layer is curved

---

[1] H. Ramage, *Nature*, **123**, 601 (1929); *ibid.*, **137**, 67 (1936); H. Ramage, J. H. Sheldon, and W. Sheldon, *Proc. Roy. Soc.* (London), **B113**, 308 (1933).

[2] H. Lundegårdh, *Zeitschr. f. Phys.*, **66**, 109 (1930); see also General Reference 16.3.

[3] O. S. Duffendack and K. B. Thompson, *Proc. Am. Soc. Testing Materials*, **36**, 310 (1936).

into a complete cylinder, an atom has more difficulty in wandering from the stream of excitation than in other sources.

The accuracy of quantitative analysis is usually limited by fluctuations in the source. Causes of these fluctuations are differential evaporation, cathode spot wandering, current fluctuations which are caused by these and other effects, and irregular train length in the case of spark sources. For this reason special sources, such as the controlled spark, discussed in Chapter 14, are of special importance in spectrochemical analysis.

16.3. Form and Preparation of the Sample. In preparing samples for burning, it is important to minimize handling and to simplify preparation procedures. If the material to be analyzed is solid and can be obtained in small, uniform sticks or bars, these can be used directly as "self-electrodes." A common source of error is inhomogeneity of the sample. When a sample is not uniform, it may be ground to a powder, mixed thoroughly, and packed in a hollow electrode of graphite or some other conducting material. The sample may also be dissolved and the resulting solution used to moisten graphite powder, which can then be packed into a graphite electrode. Sometimes a spark can be made to pass directly to a liquid surface (Fig. 15.6).

Graphite, copper, silver, and gold are used as container electrode materials, principally because of their high melting points and because they can be readily obtained in spectroscopically pure form. Graphite is much more widely used than the other three because of its desirable electrical and thermal characteristics. Somewhat higher excitation is obtained in an arc between graphite electrodes than between metallic electrodes. Pellets of graphite or other material can be compressed in briquetting apparatus, to give exact amounts of uniformly dense material for burning.

16.4. Standards for Comparison. By far the greatest part of the work involved in making a spectrographic quantitative analysis lies in preparing the standards, which must be similar in general constitution or matrix to the sample to be analyzed but which contain known amounts of the elements being determined. Fortunately, one standard sample will serve as a container of known amounts of a number of elements. There is no limit to this number except that the total quantity of varying elements must be kept low enough to avoid affecting the matrix conditions. This requirement usually means below 1 per cent of the entire sample, though in certain cases as much as 5 per cent is permissible.   A spectrograph with sufficient resolution must be used, of course, so that the lines of the various elements do not interfere.

One per cent of zinc in a sample of sodium chloride will give much less light than 1 per cent of zinc in a sample of gold, for example, because the excitation conditions set by the prevalent sodium ions in the first case are much lower than those set by the prevalent gold ions in the second case.   In analyzing for zinc in NaCl it would be necessary to make standard samples in which the matrix was NaCl, and varying amounts of zinc were added.   In analyzing gold for zinc it would be necessary to have a matrix of metallic gold to which varying amounts of zinc were added, and to have any sodium ions present in quantity in the unknown gold sample also present and constant in concentration in the standard samples.   Elements of low boiling point and ionization potential, such as the alkali metals, exert very powerful effects on the matrix, and small variations in concentration of these may produce large changes in the light emitted by a minor constituent in the same sample.   A sample of gold containing 1 per cent zinc and no copper can be expected to emit zinc lines as strongly as a similar sample containing 1 per cent of zinc and 1 per cent of copper, but if as much as 5 per cent of copper is introduced, or 1 per cent of sodium, the intensity of the zinc lines can be expected to be different.

Metallurgical standard samples can be made either by mixing alloys in the induction furnace,[4] or by dissolving the samples in acid to produce salts which can then be ground and thoroughly mixed.[5] Another procedure is to mix metallic powders with a basic matrix buffer material, such as graphite or a salt, such as ammonium sulfate or ammonium chloride, which produces few spectrum lines.   Biological samples to be examined for traces of metals can usually be digested with acids or ashed in a furnace to remove organic constituents, and then added to some matrix base that can be reproduced in preparing standards.

One of the simplest methods of preparing a standard is to take some of the actual material being analyzed and add to it known amounts of the elements to be determined.   This procedure involves extrapolation back toward zero concentration in successive approximations, however, which is much less precise than if a pure sample

---

[4] See General References 16.1 and 16.2.
[5] See General References 16.1 and 16.3.

of similar material can be obtained and used as the matrix for the addition of the elements of interest. Every spectrographic laboratory in which quantitative analyses are to be made should build up a collection of standard samples as rapidly as possible.

16.5. Burning of the Sample. The role of the excitation source is threefold: to vaporize the sample at a rate as controlled as possible; to dissociate all molecules present into their constituent atoms or atomic ions; and to excite these atoms or ions to emit radiation. When very low concentrations are involved, it is important to cause every atom of the element of interest to emit as much light as possible, and the methods of improving sensitivity discussed in § 15.3 may be invoked.

Fundamental in control of the source, however, is the necessity of treating the standard sample and the unknown sample exactly alike Such equal treatment can be attained satisfactorily only when both samples have the same matrix, are subjected to the same conditions of excitation, and are caused to emit radiation in the same way.

16.6. Selection and Use of the Spectrograph. Quantitative analyses can be made with a visual spectroscope, but this method has fallen into disuse except for rapid, short-cut analyses of fairly high concentrations. The Spekker Steeloscope (Fig. 3.4 and § 15.4) is furnished by Hilger fitted with the Insta eyepiece for this purpose. Usually a spectrograph is better than a visual spectroscope because it gives greater precision and permits use of the ultraviolet spectrum, a region where suitable lines for analysis of many elements lie. Moreover, a permanent record is given. A glass-prism spectrograph can be used, but a spectrographer limited to the visible region alone is decidedly handicapped. A quartz spectrograph of medium dispersion will serve for quantitative analyses of elements in the first three rows of the periodic table, which have comparatively simple spectra. Most analyses are made with prism spectrographs having a focal length of 6 ft or more, or with gratings of focal length 2 to 6 meters. Ferrous materials and others containing a matrix whose spectrum is complex require a dispersion of 0.15 mm/A or more. Where only a limited spectral region can be covered, more elements can be analyzed for by using the range 2400 to 4000 A than any other region of similar extent, but provision should be made if possible for covering the range 2000 to 8000 A.

It is of particular importance for quantitative analysis that background light and scattered light be kept to a minimum. The spectrograph should of course cover all spectral regions that include the lines chosen for the analysis.   It also should have sufficient dispersion so that the encroaching background will not limit to values greater than those present in the samples being analyzed the sensitivity to concentrations of the elements being determined (see § 15.3).   It should produce a spectrum plate on which as many as 10 or 20 exposures to various standard and unknown samples can be taken.

It is usually not difficult to produce sufficient radiation from a sample to obtain a satisfactory spectrogram with an exposure time of 5 min or less.   If the exposure time is less than 30 sec, it is sometimes desirable to lengthen it by artificial means, such as the use of diaphragms or rotating disks to reduce the speed of the spectrograph, since a burning time of 1 min or longer may be necessary to ensure the consumption of a truly representative sample.

A stigmatic spectrograph is especially suitable for analytical purposes, because with it simple methods of photometry can be used. Rotating-disk photometry requires uniform illumination of the slit, which can best be carried out by one of the methods discussed in §§ 6.6 and 13.2–13.3.   It is desirable also to use a spectrograph that produces straight spectrum lines.   A fairly large concave grating in a Wadsworth stigmatic mount (§ 4.7) will be found especially flexible and convenient for analytical work.

16.7.   Selection of Lines for Quantitative Analysis—The Working Curve.   If very low concentrations of a minor constituent are to be determined, it is usually necessary to use its ultimate lines for analytical purposes.   For higher concentrations, lines that lie in a more convenient region of the spectrum may be selected, but those lines should be chosen which have a straight-line *working curve* in the concentration range which is of interest.   Figure 16.2 contains a typical working curve, in which the percentage concentration of a minor constituent is plotted logarithmically against the logarithm of the ratio of the intensity of one of its spectrum lines to that of a line of the matrix.   At very low concentrations, all lines show a linear variation of intensity with the number of atoms present.   This linear variation when plotted logarithmically gives a straight line having a slope of 45 deg.   At the lowest concentrations, theory can thus be used to check the actual course of the working curve.   At higher concentrations, the values of which depend on the line under consideration, the concentrational sensitivity of the curve becomes less, and at very high concentrations an actual decrease in intensity with increasing concentration may arise from self-reversal. The working curve is then curved downward.

Two spectrum lines should be used for a concentration determination of a given element. One of these is a line of the element itself, chosen to give high, and if possible uniform, concentrational sensitivity so that the working curve will be a straight line with a 45-deg slope. The second line is one selected to lie as close in the spectrum to the first as possible, to simplify photometric problems; and similar in intensity to the first line, to simplify the comparison of their intensities. It may be a line of an element of the matrix material, of some impurity known to be present in the samples in constant amounts, or of an element especially added in constant amounts to all samples to furnish a spectrum line whose intensity remains as nearly constant as possible in all exposures. The purpose of this line

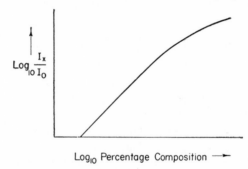

Fig. 16.2.   Typical working curve. I_0 is the intensity of a spectrum line in the matrix and I_x that of a line due to the element under analysis.

is to furnish a standard of comparison that will indicate any changes in source or photometric conditions which might affect the intensities of lines of the working element. The intensities of the working and control lines should also vary similarly with excitation conditions. Thus if the working curve is plotted as a function of the intensity ratio of the unknown line to the control line, instead of the unknown line intensity alone, variations between unknown and standard spectra are to some extent nullified. Other functions can be plotted to give the working curve, but none are so convenient as those used in Fig. 16.2.

16.8.   The Calibration Curve. If the working and control lines have about the same wavelength, which usually requires that they lie not more than 25 A from each other in the spectrum, the ratio of their

intensities can be determined from a single calibration curve (§ 13.2).
If they have widely differing wavelengths, which is usually not the
case, different calibration curves must be used for the two lines, and
the methods of heterochromatic photometry are required (§ 13.4).
Ordinarily, however, homochromatic photometry suffices for analytical purposes, since a line of the matrix or of an added internal standard
can almost always be found near a suitable line of a minor constituent.

Even when a single calibration curve can be used for the two lines,
it is not satisfactory, in general, to plot the working curve in terms
of the densities of the two lines rather than the logarithms of their
intensities, because the calibration curves are almost never linear.
This procedure may sometimes be justified in special cases over a
limited density range, but can be assumed a priori to be correct only
when the densities of the two lines are equal.   The latter is the basis
of the length-of-line method discussed below (§ 16.13).

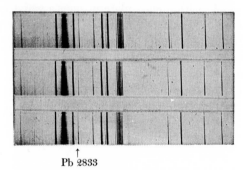

↑
Pb 2833

Fig. 16.3.   Spectrogram showing Pb lines at 2833 A in a dried sample of
condensed milk.

The methods of photographic photometry, discussed in Chapter 13,
are so straightforward, and the necessary apparatus so readily available, that there is little excuse for permitting photometric errors to
influence the results of a quantitative analysis.   They can quite
readily be kept below 2 per cent, and errors due to nonhomogeneity of
sample, variation of excitation and burning in the light source, and
other errors of handling are usually found to be much greater.

16.9. A Typical Analysis. Every quantitative spectrographic
analysis should be preceded by a qualitative analysis (Chapter 15).
Only thus can a satisfactory appraisal be made of the matrix conditions, of various constituents not of interest that might interfere with
the determination of those which are of interest, and of the approxi-

mate concentration ranges of the elements of interest. A qualitative analysis will also give some indication of the most satisfactory excitation conditions to be used.

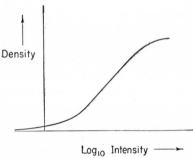

Fig. 16.4.   Calibration curve for analysis at λ = 2833 (Pb line).

We give as an example data obtained in the determination of lead in a sample of condensed milk. After a preliminary qualitative analysis, 50 mg of spectrographically pure graphite powder was placed in a porcelain evaporating dish known to have no lead contamination, and on this 50 mg of condensed milk was pipetted direct from the freshly opened can. The dish was covered loosely with a glass plate in such a way that condensed droplets of moisture would not fall back into the sample, and the escape of steam was permitted. The dish was placed in an evaporating oven and heated slowly until all moisture had escaped; it was then baked at a temperature such that only charred residue in the graphite remained, care being taken to ensure that at no time was the temperature greater than the boiling point of lead or of any lead salts that might be formed. The ash-graphite mix-

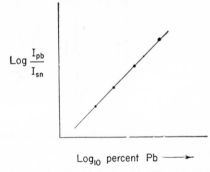

Fig. 16.5.   Working curve for Pb analysis.

ture was then placed in an agate mortar, carefully ground to a fine powder, and thoroughly mixed. Ten milligrams of the resulting powder was then packed into the cup of a preburned graphite electrode of $\frac{3}{8}$-in. diameter with a $\frac{1}{4}$-in. hole drilled in its end to a depth of $\frac{3}{8}$ in. This electrode was made the positive terminal of an electric arc, and was burned at 5 amp against a negative electrode consisting of a $\frac{1}{4}$-in. diameter pencil of pure graphite. The spectra shown in Fig. 16.3 were obtained with a Hilger Littrow quartz spectrograph, using 60-sec exposures. The plate was measured on a densitometer; the cali-bration and working curves obtained are shown in Figs. 16.4 and 16.5.

Many typical analyses involving samples of different types will be found described in the literature (see General References 16.1–16.7).

SPECIAL METHODS

The basic method described in the preceding sections was gradually evolved between 1890 and 1940 and is subject to many variations. Such investigators as de Gramont[6] worked for many years to develop methods that would be sufficiently reproducible to give quantitative results. Because of the large number of variables that govern the intensity of the spectrum lines produced by a given quantity of material, many investigators thought it impossible to gauge accurately the quantity of a substance in a mixture by means of its spectrum. Early workers suggested four different methods for measuring the quantity of an impurity present: (1) the length of the lines produced in a spark, higher concentrations producing lines which extended further from the electrode;[7] (2) the number of the lines of an element that appeared on the plate, only the ultimate lines remaining when the concentration was below certain limits;[8] (3) the intensities of the lines; and (4) the time taken for disappearance of the lines of a volatile element as it was burned out of the arc. Any of these methods can be used qualitatively, but only the third has been developed to give precise quantitative results.

Much of the credit for the development of satisfactory methods of quantitative analysis should go to de Gramont,[6] who spent years convincing his colleagues that the method could be made reproducible. Work in America was given an impetus in 1922 by a classical paper by Meggers, Kiess, and Stimson,[9] entitled "Quantitative Spectroscopic Analysis of Materials." This outlined a straightforward method of comparison of samples, relying on constancy of excitation conditions. The next major step forward resulted from the work of Gerlach and Schweitzer,[10] who introduced the method of internal standards and

[6] A. de Gramont, *Compt. Rend.*, **144**, 1101 (1907); *ibid.*, **159**, 6 (1914); *ibid.*, **171**, 1106 (1920); *Rev. Met.*, **19**, 90 (1922).

[7] J. N. Lockyer, *Phil. Trans.* (London) (I), **163**, 253 (1873); *ibid.*, **164**, 479 (1874); J. N. Lockyer and W. C. Roberts, *ibid.*, **164**, 495 (1874); A. Occhialini, *Rendiconti R. Accad. Lincei*, **9**, 573 (1929).

[8] W. N. Hartley, *Phil. Trans.* (London) (I), **175**, 50 (1884); A. G. Leonard and P. Whelan, *Proc. Roy. Soc. Dublin* (*N.S.*), **11**, 23 (1908).

[9] W. F. Meggers, C. C. Kiess, and F. S. Stimson, *Nat. Bur. Standards Sci. Paper* 444 (1922).

[10] W. Gerlach and E. Schweitzer, General Reference 16.3.

the concepts of *homologous pairs* and *fixation pairs*. This method, though now seldom used in the form envisioned by its authors, has made a very definite contribution to the basic method.

16.10.   The Method of Internal Standards.   Gerlach and Schweitzer developed this method in an attempt to avoid the necessity of maintaining a group of standard samples containing known concentrations of impurities.   They sought a method in which the comparison with standard samples of a given element-matrix combination could be done once and for all in a single laboratory, so that from published lists anyone could determine concentrations by merely matching the relative intensities of constituent and matrix lines, called *homologous pairs*.   Since the intensities of the lines of a major constituent of the matrix do not vary greatly with concentration, whereas those of the minor constituents do vary greatly, it should be possible to select strong lines of the minor constituent that at low concentrations will be equal in intensity to weak lines of the matrix. Equality of intensity would be indicated by equality of density on the plate.   Gerlach and Schweitzer found that the equality of intensity of such a pair of lines would be maintained under widely varying conditions of excitation.

A second concept introduced by Gerlach and Schweitzer was that of the *fixation pair*, another pair of lines of the matrix selected so as to be equal in intensity under the excitation conditions used but extremely sensitive in intensity ratio to variations of excitation conditions.   Thus these lines could be used to indicate the attainment of correct excitation conditions.

Many variants of the Gerlach and Schweitzer method have been described, but of these the principal contribution that remains in the basic method is the procedure of producing the working curve by using the intensity ratio of a pair of lines of the minor constituent and matrix rather than the intensity of the former line.   Pairs of lines are seldom used today either as homologous or fixation pairs, since more direct methods of determination are available.

The advantages of the method of homologous pairs are that it furnishes a null method of photometry, since it is easy to judge when the densities of a pair of lines are equal, and that it avoids the necessity of preparation of standard samples whenever an analysis is to be made.   Its great disadvantage is that it is largely a theoretical method, since it makes the assumption that matching of the fixation and homologous pairs has been carried out with a fairly small number of spectrograms, whereas in the case of an actual analysis a great many spectrograms are likely to be required before satisfactory matching is obtained.

Gerlach and Schweitzer's greatest contribution is the method of internal standards, involving use of a line of the matrix or an added material as a control in the basic method.

16.11. Methods for High Concentrations. The upper limit of concentration at which ordinary methods of quantitative spectrographic analysis become uncertain is usually given as 5 per cent, though in some cases 10 per cent concentration can be reached when only one variable element is involved. In certain cases great care must be taken when even 1 per cent of variable material is exceeded, for example when alkali metals or other elements are involved which have ionization potentials widely different from that of the matrix material. Two special methods are available, however, that can be used to make analyses at any concentration. They are not very precise but have the advantage of simplicity.

Barratt[11] made use of the fact that a working curve of a sort can be established with a series of samples of known concentrations over the entire range of 1 to 100 per cent. His method is of value when only one component of a system is being varied. Like other high-concentration methods, it suffers in comparison with wet gravimetric methods, whose precision increases with the concentration of material available, whereas that of the spectrographic method remains essentially constant at all concentrations.

The Barratt method, which can be used either photographically or visually, rests on the measurement of the relative intensities of a spectrum line produced by two different sources, using a standard specimen in one source and a specimen of the substance to be analyzed in the other. Even at such high concentrations as 50 per cent, a definite relationship exists between the ratios of the quantities of the elements in the specimens and the relative intensities of their spectrum lines if proper lines are chosen. However, this relationship is by no means the simple one that holds at low concentrations, and it is necessary to use exactly similar conditions of excitation for the two sources. Particular care must be taken in selecting lines to avoid errors due to self-reversal and to excitation differences. A series of alloys or mixtures must be prepared for use in the standard exposures, but once these have been obtained, interpolation is not difficult.

[11] See General Reference 16.1, page 169.

Barratt's apparatus consists of a spark gap having two sparks in series, with means for adjusting the sparks to equal lengths. Light from these two sources is sent through a polarizing head that is used to decrease the intensity of one beam relative to the other, and then through a visual spectroscope or a spectrograph. A working curve similar to that shown in Fig. 16.6 is set up by measuring with the instrument, for a number of standard samples, the intensity ratios of lines from the two sources. From this curve one can determine the

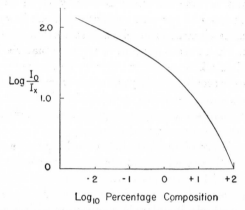

Fig. 16.6.   **Working curve obtained with the Barratt method.** I_x is the intensity of a line in the unknown element observed in one spark gap, and I_0 is the intensity of the same line from a standard sample observed simultaneously in the other spark gap.

percentage composition of an unknown sample excited in the spark. To obtain precise results, it is necessary to provide means whereby the substance to be examined can be made to produce radiation that is truly representative of its condition; production of such radiation is often difficult. The precision claimed is about 5 per cent of the quantity of material present.

A second method of measuring high concentrations involves dilu, tion, so that high concentrations become low. If we have samples containing about 20 per cent of cadmium in zinc, we can introduce this cadmium-zinc alloy as an impurity in a new matrix of graphite powder, into some metal such as zinc or copper, or into a spectrographically neutral salt such as ammonium sulfate. The concentration of the zinc having been reduced from 20 per cent to, say, 0.2 per cent by a dilution factor of 100, zinc is now determined in the ordinary way. The limitation on this method is that in diluting the sample we also dilute the precision of the results. For this reason, chemical wet methods are usually found more precise than spectrographic methods on concentrations greater than 5 per cent.

16.12. Methods for Extremely Low Concentrations. Quantitative spectrographic analyses can be carried out at any concentration at which qualitative analyses can be made, the ultimate lines being used at the lowest concentrations. The table of sensitivity limits given in § 15.1 lists the lowest concentrations that have been obtained in quantitative spectrographic analyses for the various elements. As pointed out there, it is often possible, by giving attention to certain factors, to extend sensitivity limits in a given case by several orders of magnitude below those obtained in ordinary analyses.

If, for example, one is interested in the determination of boron in steel, burning in the ordinary arc of a small chunk of steel will make possible a determination of boron in concentrations down to perhaps 1 part in 10^5. It has been possible to make analyses down to concentrations of a few parts in 10^8 by (a) more efficient feeding of the boron from the sample into the excitation stream; (b) using the method of fractional distillation discussed in Chapter 15; (c) introducing a carrier as described by Scribner and Mullin[12] (§ 15.6); (d) selecting proper excitation conditions in the source to bring out the lines of boron and make them more sensitive; (e) converting the boron in the source into a form more likely to be volatilized at the proper part of the burning cycle, as revealed by a moving-plate study (§ 15.6); and (f) using a spectrograph with such high resolution that the background does not encroach rapidly on the line (§ 15.6). Most of the methods of increasing sensitivity discussed in Chapter 15 were, in fact, originally developed for use in quantitative analysis at very low concentrations.

16.13. High-precision, Rapid, and Short-cut Methods. When truly representative homogeneous samples are prepared, spectrographic analyses can be carried out with a precision of ± 5 per cent of the minor constituent, from about 5 per cent concentration down to the lowest concentrations determinable. However, special attention, particularly to the preparation of the sample, the constancy of excitation conditions, and the accuracy of the photographic photometry, will result in increased precision. Probably the greatest uniformity claimed by any set of workers is that described by Duffendack

---

[12] B. F. Scribner and H. R. Mullin, *Jour. Res. Nat. Bur. Standards,* **37,** 369 (1946).

and his collaborators, in which reproducibility to 1.4 per cent was found in a long series of measurements made under carefully controlled conditions.

When the highest precision is not required, analyses can be made quickly by using the length-of-line method of photometry, described in § 13.11, thus avoiding the necessity of using a densitometer. A rotating disk with logarithmic opening is used, and the length of a line is then a measure of the logarithm of its intensity. Lines of a pair being compared usually lie close together in the spectrum. Since the length of each of the two lines is proportional to the logarithm of its intensity, the difference in their lengths is a direct measure of the difference in the logarithms of their intensity values. This difference equals the logarithm of the intensity ratio of the two lines, which is plotted as one of the variables in the working curve. Thus in plotting the curve it is possible to use directly the difference in position of the end points of the two lines, as measured in Fig. 16.7. This method should not be used where precision greater than ± 10 per cent is desired.

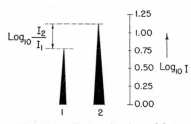

Fig. 16.7. Determination of intensity ratio of two lines by the difference in their lengths obtained with a logarithmic sector.

The limitations on precision arise from the difficulty of determining the end point of a line. Methods of etching and copying have been suggested for sharpening this end point, but all share the basic difficulty that the end point is always determined on a portion of the calibration curve of the plate that has very small slope, and therefore its location is actually indefinite.

Fagioli[13] designed an attachment for a reading comparator that splits the field of view into two sections parallel to the spectrum lines, these sections being movable relative to one another. The field is split by putting two glass plates 4 mm thick between the objective and the plate, with an arrangement for tilting these symmetrically in opposite directions by means of a handle. By this means the two lines can be put side by side in such a position that their densities match all along their lengths, and the motion necessary to accomplish this matching is a measure of their intensity ratio.

[13] O. Fagioli, *Nuovo Cimento*, **13**, 11 (1936).

In much analytical work, semiquantitative results are sufficiently precise, and direct eye comparison of spectrum lines can often be made to give useful values. The densities of the lines used to produce the working curve can be judged, and the intensities of the corresponding lines in the samples to be determined can be quickly assigned to locations between two known densities. In this way, after some experience, it is possible to make a surprisingly accurate interpolation that may well come within ±25 per cent of the amount of material present. The lines must be photographed under controlled conditions, however.

16.14. Methods for Special Elements. When analyses for elements not ordinarily considered susceptible to spectrochemical analyses must be made spectrographically, special methods must be used. The methods of preparation and excitation required are similar to those discussed in § 15.7, but the prime need is careful consideration of the theoretical basis of the controlled excitation of atoms to emit radiation.[14] The primary problem involved in working quantitatively with such trace elements as sulfur or chlorine is the production under controllable conditions of spectrum lines at the concentrations desired.

16.15. Photoelectric Methods of Analysis. Increasing use of spectrochemical methods in industry has caused much attention to be given to the development of more rapid methods than those involving photography. Sawyer and his collaborators,[15] in addition to improving the precision of the analytical process, have done much to speed it up by shortening the time of plate processing and in other ways. To bring still closer the day of the automatic analytical recorder, photoelectric methods of photometry have been applied to problems of quantitative analysis (see § 12.17).

The application of the Geiger-Müller counter to spectrochemical analysis has been investigated by Duffendack and Morris,[16] by Hanau and Wolfe,[17] and by Nahstoll and Bryan.[18] Many workers have

---

[14] W. F. Meggers, *Jour. Opt. Soc. Am.*, **31**, 39 (1941); G. R. Harrison, *Metals and Alloys*, Nov. 1936.

[15] H. B. Vincent and R. A. Sawyer, *Metal Progress*, **36**, 35 (1939); *Jour. Opt. Soc. Am.*, **32**, 686 (1942); R. A. Sawyer and H. B. Vincent, *Jour. Opt. Soc. Am.*, **31**, 47 (1941); H. H. Grossman, R. A. Sawyer, and H. B. Vincent, *ibid.*, **33**, 185 (1943).

[16] O. S. Duffendack and W. E. Morris, *Jour. Opt. Soc. Am.*, **32**, 8 (1942).

[17] R. Hanau and R. A. Wolfe, *Jour. Opt. Soc. Am.*, **37**, 989 (1947); *ibid.*, **38**, 377 (1948).

[18] G. A. Nahstoll and F. R. Bryan, *ibid.*, **37**, 990 (1947).

investigated the use of photocells and amplifiers, and photomultipliers, in the direct measurement of the intensities of strong spectrum lines. Dieke and Crosswhite have described the adaptation of a large grating spectrograph in a Wadsworth mounting to photoelectric measurement of emission spectra, as discussed in § 12.17.

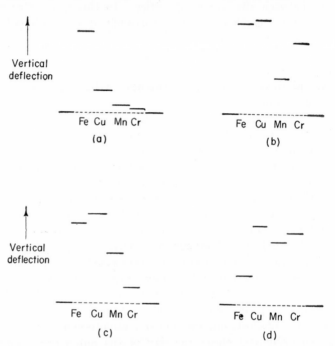

Fig. 16.8. Oscilloscope patterns obtained by Dieke and Crosswhite in the analysis of steel samples for copper, manganese, and chromium. A weak iron line serves as a reference. (a) Pattern for electrolytic iron. (b) Chrome-molybdenum steel: Cu, 0.06%; Mn, 0.65%; Cr, 0.91%. (c) Manganese steel: Cu, 0.12%; Mn, 1.4%; Cr, 18%. (d) Stainless steel: Cu, 0.59%; Mn, 4.1%; Cr, 20%.

Dieke and Crosswhite have also described [19] a photoelectric method of spectrochemical analysis in which an oscilloscope is used as the indicating device, with a 931 A or 1P28 RCA photomultiplier tube placed at each spectrum line to be measured. Sensitivity was found ample for reasonably strong lines. In analyzing a steel sample for copper, manganese, and chromium, for example, suitable strong lines

[19] G. H. Dieke and H. M. Crosswhite, *Jour. Opt. Soc. Am.*, **36**, 192 (1946).

of each element were selected, together with an iron line to serve as control line. A rotating switch was used to connect the output of each tube successively to the oscilloscope for 0.4 sec. The time scale of the oscilloscope was synchronized with a rotating switch so that the repeated traces of each line always fell on the screen in the same position. A small condenser was inserted in the circuit to increase the time constant, thus eliminating the influence of short-period fluctuations. Any changes in light intensity caused the whole pattern to fluctuate up and down on the screen, so the traces were evaluated in terms of the deflections for the iron line. The patterns obtained with four different steel samples by Dieke and Crosswhite are shown in Fig. 16.8.

In a second method introduced by Dieke and Crosswhite[19] they caused the iron line to produce a horizontal deflection and the other lines vertical deflections on the oscilloscope. Traces were then obtained as shown in Fig. 16.9. In these the slope of each line gives a measure of the concentration of the corresponding material. A suitable transparent scale can be attached to the screen to make direct quantitative determinations possible.

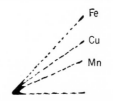

Fig. 16.9. Oscilloscope pattern obtained with standard element on horizontal axis and unknown elements (Cu, Mn) on vertical axis. An AC source is used. The sample is the same as that used in producing Fig. 16.8b.

A photoelectric spectrometer with auxiliary equipment to integrate the photocurrents produced by spectrum lines, designated the Quantometer, has been described by Hasler and Dietert.[20] Commercial instruments of this sort are furnished by the Applied Research Laboratories. In this instrument, which is basically a small grating spectrograph, up to 12 electron-multiplier tubes are employed to detect the appropriate spectrum lines for the various elements to be determined. While the sample is burned in the source the photocurrents generated in the various multipliers are amplified and then in effect used to drive small motors attached to mechanical counters. The source is kept in operation until the counter operated by the photocurrent from the "standard" or control line reaches a preset reading. The readings of the counters attached to the other tubes then correspond to the percentages of the various elements being measured. Various parts of the Quantometer are shown in Fig. 16.10.

---

[20] M. F. Hasler and H. W. Dietert, *Jour. Opt. Soc. Am.*, **34**, 751 (1944).

Another direct-reading spectrochemical installation, which is manufactured commercially by Baird Associates, has been described by Saunderson, Caldecourt, and Peterson.[21] A 2-meter concave grating in an Eagle mounting is used, and electron multiplier photo-tubes are mounted behind appropriate exit slits in the focal plane to measure the intensity of a spectral line from each element being determined. The currents from the multiplier phototubes are col-

Fig. 16.10.   The Applied Research Laboratories' Quantometer.

lected in condensers, which are then discharged through resistors whenever they reach a certain voltage. The number of discharges occurring during a controlled period of operation is made to operate a "clock" for each element, which is calibrated directly in percentage concentration.

Although such devices give analytical results very quickly and are sufficiently precise for most purposes, their complexity and cost make

---

[21] J. L. Saunderson, V. J. Caldecourt, and E. W. Peterson, *Jour. Opt. Soc. Am.*, **35**, 681 (1945); R. O'B. Carpenter, E. DuBois, and J. Sterner, *ibid.*, **37**, 707 (1947).

them of value principally in large installations, as in foundries, where thousands of analyses must be made per week. Development of the iconoscope or the image dissector tube to the point of usefulness for precision measurements may make possible recording analytical installations that do not require the complexity of an additional phototube and circuit for each spectrum line studied.

GENERAL REFERENCES

16.1. F. Twyman, *The Spectrochemical Analysis of Metals and Alloys.* Brooklyn: Chemical Publishing Company, Inc., 1941.

16.2. D. M. Smith, *Metallurgical Analysis by the Spectrograph.* London: British Non-ferrous Metals Research Association, 1933.

16.3. W. Gerlach and E. Schweitzer, *Foundations and Methods of Chemical Analysis by the Emission Spectrum.* London: Adam Hilger, Ltd., 1931.

16.4. H. Lundegårdh, *Die quantitative Spektralanalyse der Elemente,* I (1929); II (1934). Jena: Fischer.

16.5. W. R. Brode, *Chemical Spectroscopy,* 2d ed. New York: John Wiley & Sons, Inc., 1942.

16.6. R. A. Sawyer, *Experimental Spectroscopy.* New York: Prentice-Hall, Inc., 1944.

16.7. H. Mark, in *Spektroskopische und radiometrische Analyse,* Teil I. Leipzig: Akademische Verlagsgesellschaft, 1933.

See also General References 15.4 to 15.19, inclusive.

CHAPTER 17

Spectroscopy of the Infrared Region

THE INFRARED REGION OF THE SPECTRUM may be taken to include the wavelength range from 0.75 μ to about 1 mm and may be subdivided, on the basis of the instrumental techniques appropriate to each subdivision, into the photoelectric infrared, the near infrared, and the far infrared.

The photoelectric infrared covers the approximate range 0.75 to 3 μ. The lower boundary is set by the wavelength-sensitivity curve of the human eye. Except for use of the eye, radiation of the these long wavelengths can be detected and measured in the same way as visible radiation, and the use of spectrographs suitable for the visible region, both prism and grating, can be extended well into the photoelectric infrared. Photographic emulsions and photoelectric cells can be made with a usable sensitivity over much of the region. At the longer wavelengths, however, photoelectric processes—including that of the photographic emulsion—begin to lose their sensitivity. Not far beyond 3 μ, the detection of radiation is best accomplished through its heating effect, and spectrometric techniques are modified accordingly.

The near infrared might be called the "prism infrared," because prism materials transparent to the region are readily obtainable. Most near infrared spectrometers have prism optics, though gratings are also used occasionally. The long wavelength limit to the near infrared is set by the transmission of readily obtainable prism materials and lies at about 25 μ, where the absorption of potassium bromide gets prohibitively large. To be sure, materials are known that are transparent beyond 25 μ, but for reasons discussed later, the reflection grating is usually preferred at these wavelengths.

The far infrared extends from 25 μ to the ill-defined borderland between the infrared and microwaves (radar waves) in the neighborhood of 1 mm. Throughout the far infrared the most generally used

472

dispersing element is the *echelette grating*, that is, a grating whose lines have been so ruled that radiation of a given wavelength is largely concentrated in one order (see § 2.5). Other techniques such as residual rays may be applied in special cases. Far infrared radiation, in default of more sensitive methods, must be detected by its heating effect. Because the energy of infrared sources is greatly reduced in the far infrared and the problem of extraneous radiation is much more acute, the precautions required to obtain accurate radiation measurements are more elaborate than those used at shorter wavelengths.

It is an interesting coincidence that this subdivision of the infrared agrees in a general way with the division of molecular energy levels into electronic, vibrational, and rotational levels, as discussed in Chapter 11. The lower electronic levels and a few higher vibrational overtones lie in the photoelectric infrared, most vibrational fundamentals lie in the near infrared, and the frequencies of molecular rotation lie in the far infrared. The fact that there is no natural boundary for atomic or molecular energy levels in the 0.75 μ region emphasizes the artificiality of segregating the photoelectric infrared from the visible portion of the spectrum. The ensuing discussion of the techniques of infrared spectroscopy will be concerned only with the near and far infrared, the techniques of the photoelectric infrared being more closely similar to those considered in previous chapters.

17.1. Radiation Sources and Filters for Infrared Spectroscopy. All but a small fraction of infrared spectroscopic studies are concerned with absorption spectra, for which a source of continuous infrared radiation is needed. Incandescent solid bodies at temperatures of 1000 to 1500°C meet this requirement best. Such bodies emit radiation roughly in accordance with the Planck blackbody equation (see Chapter 8) and therefore emit radiation throughout the infrared. The fact that the intensity of the radiation varies somewhat rapidly with wavelength is an inconvenience, especially at the longer wavelengths. When quasi-monochromatic radiation is wanted, the easiest procedure usually is to select the desired wavelengths from the continuum of an incandescent source. Among the many devices that have been used for this purpose are selective filters, selective reflectors and focal isolation.

A wide variety of substances have been used for infrared filters. Powder filters, as described by Pfund,[1] and Christiansen filters[2]

---

[1] A. H. Pfund, *Phys. Rev.*, **36**, 71 (1930); *Jour. Opt. Soc. Am.*, **23**, 375 (1933).
[2] R. B. Barnes and L. G. Bonner, *Phys. Rev.*, **49**, 732 (1936).

(§ 14.30) are particularly flexible with respect to the wavelength ranges to which they are applicable. Soot-blackened paper is sometimes used for its transmissivity at long waves and opacity in the near infrared region. In general, filters are more valuable for the elimination of undesired radiation, especially short-wave radiation, than for the isolation of a narrow range of wavelengths.

It has been known for many years[3] that crystals possess reflecting powers approaching those of metals at characteristic wavelengths in the infrared region. For any given crystal the high reflectivity is confined to one or two narrow characteristic bands in the spectrum. Radiation corresponding to these bands can be isolated from a continuous source by the successive reflection of the continuous radiation from plane surfaces of the crystal.[4] Because the reflectivity of a crystal at other than the characteristic wavelengths is very small, three or four successive reflections leave a residue of only the characteristic wavelengths, whence the name *residual rays*.

A selective reflector of a different type has been suggested by White.[5] The reflector makes use of the fact that a plane grating gives specular reflection of wavelengths longer by a factor of roughly 1.5 than the grating spacing, and disperses shorter wavelengths at angles considerably different from the specular. Such a grating can thus be used as a selective "cutoff" reflector, the cutoff wavelength being about 1.5 times the grating space. Echelette gratings are usually employed for this purpose because they put very little short-wave radiation into the specularly-reflected central image. This type of filter, for which replica gratings are quite suitable, has been successfully applied to the reduction of scattered radiation in infrared spectrometers. Reduction by as much as a factor of 10 has been realized with one filter, and with several in series the possibilities are even more favorable (compare Figs. 5 and 10 given by White[5]).

Another ingenious method for selecting a narrow range of wavelengths in the far infrared makes use of the transparency of quartz beyond 50 μ. The refractive indices of quartz below 8 μ and above 30 μ are so markedly different (for example, 1.5 at 3 μ, 1.4 at 5 μ, and varying from 2.13 at 33 μ to 1.94 at 300 μ) that the conjugate foci of a quartz lens have greatly differing values for the near and the far

---

[3] E. F. Nichols, *Wiedemanns Annalen*, **60**, 401 (1897).

[4] See, for example, General Reference 17.5, page 383.

[5] J. U. White, *Jour. Opt. Soc. Am.*, **37**, 713 (1947); replica grating filters may be purchased from the Perkin-Elmer Corp., Glenbrook, Conn.

infrared.   By placing a small source rich in far infrared radiation at
one conjugate focus for a lens of assumed index 2.2 and an opaque
screen at the other conjugate focus, Rubens and Wood [6] were able to
bring the long waves to a focus at the screen, while the short waves
were not convergent.   Perforation of the screen at the focal point
allowed the passage of the focused radiation, after which its approximate wavelength was measured interferometrically to be about 107 μ.
This procedure of "focal isolation" would appear to be useful for study
of the borderland between infrared and microwaves, particularly
with lenses of other materials in addition to quartz.

The two most commonly used infrared sources are the Nernst
glower and the Globar, but occasionally other sources have some
special applicability.   The Welsbach lamp and a quartz-jacketed
high-pressure mercury arc have been used in the region beyond 50 μ.
In the photoelectric infrared it is occasionally of advantage to utilize
a tungsten filament lamp as a source, though necessarily within the
region over which the envelope is transparent.

The Nernst glower (§ 8.8) was originally developed by its inventor
as an incandescent light.   It is an excellent infrared source because
of its high emissivity and its simplicity of construction and of operation.   The glower consists of a filament prepared [7] by sintering a
finely powdered mixture of various oxides, particularly those of
zirconium, thorium, and cerium, held together with a binder.   The
filament is maintained at incandescence electrically, for which purpose
platinum leads are attached to it with appropriate sealing techniques.
When the filament is operated at a temperature above 1500°C, its
emission curve resembles that of a blackbody fairly closely.   At lower
temperatures, the short-wave end of the emission curve is quite
irregular because of the selective emission of the metallic oxides.

The filament of the Nernst glower has a large *negative* temperature
coefficient of electrical resistance and is customarily heated by flame
or other external means to lower its resistance at the start of operation.
At a temperature of several hundred degrees centigrade, this resistance
is low enough to pass sufficient current at the operating voltage to
bring the lamp to incandescence.   It is then necessary to ballast the
lamp by a voltage regulator or series resistance to keep it from burning

[6] General Reference 17.6, page 523.
[7] H. D. Griffith, *Phil. Mag.* (6) **50**, 263 (1925); R. A. Friedel and A. G. Sharkey, Jr.,
Rev. Sci. Inst., **18**, 928 (1947).

out.   Typical operating data for a Nernst filament used as an infrared
source are shown in Table 17.1.

TABLE 17.1

DATA ON NERNST GLOWER AND GLOBAR INFRARED SOURCES

Specifications	Nernst lamp	Globar
Length of element, centimeters	2–5	5–10
Diameter of element, millimeters	1.5	6
Operating potential drop, volts	About 100	50–60
Current, amperes	0.2–0.5	3–5
Power, watts	20–50	150–250
Approximate temperature, °C	1600–1700	1200
Wavelength of radiation peak, microns	1.4	1.8

The Globar (§ 8.8) is a rod of carborundum (silicon carbide).   Its
temperature coefficient of electrical resistance is negative but rather
small.   It conducts sufficiently in the rod sizes customarily used as
infrared sources to require no external preheating.   Ballasting is not
necessary with a Globar to prevent its burning out, but some sort of
voltage regulation is desirable to maintain constancy of radiation.
The Globar surface is very rough, which accounts in part for the
excellence of its radiance.   The attachment of electrical leads to the
Globar is not a critical problem because of its ruggedness.   Usually
the ends of the rod are metallized and fitted into metallic sockets
which serve as electrodes.   Operating data are shown in Table 17.1.

The choice between the Nernst glower and Globar as an infrared
source depends on the spectral region in which radiation is wanted.*
The advantages of the Nernst glower are its low operating wattage
and high intensity in the short-wave region.   The Globar is more
useful at longer wavelengths ($>10\ \mu$), where it has considerably more
energy relative to its short wavelength peak than the Nernst glower.
The latter is physically smaller, and an enlarged image of it may be
needed to fill completely the slits of a spectrometer, especially when
these are opened wide at the longer wavelengths.   The large amount
of heat dissipated by the Globar usually necessitates a water-cooling
arrangement.

---

* The Globar is made by the Carborundum Corporation, Niagara Falls, N. Y.
The Nernst glower can be obtained from the Stupakoff Ceramic and Manufacturing
Company, Latrobe, Pa., or from National Technical Laboratories, South Pasadena,
Calif.

17.2. Prism Spectrometers for the Infrared. The optics of both prism and grating infrared spectrometers are fundamentally the same as those of spectrometers described in Chapters 3 and 4. However, all infrared spectrometers are monochromators and all use mirror optics. The monochromator arrangement is dictated by the nature of infrared detectors, and mirror optics by the opacity of glass in the infrared and the wide spectral range to be covered, which makes it infeasible to construct suitable lenses of any material whatever.

Prism instruments are the most widely used. They are quite satisfactory in the near infrared, are relatively simple to operate, and when well designed give adequate resolving power for most purposes. Grating instruments must be used in the far infrared because of the lack of suitable prism materials. They have the advantage of high resolving power and are used in the near infrared when high resolution is essential. Some of the complications inherent in grating instruments are considered below.

Table 17.2 shows the wavelength ranges over which various prism materials are reasonably transparent. Rock salt is the most widely used of these. It is transparent to about 15 μ, but below 5 μ its

TABLE 17.2

Infrared Prism and Window Materials

Material	Region of usable transparency (prisms)	Wavelength of residual rays, microns
Glass	Up to 2.5μ	. . .
Quartz	3.5μ	9; 21
Lithium fluoride	6μ	20
Calcium fluoride (fluorite)	9μ	33
Sodium chloride (rock salt)	15μ	52
Potassium chloride (sylvine)	21μ	63
Potassium bromide	27μ	82
Silver chloride*	28μ	. . .
Thallium bromoiodide (KRS-5)	40μ	120

* Windows only.

dispersion is poor, and other prism materials must be used if the best performance of a prism instrument is to be obtained at the short wavelengths. Fluorite and lithium fluoride are excellent here. For the range from 15 to 25 μ, potassium bromide is suitable, and from

25 to 40 μ, thallium bromoiodide.[8] All these materials are commercially available in blanks for window or prism fabrication.*

The traversal of the infrared spectrum by a prism monochromator is accomplished by the rotation of the dispersing element in such a way that the dispersed wavelengths are brought successively to a focus at the exit slit. The two most widely used optical arrangements for this purpose are the Wadsworth and the Littrow mountings (see Chapter 3). In the Wadsworth mounting, the prism and the plane mirror, the latter usually lying in such a position as to constitute an extension of the prism base, are rotated together about a vertical axis through the center of the prism base. Under these conditions the angular deviation of a monochromatic beam traversing the prism at minimum deviation is exactly nullified by reflection from the mirror, although lateral displacement and inversion of the beam result. The lateral displacement, which is equal to the length of the prism edge for a 60-deg prism, is practically independent of the wavelength. Accordingly, when optical arrangements have been made for radiation of one wavelength to traverse the prism at minimum deviation and come to a focus at the exit slit, the whole spectral range of the prism may be scanned at minimum deviation merely by rotation of the prism-mirror combination about the above-mentioned axis.

In the Littrow mounting, the plane mirror is placed roughly normal to the dispersed beam emerging from the prism. For one particular wavelength, which varies of course with the orientation of the mirror, the emergent beam is reflected exactly upon itself and retraces its path through the prism. The return paths of slightly longer and shorter waves, however, differ from their initial paths, and consequently further dispersion occurs. The spectrum may be scanned simply by rotation of the Littrow mirror about a vertical axis. If the prism remains fixed with respect to the incoming beam, however, only one wavelength passes through the prism at minimum deviation

The two chief advantages of the Littrow mounting are the doubled dispersion obtained from a given prism train, and the compactness and economy that result from the use of the same concave mirror as a collimator and as a focusing mirror. To illustrate the latter point, several optical systems frequently used in infrared spectrometers are

---

[8] O. F. Tuttle and P. H. Egle, *Jour. Chem. Phys.*, **14**, 571 (1946); E. K. Plyler, *Jour. Chem. Phys.*, **15**, 885 (1947).

*Purchasable from the Harshaw Chemical Company, Cleveland, Ohio, or from the Optavac Company, 112 Bickford Street, Boston 30, Mass.

shown in Fig. 17.1. Figure 17.1a shows an arrangement using the Wadsworth mounting. S_1, S_2 are the entrance and exit slits; C, the collimating mirror; F, the focusing mirror; and P, M_w, and A, respectively, the prism, plane mirror, and axis of rotation (perpendicular to the plane of the sketch) of the Wadsworth system. C and F can be either spherical or off-axis parabolic mirrors. Parabolic mirrors avoid astigmatism and spherical aberration but are more difficult to make than the spherical. It is to be noted that two are required.

Figure 17.1b depicts a widely used form of the Littrow mounting in which the double-duty mirror OP is an off-axis paraboloid. The beam returning from the Littrow mirror M_L is indicated by dotted lines, which show that the return beam is made to deviate slightly from the initial path. With the help of a small plane mirror, M_2, the return beam is deflected just before it reaches the entrance slit, S_1, and instead is brought to a focus at the exit slit, S_2. The spectrum is scanned by rotation of M_L about a vertical axis at A.

When an on-axis paraboloid is used in the Littrow arrangement, the rather large angle between the collimated beam and the beam from the slit S_1 results in considerable astigmatism. An ingenious variant (Fig. 17.1c) of the Littrow scheme was suggested by Pfund [9] to avoid astigmatism from an on-axis paraboloid. The essential feature is the Pfund mirror, M_P, a plane mirror with a small central hole. This mirror is placed immediately behind the entrance and exit slits, S_1 and S_2, which are located respectively just above and just below the optic axis, OA, of the on-axis paraboloid mirror C. OA passes through the center of the small hole in M_P, the hole being large enough so that the entering beam diverging from S_1 and the return beam focused on S_2 have free passage. The two beams are not shown separately, since their projections upon the plane of the drawing coincide. The light losses associated with two reflections from M_P and with the hole in M_P can be made small and are a low price to pay for the high optical quality gained by the on-axis use of C. The Pfund mirror introduces additional stray radiation, the effect of which may be minimized by blocking out the unused central portion of C so that radiation from this portion does not reach the exit slit S_2.

The complete optical scheme for a prism spectrometer includes some means for focusing the radiation to be studied on the entrance slit. A concave spherical mirror usually is sufficient for this purpose.

---

[9] A. H. Pfund, *Jour. Opt. Soc. Am.*, **14**, 337 (1927).

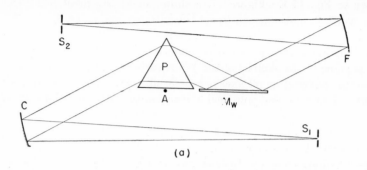

(a)

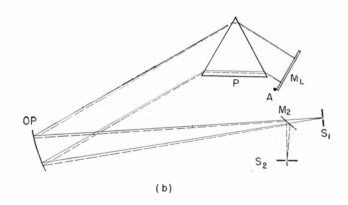

(b)

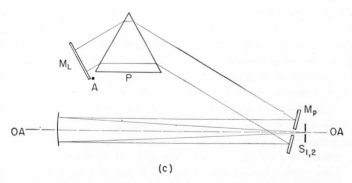

(c)

Fig. 17.1. Typical optical systems for infrared prism spectrometers. (a) Wadsworth mounting. (b) Littrow mounting with off-axis paraboloid. (c) Littrow mounting with Pfund pierced-mirror arrangement.

For absorption spectra, the incandescent source is focused on the slit with a mirror whose focal length allows adequate separation of source from mirror and ample room for absorption cells, shutters, and the like that must be placed in the beam.   The beam emerging from the exit slit of the spectrometer is commonly focused on the thermal detector by means of an elliptical mirror.   This type of mirror concentrates a reduced image of the exit slit on the detector with great efficiency but is quite expensive to make; in many instruments a spherical mirror of appropriate aperture would serve about as well.

A prism $2\frac{1}{2}$ in. high, having a 3-in. base, is a size commonly used in infrared spectrometers.   With a 60-deg rock-salt prism of this size used in the optical arrangement shown in Fig. 17.1b, a resolving power of about 200 should be realized at 5 μ and about 400 at 14 μ. These values correspond to wave-number separations of 10 cm^{-1} and 2 cm^{-1}, respectively.   The resolving power of a spectrometer at short wavelengths is governed by the excellence of the optics (optical quality of the off-axis paraboloid, alignment, and similar factors), whereas at the longer wavelengths the optical arrangement is not so critical.   There the limiting factor is the small amount of energy available from the source, which forces the use of wide slits and a consequent reduction in resolving power.

The wavelength calibration of a prism instrument consists of a plot, on an adequately large piece of graph paper, of the prism-table or Littrow-mirror orientation as a function of the wavelength brought to focus on the exit slit.   The orientation may be expressed in any convenient fashion, which means that the ordinate is usually in terms of screw turns, counter readings, fiducial-mark numbers, or some other index of prism-table setting.   The calibration curve is ordinarily determined [10] with the help of the precise wavelengths for sharp vapor-absorption bands in certain simple molecules such as ammonia (3 and 8-to-12 μ regions), water (6 μ), carbon dioxide ($4\frac{1}{2}$ and 15 μ), and methanol (20 μ region).   The wavelengths of the absorption bands in these substances were originally measured [11, 12] with grating spectrometers (described in §17.3).

Until quite recently the setting up of a prism spectrometer for infrared involved both a long apprenticeship on the part of the

---

[10] See, for example, D. S. McKinney and R. A. Friedel, *Jour. Opt. Soc. Am.*, **38**, 222 (1948).

[11] R. A. Oetjen, Chan-Lan Kao, and H. M. Randall, *Rev. Sci. Inst.*, **13**, 515 (1942).

[12] A. Borden and E. F. Barker, *Jour. Chem. Phys.*, **6**, 553 (1938).

operator, preferably in a laboratory where infrared research was in progress, and the construction of an instrument on a made-to-order basis in an instrument shop.   There are now on the market, however, several prism instruments that can be set up and put into operation by those who have had no previous infrared experience.   Figures 17.2 and 17.3 show infrared prism spectrometers marketed respectively by the Perkin-Elmer Corporation, Glenbrook, Conn., and the National Technical Laboratories, South Pasadena, Calif.   Both of these instruments use the Littrow arrangement shown in Fig. 17.1b, high-

Fig. 17.2.   Perkin-Elmer Model 12C infrared spectrometer.
(Courtesy Perkin-Elmer Corp.)

speed thermal detectors, and a commercial pen recorder.   The resolution attained by both instruments is good for prism instruments of this size and is satisfactory for most industrial control uses and for many research purposes.

17.3.   **Grating Spectrometers.**   Infrared wavelengths are of such size that the optimum grating spacing is of the order of 0.01 mm in the near infrared and 0.1 mm or more in the far infrared.   It is therefore possible to make transmission gratings for the latter region by winding wire of the appropriate diameter upon a flat frame.   Such gratings, which were once extensively used, have been superseded by ruled gratings of the echelette type (see § 2.5).   Echelette gratings, because of their ability to concentrate most of the available radiation

Fig. 17.3.   National Technical Laboratories Model IR-2 infrared spectrometer. This instrument is often called the Beckmann infrared spectrometer.   (Courtesy National Technical Laboratories.)

into one order, have opened up spectral regions that could have scarcely been studied otherwise.

It was said earlier that gratings are used in the near infrared when high resolution is indispensable, and throughout the far infrared because of the lack of prism materials.   The optical arrangement of the grating spectrometer proper does not differ greatly from the Littrow mounting for prism instruments shown in Fig. 17.1b and c, in which the prism and Littrow mirror combination is replaced by a plane grating.   Grating instruments of these two types have been described respectively by Randall [13] and J. D. Hardy.[14]   In the former, with which much work on rotational absorption of small polyatomic molecules has been carried out, the off-axis paraboloid is large (a semicircle of 24 in. diameter and of 36 in. focal length) and fills a grating 10×22 in.   This large size makes the instrument highly effective in the region beyond 50 μ, where the radiation from the source is extremely weak.

A difficulty in the use of gratings in the infrared is the overlapping of different spectral orders, which is especially troublesome because of the high source intensity of radiation at $\lambda/2$, $\lambda/3$, and so on, compared to that at λ.   The radiation must therefore be purified in some way before it enters the spectrometer.   This purification can be satisfactorily accomplished in the near infrared by the use of a low-dispersion prism monochromator in front of the grating monochromator; but at wavelengths beyond 25 μ, filters opaque to short waves must be used.   Thin plates of fused quartz are suitable for elimination of radiation between 10 and 50 μ, and hard paraffin, metallic blacks, specially prepared powder filters, and soot-blackened paper have also been used.   The reflection filter of White [5] mentioned in § 17.1 can also be employed with great effectiveness.

At the present time, grating spectrometers for the infrared are not available commercially, although there are numerous custom-built instruments in research laboratories in the United States.   Most of these are equipped with gratings ruled on the engine at the University of Michigan.   Figure 17.4 is a reproduction of a record of the far infrared absorption spectrum of deuterium oxide vapor made with the grating instrument described by Randall [13] and located at the Randall Laboratory of Physics at the University of Michigan.

17.4.   The Measurement of Infrared Absorption.   Because infrared spectra are nearly always studied as absorption spectra, the technique of absorption measurements in this region will be consid-

---

[13] H. M. Randall, *Rev. Sci. Inst.*, **3**, 396 (1932).

[14] J. D. Hardy, *Phys. Rev.*, **38**, 2162 (1931).

ered in some detail. Methods for the measurement of spectral radiation in the infrared region, including amplification and recording of detector output, were discussed in Chapter 12. The special features of infrared absorption measurement other than detection, amplification, and recording will be described here.

Infrared-absorption measurements are carried out on substances in any of the three states of aggregation. The techniques used in handling the samples are not elaborate. The absorption cell is placed in the optical path somewhere between the source and the entrance slit, usually just in front of the latter. The cell windows are ordinarily of polished rock salt several millimeters thick unless the

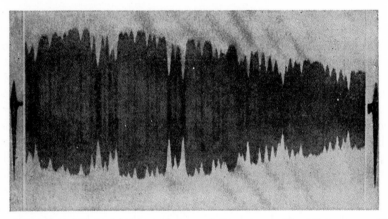

Fig. 17.4. A record of the spectrum of deuterium oxide ("heavy water") vapor in the spectral region 34μ to 38μ. (Courtesy Prof. H. M. Randall and Dean R. A. Sawyer.)

spectral region under investigation lies beyond 15 μ, in which case potassium bromide or some other suitable material is used. The cell windows must be large enough to admit the entire collimated beam from the source, which means that in practice they are 2 to 5 cm in diameter.

In the study of gases, the windows are fastened on the ends of a glass or metal cylinder with an appropriate cement. The sample is admitted to the cell through side tubes in the cylinder, and the gas pressure is adjusted to give the optimum absorption. In general, absorption spectra of gases are obtained at several pressures, because the optimum pressure for the resolution of fine structure in one spectral region is usually too high or too low for best resolution in other regions.   If the vapor pressure of the substance under study is low at room temperatures, sufficient absorption may be obtained by increasing the length of the absorption cell or by raising the cell temperature.   Neither of these expedients is entirely satisfactory, the first because of the awkwardness of long cells and the latter because of the difficulty of sealing rock salt to other materials over a wide temperature range.   The length of gas absorption cells in general use varies from about 10 to 30 cm, and the gas pressures used may run from 5 mm or even less for strongly absorbing substances like fluorocarbons to half an atmosphere for weak absorbers such as hydrogen chloride or water vapor.

The difference in densities between a liquid and its vapor under standard conditions being nearly a thousandfold, a thousandfold shorter path length should be sufficient in a liquid to produce the same infrared absorption.   From the figures given above, we should expect that liquid cells should have a length (usually called "thickness") of 0.1 mm or less.   Actual practicable cell thicknesses run from 0.01 to 1.0 mm, the average being around 0.05 mm.   Liquid cells usually consist of a metallic gasket or spacer of a thickness equal to the desired path length, which is placed in sandwich form between the two rock-salt plates serving as cell windows.   Liquid is put into the cell either through an orifice in the gasket or before the cell is assembled.   In the latter procedure, one window is laid flat and the gasket is placed upon it.   A drop or so of the liquid to be studied is placed in the shallow receptacle so formed, and the other window is then put on top of the gasket in such a way that all air is squeezed out.   The resulting sandwich is held together by metallic clamps.   Highly volatile liquids cannot be handled in this way, and must be placed in cells by the former technique.   An absorption cell for volatile liquids has been described by Gildart and Wright.[15]

In quantitative analysis of liquid mixtures by their infrared spectra, it is highly important to have a cell of reproducible thickness, because for highest accuracy the spectra of unknown and standard samples should be measured in cells of the same thickness.   The best means of ensuring reproducible cell thickness is to employ a cell of a fixed thickness that is never changed, and to use this cell for all analyses of

---

[15] L. Gildart and N. Wright, *Rev. Sci. Inst.*, **12**, 204 (1941).   Additional references to construction of absorption cells will be found in this paper.   See also General Reference 17.9.

a given kind of mixture. A disassembled cell will never regain exactly the same thickness after reassembly, and therefore a cell should not be taken apart if it is to be used again for quantitative analyses based on working curves (§ 17.6) obtained previously. A typical cell design is shown in Fig. 17.5.

Since the density of solids is of the same order as that of liquids, the path length in solid media for optimum infrared absorption is about 0.1 mm. If a solid can be fabricated by rolling, melting, deposition, and similar methods into a thin sheet or plate of this thickness, it offers no difficulty. The optical quality of the sheet for visible

Fig. 17.5.   Liquid absorption cell for infrared spectrometer.

wavelengths is unimportant. Solids that cannot be made into sheets or plates can sometimes be studied in the form of a thin powder layer deposited on a rock-salt plate by sedimentation. This technique has been used by Pfund,[1] Wright,[16] and others. Solids are also occasionally examined in solution, but this procedure has limitations. It can almost never be used for study of substances soluble only in water; even for substances soluble in organic solvents, it requires the use of two or more solvents so that the spectral regions of absorption of one solvent can be examined in a different solvent that is transparent in those regions. The particular solvents chosen for a given solid depend

---

[16] N. Wright, *Jour. Biol. Chem.*, **120**, 641 (1937).

on the spectrum expected for the solid and on its solubilities. Often it is useful to examine a solid in the form of a suspensoid or "mull" in an inert liquid medium such as Nujol.[17] As for solutions, the regions of absorption of the medium interfere with the measurement of the spectrum of the suspended solid (see General Reference 17.1, page 11).

It is customary to present the results of an infrared absorption study as a graph of per cent transmission plotted against wavelength in microns or wave number in cm^{-1}. Some infrared spectrometers produce such a record automatically and hence may properly be called *infrared spectrophotometers*. Most instruments, however, produce records from which transmission curves can be computed. At every point on these records, there must be explicit or implicit indication of the wavelength and the deflections corresponding to (a) the transmission of the sample, (b) 100 per cent transmission, and (c) zero transmission. All of these except the last vary greatly through the spectrum, but they must be known if the per cent transmission of the sample as a function of wavelength is to be obtained.

Wavelength is generally indicated on the record by some kind of fiducial mark made at convenient intervals during the recording. These marks are related to wavelength when the instrument is calibrated (see § 17.2) and their reliability may be checked easily with reference to the well-known absorption bands of water and carbon dioxide, or other convenient standards. The deflection for zero transmission can be indicated as often as desired by the insertion of an opaque shutter in front of the absorption cell, but the 100 per cent transmission deflection is rather more complicated to record. This deflection varies considerably with wavelength in approximate accord with the blackbody curve. At any particular wavelength, moreover, it is a function of slit width, source temperature, and other factors such as scattered radiation within the instrument and absorption and reflection in the optical path outside the absorbing substance. By careful regulation of these factors, it is possible to obtain a 100 per cent transmission curve throughout the spectrum which is sufficiently reproducible for most purposes except those of quantitative chemical analysis.

When the spectral record of a particular substance has been obtained, it still has to be translated into a per cent transmission vs.

---

[17] R. B. Barnes, E. F. Williams, *et al.*, *Ind. Eng. Chem.*, *Anal. ed.*, **19**, 620 (1947).

wavelength curve with the help of the 100 per cent transmission curve. The translation step is time-consuming, and various methods for its elimination have been suggested. One of these consists of a device for forcing the instrument to give a horizontal straight line as the 100 per cent transmission curve. Inasmuch as the slit widths have to be changed several times during the scanning of the spectrum anyway, a straight line for the 100 per cent transmission curve might be obtained by varying the slit width continuously as the spectrum is scanned, the rate of variation being governed by a cam so as to compensate for the blackbody curve and other variables. The difficulty here is the exceedingly fine control of slit width needed at the short wavelengths near the peak of the blackbody curve, where the curve is very steep and slit widths are very narrow. If electronic amplification is used, control can also be exercised by continuous variation of amplifier gain as the spectrum is scanned. A combination of these two devices has been described by White.[18]

The more basic and more satisfactory way to produce a record of per cent transmission is to provide a mechanism within the spectrometer by which the actual transmission of the sample is compared automatically and continuously with 100 per cent transmission as the spectrum is scanned. Such a mechanism converts the spectrometer into an automatic-recording infrared absorption spectrophotometer. The fundamental principles of infrared absorption spectrophotometers are essentially the same as those for the visible and ultraviolet (Chapter 14), the differences in detail arising from differences in sources and detectors. Various arrangements have been described by Hardy and Ryer,[19] Wright and Herscher,[20] and others.[21]

The optical system of a commercial instrument[22] having several features in common with those of Hardy and Ryer[19] and Wright and Herscher[20] is shown in Fig. 17.6. Radiation from a Globar source is received on two identical spherical mirrors so located that the two source-to-mirror beams make an angle of about 135 deg. The two collimated beams then pass through two identical cells, one holding the sample and the other the reference standard with respect to which the transmission of the sample is to be measured. By defini-

---

[18] J. U. White, *Jour. Opt. Soc. Am.*, **36**, 362A (1946).

[19] J. D. Hardy and A. I. Ryer, *Phys. Rev.*, **55**, 1112 (1939).

[20] N. Wright and L. W. Herscher, *Jour. Opt. Soc. Am.*, **37**, 211 (1947).

[21] R. F. Wild, *Rev. Sci. Inst.*, **18**, 436 (1947).

[22] W. S. Baird, H. M. O'Bryan, George Ogden, and Dorothy Lee, *Jour. Opt. Soc. Am.*, **37**, 754 (1947).

tion, the transmission of the reference cell is 100 per cent and the instrument functions so as to determine the ratio of the transmission of the sample to that of the reference. For example, the per cent transmission of a substance in solution would be determined with respect to a reference cell containing the solvent at a thickness equivalent to that of the solvent in the sample cell.

The beams pass through the two cells at right angles to each other and proceed to a point of intersection at which a rotating-sector interrupter is located. One sector of this interrupter is a plane

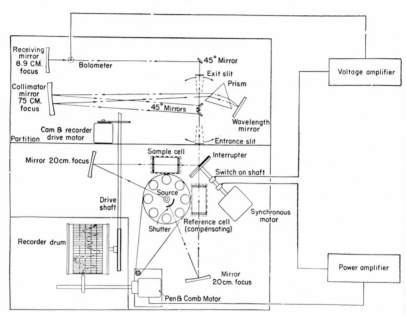

Fig. 17.6. The optical system of the Baird Associates' recording infrared spectrophotometer.   (Courtesy Baird Associates.)

mirror; and when this sector is at the beam intersection, the beam from the sample cell is reflected onto the entrance slit of the spectrometer while the beam from the reference cell is occulted. The other sector is simply an opening through which both beams pass, the reference beam proceeding to the entrance slit and the sample beam passing harmlessly off to one side. From the entrance slit onward, the optical path followed by radiation of any given wavelength is identical for both beams.

When the radiation at a particular wavelength, say 10 μ, is incident on the exit slit of the spectrometer, this radiation will remain constant with time if the 10-μ radiation from the source is constant and if the reduction in intensity which results from passage through the two absorption cell systems is the same for both.   However, when the sample cell absorbs more 10-μ radiation than the reference cell, the intensity of this radiation at the exit slit will "flicker" with the frequency of the rotating-sector interrupter.   The amplitude of the flicker depends on the absorption of the sample, and could in principle be measured directly to determine the per cent transmission.   Complications of the sort discussed in § 14.28 and in Wright and Herscher's article are avoided, however, if a null method is used.   By reducing the intensity of radiation in the reference beam to match the smaller intensity of the sample beam, one can determine the latter from the amount of reduction required.

In the instrument show in Fig. 17.7, the reference beam is capable of reduction by means of a comb-shaped shutter, the teeth of which are triangular in shape.   The shutter is driven by a motor whose source of current is the bolometer on which the flickering beam ultimately falls.   The bolometer current is first amplified by an AC amplifier tuned to the flicker frequency (§ 12.8), the value of which is of course determined by the sector interrupter.   This current causes the shutter motor to move the shutter into the reference beam until the flicker disappears.   Simultaneously, the amount of motion of the shutter is recorded.   By adjustment of the size and shape of the teeth in the shutter, it is possible to establish a linear relationship between this motion and the per cent transmission, so that the record of shutter motion is also a record of per cent transmission.

The spectrum is scanned by rotation of the Littrow mirror (§ 17.2), marked WAVELENGTH MIRROR in Fig. 17.6.   The same motor that drives the mirror also drives the recorder drum, giving thereby a direct relationship between wavelength and drum orientation.   As the spectrum is scanned, the drum rotates and a recording pen connected to the shutter traces out the per cent transmission curve on a paper chart properly ruled in transmission and wavelength coordinates.   A typical curve is shown in Fig. 17.8.

The use of AC amplification has the advantages mentioned in § 12.8.   In addition, it enables a traversal of the spectrum without interruption from one end to the other.   Ordinarily it is necessary to stop an infrared spectrometer while the slit width is being changed to compensate for change in the radiation curve.   In the Baird instrument the slit-width change can be made continuously, because any energy changes produced by changing slit width affect both sample and reference beams equally, and therefore the intensity ratio of sample beam to reference beam is not affected.   Inasmuch as the sample-beam and reference-beam intensities are balanced by the

Fig. 17.7.   Baird Associates' recording infrared spectrophotometer.
(Courtesy Baird Associates.)

mechanical shutter, the slit-width drive does not have to operate so as to compensate the radiation curve with high precision.

A double-beam instrument has many possibilities in addition to its designed use as a spectrophotometer.   A valuable application lies in the measurement of differential spectra of chemical substances known to differ in some important way (in physiological activity, for example) but without known difference in chemical composition.   It is also apparent that such differential spectra offer interesting possibilities in control of purity of chemical preparations.

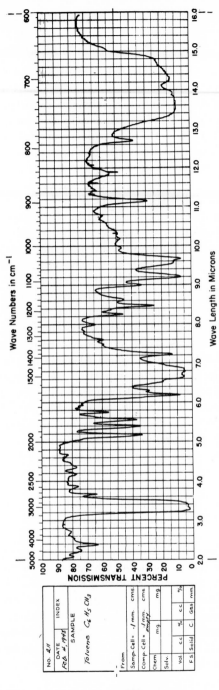

Fig. 17.8. Infrared transmission spectrum of toluene as recorded by the Baird Associates' spectrophotometer. (Courtesy Baird Associates.)

493

APPLICATIONS OF INFRARED SPECTROSCOPY

As was mentioned above, infrared spectroscopy has been most widely applied in the analysis of chemical compounds by means of their infrared absorption. However, extensive researches have also been carried out in the fields of emission and reflection spectra (General References 17.2, 17.3, 17.4). The emission spectra of gases have been used to extend spectral series into the infrared region, as in the Paschen, Brackett, and Pfund series in the atomic hydrogen spectrum; and the infrared spectrum of the "blackbody" radiator furnished the experimental basis on which Planck first proposed the quantum hypothesis. The reflection spectra of crystals, apart from their utility in the isolation of narrow spectral regions, have been widely studied in connection with crystal structure and composition as well as related properties such as specific heat. The reflection spectra of crystals are as characteristic of the crystal as their absorption spectra, and could be used for identification. The techniques of absorption spectra are more generally applicable, however.

17.5. Qualitative Chemical Analysis by Infrared Absorption Spectra. In order that results of infrared-absorption studies made under different conditions may be compared, research workers in this field usually indicate, explicitly or implicitly, the path length, pressure, temperature, and slit width at each wavelength, and any other pertinent information. However, it has proved impossible to follow the convention, used in the field of visible and ultraviolet spectrophotometry, of plotting extinction coefficients calculated from Beer's law (see Chapter 14). The reason is not necessarily that Beer's law does not hold in the infrared but rather that experimental determination of extinction coefficients meets with difficulties that are quantitatively small in the visible and ultraviolet but may be overpowering in the infrared. Hence the percentage transmission values given in an infrared absorption spectrum have at best a semiquantitative significance, for which reason absorption bands are frequently listed in tables of infrared spectra on a qualitative scale as "very weak," "weak," "medium," "strong," or "very strong."

In the past, the two most important difficulties to overcome have been the effects of slit width and of scattered radiation, corrections for both of which are difficult to apply at every wavelength in the infrared for which extinction coefficients are to be calculated. With commercial spectrometers of high optical quality now available, these difficulties can be considerably reduced and very probably will be in the near future. Additional trouble with accurate control and measurement of liquid absorption-cell thicknesses and with the photometric comparison of two beams is also involved, but it appears that infrared extinction coefficients are a realizable goal.

It might reasonably be concluded from the foregoing paragraphs that the use of infrared absorption spectra for chemical analysis would be out of the question, particularly if the analysis has to be quantitative. However, the fact is that both qualitative and quantitative analyses are possible. The effects that prevent a determination of extinction coefficients are nevertheless quite reproducible for one instrument at one wavelength and can therefore be taken into account empirically, even though it is impossible to measure them accurately. The procedures used in infrared analysis are described below, and from them an understanding of applicability of this new analytical tool can be gained. We point out here some of the general advantages of chemical analysis by infrared means.

Infrared analyses can be carried out rapidly on a very small amount of sample (< 0.1 gram) if it does not require special preparation for spectroscopic study. The analytical procedure is not destructive; that is, the sample can be recovered quantitatively after the spectral data have been obtained. This feature is especially valuable for chemically fragile substances, on which infrared radiation produces no chemical action apart from its heating effect, in contradistinction to ultraviolet radiation. For the analysis of chemical and biological materials, where the total sample at the disposal of the investigator may be only 10 or 20 mg, these features are especially valuable. It is apparent that after special modifications for his purposes, the biochemist will find the analytical use of the infrared spectrometer to be as powerful a tool as it is for the industrial organic chemist.

The limitations of analysis by infrared means are several. It has been employed primarily in the analysis of organic compounds, although the advantages it offers to the inorganic chemist would appear to be considerable. However, the facts that water is opaque throughout the near infrared and that most atoms and monatomic ions do not absorb at all in this region eliminate the infrared spectrometer as an analytical tool for many inorganic problems. In the past, the experimental difficulties encountered in constructing and maintaining a good spectrometer have been sufficiently formidable to rule out the use of infrared in many laboratories, but this limitation is to a large extent removed by the availability of rugged and reasonably priced commercial instruments.

In Chapter 11 it was stated that near infrared spectra arise from molecular vibration, while far infrared spectra are due to molecular rotation. Because of the relative simplicity and availability of prism spectrometers, at present all chemical analysis by infrared means is carried out in the near infrared. Necessarily, then, the qualitative analytical conclusions are drawn from spectroscopic observations of molecular vibrational frequencies. It is well known from experience that the vibrational spectrum of a polyatomic molecule can be classified approximately into those frequencies which are characteristic of the molecule as a whole and those which are characteristic of small groups of atoms within the molecule. These latter frequencies (compare Table 11.2) occur in a molecular spectrum whenever the groups giving rise to them are present in the molecule, regardless of the structure of the molecule as a whole. It is a further result of experience that the infrared spectrum of a mixture containing different molecular species is simply the superposition of the individual infrared spectra of the various molecules present. Whenever the spectrum of a mixture is not a superposition of the spectra of the substances that were mixed together to form it, one can conclude that some sort of reaction has occurred in which some change has been made in the molecular structure of one or more of the original substances.

The following kinds of qualitative information may be obtained from the infrared spectrum of an unknown substance or mixture:

1. If the material is known to be a single chemical substance and is presumed to be one of a number (large or small) of substances whose spectra have previously been determined, comparison of the spectrum of the unknown with the others will quickly establish which, if any, of the presumed substances it is. This comparison is probably the most useful qualitative infrared procedure.

2. If the material is known to be a single chemical substance of undetermined structure, the spectrum can show the presence or absence of various groups of atoms and thus can lend powerful aid to a determination of the structure or essential parts of it.

3. If the material is a single chemical substance of questionable purity, comparison of its spectrum with the spectra of suspected impurities can often establish the presence of certain impurities, together with a rough estimate of the amount of impurity. Of course

the sensitivity of the method depends on the spectra of the substance and of the impurities. Under favorable conditions it is possible to identify impurities present in amounts less than 1 per cent, sometimes much less (0.01 per cent).

4. If the material is a mixture of chemical substances, comparison of its spectrum in a systematic way with the spectra of substances conceivably present in the mixture can lead to identification of the components of the mixture, together with a rough estimate of their percentages.

It is apparent that one must have a table of group frequencies and a catalogue of spectra of pure substances if one is to carry out the analytical procedures just outlined. Extensive tables of character-istic group frequencies like Table 11.2 have been given by various authors.* These frequency values are easily reproducible from one spectroscopic setup to another and can be relied upon for analytical purposes. The situation is not quite so simple, however, with respect to catalogues of absorption spectra. For one thing, although existing catalogues give many absorption curves,† it is quite probable that a given analytical problem will call for spectra not previously published. Moreover, in comparing spectra of unknown substances with known spectra, there is a great advantage in employing spectra obtained on the same instrument and under comparable circumstances. For this reason a laboratory carrying out qualitative analyses by infrared means customarily sets up its own collection of absorption curves. The systematic use of catalogues of infrared spectra in industrial research laboratories has been described by Wright[23] and by Barnes, Gore, Liddel, and Williams (General Reference 17.1).

17.6. Quantitative Chemical Analysis by Infrared Absorption Spectra. Quantitative analyses of mixtures of organic compounds are usually feasible despite the previously mentioned difficulties that prevent the accurate measurement of extinction coefficients. The difficulties are sidestepped by determining the infrared absorption of the unknown at various wavelengths under carefully controlled con-ditions and comparing these absorptions quantitatively with those measured for various standard samples under identical conditions.

---

* See, for example, Tables 1–4 in General Reference 17.1 and Fig. 6 of General Reference 17.9.

† Reference 17.1 gives spectra for some 363 compounds, mostly limited to the range 5–10 μ. General Reference 17.7 gives curves for several hundred hydrocarbons; and General Reference 17.4, though compiled many years ago, is still occasionally useful.

[23] N. Wright, *Ind. Eng. Chem., Anal. ed.*, **13**, 1 (1941).

Among the factors that must be controlled are the temperature of the sample, its pressure if it is studied as a gas, the absorption path length (if the sample is studied as a liquid, this is the cell thickness and must be reproducible to 1 per cent or better), spectrometer slit widths, and wavelength settings.

When these variables are controlled, it is possible in principle to analyze a mixture of n components by determining the fractional transmissions, T, at n wavelengths and solving the set of n simultaneous linear equations, obtained from Beer's law (compare Eqs. 14.7 and 14.8), relating T to fractional composition X:

$$-\log T_1 = \sum_{j=1}^{n} C_{1j}X_j$$

$$-\log T_2 = \sum_{j=1}^{n} C_{2j}X_j \qquad (17.1)$$

$$\cdot \cdot \cdot \cdot \cdot \cdot \cdot \cdot \cdot \cdot \cdot \cdot \cdot \cdot \cdot$$

$$-\log T_n = \sum_{j=1}^{n} C_{nj}X_j$$

Here T_n is the fractional transmission of the mixture at λ_n, X_j is the fractional amount of component j in the mixture, and C_{nj} is the value of $(-\log T_n)$ when $X_j = 1$, that is, the value of $(-\log T_n)$ at wavelength λ_n for the pure component j.

Since all quantitative analyses by infrared absorption are carried out by some variant of the above procedure, it is necessary to consider the practical restrictions which apply to its use:

1. Beer's law must hold in effect for the *range of compositions over which analyses are to be made.** Its validity is best determined by carrying out actual analyses on samples of known composition. If analysis is impossible because of the magnitude of deviations from Beer's law, such a trial procedure will show it and will reveal as well any other practical impediments to accurate analysis, such as the variation in scattered light in the spectrometer at a fixed wavelength with variation in sample composition.

2. The n wavelengths at which T_λ's are determined must be selected judiciously to give the best analytical accuracy for the mixture in

---

* Beer's law says that log (I_0/I_c) is a linear function of the concentration c. This relationship may not hold for measurements of I_0/I_c on a given spectrometer for a given substance over the desired concentration range. However, it may be possible to apply corrections for scattered light and the like, so that Beer's law does hold. In such a case, Beer's law may be said to hold "in effect."

the spectral range involved. Clearly, one must not select two wavelengths for which C_{1j} is approximately the same multiple of C_{2j} for every j. Likewise, one cannot expect to find n wavelengths at the first of which only component 1 absorbs, at the second of which only component 2 absorbs, and so on. Such a fortuitous circumstance will be especially improbable if one is analyzing, as is often the case, a mixture of chemically similar substances. The closer one can approach to this ideal situation, however, the greater the accuracy and the ease with which the analysis can be carried out.

3. Since Eqs. (17.1) assume the constancy or reproducibility of the various factors previously mentioned, such as slit widths, wavelength settings, and cell thickness, these factors must be controllable. Of particular importance is cell thickness, the reproducibility of which is vital. It is therefore customary in quantitative work to use a permanently assembled cell of fixed thickness for all the measurements involved in a given analysis.

In practice, analyses are usually made with n smaller than 5, and usually with $n = 2$ or 3, although as many as 10 components have been determined in hydrocarbon mixtures. For $n = 2$, the analytical problem frequently calls for the determination of small amounts of component 1 in the presence of 90^+ per cent of component 2. In such an instance, the analytical procedure can be speeded up as well as made more accurate by preparing from standard samples an analytical "working curve." This curve consists of a plot of log T at λ_1 against X_1 over the range, say 0 to 0.1, within which X_1 is expected to lie. The value of X_1 for an unknown can then be read directly from the working curve when the value of log T at λ_1 has been measured for the unknown. In special cases, this procedure can be followed in the determination of two or more components $X_1, X_2, X_3, \ldots$ when they are present in amounts small by comparison with the largest component, provided that each working curve (at λ_1 for X_1, at λ_2 for X_2, . . .) is uninfluenced by variation in the amounts of the other components. Strictly, this proviso is equivalent to the ideal situation mentioned under restriction 2, above. However, in the equation

$$-\log T_1 = C_{11}X_1 + C_{12}X_2 + C_{13}X_3 + \ldots + \text{constant} \quad (17.2)$$

to a fair approximation one can neglect the terms $C_{12}X_2\ C_{13}X_3, \ldots$ when C_{11} is much larger than $C_{12}, C_{13}, \ldots$, and $X_1, X_2, X_3, \ldots$ are all small. The constant is the contribution of the largest component, which is present in fixed amount both in the known samples used in making up the working curve and in the unknowns. Extensive discussion of analytical methods by means of working curves will be found in General Reference 17.1 and in various other places. [23, 24]

Quantitative analyses by means of infrared absorption are carried out either on liquid or on vapor samples. Provided the problem of controlling sample thickness can be solved with suitable accuracy, as by the use of an internal standard,[17] there appears to be no reason in theory or in practice why one cannot also make analyses on solids whose near infrared absorption is suitable for the purpose. Infrared quantitative analysis is especially valuable in the determination of closely similar chemical compounds such as geometrical isomers. It has been mentioned earlier that aqueous solutions cannot ordinarily be analyzed by means of their near infrared absorption.

17.7. The Determination of Molecular Structure from Infrared Spectra. It was mentioned in § 11.4 that the absorption of infrared radiation by a vibrating and rotating molecule depends on the presence of a molecular dipole moment. When the dipole moment changes temporarily during the course of a particular vibration of the molecule, infrared radiation of the frequency of that vibration can be absorbed by the molecule. Those molecular vibrations which are attended by no change in the dipole moment do not absorb infrared. Likewise, those molecules which at rest possess no dipole moment cannot absorb infrared radiation by rotation alone, but if the molecular dipole moment changes, during a simultaneous vibration and rotation, the combined frequencies (both sum and difference) of vibration and rotation can be absorbed.

It has been known for some years that spectroscopic activity of molecular vibrations and rotations is strongly dependent on their symmetry.[25, 26] In fact, it is possible to work out tables of selection rules for infrared and Raman spectra purely on the basis of molecular symmetry. With no more detailed knowledge of a particular molecule than the number and kind of atoms in it and the symmetry of their arrangement, one can determine the number of molecular frequencies which appear in infrared absorption and in the Raman effect

[24] J. R. Nielsen and D. C. Smith, *Ind. Eng. Chem., Anal. ed.*, **15**, 609 (1943).

[25] C. J. Brester, *Zeitschr. f. Physik*, **24**, 324 (1924).

[26] G. Placzek, *Handbuch der Radiologie*, Vol. VI, part 2, pages 205 *ff*. Leipzig, Akademische Verlags., 1934.

(Chapter 18), together with other results such as the number of frequencies that occur simultaneously in both. The procedure used in determination of molecular structure from infrared and Raman spectra is as follows:

1. Observe both spectra.
2. Assume a molecular model, and from the selection rules predict the number and type of frequencies to appear in both spectra; if possible, estimate the approximate spectral positions of the frequencies.
3. Compare the observed spectra with the predictions of the model.
4. Accept or reject the model.

In principle, this process should be repeated for every possible molecular symmetry compatible with the number and kind of atoms, but in practice it is usually necessary to consider only the smaller number of structures consistent with additional restrictions such as those of chemical valence. It is, however, a frequent practical result that two or more models appear to explain the spectra equally well. In such instances, additional spectroscopic data are needed and can often be obtained by such expedients as the study of isotopic spectra. For molecules of interest to the organic chemist, deuterium is a valuable tool in spectroscopic analysis.[27]

The determination of molecular symmetry is usually insufficient for a complete specification of the interatomic bond angles in a molecule and *never* determines the interatomic distances. The evaluation of interatomic distances and angles by spectroscopic means is accomplished through a determination of molecular moments of inertia, which are involved in the frequencies of molecular rotations. However, this procedure* is severely limited by the fact that for a rigid molecule there are at most three moments of inertia. Hence

---

[27] F. Halverson, "The Use of Deuterium in the Analysis of Vibrational Spectra," *Rev. Mod. Phys.*, **19**, 87 (1947).

* There is another procedure for obtaining interatomic bond angles in small molecules or atomic groups. The equations for the vibrational frequencies of a molecule sometimes involve the interatomic angles explicitly. If all the other parameters—mostly force constants—are known, the angles can be obtained by substituting the proper observed molecular frequencies in the equations and solving for the bond angles. Ordinarily, this method suffers in accuracy and reliability for one or more of the following reasons: (1) the calculated bond angle is highly sensitive to small errors in observed frequency or in force constants; (2) the frequency equations are derived from a potential function of unknown validity; (3) force-constant values must be assumed or carried over from other molecules.

only three numerical values (at most) can be obtained from the moments of inertia unless additional molecular species derived from isotopes are available. If the number of parameters of this sort is sufficient, together with molecular symmetry, to determine the molecular geometry completely, then the molecular structure can be worked out completely by spectroscopic means. This limitation means in practice that only the structures of molecules with relatively few atoms or high symmetry can be completely determined spectroscopically. In addition to the numerous diatomic molecules whose interatomic distances have been thus evaluated, carbon dioxide, water, ammonia, methane, hydrogen sulfide, and a few other small molecules have been worked out by analysis of near and far infrared absorption spectra. Larger and less symmetrical molecules are not, in general, amenable to this type of treatment.

The results of many spectroscopic studies on molecular structure are discussed in the monograph of Herzberg (General Reference 17.8), to which the reader is also referred for details on such related topics as the determination of thermodynamic quantities from spectroscopic data.

17.8. Astrophysical and Biological Applications of Infrared Spectroscopy. The interpretation of the spectra of water, carbon dioxide, ammonia, and methane mentioned in the preceding section has made possible an interesting application of infrared spectroscopy to astrophysics. In 1932, Adams and Dunham[28] found absorption bands in the photographic infrared spectrum of the planet Venus similar to those shown in Fig. 1.9b. These were soon interpreted [29] as very high overtones of the carbon dioxide infrared absorption bands and demonstrated that the atmosphere of Venus contains large amounts of this gas. This work led to similar studies of the atmospheres of the other planets and resulted in the still more remarkable discovery that the atmospheres of Jupiter and Saturn contain enormous amounts of methane and ammonia.

The early work on the planetary atmospheres was carried out in the photographic infrared because neither photocells nor radiometric devices were sufficiently sensitive for the measurement of astronomically available intensities in the infrared region. With the development of the lead sulfide photoconductive cell (§ 12.13), this limitation was removed and extension of all kinds of astrophysical studies into

---

[28] W. S. Adams and T. Dunham, Jr., *Pub. Astron. Soc. Pacific*, **44**, 243 (1932).
[29] A. Adel and D. M. Dennison, *Phys. Rev.*, **43**, 716 (1933).

the near infrared was begun.   Kuiper[30] has examined planetary atmospheric spectra out to nearly 3 μ and has confirmed the existence of ammonia and methane on Jupiter and Saturn and on Titan, the largest satellite of Saturn.   According to his studies, there is somewhat less ammonia on Saturn than on Jupiter; and although both planets have large amounts of methane, the methane absorption in the rings of Saturn is less than that in the planet itself.   Stebbins and Whitford [31] have studied infrared radiation from the region of the center of our galaxy, and the solar spectrum out to 2.5 μ is the subject of an extensive series of investigations by astronomers of the McMath-Hulburt Observatory.[32]

The application of infrared absorption spectra to the solution of biological and biochemical problems was rather late in comparison with the extensive use made by organic chemists, primarily because of instrumental difficulties that since have largely been removed.   For many biochemical problems, infrared absorption spectra offer aid that cannot be obtained by any other physical methods, particularly ultraviolet spectra.   A wide variety of highly important biological substances—hormones, amino acids, carbohydrates, and saturated fatty substances, to cite several classes—exhibit either little ultraviolet absorption at wavelengths above 2000 A or else show absorption characteristic only of a small chromophoric group that does not enable the biochemist to identify or analyze for the remainder of the molecule.   On the other hand, the infrared spectra of these substances, besides revealing the presence of specific groups, exhibit features characteristic of the molecule as a whole.   For example, infrared examination of two compounds that differ only in being geometrical isomers nearly always makes possible a sharp distinction between them.

The steroids may be cited as an example of the kind of biochemical substance to which the above remarks apply.   This class of compounds, which includes many of the sex hormones, consists of a large saturated hydrocarbon ring system to which various side groups are attached.   The ketosteroids, for example, have a carbonyl side group.   The carbonyl group shows an ultraviolet absorption, to be sure, but it is characteristic of the absorption of ketones in general.   The presence and location of other side groups do not affect this absorp-

[30] G. P. Kuiper, *Astrophys. Jour.*, **106**, 251 (1947).

[31] Joel Stebbins and A. E. Whitford, *Astrophys. Jour.*, **106**, 235 (1947); *Sky and Telescope*, **7**, 123 (1948).

[32] R. R. McMath and O. C. Mohler, *Sky and Telescope*, **7**, 143 (1948).

tion, and therefore the ultraviolet region does not afford a means of distinguishing these various compounds, the physiological properties of which may differ radically. On the other hand, the infrared spectrum shows not only the characteristic carbonyl absorption as well as that of any other side group but also shows features indicative of the location of the groups.

The advantages of infrared for work with steroids were appreciated by Furchgott and his associates[33] as well as by Dobriner and collaborators. The latter, in a classical paper[34] on the application of infrared spectrometry to the fractionation of urinary ketosteroids, not only studied crude mixtures of the ketosteroids but also analyzed spectroscopically the products obtained by chromatographic fractionation of the mixtures. The ketosteroids were usually studied in carbon disulfide solution, the technique normally requiring somewhere between 1 and 4 mg of steroid sample. Dobriner and his coworkers found that the various compounds that they were able to obtain in pure form had quite specific infrared spectra, in contrast to their ultraviolet absorption. The small samples were undamaged by infrared radiation and could be recovered quantitatively after spectra had been obtained. When they were dealing with mixtures containing one or more substances of hitherto unknown composition and structure, the infrared spectra helped in two ways: in concentrating the unknown material by chromatographic fractionation, infrared spectra were used to trace the unknown in the various fractions; in elucidating the structure of the unknown, the spectra indicated the nature of side groups present. Dobriner's paper furnishes an excellent summary of the way in which infrared can be used in biochemical problems, and the interested reader should also consult it for details of the technique used in the ketosteroid work.

General References

17.1. R. B. Barnes, U. Liddel, V. Z. Williams, and R. C. Gore, *Infrared Spectroscopy*. New York: Reinhold Publishing Corp., 1944.

17.2. C. Schaeffer and F. Matossi, *Das ultrarote Spektrum*. Berlin: Julius Springer, 1930.

17.3. J. Lecomte, *Le Spectre infrarouge*. Paris: Presses Universitaires, 1928.

---

[33] R. F. Furchgott, H. Rosenkrantz, and E. Shorr, *Jour. Biol. Chem.*, **171**, 523 (1947), and earlier references there cited.

[34] K. Dobriner, S. Lieberman, C. P Rhoads, R. N. Jones, V. Z. Williams, and R. B. Barnes, *Jour. Biol. Chem.*, **172**, 297 (1948).

17.4. W. W. Coblentz, *Investigations of Infrared Spectra*, Washington, D.C., 1905–08. Vol. 1 (October, 1905): Part I, Infrared absorption spectra; Part II, Infrared emission spectra. Vol. 2 (December, 1906): Part III, Infrared transmission spectra; Part IV, Infrared reflection spectra; Part V, Infrared reflection spectra; Part VI, Infrared transmission spectra; Part VII, Infrared emission spectra.

17.5. John Strong, *Procedures in Experimental Phsyics*. New York: Prentice-Hall, Inc., 1938.

17.6. R. W. Wood, *Physical Optics*. New York: The Macmillan Company, 1934.

17.7. National Bureau of Standards, American Petroleum Institute Project No. 44: *Thermodynamic and Spectroscopic Data on Hydrocarbons*, 1945 *et seq.*

17.8. G. Herzberg, *Infrared and Raman Spectra*. New York: D. Van Nostrand Company, Inc., 1945.

17.9. V. Z. Williams, "Infrared Instrumentation and Techniques," *Rev. Sci. Inst.*, **19**, 135 (1948).

CHAPTER 18

Raman Spectroscopy

WHEN A BEAM OF LIGHT PASSES THROUGH A MATERIAL MEDIUM, some of the light is transmitted, some absorbed, and some diffused or "scattered." The scattered portion is ordinarily very small and originates from several scattering processes. Even in a macroscopically uniform medium, microscopic inhomogeneities give rise to scattering, especially if their dimensions approximate the wavelength of the light. If the inhomogeneities are randomly distributed particles, as for example in tobacco smoke, the scattering is called *Tyndall scattering.* If the inhomogeneities are transitory fluctuations in the index of refraction of the medium that arise from local density fluctuations, the scattering is called *Rayleigh scattering.* A third type of light scattering, called the *Raman effect* after the Indian physicist who discovered it in 1928,[1] arises directly from variations in the "index of refraction" of individual molecules.* These variations, which are produced by molecular rotation and vibration, are relatively slight, and the intensity of the light involved in the Raman effect is correspondingly low.

18.1. The Raman Effect. When scattered monochromatic radiation is examined spectrographically, it is found to be no longer monochromatic but to consist of the original frequency (Tyndall and Rayleigh scattering) plus several new frequencies (Raman effect). The spectral location of the new frequencies, together with other properties such as their intensities and polarizations, are characteristic of the scattering substance. From such data it is possible to draw conclusions about the nature of the substance, a possibility that accounts for the wide usefulness of Raman spectroscopy.

---

[1] C. V. Raman, *Ind. Jour. Physics*, **2**, 387 (1928).

* The "index of refraction" of a single molecule is more commonly called the *molecular refractivity.* It is directly related to the molecular polarizability discussed later (§ 18.10).

For a particular scattering material, a set of Raman frequencies is associated with each frequency in the exciting radiation; that is, two different exciting wavelengths will give rise to two different sets of scattered frequencies. However, these two sets are not independent. If the scattered frequencies are known for one exciting wavelength, the analogous frequencies for another exciting wavelength can be calculated readily. The reason is that the number and magnitude of the frequency shifts introduced by the Raman effect in a particular substance is the same irrespective of the frequency of the exciting radiation. This point is illustrated in Fig. 18.1, which shows schematically the spectrum scattered by the simple molecule carbon disulfide when the exciting radiation consists of the two mercury lines

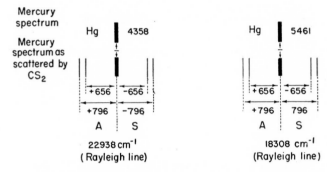

Fig. 18.1. Schematic diagram of the Raman spectrum of carbon disulphide

at 18,308 and 22,938 cm^{-1}. These are the wave numbers of the green and blue mercury lines at 5461 and 4358 A, respectively.

It will be seen in Fig. 18.1 that the pattern of Raman lines is the same for the two exciting frequencies. The numerical values of the shifts introduced by the Raman effect are shown above the arrows that indicate the shifts. The numbers are obtained by taking the *difference* between the absolute wave number of each Raman line and the wave number of the mercury line that excites it. Thus the figures $+656$ and -656 for the two shifts nearest the Hg-4358 line were derived by subtracting 22,938 cm^{-1} from 23,594 and 22,282, the last two numbers being the spectroscopically measured wave numbers of the two Raman lines. Because the Raman shifts depend on frequency differences rather than absolute frequencies, the symbol $\Delta\bar{\nu}$ is often used to denote their magnitude in wave numbers.

As is apparent from Fig. 18.1, Raman shifts occur symmetrically above and below the exciting frequency. Those that occur above are called *anti-Stokes lines* (denoted by A in the figure) to distinguish them from the lines on the low-frequency side, which are called *Stokes lines* (denoted by S). The terminology arose from an old rule, Stokes' law of fluorescence, which holds that scattered radiation never has a higher frequency than the exciting radiation. Anti-Stokes lines are nearly always much weaker than Stokes lines. Although they are of theoretical interest, they are of little practical importance, since Raman spectra are universally studied by means of the more intense Stokes lines.

In addition to the shift in frequency, there are several other ways in which Raman scattering differs from the other types. Tyndall and Rayleigh scattering are coherent; that is, there is a definite phase relationship between the incident and the scattered light, whereas Raman scattering is incoherent, with only random phase relationship. Raman lines frequently show marked depolarization, whereas the accompanying Rayleigh line is highly polarized. The intensity of Raman lines in liquids is from one-hundredth to one one-thousandth that of the Rayleigh line, and in vapors the ratio may be as small as 1 in 10,000. In a clear crystalline solid, on the other hand, the intensity of Raman scattering may approach that of the Rayleigh type, because the latter is especially weak.

18.2. Technique of the Raman Effect. Because the Raman effect is so feeble, a special though simple optical technique is required to detect and study it. The technique is based on that used by R. W. Wood[2] for the investigation of fluorescence. The basic requirement is an intense source of monochromatic radiation. Thus light source L in Fig. 18.2 sends its radiation in the direction of the arrow I into the transparent tube T (sometimes called a Wood's tube). One end of the tube has an optically flat window W and the other end is drawn into the horn-shaped form indicated in the figure. The horn H is blackened to trap stray reflected radiation. Radiation entering the tube is scattered in all directions by the liquid or gas contained therein, but only that part scattered along the direction R (perpendicular to I) is studied spectroscopically. The symbol S stands for the spectrograph.

Looking into the tube T from the spectrograph, one views the light

---

[2] R. W. Wood, *Nature*, **122**, 349 (1928); *Phil. Mag.*, **6**, 729 (1928).

scattered by a long column of material against the black background of the horn H. No direct or reflected radiation should be seen, but only Rayleigh and Raman scattering. The long column serves to increase the total intensity of scattering along the direction R, and the right angle between I and R minimizes direct and reflected radiation.

18.3. Sources for Excitation of the Raman Effect. The Raman effect would be easier to work with if an intense source of sharply monochromatic radiation of, say, 5000 A wavelength were available. Since there is none, existing sources must be adapted to do the job. An intense source of some kind of line spectrum, usually the mercury-vapor arc, is the starting point. Other vapor arcs, both metallic and nonmetallic, have been employed, as for example the helium discharge tube, but the mercury spectrum has proved the most generally useful. Mercury arcs of various kinds are discussed in detail in Chapter 8.

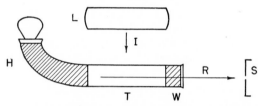

Fig. 18.2.   Optical arrangement for the study of the Raman effect.

Many of these, including several inexpensive commercial types, are suitable for Raman work, the choice of a particular arc being dictated by the substances to be studied, the spectrograph to be employed, and related considerations.[3]

One of the great advantages of the mercury spectrum is the number of fairly widely separated intense lines, which are located at 2537, 3650, 4047, 4358, 5461, and 5770–5790 A. The selection of one of these as the source of excitation for the Raman spectrum of a particular material is based on the properties of the material. The intensity of both Rayleigh and Raman scattering increases with the fourth power of the exciting frequency, so that the highest frequency (lowest wavelength) would always be chosen if other factors were not involved. The most important factor is the absorption spectrum of the substance. If the substance absorbs radiation of the frequency

---

[3] D. H. Rank and J. S. McCartney, *Jour. Opt. Soc. Am.*, **38**, 279 (1948).

in question, the scattered light will probably be fluorescent.* Even if fluorescence is missing, the scattered spectrum will be reabsorbed, and it will be difficult, if not impossible, to detect the Raman spectrum. Most substances in thick layers (Fig. 18.2), particularly organic compounds, absorb ultraviolet radiation of 2537 A, and therefore the use of this line is confined to relatively rare instances when the scattering substance is quite transparent to 2537 A and the requirement of an all-quartz system can be met.

The most commonly used lines are the blue 4358 line, the violet 4047 line, and the green 5461 line, in that order. The 4358 line combines the advantages of high transmissibility through many materials, high photographic activity, and good exciting power. In addition, most glass-prism spectrographs have high dispersion and resolving power in the blue region. The mercury spectrum contains no lines of appreciable intensity between 4358 and 4916 A, which gives an open region of 2600 cm^{-1} for the Stokes lines from λ 4358. The violet line can be used for excitation of Raman shifts greater than 2000 cm^{-1} if the scattering substance permits, because these shifts will appear in the same open region (4358 to 4916 A). The 5461 line is used only with substances whose absorption of blue light is too strong to permit the use of 4358.

The mercury arc, like any other source found thus far, still falls short of the ideal in two important ways: (a) the spectral lines in the source are often so close together (for example, the mercury lines at 4047 and 4358 A) that Raman shifts excited by one line may overlap, and hence be concealed by, another line or by Raman shifts from another line; (b) there is continuous as well as monochromatic radiation in the source. If the continuous radiation, generally termed *background*, has even 0.1 per cent of the intensity of the exciting line, the Rayleigh scattering of the background may mask or interfere seriously with the detection of the Raman lines. These two shortcomings are mitigated considerably by the use of radiation filters.

18.4. Filters for the Raman Effect. Most of the optical filters used in Raman work are designed to isolate the above-mentioned mercury lines. Since the interested reader can find detailed ac-

---

* The lesser usefulness of fluorescence (see § 11.13), which is a phenomenon closely related to the Raman effect, is the result of its usually diffuse, continuous spectrum, from which detailed conclusions are hard to draw. The Raman spectrum, which is discrete and sharp-lined, gives more information.

counts[4] of filters for this purpose in the literature, Table 18.1 lists only a few of the more commonly used line-filter combinations.

TABLE 18.1

MERCURY-LINE FILTERS FOR THE RAMAN EFFECT

Hg-2537: This line is ordinarily used without preliminary filtering, especially since it is possible to excite it preferentially in a "resonance lamp." However, the procedure of filling the spectrograph case with mercury vapor is sometimes followed (the vapor pressure of mercury at room temperature is sufficiently high), which sharply absorbs the Rayleigh-scattered 2537 line. By this device, Raman shifts of only a few wave numbers can be detected; this detection would be impossible if the Rayleigh line were of its usual intensity.

Hg-3650: The nickel-oxide glass filter (for example, Corning No. 5874) first devised by Wood, isolates this line reasonably well.

Hg-4047: Corning Noviol O glass (No. 3060) or a dilute solution of sodium nitrite will readily remove Hg-3650. To eliminate longer wavelengths than 4047, a solution of iodine in carbon tetrachloride is suitable.

Hg-4358: Wavelengths below 4358 are absorbed quite satisfactorily by saturated aqueous sodium nitrite solution. Praseodymium salts (such as the chloride) are excellent for cleaning up background from 4400 to 4800 A, and a rhodamine dye (duPont Rhodamine 5GDN Extra) is good from 4600 to 5400.

Hg-5461: Wavelengths below 5461 are removed by basic potassium chromate solution, and those above by cupric sulfate solution. The 5770–5790 yellow doublet falls in the same region with 1000 cm^{-1} Stokes shifts from 5461. It is difficult to remove the yellow lines completely, but a filter of saturated neodymium chloride can reduce their intensity so greatly that Raman lines in their immediate neighborhood can be uncovered.

Hg-5770–5790: The yellow doublet is rarely used but may be called for if the scattering substance absorbs green light too strongly, or if it is necessary to resolve some ambiguity in a spectrum excited by Hg-5461. For this purpose a dilute water solution of the dye cyanosine or certain of its derivatives can be used to absorb Hg-5461.

Most of the filters listed in Table 18.1 are solutions, the use of which requires special containers. Glass and plastic filters of equally good spectral characteristics could doubtless be used, but they are not so readily obtained or adaptable.

18.5. Arrangement of the Excitation Unit. To increase the intensity of illumination, it is customary to use more than one mercury arc, the number varying from 2 to as many as 12. In addition, the radiation incident upon the scattering substance is further enhanced

---

[4] K. W. F. Kohlrausch, General Reference 18.6, page 34.

by some kind of collimating device, such as a cylindrical mirror placed on the opposite side of the arc from the scattering tube, or a cylindrical lens between the arc and the tube.   Wood[5] ingeniously combined the latter with a filter by using a cylindrical tube filled with sodium nitrite solution as the lens.

When a large number of arcs and filter holders are used, it is found convenient in general to mount the arcs, filter holders, and scattering tube with their axes vertical.   This change in direction requires a plane mirror between the tube and the spectrograph, to deflect the scattered light at an angle of 90 deg.   The heat generated by the arcs is always considerable, and both air and water cooling of the excitation unit are usually necessary.   Sometimes a filter solution may be circulated as a refrigerant to keep the number of media between the source and scattering tube to a minimum.   An excitation unit with six General Electric type H-2 mercury arcs and elliptical reflectors for each is shown in Fig. 18.3.

18.6.   The Scattering Tube.   The size of the Wood's tube (T in Fig. 18.2) depends on the size of the arcs used, the relative scarcity of the scattering material, whether gases or liquids are being studied, and other factors.   For liquids the tube commonly has a volume of 10 to 100 cc.   Volumes less than 10 cc can be used, but the quality of the spectrum suffers when the volume drops below 1 cc.   Many substances require only a little preliminary attention before introduction into the tube; for these, it is convenient to have a ground-glass stoppered tube.   Other materials, however, may need special treatment to remove suspended matter, fluorescent impurities, and the like, for which direct distillation into the tube is required and perhaps sealing of the tube under nitrogen or other inert gas.   Hence every laboratory working extensively with the Raman effect uses many different sizes and kinds of tubes.

Special techniques are required if the substance is to be studied at temperatures or pressures markedly different from 20°C and 1 atmosphere.[6, 7]   When the substance cannot be examined in any other form than that of a crystalline powder, the technique described above is also inadequate.   Even though these different conditions of temperature, pressure, and state of aggregation are not uncommonly en-

---

[5] General Reference 18.7, page 448.

[6] See, for example, G. B. B. M. Sutherland *et al.*, *Proc. Roy. Soc.* (London), **176**, 484 (1940).

[7] W. V. Houston and C. M. Lewis, *Proc. Nat. Acad. Sci.*, **17**, 229 (1931).

Fig. 18.3. Excitation unit for the Raman effect. The blackened light horn on the Wood's tube may be seen at the top, and the glass cylinders containing filter solutions and refrigerant in the center. The base of the entire unit fits an optical bench, from which it can be removed and later replaced without disturbing the alignment.

countered, the techniques thus far developed to cope with them are not entirely adequate, and they add much difficulty to the study of the Raman effect. As it happens, they can sometimes be avoided by putting the substance into solution. Solutions may be studied readily by the Raman effect if they can be "cleaned up," that is, made optically clear, and if sufficient concentration (volume fraction of solute larger than 0.01) can be obtained in a suitable solvent. Fortunately, water is a good solvent because its Rayleigh and Raman scattering of radiation above 4000 A are very weak. The use of solution spectra is contingent upon some kind of assurance that action of the solvent on the solute may be disregarded; conversely, solution spectra may furnish information about the interaction of solute and solvent (§§ 11.13 and 14.2).

18.7. **Spectrographs for the Raman Effect.** A research worker who wishes to undertake the study of Raman spectra can adapt an existing spectrograph that may not have been designed specifically for Raman work; he can purchase a commercial spectrograph designed especially for Raman work; or he can construct his own instrument. The first of these three choices is the most desirable if he happens to work in a laboratory already equipped with a good prism instrument. The chief requirements are high speed, moderate resolving power, and fair dispersion. A camera lens of $f/10$ or faster is virtually essential, but lenses whose numerical apertures are faster than $f/4.5$ generally have focal lengths, and hence linear dispersions, which are inconveniently small. With the coarse-grained high-speed emulsions on which Raman spectra are most often photographed, a linear dispersion smaller than 0.03 mm to the angstrom results in a serious loss of resolving power. A single-prism instrument usually does not have sufficient dispersion, but multiplication of the number of prisms introduces light losses by reflection, absorption, and scattering that may seriously reduce the speed. Fortunately, the resolution demanded in Raman spectroscopy is ordinarily not high—a resolving power of 5000 at 4500 A is sufficient for most purposes—because of the large natural breadth of Raman lines.

Among the commercial glass-prism spectrographs which have been successfully used for Raman work but which were not specially designed therefor, are the Steinheil three-prism instrument, the Zeiss three-prism constant-deviation instrument shown in Fig. 3.8 (both of these have more than one camera, and can therefore be used at different dispersions), the Hilger E-494 single-prism medium glass spectrograph, and the Bausch & Lomb equivalent of this (Chapter 3).

The longer focal-length spectrographs are generally too slow. The Littrow mount is also considered disadvantageous for Raman work because of the relatively large amount of stray reflected light. For study of the Raman effect in the ultraviolet with Hg-2537 excitation, the Hilger medium quartz instrument (Model E-498 or any of its predecessors, such as E-315) is satisfactory.

Some of the instruments mentioned above are no longer manufactured, and even if they were, their purchase for the study of Raman spectra would be a questionable procedure in view of the availability of commercial spectrographs designed for Raman work. Among these latter may be mentioned the Hilger E-518 single-prism $f/4$ and E-612 two-prism $f/1.5$ instruments, and the Lane-Wells No. 40A three-prism spectrograph.* The latter uses a spherical mirror in the camera, the spherical aberration being corrected by a glass element of the Schmidt type. The effective aperture is $f/3$, a good compromise between speed and linear dispersion for the prism train which is used.

Until a few years ago, the use of grating spectrographs for the Raman effect was impractical because of the loss that accompanies the dispersion of the light into the various orders. With the development by Wood of the technique of ruling echelette gratings for short wavelengths, however, the use of the grating has become a decided advantage. A 15,000-line-per-inch grating that puts 75 per cent of the blue light incident upon it into a single first order is much more conservative of light than a prism train of the same aperture and comparable resolving power. At least a half dozen grating instruments have been used in the United States for Raman work, of which two will be described briefly.

Figure 18.4 shows the optical arrangement of a plane-grating Raman spectrograph at the Johns Hopkins University, designed and built by Lord and Miller.[8]† An off-axis parabolic mirror C (6 in.

---

* The Lane-Wells Company, 717 North Lake Avenue, Pasadena 19, Calif.

[8] R. C. Lord, Jr., and F. A. Miller, *Jour. Chem. Phys.*, **10**, 328 (1942).

† This instrument was described in the Ph.D. dissertation of F. A. Miller (April, 1941) and a published description of an instrument built with the help of this dissertation has been given by Stamm.[9] The reader may consult Stamm's paper for details of design, construction, and performance.

[9] R. F. Stamm, *Ind. Eng. Chem., Anal. ed.*, **17**, 318 (1945)

diameter, 4 in. off axis) is the collimator. Light enters at the slit S, is deflected through almost 90 deg by the mirror M astride the collimator axis A, and falls on the collimator. Since the slit is in effect at the focus of the collimator, light reflected from the collimator is rendered parallel and proceeds to the plane grating G. The rectangular ruled surface of G ($6\frac{1}{4} \times 4\frac{1}{4}$ in.) does not cover the entire grating blank, which means that the part of the grating blank near M has to protrude out over the axis A if the parallel beam from C is to cover the ruled surface. By means of the mirror M, the slit can be located at the point S instead of at the point A, and vignetting of the incoming beam by the grating blank can be avoided. The diffracted

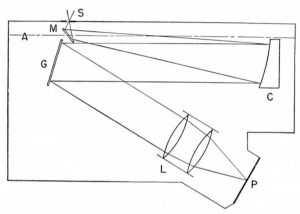

Fig. 18.4.   Optical arrangement of a plane-grating Raman spectrograph.

beam from the grating enters the camera lens L and is brought to a focus at the photographic plate P.* A Raman spectrum excited by Hg-5461 and photographed with a camera lens of 27 in. focal length, $f/5.4$, in 45 min, is shown in Fig. 18.5.

The advantageous features of such a spectrograph as compared with a prism instrument are its high resolving power and angular dispersion, coupled with high speed and freedom from stray light. The latter characteristic is especially good, because the only sources of stray light up to the first element of the camera lens are the three reflecting surfaces M, C and G, whereas the stray light associated with

---

* Lenses of the Petzval type designed especially for this instrument and having focal lengths of 18 and 27 in. can be purchased from the Perkin-Elmer Corporation, Glenbrook, Conn. With these lenses, respective dispersions of 0.027 and 0.040 mm to the angstrom are obtained

the various kinds of scattering from prisms may be considerable in a multiple-prism system. The use of the off-axis collimating mirror avoids such troubles as spherical and chromatic aberration. The reasons for the plane grating are two: a concave grating has a definite curvature, which fixes the focal length and hence the speed and dispersion of the instrument. Moreover, a special mounting of a concave grating is required to give a stigmatic spectrum, and with this mounting the spectrum cannot be scanned for photoelectric detection by simple rotation of the grating.

The adaptation of the instrument shown in Fig. 18.4 to photoelectric measurement of spectra (Chapter 12) can be accomplished in two ways. If scanning of the spectrum by motion of the exit slit and photomultiplier across the spectrum in the focal plane is desired, apparatus for the purpose can be installed in the place occupied by the plateholder. If one prefers to scan by rotation of the grating, the

Fig. 18.5.   Raman spectrum of cyclooctatetraene taken with a plane-grating spectrograph.   Scattering volume, 4 cc; excitation unit as in Fig. 18.3, photographed on Eastman 103B emulsion in 45 min.

spectrograph can be changed very readily to an autocollimating arrangement. The off-axis mirror acts both as collimating and as focusing mirror, and the mirror M is split horizontally so that one half can reflect the beam from the entrance slit to the collimator and the other half can receive the converging beam from the collimator and reflect it to the exit slit.

The adaptation of a Wadsworth-mounted concave-grating spectrograph to Raman work has been described by Rank and coworkers.[10] The concave grating used had a 15-ft radius and was so ruled as to concentrate 40 per cent of the incident blue light into one of the second orders. The Wadsworth mirror was 10 in. in aperture and worked at approximately $f/10$. The linear dispersion of this instrument was so large (about 0.25 mm to the angstrom) that very wide slits (0.6 mm) could be used without impairment of its usefulness for the Raman effect. In consequence, it was well suited for photo-

---

[10] D. H. Rank and R. V. Wiegand, *Jour. Opt. Soc. Am.*, **36**, 325 (1946), and earlier references there cited.

electric detection, for which purpose total light flux rather than flux incident on unit area is the desideratum.

Scanning of the spectrum with the Wadsworth mounting requires motion of the exit slit, no matter what scanning arrangement is used. In the Rank instrument, the spectrum was scanned by rotation of the grating. To compensate for the change in focal length with grating orientation, the exit slit was moved synchronously along a fixed line drawn from the center of the slit to the center of the grating. The detecting element, which had to be moved along with the exit slit, consisted of a photomultiplier tube (RCA 1P21) refrigerated by "dry ice." The output of the detector was amplified further and fed to a photographically recording galvanometer. A sample record obtained with this instrument is shown in Fig. 18.6.

18.8. Measurement of Intensity and Polarization of Raman Lines. Until the pioneer work of Rank[10] pointed the way to photoelectric determination of intensities in Raman spectra, the photographic method of intensity measurement had been universal. The usual difficulties of photographic photometry (Chapter 13) are accentuated in Raman work by the low intensity level, the high background associated with Rayleigh scattering of the continuum, and the wide range of breadth and sharpness among Raman lines. The fact that relatively coarse-grained emulsions such as Eastman types I and 103 (see Chapter 7) are used because of their speed adds to the difficulty.

As a result, the practice has been to avoid quantitative determination of intensities in Raman spectra whenever possible. A common method is to estimate by eye the photographic density of the various Raman lines, and to report these estimated values on some arbitrary approximate scale, such as one of 0 to 10. The inadequacy of such a procedure is apparent to anyone familiar with the vagaries of the eye and the photographic plate. It shows up strongly in the literature of the Raman effect, in which contradictory intensity results from different observers abound. In view of the greater usefulness of Raman spectra when quantitative intensity measurements are available, much wider application of photoelectric detection seems inevitable.

When reliable quantitative intensities are absolutely necessary, the procedures outlined in Chapters 12 and 13 are followed. One instance in which such data are essential is the quantitative chemical analysis of liquid mixtures, to which further attention is paid below. Another is the determination of the state of polarization of the individual Raman lines, which is a property of basic significance.   If a polarizing device such as a Nicol prism or a piece of Polaroid sheet is placed at the point R in the beam of scattered light in Fig. 18.2, the Raman lines observed spectroscopically are found to change in inten-

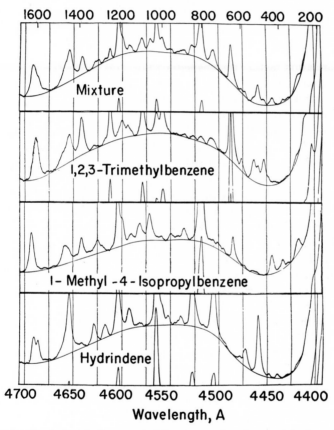

Fig. 18.6.   Photoelectrically recorded Raman spectra of several hydrocarbons.
(Courtesy Prof. D. H. Rank).

sity, not only with respect to the Rayleigh scattering but also with respect to each other.   In other words, the Raman lines are, to a greater or lesser extent, polarized.

The state of polarization of a Raman line is described in a precise fashion by its *depolarization factor*. This factor is the ratio of the intensities of the line measured when the polarizing device is oriented so that its polarizing direction is respectively in the plane of Fig. 18.2 and perpendicular to that plane but is in both instances perpendicular to R. These two intensities are conventionally* called $I_\perp$ and $I_{||}$, from which the definition of the depolarization factor, ρ, is

$$\rho = \frac{I_\perp}{I_{||}} \qquad (18.1)$$

When the incident radiation is natural, or unpolarized, light, the depolarization factor (then called ρ_n) takes on values from 0 to $\frac{1}{2}$ for Rayleigh scattering and from 0 to $\frac{6}{7}$ for Raman lines. However, Rayleigh scattering usually has ρ_n very close to zero, that is, strongly polarized, whereas no such generalization can be made concerning Raman lines. For the latter, the exact value of ρ_n is $\frac{6}{7}$ when the line originates from a nontotally symmetrical molecular vibration and is less than $\frac{6}{7}$ (frequently approaching zero) when the molecular vibration is totally symmetrical (compare § 11.5 and Fig. 11.3).

The fact that the polarization of a Raman line is related to the symmetry of the molecular vibration from which the line originates is of foremost importance in the interpretation of Raman spectra. In the elucidation of molecular structure from Raman and infrared spectra, the number of lines for which ρ_n equals $\frac{6}{7}$ and the number for which ρ_n is less than $\frac{6}{7}$ is the basis on which many possible structures may be eliminated from consideration, and is sometimes definitive for the correct structure. Unfortunately, the determination of depolarization factors is beset with experimental difficulties. Most of the trouble is associated with the fact that the incident radiation has to be sharply directional. This requirement essentially restricts the excitation unit to a maximum of two arcs, and in addition necessitates the use of baffles between the arcs and the scattering tube. The insertion of the Nicol prism or other analyzing device further reduces the intensity, so that exposure times are increased by a factor of 10 or more over those in which polarization measurements are not made. In many methods, the perpendicular and parallel components are photographed successively rather than simultaneously, which of

---

* The convention is based on the plane of the electric vector of the incident light rather than the plane of Fig. 18.2. Sometimes $I_\perp$ and $I_{||}$ are called I_S and I_P, or I_σ and I_π, respectively, from the first letters of *senkrecht* (German for "perpendicular") and "parallel."

course introduces another factor of 2.   Detailed discussion of the techniques and precautions used in polarization measurements by photographic means may be found in several places.[11, 12, 13]

The photoelectric measurement of depolarization factors offers great promise with respect both to speed and to accuracy.   The chief limitation is the noise level of the detecting and amplifying system, which sets the lower limit of detectability.   A consequence is that many weak lines cannot be detected at all under the special conditions of excitation required for polarization work.   However, the photoelectric method is still new, and further reduction of the noise level (for example, by refrigeration of the detector to still lower temperatures) may be possible.   The reader is referred to the papers of Rank and coworkers[10, 14] for the details of the photoelectric measurement of depolarization factors.

18.9. Applications of the Raman Effect.   It has been mentioned earlier that the Raman effect arises from molecular vibration and rotation.   Conversely, the interpretation of Raman spectra leads to information about the vibrational and rotational energy levels of molecules.   Since we saw in Chapters 11 and 17 that infrared absorption spectra also arise from the vibrational and rotational energy levels, we note that *infrared spectra and Raman spectra give the same kind of molecular information.*   However, because the techniques of the two differ greatly, it is sometimes advantageous to use the one rather than the other in attacking a particular problem.   The choice is essentially one based on the convenience or applicability of the techniques, however, and not on the type of information to be obtained.   Some of the factors on which one may base the decision as to whether infrared or Raman spectra, or both, should be used to solve a given problem are the following:

1. *Equipment.*   If a laboratory is already equipped with an infrared spectrometer, clearly infrared spectroscopy will be the selected technique so far as the equipment factor is concerned, and conversely if Raman equipment is available.   If neither is available but an adaptable spectrograph is at hand (see § 18.2), it is relatively easy to set up Raman equipment.   In the event that new equipment must

[11] J. Cabannes and A. Rousset, *Ann. de Physique* (10) **19**, 229 (1933); *Ann. Chim. Physique*, **19**, 229 (1933).

[12] A. W. Reitz, *Zeitschr. f. physik. Chemie*, **B33**, 368 (1936).

[13] A. Langseth, J. U. Sørensen, and J. R. Nielsen, *Jour. Chem. Phys.*, **2**, 402 (1934).

[14] M. R. Fenske, D. H. Rank, *et al.*, *Ind. Eng. Chem.. Anal. ed.*, **19**, 700 (1947).

be purchased or constructed, the decision as to which kind to purchase or construct will be based on other factors.

2. *State of aggregation of material to be studied.* Since infrared spectra of gases are much easier to obtain than Raman spectra of gases, the former technique is strongly to be preferred for such tasks as quantitative chemical analysis in the vapor state. Liquids are about equally well studied in both, whereas the spectra of most solids are not readily obtained in either, with the preference in favor of the infrared. It should be mentioned that one kind of molecule, the symmetric diatomic molecule like H_2 or N_2, does not absorb infrared radiation. The Raman spectra of several such gases have been studied for various purposes, as for the determination of the ratio of orthohydrogen to parahydrogen in mixtures of the two, but the technique is not easy.

3. *Solutions.* Because the intensity of Raman scattering by a solute is approximately proportional to its volume per cent, the Raman effect of dilute solutions is hard to obtain (compare § 18.1). Study of the infrared absorption of a solute in dilute solution, on the other hand, is scarcely more difficult than that of a pure liquid, provided solvents are available whose own infrared absorption does not obscure the spectrum of the solute. One advantage of the Raman effect is that water is a good solvent to use because of its very simple and very weak spectrum. Water is black to the infrared and is virtually out of the question as a solvent in which to study infrared absorption.

4. *Colored substances.* Any material that absorbs visible radiation of longer wavelength than 5000 A even weakly is a poor prospect for the Raman effect, whereas color is of no hindrance to the infrared spectroscopist. Furthermore, substances which are decomposed or otherwise altered chemically by the action of light, which fluoresce, or which cannot be prepared in an optically transparent form had better be studied in the infrared. Sometimes the fluorescence of a material can be suppressed sufficiently to enable study of the Raman effect by the addition of a quenching agent such as nitrobenzene or iodide ion, but the spectra then obtained are usually of inferior quality.

5. *Wavelength range.* Most infrared spectrometers are limited by their rock-salt optics to wavelengths below 15 μ, that is, to wave numbers above about 700 cm^{-1}. Many molecules, however, especially large ones and those with heavy atoms, exhibit a goodly fraction of their fundamental vibrations in the range 50 to 700 cm^{-1} (15 to

200 μ). Since the Raman effect is regularly photographed over the range 0 to 4000 cm^{-1}, the wavelength limitation does not apply. To be sure, the width of the Rayleigh line sets a lower limit to the detectable frequency, but this limit can be pushed to very low values by complementary filters, if necessary.

6. *Overtones.* A well-established experimental rule exists that the intensity of overtones and combination tones relative to that of fundamentals in the Raman effect is very small (0.01 or less), whereas in the infrared the ratio is more nearly 0.1. This difference gives the Raman effect a great advantage for many purposes. It simplifies the Raman spectrum and makes possible an easy differentiation between overtones and fundamentals. It sometimes permits a ready analytical discrimination between two substances in a mixture where infrared methods fail because the overtones of one substance coincide with fundamentals of the other.

18.10. Determination of Molecular Structure. The combined use of infrared and Raman vibrational spectra for the determination of the geometrical configuration of molecules was discussed briefly in § 17.7. Because the selection rules often permit the appearance of certain vibrational frequencies in the infrared spectrum alone or in the Raman spectrum alone and sometimes even require the two spectra to be mutually exclusive, it is necessary to have both kinds of spectra to make a thorough structural determination.

As was indicated in §§ 11.5 and 17.7, the selection rules for the Raman effect as well as for the infrared are a consequence of the symmetry of molecular vibrations. For the Raman effect, this relationship arises from the fact that the refractivity of a molecule usually changes, even though the change is very slight, when the molecule vibrates. The molecular refractivity is directly connected with the molecular polarizability, that is, with the ability of the molecule to be polarized under the action of an electric field such as the alternating field of a light wave. Because a polarized molecule is one in which the center of negative electrical charge has been displaced with respect to the center of positive charge by the electric field, the binding of the electrons to the positively charged atomic nuclei in the molecule is the factor that determines the polarizability. Consequently, when the binding changes as a result of a change in the positions of the nuclei relative to one another, the polarizability may be expected to change.

An examination of the influence of molecular vibration on the polarizability shows that often the symmetry of a vibration prevents any change in polarizability arising from that vibration. For example, if the atoms move during a vibration so that their displacements are antisymmetric to a center of symmetry, the polarizability change produced by each atom is annulled by the antisymmetric displacement of the atom across the symmetry center from it, and the net effect on the polarizability is zero. Such vibrations therefore do not give rise to Raman lines. On the other hand, if the atoms move so as to preserve all the symmetry inherent in the geometrical form of the molecule at rest (a totally symmetrical vibration: § 11.5), the vibration affects the polarizability and the vibration appears in the Raman effect with relatively high intensity and low depolarization factor. Any vibration in which the atoms move with less than the total symmetry of the molecule but still produce a change in the polarizability gives rise to a Raman line, usually of medium or low intensity and with a depolarization factor of $\frac{6}{7}$.

The procedure given first in § 17.7 for the determination of molecular structure from infrared and Raman spectra is here repeated:

1. Observe both spectra.

2. Assume a molecular model and predict the selection rules for both spectra; if possible, estimate the approximate spectral positions of the frequencies.

3. Compare the observed spectra with the predictions of the model.

4. Accept or reject the model.

This procedure sometimes cannot be applied in strictly logical fashion because of practical difficulties such as indecision between two models with similar selection rules or the failure of certain frequencies to appear in one spectrum or the other despite the assent of selection rules. Often in such cases, as has been mentioned earlier, the difficulty may be resolved with the help of isotopic derivatives.

The vast majority of studies of molecular structure by means of the Raman effect have not followed the process outlined above because the symmetry of most molecules is too small and the number of vibrational degrees of freedom is too large. When little symmetry is present, the selection rules are lax, and it is unlikely that a definite conclusion can be drawn about the geometrical form of the molecule. Nonetheless it is often possible to reach conclusions of value to the chemist by methods of analogy. The procedures are similar to those followed in the application of infrared spectra to the same kind of problems.

As we saw in Chapter 11, the vibrational frequencies in the spectrum of a polyatomic molecule can be divided roughly into those characteristic of the molecule as a whole and those characteristic of small groups of atoms within the molecule (compare Table 11.2). Since these latter frequencies appear in the spectrum of any compound containing the groups, they serve as a means for ascertaining the presence of a particular group in a molecule. The nature of the information on which such structural conclusions are based is the same for the Raman effect as for infrared absorption, namely, vibrational frequencies and intensities. Therefore the methods of drawing conclusions are the same as those already discussed in § 17.7. We shall be content to cite several simple examples of the use of Raman spectra in qualitative structural studies, referring the reader to the general references on the Raman effect for further details and for specific references to the voluminous literature on this kind of investigation.

1. *Orientation of groups in the benzene ring.* The Raman spectra of benzene derivatives have been extensively studied, especially by Kohlrausch and his school.[15] They have demonstrated that the spectra of *ortho-*, *meta-*, and *para-* substituted derivatives have characteristic differences which enable one to discriminate between the positions of substitution. For example, all *meta*-substituted benzenes have an intense, strongly polarized line at 995 cm^{-1}, which is not present in *ortho* and *para* compounds. The latter two can be distinguished by the richer spectrum of the *ortho* and by a line in the neighborhood of 625 cm^{-1} in the *para*, which is usually absent from the *ortho* derivatives. These characteristics can be used to determine from the Raman spectrum the position of substitution in a benzene derivative whose structure is unknown.

2. *Cis-trans isomerism.* Many isomers of the *trans* structure have either a genuine center of symmetry or a sufficient approximation thereto to make effective the selection rule that excludes from the Raman effect all vibrations antisymmetric to the center. This rule does not apply to *cis* isomers, which do not have a center of symmetry. One can therefore determine which of a pair of isomers is the *cis* and which the *trans* because of the smaller number of strong

[15] K. W. F. Kohlrausch, General Reference 18.6, page 354.

Raman lines in the latter. If both Raman and infrared spectra are available, the question can be answered more positively. In the infrared spectrum of the *trans* isomer, absorption bands corresponding to strong Raman lines should be weak or missing. In the Raman spectrum, the frequencies of strong infrared bands should be observed weakly, if at all, as in the spectrum of *trans*-butene-2.[16] This procedure is not applicable to those cases of *cis-trans* isomerism in which the *trans* isomer departs markedly from the centrosymmetric, and it is sometimes difficult to apply when the objective is to determine whether a substance is of the *cis* or *trans* form, rather than to determine which of two isomers is one and which the other. It has been remarked by Rank, Fenske *et al.*,[14] however, that the double-bond frequency in the region about 1660 cm^{-1} is some 20 cm^{-1} higher in the *trans* form for many hydrocarbons.

3. *Structure of substances in aqueous solution.* The chemist has long been interested in the question of structure of the compounds formed when such gases as CO_2, SO_2, and NH_3 are dissolved in water. The Raman effect has given a semiquantitative answer to the question for these three molecules: the vibrational Raman spectra of the dissolved substances are essentially the same as those of the pure gases;* in other words, so far as one can determine with Raman spectra, the process of solution has resulted in little change in the molecular structure, and in particular has not produced spectroscopically detectable amounts of H_2CO_3, H_2SO_3 or NH_4OH. A rather surprising by-product of the study of aqueous NH_3 is spectroscopic evidence for free rotation of the ammonia molecule in the solution. Langseth[17] has found that the rotational fine structure of one of the vibrational Raman lines of aqueous ammonia indicates the same set of rotational energy levels as those possessed by the rotating gas molecule.

18.11. Qualitative and Quantitative Chemical Analysis. The use of the Raman effect for qualitative chemical analysis rests on exactly the same principles as the use of infrared absorption for the

[16] H. Gershinowitz and E. B. Wilson, Jr., *Jour. Chem. Phys.*, **6**, 247 (1938).

* For SO_2 the Raman spectrum of the vapor is less complete than that of the pure liquid, with which it agrees so far as it goes. The spectrum of aqueous SO_2 agrees closely with that of pure liquid SO_2. The Raman spectrum of NH_3 changes somewhat on passing from gas to liquid, the change consisting of frequency shifts of the sort usually associated with hydrogen bonding. The frequency differences between pure liquid NH_3 and aqueous NH_3 are negligible.

[17] A. Langseth, *Zeitschr. f. Physik*, **77**, 60 (1932).

same purpose (§ 17.5). Accordingly, the selection of the one technique or the other for qualitative analysis depends on other considerations than basic principles. These considerations have been summarized in § 18.9, where the two techniques are compared.

The basis for the use of Raman spectra in quantitative analysis, on the other hand, differs from that for infrared absorption spectra. The fundamental assumption for the latter use is the validity, under the special conditions of the analysis, of Beer's law (§ 17.5). The analytical use of Raman spectra, on the other hand, depends on the assumption that the intensity of Raman scattering by one component in a fixed volume of a mixture is linearly proportional to the number of molecules of that component present. This is a very simple relationship, but there are good theoretical as well as experimental reasons for believing it to be an accurate one in many mixtures.* Thus the complete quantitative analysis of a mixture in principle can be carried out directly by the measurement of the intensity of one Raman line for each component, once the intensities of these lines in the pure components have been determined under the standard conditions of the analysis.

Actually, the use of Raman spectra for quantitative analysis is more complicated than is implied in this discussion, but the complications are those of practice rather than principle. One must first of all be on the alert for possible reaction between the components of a mixture that results in the disappearance of molecules of the original components and the appearance of new molecules. The qualitative analysis of the mixture by means of its Raman spectrum is the best indication of this kind of change insofar as its effect on the quantitative analysis is concerned. If the Raman spectrum of a mixture is a superposition of the spectra of the components, the indication is that no reaction of significance for quantitative analysis has occurred. This conclusion can be checked by quantitative spectroscopic study of solutions whose compositions are fixed in advance.

Another complication encountered in practice is fluctuation in the intensity of the light source. This unpredictable source of variation in the intensity of the scattered light can be compensated by the inclusion of a fixed amount of an *internal standard* in the mixture. The

---

* To be sure, quantitative analysis by means of empirical working curves (compare § 17.6) can be carried out even if Raman intensities do not bear a linear relationship to the number of molecules. This procedure may be complicated for mixtures of several components.

intensities of the lines of the components are then measured with respect to some line of the standard, these relative values being unaffected by external changes in illumination.   Carbon tetrachloride, a relatively unreactive substance having a strong, simple Raman spectrum, is frequently used for this purpose.   The internal standard, of course, serves to eliminate other external variables, such as the size of the scattering tube, filter densities, and the like, but these are generally easy to control anyway, the use of the internal standard being a great convenience rather than an absolute necessity.

In view of the rather straightforward nature of quantitative analysis by Raman spectra, it might be asked why the method is not used more often.   The answer lies partly in the limitations of the Raman effect itself as outlined in § 18.9, such as the necessity for an optically clear, nonfluorescent, almost colorless liquid scatterer of considerable volume, and partly in the nuisance of accurate measurement of light intensity from the blackening of a photographic emulsion.   To photograph the Raman spectrum to the required density, to process the plate, to measure the densities of lines for both standard and unknown, and to convert these densities to percentage composition usually takes several hours.   This time often compares unfavorably with that required for other methods of analysis, particularly infrared methods.

It is apparent, however, that whenever these two kinds of objections can be eliminated—the one by the nature of the substance to be studied, the other by the elimination of the photographic process in favor of photoelectric intensity measurement—the Raman effect offers great possibilities for rapid, easy, and accurate analysis of mixtures that are troublesome with any other method.   As an example of what one may expect in this direction, the reader is referred to the papers of Rank and his associates on the photoelectric Raman analysis of hydrocarbon mixtures.[14]   An excellent résumé of quantitative analytical procedures that use the photographic process is given in an article by Stamm.[9]

GENERAL REFERENCES

18.1.   S. Bhagavantam, *The Scattering of Light and the Raman Effect*.   Andhra University, Waltair, India, 1940.
18.2.   G. Glockler, "The Raman Effect," *Rev. Mod. Phys.*, **15**, 111 (1943).
18.3.   G. Herzberg, *Infrared and Raman Spectra*.   New York: D. Van Nostrand Company, Inc., 1945.

18.4. J. H. Hibben, *The Raman Effect and Its Chemical Applications.* New York: Reinhold Publishing Corp., 1939.

18.5. K. W. F. Kohlrausch, *Der Smekal-Raman-effekt.* Berlin: Julius Springer, 1931; also *Ergänzungsband* to above. Berlin: 1938.

18.6. K. W. F. Kohlrausch, *Ramanspektren.* Leipzig: Akademische Verlag. (Reprinted by Edwards Brothers, Ann Arbor, Mich., 1943.)

18.7. R. W. Wood, *Physical Optics.* New York: The Macmillan Company, 1934.

CHAPTER 19

Spectroscopy of the Vacuum Ultraviolet

THE REGION OF THE SPECTRUM having wavelengths shorter than 2000 A is frequently called the *vacuum ultraviolet* because the high absorption of most gases in this region makes it essential to work with spectroscopic equipment that has been evacuated or has been filled with a transparent gas such as hydrogen or helium.

The earliest vacuum spectrograph was made by Schumann,[1] who employed a fluorite dispersing system and photographic emulsions that he made as free as possible from gelatin, to extend the limit of the spectrum from about 1850 to 1200 A.   He was not able to measure wavelengths.   The use of a concave-grating vacuum spectrograph by Lyman[2] permitted determination of wavelengths in the range that had been photographed by Schumann, a range now referred to as the *Schumann region*.   Lyman also extended the short-wave limit of spectrography to about 500 A (see General Reference 19.1).   The development of the hot spark (§ 8.22) enabled Millikan[3] to extend the short-wavelength limit of observations to below 200 A.   More recently, the use of gratings at grazing incidence in combination with sources of high excitation energy has resulted in closing the gap between the short-wave ultraviolet and long-wave X-ray regions (General References 19.2 and 19.3).   Using such techniques, Edlén[4] has observed radiation as short as 4 A, though at wavelengths below 10 A, X-ray methods become superior.

Vacuum-ultraviolet spectroscopy has been particularly useful in the study of atomic emission spectra corresponding to high excitation energies, as for example in singly and multiply ionized atoms.   Spectra in this region have also been useful in elucidating astrophysical

---

[1] V. Schumann, *Akad. Wiss. Wien*, 102, 2A, 625 (1893).

[2] T. Lyman, *Astrophys. Jour.*, 5, 349 (1906).

[3] R. A. Millikan, *Proc. Nat. Acad. Sci.*, 7, 289 (1921).

[4] B. Edlén, personal communication.

problems such as those of the gaseous nebulae, in investigations of molecular spectra corresponding to high excitation energies, in investigations of the solid state, and to a more limited extent in the study of certain organic compounds of biochemical interest.

SPECTROGRAPHS FOR THE VACUUM ULTRAVIOLET

19.1. **General Considerations.** Spectrographs for the vacuum-ultraviolet region must be designed to reduce to a minimum the absorbing effects of atmospheric constituents. This reduction may be accomplished by enclosing the spectrograph in a vacuum-tight case, so that the air can be exhausted therefrom, or by filling the case with a gas having comparatively low absorption. The former method is used almost exclusively.

Of atmospheric constituents, oxygen produces the most troublesome absorption. Absorption bands of O_2 begin near 1950 A, converging to a limit near 1760 A, beyond which there is a continuum.[5-7] The region from about 1300 to 1100 A is comparatively transparent. A second continuum extends from 1100 A to 300 A or less. The maximum of absorption is at 1450 A, where a path length of 0.0014 cm of O_2 at normal temperature and pressure is sufficient to reduce the intensity of radiation by one-half. Thus, in order to obtain transmission of one-half the incident radiation in this region through a path length of 4 meters, it is necessary to reduce the partial pressure of oxygen in a vacuum spectrograph to about 0.001 mm Hg. In practice, the partial pressure is usually reduced to values ranging between 10^{-4} and 10^{-5} mm.

Nitrogen absorption bands begin at about 1450 A and extend to 990 A, beyond which there is a continuum.[8] The relative transparency of nitrogen to wavelengths longer than 1450 A has made possible its use in fluorite spectrographs in lieu of a vacuum. Contamination of the nitrogen with oxygen or water vapor may cause difficulties, however.

Water vapor exhibits two absorption continua starting at 1780 A and 1340 A, with a series of bands superposed.[9, 10]

The rare gases helium, neon, argon, krypton, and xenon have com-

[5] S. W. Leifson, *Astrophys. Jour.*, **63**, 73 (1926).

[6] J. Curry and G. Herzberg, *Ann. d. Physik*, **19**, 800 (1934).

[7] R. Ladenberg, Voorhis, and J. C. Boyce, *Phys. Rev.*, **40**, 1018 (1932).

[8] R. Birge and J. Hopfield, *Astrophys. Jour.*, **68**, 257 (1928).

[9] G. Rathenau, *Zeitschr. f. Physik*, **87**, 32 (1933).

[10] J. J. Hopfield, *Phys. Rev.*, **53**, 931 (1938).

paratively little absorption except at relatively short wavelengths and are present in such small quantities in the air as to be unimportant in contributing to the absorption of the residual atmosphere left in spectrographs (see General References 19.2 and 19.3). Argon exhibits absorption from 1066 to 800 A, with a continuum beyond, and neon absorbs from 743 to 575 A with a continuum beyond that point. Hydrogen has negligible absorption to about 1200 A, and this gas and helium have been used to wash out and fill vacuum spectrographs. Hydrogen must be used with care because of the danger of explosion. Preliminary washing with nitrogen will greatly reduce the hazard of explosion in the spectrograph proper.

Three principal types of dispersing systems are used in vacuum spectrographs: (1) prism systems, (2) concave gratings illuminated at normal incidence, and (3) concave gratings illuminated at grazing incidence. Prism instruments are limited to the range of the Schumann region, extending to about 1200 A, because of the lack of suitable material for prisms and lenses with appreciable transmission beyond this point. Concave gratings illuminated at grazing incidence are used for the range from 2000 A to the shortest wavelengths observed.

Vacuum spectroscopes are usually designed for photographing the spectrum, although other types of radiation detectors have been used (§ 19.8). Light sources must be operated in a vacuum or in an atmosphere comparatively free from oxygen or other absorbing gases. If the light source is separate from the spectrograph and a window is interposed between the source chamber and the spectrograph housing, the absorbing characteristics of suitable window material limit the working range to 1000 A or above. For shorter wavelengths, it is essential that no window material be interposed in the light path except for thin organic films that have been found transparent at very short wavelengths.

19.2. Prism Spectrographs. The absorption of quartz is so great at wavelengths shorter than about 1850 A as to make it unusable as a prism or lens material for vacuum ultraviolet spectroscopy. The only materials suitable for lenses and prisms in this region are natural fluorite (CaF_2) and synthetic crystals of calcium fluoride or lithium fluoride. All these crystals are isotropic. The absorption of natural crystalline fluorite increases rapidly below about 1250 A.[11, 12] Syn-

---

[11] E. C. Schneider, *Phys. Rev.*, **45**, 152.

[12] W. M. Powell, Jr., *Phys. Rev.* **45**, 154 (fluorite); **46**, 43 (quartz) (1934).

thetic lithium fluoride has somewhat better transmission,[13] being usable in some cases to about 1100 A, and the transmission of synthetic calcium fluoride extends almost as far. Of these two synthetic crystalline materials, both grown in large crystals by Stockbarger, calcium fluoride is somewhat harder and may be optically worked more easily. The short-wavelength absorption of synthetic lithium fluoride increases if it is exposed to short-wave ultraviolet radiation

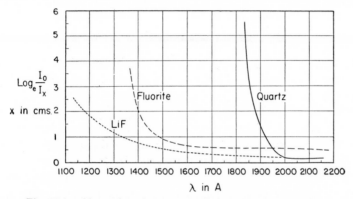

Fig. 19.1. Absorption of quartz, fluorite, and lithium fluoride.
(From data in Gen. Ref. 19.2)

of high intensity or if it is bombarded with gaseous ions.[14] This phenomenon is somewhat analogous to the "solarization" of quartz upon exposure to ultraviolet radiation. As in the case of solarized quartz, heating tends to restore the original transmission.

The working of the optical components of prism systems requires great precision in the grinding and polishing of the surfaces because of the short wavelengths involved. Thus at 1450 A the precision must be approximately four times as great as that required at the wavelength of the sodium D lines in the visible spectrum, for equal freedom from lens aberrations and other image defects.

The absorption of quartz, fluorite, and lithium fluoride is shown in Fig. 19.1, and the dispersion of fluorite and lithium fluoride in Fig. 19.2.

Prism instruments are chiefly useful for such investigations in the Schumann region as do not require the highest dispersion. It is pos-

---

[13] E. G. Schneider, *Phys. Rev.*, **49**, 341 (1936).
[14] E. G. Schneider, *Jour. Opt. Soc. Am.*, **27**, 72 (1937).

sible to design prism instruments that are comparatively compact and hence easily pumped out. They serve adequately for exploratory work down to about 1250 A and for the study of simple ⌐mission and absorption spectra.

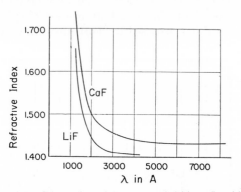

Fig. 19.2.   Dispersion of fluorite and lithium fluoride. (From data in Gen. Ref. 19.2.)

Many types of prism instruments have been designed. The spectrograph of Cario and Schmidt-Ott,[15] shown in Fig. 19.3, is typical. A 60-deg fluorite prism is used with fluorite collimating and telescope lenses of 0.8 cm aperture and 10 cm average focal length. The focal

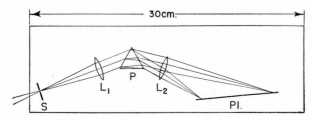

Fig. 19.3.   Diagram of small vacuum spectrograph of Cario and Schmidt-Ott.[15] S, slit; L_1, fluorite collimator lens; P, fluorite prism; L_2, fluorite telescope lens; Pl, plate.

length changes markedly as a function of wavelength, which necessitates tilting the plate at an acute angle to the optic axis of the telescope lens. Two somewhat similar designs of spectrographs by

---

[15] Cario and Schmidt-Ott, *Zeitschr. f. Physik*, **69**, 719 (1931).

McLennan[16] are shown in Figs. 19.4 and 19.5. Fluorite-prism vacuum spectrographs of the Littrow type have also been used. Some prism instruments of comparatively large size and high resolving power have been built, but it is more customary to employ concave-grating instruments when high resolution is desired. Because of the

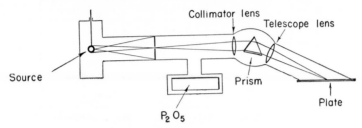

Fig. 19.4. Small fluorite spectrograph designed by McLennan.[16]

high dispersion at short wavelengths and the large angle of plate tilt used in prism spectrographs, comparatively large linear dispersion is, of course, obtained. For example, the plate factor of the Cario and Schmidt-Ott instrument is about 6 A/mm at 1400 A.

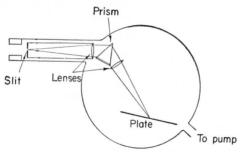

Fig. 19.5. Alternative design of small fluorite spectrograph by McLennan.[16]

19.3. Normal-Incidence Grating Spectrographs. When used at normal incidence, the reflecting power of grating surfaces is important in determining the range in the vacuum ultraviolet which may be covered successfully. The reflecting powers of various metals and other substances near 1000 A are shown in Table 19.1 [17, 18] and curves

[16] J. C. McLennan, D. S. Ainslie, and D. S. Fuller, *Proc. Roy. Soc.* (London), **95B**, 316 (1919); J. C. McLennan, A. C. Lewis, *Proc. Roy. Soc.* (London), **98B**, 109 (1920).
[17] A. H. Pfund, *Jour. Opt. Soc. Am.*, **12**, 467 (1926).
[18] P. R. Gleason, *Proc. Nat. Acad. Sci.*, **15**, 551 (1929).

of reflection coefficients are given in Fig. 19.6.[19] At wavelengths longer than about 1000 A, aluminum is the best reflector, whereas below that wavelength platinum is superior to aluminum but not quite so good as quartz. For the Schumann region, aluminum is the

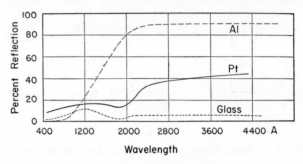

Fig. 19.6.   Reflection of aluminum, platinum, and glass at normal incidence as a function of wavelength.   From data of G. B. Sabine.[19]

surface of choice. Speculum-metal gratings have been used at wavelengths as short as 200 A but are not so employed in instruments of recent design. The reflection of glass compares favorably with that

TABLE 19.1

REFLECTING POWER OF SUBSTANCES IN THE ULTRAVIOLET
NEAR 1000 A FOR NORMAL INCIDENCE

(Data from General References 19.1 and 19.3, based on articles by
A. H. Pfund and P. R. Gleason)

Substance	Coefficient, %
Silver	5.1
Speculum metal	5.2
Gold	6.3
Selenium	6.5
Tellurium	7.2
Platinum	8.0
Glass	8.5
Quartz	13.5

of aluminum or other metals below 1000 A. Gratings ruled on glass, without subsequent coating by metallic films, are often used in this region. Glass has the particular advantage of not tarnishing and of being cleaned easily if it becomes coated with surface films. Usually

---

[19] G. B. Sabine, *Phys. Rev.*, **55**, 1064 (1939).

a grating for this region is lightly ruled on speculum metal or glass and an aluminum surface is then evaporated on this. If a grating is lightly ruled, with reflecting areas between the grooves, the transmission factor of the spectrograph is somewhat improved.[20]

Normal-incidence gratings for the vacuum ultraviolet are usually ruled with 15,000 or 30,000 lines to the inch. The rulings are usually very similar to those used for the longer-wave ultraviolet and visible regions of the spectrum.

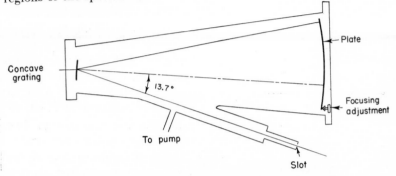

Fig. 19.7. Normal-incidence vacuum grating spectrograph. Designed by K. T. Compton and J. C. Boyce.[21]

A normal-incidence grating spectrograph designed by Compton and Boyce[21] is shown in Fig. 19.7. The spectral range from the direct image of the slit to 2500 A is covered on a 24-in. photographic plate. The shortest wavelengths that have been photographed with this instrument are about 300 A. The grating is of 2-meter radius and is ruled on glass, with 30,000 lines to the inch. The plate factor is about 4 A/mm at the normal. Hilger has manufactured a normal-incidence vacuum spectrograph based on a design by Sawyer[22] which is typical of many instruments. The grating is of 1-meter radius, ruled 15,000 lines to the inch. The plate factor is about 16.6 A/mm, the entire spectral range up to about 3000 A being photographed on one plate. A 6-meter grating instrument of similar design has been constructed at the Massachusetts Institute of Technology.[23] This spectrograph was arranged so that plates could be removed and replaced without destroying the vacuum in the instrument.

[20] R. A. Millikan, I. S. Bowen, and R. A. Sawyer, *Astrophys. Jour.*, **53**, 150 (1921).
[21] K. T. Compton and J. C. Boyce, *Rev. Sci. Inst.*, **5**, 218 (1934).
[22] R. A. Sawyer, *Jour. Opt. Soc. Am.*, **15**, 303 (1927).
[23] G. R. Harrison, *Rev. Sci. Inst.*, **4**, 651 (1933).

19.4. Grazing-Incidence Grating Spectrographs. The shortest wavelengths that have been photographed with normal-incidence grating spectrographs lie at about 200 A,[24] the limit being set by the low reflectivity of grating surfaces for shorter wavelengths, as discussed in § 19.3. Hoag[25] first demonstrated that shorter wavelengths could be photographed by using high angles of incidence. As the angle of incidence becomes large, the reflection coefficients of many materials become quite high, even in the extreme ultraviolet range. Gratings ruled on glass are entirely satisfactory for use in this way.

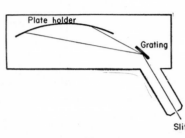

Fig. 19.8. Schematic diagram of grazing-incidence vacuum grating spectrograph.

An investigation by Edlén[26] showed that the shortest wavelengths that could be photographed with a particular grating were 320, 160, 75, and 53 A for angles of incidence of 0, 60, 80, and 85.6 deg, respectively, other conditions being comparable. Angles of incidence near 90 deg are used to reach the shortest wavelengths.[26-29]

A typical grazing-incidence spectrograph is illustrated in Fig. 19.8. Siegbahn[29] has constructed such instruments for use with X rays, and similar spectrographs have been used by Edlén[30] and others for ultraviolet spectrography. The gratings used vary in radius from 1 to 5 meters and are usually ruled with about 15,000 lines to the inch. The linear dispersion at grazing incidence is considerably greater than at normal incidence and varies rapidly with wavelength. Thus at 80-deg incidence a 1-meter grating ruled 14,500 lines to the inch has plate factors of 6.5 A/mm and 2.5 A/mm at 1000 A and 100 A, respectively. The same grating at normal incidence has a plate factor of 16.6 A/mm. Grazing-incidence spectrographs with gratings of 21-ft radius have been constructed by Kruger.[31]

The resolving power of a grating at grazing incidence is considerably

[24] R. A. Millikan and R. A. Sawyer, *Science*, **50**, 138 (1919).

[25] J. B. Hoag, *Astrophys. Jour.*, **66**, 225 (1927).

[26] B. Edlén, *Nova Acta Reg. Soc. Sci. Ups.*, IV, **9**, No. 6 (1934).

[27] F. Tyren, *Zeitschr. f. Physik*, **111**, 314 (1938).

[28] A. Ericson and B. Edlén, *Zeitschr. f. Physik*, **59**, 656 (1930).

[29] Siegbahn and Magnusson, *Zeitschr. f. Physik*, **95**, 133 (1935).

[30] B. Edlén, *Zeitschr. f. Physik*, **100**, 621 (1936).

[31] P. G. Kruger, *Rev. Sci. Inst.*, **4**, 128.

different from that at normal incidence. The effects of large incidence angles on aberrations and resolving power have been investigated by several workers.[32-35] The adjustment of grazing-incidence instruments is also somewhat more complicated than is that of normal-incidence instruments.[36]

Over the range in which both grazing-incidence and normal-incidence grating spectrographs are useful, the choice between the two types depends upon the application. If the greatest precision in wavelength determinations is desired, the more nearly normal dispersion and greater freedom from aberrations in the normal-incidence type may be of advantage. If, however, the weakest lines are to be observed, the greater reflecting power at grazing incidence may favor the use of an instrument of the grazing-incidence type.

19.5. Housings and Vacuum Equipment. Housings should be so constructed that all seals and joints are easily accessible for inspection and for the repair of leaks. It is desirable that the volume of the housing be kept small in order that the system may be evacuated in minimum time. However, sufficient room should be provided for ease of adjustment and replacement of optical components.

Some instruments are built with external controls by means of which adjustments may be made from the outside while the instrument is evacuated. Air locks are also sometimes provided whereby plates may be changed or the slit may be inspected and the light source replaced without breaking the vacuum in the entire instrument.[23] Such features make for ease and rapidity of manipulation.

If a vacuum spark is used without interposition of a protecting window between it and the slit (as must be done for work below the transmission of suitable window materials), considerable sputtering of the slit jaws may occur. The slit must then be cleaned frequently. Stellite jaws stand up somewhat better under such circumstances than do steel jaws.

Diffusion pumps backed by mechanical pumps are most convenient to use for evacuating the chambers of vacuum spectrographs. The pumps should be of adequate capacity to reduce the pressure to the desired working range within a reasonable time. A pumping time of

[32] J. Mack, J. Stehn, and B. Edlén, *Jour. Opt. Soc. Am.*, **22**, 245 (1932).
[33] I. S. Bowen, *Jour. Opt. Soc. Am.*, **23**, 313 (1933).
[34] Anderson and J. Mack, *Jour. Opt. Soc. Am.*, **24**, 292 (1934).
[35] J. Mack and J. Stehn, *Jour. Opt. Soc. Am.*, **23**, 184 (1933).
[36] Rathenau and Perlkamp, *Physica*, **2**, 125 (1935).

1 hr or less is usually considered reasonable. Vacuum gauges should be provided both to check the operation of the diffusion pump and to check the pressure in the spectrograph chamber. A simple discharge tube serves as an excellent working gauge.

ACCESSORY APPARATUS

19.6. Light Sources. For wavelengths shorter than 500 A, sparks are the most useful sources. The so-called "hot spark" in vacuum is the source most frequently used in this range. At somewhat longer wavelengths, either vacuum sparks or discharge tubes in helium may be used. Various other sources are satisfactory in the Schumann region, including (a) sparks, (b) vacuum arcs, (c) hydrogen discharge tubes, (d) hollow-cathode discharges, and (e) the vacuum furnace. In the range above which nitrogen transmits radiation (about 1400 A), this gas may be used instead of a vacuum surrounding a spark or arc discharge.

The foregoing sources and their characteristics are described in Chapter 8.

19.7. Photographic Materials. Ordinary photographic plates are not usable in the vacuum ultraviolet region without special treatment because of the high absorption of gelatin in this region. The absorption of gelatin begins to rise at about 2200 A and becomes extremely marked before the limit of transmission of quartz is reached at 1850 A.

Schumann[1] prepared plates satisfactory for photography of the region to 1200 A (General Reference 19.1). He tried various methods of preparing plates, including the coating of pure silver bromide on glass and the coating of the surface of thin gelatin films with silver bromide. In his final process, the one still used today in the manufacture of Schumann plates, an emulsion is formed in which the proportion of silver bromide to gelatin is quite high. After sensitization by heating, this emulsion is dried and washed with water. The emulsion is then dissolved in water to a high dilution, flowed onto the glass plates, and allowed to settle. After the suspension has settled, the extra fluid is poured off and the remaining emulsion is dried. Schumann plates are, if properly prepared, responsive to the shortest wavelengths which can be photographed. The emulsions are apt to be somewhat nonuniform, however, and Schumann plates are therefore not well adapted to photographic photometry.

Plates prepared for the photography of positive rays have a high proportion of silver bromide to gelatin (although not so high as in Schumann plates) and have been used in ultraviolet spectroscopy (General Reference 19.3).   Such plates are manufactured in England by Ilford, Ltd., and in the United States by the Eastman Kodak Company.   A method of sensitizing ordinary plates to the vacuum ultraviolet region was developed by Duclaux and Jeantet,[37] in which most of the gelatin is eaten away from the emulsion by sulphuric acid, leaving a surface layer in which silver bromide is highly concentrated. They also tried other methods of digesting away the gelatin, including enzyme digestion, but none of these were as successful. The plates produced by sulphuric acid digestion have high sensitivity, but the emulsion is quite fragile, and this method of processing plates has not been used extensively.

Duclaux and Jeantet[37] also sensitized plates by coating them with thin layers of oil that absorbed energy in the vacuum ultraviolet range and converted it into fluorescent radiation in the near ultraviolet and visible region. Lyman used such plates for vacuum ultraviolet spectroscopy to 500 A (General Reference 19.1).   Many types of machine oils and other mineral oils are satisfactory for this purpose.[38] Since the fluorescent radiation that results in exposure of the emulsion is comparatively constant in spectral quality for different regions of excitation, plates treated in this manner show comparatively uniform spectral response throughout the range in which the oil absorbs.[39] The oil must, of course, be washed off with a suitable solvent after exposure prior to development.

It is somewhat difficult to coat plates with oil uniformly in the laboratory, and some variation from plate to plate is to be expected. Eastman spectroscopic plates are available coated with an organic fluorescent material that is washed off with ethylene chloride after exposure and prior to development.   These plates show somewhat greater uniformity than oiled emulsions, but even they are subject to a certain amount of variation.   Eastman ultraviolet-sensitized plates may be obtained in emulsions of various speed, contrast, and grain size.

No coated plates appear to have as high resolving power as the best

[37] Duclaux and Jeantet, *J. de Phys. et Rad.*, **2**, 154 (1921).
[38] G. R. Harrison, *J. Opt. Soc. Am. and Rev. Sci. Inst.*, **11**, 113, 341 (1925).
[39] G. R. Harrison and P. A. Leighton, *J. Opt. Soc. Am.*, **20**, 313 (1930); **38**, 899 (1931).

Schumann plates, but their resolution is sufficient for most applications (General Reference 19.3).

19.8. Nonphotographic Radiation Detectors. Photoelectric detection has been used in vacuum ultraviolet spectroscopy to a limited extent.[40, 41] Platinum makes a satisfactory photoemissive surface. If traces of gas are present, the photoelectric threshold of platinum is at about 3000 A, but if the cell is thoroughly outgassed, the threshold is shifted to about 1960 A. Such cells have the advantage for some applications of being sensitive only to the vacuum ultraviolet region.

Thermoluminescent detection based on a method developed by Hoffmann[42] has been used by Lyman.[43] Copper film is coated with a mixture of calcium sulphate and a small amount of manganese sulphate deposited from a water solution. The dried plates are heated to redness for a few minutes. Following such treatment, exposure of the plates to radiation longer than 1300 A causes them to store energy that is released as visible luminescence if the plates are subsequently heated to about 180°. For a permanent record, the luminescence may be photographed.

Photochemical processes may be used for measuring the total radiant energy in the vacuum ultraviolet region. The formation of ozone from molecular oxygen, for which the quantum yield is 2, has been used for this purpose (General References 19.2 and 19.3). If oxygen is passed through an absorption cell exposed to radiation of the wavelength at which the intensity is to be measured, the amount of ozone formed in a given time may be determined chemically, and the total radiant energy involved in the reaction may be determined from the ozone yield.

19.9. Accessories for Absorption Measurements. Absorption spectrophotometric measurements of organic materials in the vacuum ultraviolet region have been made with the use of a Spekker photometer (Chapter 14) equipped with fluorite optics. Direct methods of photographic photometry have been more generally employed.

Absorption cells for gases or liquids for use in this region must, of course, be fitted with end plates of fluorite, lithium fluoride, or calcium fluoride. The absorption of the end plates then limits the working range to the Schumann region. The absorption of gases may

---

[40] W. M. Powell, Jr., *Phys. Rev.*, **45**, 154; **46**, 43 (1934).

[41] W. M. Preston, *Phys. Rev.* **57**, 887 (1940).

[42] M. W. Hoffmann, *Wied. Ann.*, **60**, 269 (1897).

[43] T. Lyman, *Phys. Rev.*, **48**, 149 (1935).

also be measured by introducing the gas into the spectrograph itself. The pressure may be adjusted to give absorption of the desired magnitude for the path length involved.

The absorption of solid materials has been investigated by coating them in thin layers on thin films of celluloid or collodion. With proper precautions as to the thickness of film, this method may be used throughout the Schumann region (General Reference 19.3).

APPLICATIONS

19.10. Atomic Spectra. By far the greatest number of investigations in the vacuum ultraviolet region has been concerned with atomic spectra. This work is reviewed in the references listed at the end of this chapter.

Atomic spectra have been studied both in emission and absorption. For many atoms, the second and higher spectra (corresponding to singly and multiply ionized atoms) occur principally in this region of the spectrum. Vacuum ultraviolet spectroscopy has therefore permitted the study of energy transitions not accessible in any other region. The tenth and higher spectra (representing ninefold and higher states of ionization) have been observed for many of the elements, and for copper the nineteenth spectrum (corresponding to eighteenfold ionization) has been photographed. Atomic absorption lines corresponding to transitions from completed shells have been observed in the vacuum ultraviolet, particularly by Beutler (General References 19.2 and 19.3). These correspond to X-ray spectra, except that the multiplicities are more easily observable and therefore represent an interesting transition from optical to X-ray spectra.

19.11. Wavelength Standards. The earliest wavelength standards in the Schumann region were those of the emission lines in the molecular spectrum of hydrogen. Schumann photographed the emission lines of molecular hydrogen with a fluorite prism spectrograph to about 1270 A. Lyman, however, was the first to measure the wavelengths of these lines. Using a concave grating at normal incidence, he measured the wavelengths of a large number of lines (General Reference 19.1). By comparing his plates with Schumann's maps, Lyman determined by interpolation the wavelengths of all the rest of the hydrogen emission lines that had been observed up to that time. His table of lines served as the standard of wavelengths for the vacuum ultraviolet for many years.

More recently,[44, 45] computed wavelengths of the spectrum lines of neutral atomic hydrogen and of singly ionized atomic helium have been used as wavelength standards in the vacuum ultraviolet. Wavelengths so computed from formulas for spectral series (§ 9.8 and Chapter 10) have a high degree of accuracy. Especially for helium, these computed wavelengths extend into regions much shorter than those in which accurate wavelength determinations can be made by normal-incidence grating spectrographs.

One method that has been used extensively for standardizing the wavelengths of emission lines of various elements in the region from 2000 to 160 A is to determine the wavelengths of these lines by comparison of their higher-order spectra with the first-order spectrum of the iron lines in the visible and ultraviolet (General References 19.2 and 19.3). Difficulties are encountered in this method because of the differences in the positions or profiles of lines in different orders, or of lines arising from illumination of the grating in slightly different aspects by two different sources, the so-called "errors of coincidence." The second difficulty is overcome by exciting the lines of the comparison substance in the source used to excite lines of the substance under investigation, the two spectra being photographed simultaneously. The first difficulty may be overcome by application of the combination principle (Chapter 10 and General Reference 19.3). Successive applications of the combination principle permit the extension of standard determinations to very short wavelengths.

Interferometric methods have been used for the precise determination of wavelength standards in the vacuum ultraviolet,[46] but only to a limited extent (Chapter 20).

19.12. Molecular Spectra. Molecular spectra have been studied in the vacuum ultraviolet both in emission and absorption. The spectra of many polyatomic molecules and diatomic molecules or molecular ions have been investigated. The literature has been reviewed by Sponer.[47]

In general, the vibrational structure, but not the rotational structure, is resolvable in such spectra, though even the vibra-

---

[44] F. Paschen, *Preuss. Akad. Wiss. Berlin Ber.*, page 662.

[45] W. G. Penney, *Phil. Mag.*, **9**, 661 (1930).

[46] D. L. MacAdam, *Phys. Rev.*, **50**, 185 (1936).

[47] H. Sponer, *Molekülspektren und ihre Anwendung auf chemische Probleme.* Berlin: Julius Springer, 1936.

tional structure is sometimes so complicated as to appear continuous, Whether or not spectra will be observed in a particular region of the vacuum ultraviolet for a particular molecule depends on the magnitude of the energy changes involved in transitions between possible electronic energy states. Particularly in molecules in which a closed outer shell is formed in the unexcited state, the transition to the first excited state is quite high and may give rise to bands in the vacuum ultraviolet region. However, all molecules without exception absorb somewhere in the vacuum ultraviolet.

Many organic compounds of biochemical interest have their principal absorption in this region. Some endeavor has been made to investigate such spectra, particularly from the purely empirical point of view, but the field has not been studied extensively.

19.13. Miscellaneous Applications. Electronic transitions in solids are of special interest from the standpoint of the theory of the solid state. Soft X-ray spectra have been used for studying such transitions, but except for some of the technical difficulties involved, there are advantages in the use of the vacuum ultraviolet region from about 300 to 100 A. Data so obtained are useful in theoretical explanations of the transmission and absorption bands of dielectrics, and of the phenomena of photoconductivity, phosphorescence, and fluorescence.

Observations of emission spectra in the vacuum ultraviolet have been useful in astrophysical studies in explaining unusual types of spectra observed in nebulae and stars. Emission spectra of nebulae associated with hot stars are assumed to arise from excitation by ultraviolet of very short wavelengths coming from the stars. By observing the intensities of the Balmer emission lines of hydrogen, the total intensities of the ultraviolet continua of such stars beyond 912 A have been estimated. From such estimates, it has been inferred that the blackbody surface temperatures of these stars reach values as high as 100,000°K. Vacuum ultraviolet studies have also helped to explain the energy transitions giving rise to many of the lines in the spectra of stars and nebulae.

The photochemical and photobiological effects of ultraviolet radiation in the Schumann region are quite marked. Several photochemical reactions have been studied in this region. The bactericidal effects of Schumann radiation have also been investigated, as well as the lethal effects of such radiation on other types of cells.

These miscellaneous applications of vacuum ultraviolet spectroscopy are discussed in greater detail in General Reference 19.3, which gives considerable additional bibliographical material.

GENERAL REFERENCES

19.1. T. Lyman, *Spectroscopy of the Extreme Ultraviolet.* New York: Longmans, Green & Co., Inc., 1928.

19.2. H. Bomke, *Vacuumspektroskopie.* Leipzig: J. A. Barth, 1937.

19.3. J. C. Boyce, "Spectroscopy in the Vacuum Ultraviolet," *Rev. Mod. Phys.*, **13**, 1 (1941).

CHAPTER 20

Interferometric Spectroscopy

Two specialized types of spectroscopic problems require instruments having resolving powers greater than those provided by ordinary spectroscopes. In the first, of which hyperfine and isotope-structure studies involving the atomic nucleus are typical, it is desired to separate very close and narrow lines that at medium resolution

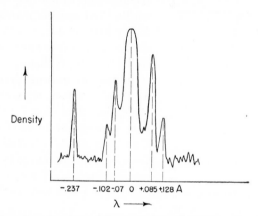

Fig. 20.1. Hyperfine structure of the green line Hg-5461A, after R. W. Wood.

appear as single lines. In the second, it is desired to measure wavelengths as precisely as possible; and the narrower and more highly resolved a line, the more closely can the position of its intensity maximum be determined.

A densitometer tracing of the hyperfine structure of the green mercury line 5461 A, as photographed in the sixth order of a 15,000-line-per-inch plane grating by R. W. Wood[1] is shown in Fig. 20.1. Though this line appears sharp and single in ordinary

[1] R. W. Wood, *Phil. Mag.*, 8, 205 (1929).

spectroscopes, it is seen actually to consist of a large number of components, whose origins have been elucidated by Schüler and Schmidt.[2] This multiplicity of lines arises from the fact that each isotope of mercury, of which a number exist in nature, emits light of a slightly different frequency, while in addition the odd-numbered isotopes emit lines corresponding to this transition which show hyperfine structure.

The complex structure shown in Fig. 20.1 can be observed only in light from a cooled mercury arc run under low current. In an ordinary arc the lines are so broadened that they merge into a single line. Thus when the ultimate in resolution is required, special attention must be given both to the source emitting the light to be resolved and to the spectroscope resolving it into lines.

Four principal types of instruments are available to give resolving powers in excess of 200,000. These are the large diffraction grating having more than 10 cm of ruled width, the Lummer-Gehrcke plate, the Fabry-Perot etalon, and the Michelson echelon as put into more practical and useful form by Williams. All of these, including the grating, may be classed as interferometers, since they produce their high resolution by the interference of from 20 to 200,000 beams of light into which retardations ranging from 500,000 wavelengths down to 1 are introduced. These various high-resolution spectroscopes are compared in § 20.3 and are described individually in later sections.

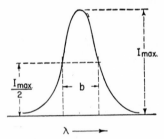

Fig. 20.2. Typical line shape illustrating half breadth, b.

20.1. Line Broadening and Its Causes. No spectrum line is truly monochromatic but consists of a distribution of intensity as a function of wavelength similar to that shown in Fig. 20.2. A so-called "sharp" line emitted by an electric arc in the visible spectrum is usually at least 0.03 A wide. Since the actual breadth of a line is somewhat indeterminate, it is conventional to use the half-intensity breadth b, the breadth at the intensity level which is half that at the maximum. From the Rayleigh criterion (§ 2.2 and 6.2) it follows that two lines of equal intensity and similar shape will be resolved when separated by approximately 1.2 times their half-intensity breadth.

[2] H. Schüler and Th. Schmidt, *Zeitschr. f. Phys.*, **98**, 239 (1935).

In an actual spectrogram the observed shape of a line indicates the variation of its density with wavelength. The true intensity distribution may be found by using one of the photometric methods discussed in Chapter 13. This distribution is influenced by the resolving power of the spectroscope used, which may conveniently be expressed in terms of "apparatus half breadth," by the thickness of the emitting layer and the degree of absorption by atoms or ions in that layer, by such physical conditions of the emitting system as pressure and temperature, and by the structure of the atom itself.

The natural half breadth of a spectrum line, that is, the minimum half-intensity breadth obtainable under any conditions, depends on the internal structure of the atom from which it is emitted; it ranges from about 0.0001 A for most lines to much larger values in special cases. Usually this natural half breadth is negligible compared with the broadening introduced by external factors. The magnetic moment of the nucleus produces a hyperfine structure or splitting of the line into a number of components, and mixtures of isotopes similarly produce multiple lines, but these contribute to line broadening only when other factors cause the components to merge into a single pattern.

The temperature motion of an emitting atom or molecule gives rise to Doppler broadening (§ 10.7) because of the random variations of velocity possessed by the emitters in the line of sight. Since this type of broadening varies directly as the square root of the absolute temperature and inversely as the square root of the mass of the emitting particle, it can be reduced greatly by using lines emitted by heavy atoms and by exciting them at low temperatures or in an atomic beam. The Doppler broadening of a line emitted by a hydrogen atom at 3000°K may amount to several tenths of an angstrom.

Pressure broadening, which results from collisions of the emitting atom with more or less inert surrounding atoms, is likely to be not more than 0.001 A per centimeter of pressure for the lower members of a spectral series. Since the stationary states that involve the outer reaches of the atom are more seriously affected by collisions than those farther in, the higher members of a series show greater pressure broadening, coupled with shifts in wavelength arising from this cause.

Resonance broadening results when an atom is immersed in a dense cloud of atoms of its own kind with which strong interactions take place, forming temporary quasi molecules. In lower members of a series resonance may broaden a line by angstroms or even hundreds of angstroms; this effect accounts for the great breadths sometimes observed even at moderate pressures in the sodium D lines and in the equivalent lines of ionized calcium.

Small magnetic fields originating within and outside the atom give rise to an incipient splitting of spectrum lines caused by the Zeeman effect and thus influence broadening. Electric fields similarly produce Stark-effect broadening. Therefore high current densities, great ion densities, and strong electric and magnetic fields must be avoided if narrow lines are to be produced.

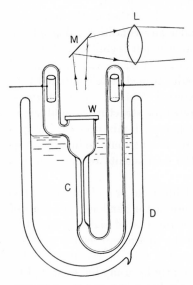

Fig. 20.3. Geissler tube immersed in liquid air for cooling. D, Dewar vessel; C, capillary for discharge; W, window; M, front-surface mirror; C, condensing lens.

Finally, the narrowest lines are produced by the thinnest emitting layers of luminous material. As the light passes through the emitting medium the shape of each line gradually changes, the center being built up less rapidly than the outer edges due to self-absorption, and the line gradually becomes wider and flatter.[3]

Tolansky[4] has given an extensive discussion of the causes of line broadening and of the production of narrow lines from special sources.

20.2. Line Sources for High-Resolution Spectroscopy. The above discussion indicates that to obtain the sharpest lines it is desirable to select lines of low natural breadth emitted by heavy atoms of single isotopic elements having zero nuclear moment, and to excite these with low current densities, at low temperatures and pressures, in thin emitting layers. Almost all of these conditions lead in the direction of reducing intensity, and to arrive at a useful light source it is necessary to compromise some of the above factors in favor

[3] See J. C. Slater, *Phys. Rev.*, **25**, 783 (1925).
[4] S. Tolansky, General Reference 20.4, pages 19–85.

of others. The 5461 A line of mercury isotope 198 is a suitable line[5] when emitted under carefully controlled conditions.

A Geissler discharge, in a permanent gas as distinguished from a vapor such as mercury, can be cooled with liquid air or other liquids to very low temperatures. Krypton tubes can in this way be made to give extremely sharp lines whose wavelengths can be measured to 1 part in 50 million. A typical arrangement for cooling a Geissler discharge is shown in Fig. 20.3.

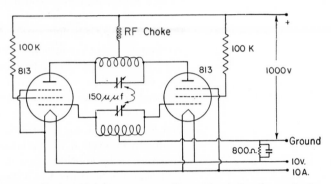

Fig. 20.4. Typical high-frequency oscillator circuit for the excitation of the electrodeless discharge. The oscillator frequency will be roughly 10 mega-cycles/sec when the inductances consist of about 10 turns each of about $2\frac{1}{2}''$ in diameter.

The electrodeless discharge[6] can be made to emit very narrow lines, since it can be operated at extremely low pressures, and thin luminous sheets can be excited. Since external electrodes can be used, the making of suitable discharge tubes, preferably of fused silica, is simple, and contamination of contents is reduced. A low pressure of inert gas such as argon may be included to initiate the discharge, and a heavy metal can then be excited as its vapor pressure builds up. The gas pressure for maximum light intensity is usually rather critical. A typical oscillator circuit for high-frequency electrodeless excitation is shown in Fig. 20.4.

The hollow-cathode discharge of Paschen already described in

[5] J. H. Wiens, *Phys. Rev.*, **70**, 910 (1946); W. F. Meggers, *Jour. Opt. Soc. Am.*, **38**, 7 (1948).

[6] L. Dunoyer, *Comptes Rend.*, **152**, 592 (1911); L. and E. Bloch, *Zeeman Verhandelingen* (1935), page 19; S. Tolansky and S. A. Trivedi, *Proc. Roy. Soc.* (London) **A175**, 336 (1940).

§§ 8.19 and 15.7 has been modified by Schüler[7] to permit cooling and production of extremely narrow lines. A convenient form of this tube is shown in Fig. 20.5.

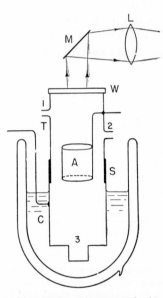

Fig. 20.5. Diagram of the Schüler cooled hollow-cathode discharge tube. The cathode *C* is of metal such as brass or iron, and the tube *T* is of glass. The glass-to-metal seal *S* must either withstand refrigeration or else be kept warm enough, by separate heating, to maintain a vacuum-tight joint. A gas such as argon is circulated (entrance at 1, exit at 2) and the discharge occurs mainly in the crevice at 3. *A*, anode; *D*, Dewar vessel; *W*, window; *M*, front surface mirror; *L*, condensing lens.

When the ultimate in line sharpness is required, the atomic beam source should be used. This source, developed by Bogros[8] and by Dobrezov and Terenin[9] (see also General Reference 20.6), almost completely eliminates the Doppler broadening by ensuring that the emitting atoms have no velocity component along the direction of viewing. As shown in Fig. 20.6, the material whose atoms are to emit light is vaporized in a small furnace, and atoms are ejected through two narrow slits so that a beam of atoms is formed. This beam can be excited by radiation, by electrons, or by another beam, to emit light that can be studied in a direction at right angles to the motion of the atoms. Various workers have in this way produced spectrum lines so narrow that resolving powers of several million were required to reduce the apparatus half breadth below the natural half breadth of the lines. Atomic beam sources are relatively faint, however, and this difficult technique is to be used only when extremely narrow lines are needed.

20.3. Selection of a Spectroscope of High Resolving Power. When lines must be resolved which lie closer than 0.1 cm⁻¹ apart, that is,

lines that in the mid-range of the spectrum are separated by less than 0.025 A, it is necessary to use a spectroscope of high resolution.

[7] H. Schüler, *Zeitschr. f. Physik*, **35**, 323 (1926); *ibid.*, **59**, 149 (1930).

[8] A. Bogros, *Comptes Rend.*, **183**, 124 (1926) and *Ann. d. Physique*, **17**, 199 (1932).

[9] L. Dobrezov and A. Terenin, *Naturwiss.*, **16**, 656 (1928).

Resolving power, discussed in Chapter 2, was defined as $P_r = \lambda/d\lambda$. P_r for ordinary spectroscopes was found to range from 5000 to 200,000; in the present chapter we are concerned with values of P_r lying between 200,000 and 5,000,000 or more. A concept which is sometimes more convenient to use than resolving power is the "limit of resolution" $d\sigma$,* which expresses the wave number difference of the two closest lines of equal intensity that can just be resolved. Since $\lambda\sigma = 10^{-8}$,

$$d\sigma = \frac{\sigma d\lambda}{\lambda} = \frac{\sigma}{P_r} \qquad (20.1)$$

where σ is the wave number, and the other symbols are as used throughout this book. Thus at 5000 A (20,000 cm^{-1}) an instrument

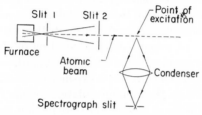

Fig. 20.6.   Schematic diagram of an atomic beam source.

having a resolving power of 500,000 has a limit of resolution of 0.040 cm^{-1}. The resolving power of an instrument is likely to vary with wavelength, whereas the limit of resolution, which is a quantity of more fundamental interest, in certain instruments remains essentially constant over an extended wavelength range.

Several grating spectrographs have been constructed having measured resolving powers greater than 200,000, the upper limit thus reached lying between 400,000 and 600,000. When a good grating is available, it is probably most convenient when resolution in this range is desired, since it suffers less from overlapping orders than the other high-resolution spectroscopes, has a more extensive free spectral range (the wavelength interval covered by one order without being overlapped by the previous and succeeding orders), has more nearly linear dispersion, and is probably less wasteful of light. The limitations of the grating at high resolution are discussed in § 20.4.

If a grating cannot be used, a Fabry-Perot etalon is frequently found next best. In fact, this type of interferometric spectroscope

---

* Tolanksy's "resolving limit"; see General Reference 20.4, page 87.

(§ 20.6) is so superior to other types for most purposes that it seems probable that it will ultimately supersede them for all but a few special purposes. The etalon is cheapest, most readily available, most flexible, and freest from gho st lines, and can be made to give the highest resolution of all interferometers. Like the Lummer-Gehrcke plate and the echelon, its free spectral range is small, so for all but the narrowest patterns it must be crossed with a spectroscope of low resolution. Because the dispersion of the etalon varies rapidly, more involved calculations are required to reduce wavelengths determined with it than with other interferometers except the Lummer plate, but this difficulty has been considerably reduced by recent computational devices.

The Lummer-Gehrcke plate (§ 20.5) is almost outdated. Though only slightly more expensive than the etalon, it is much less flexible. For a long time its greatest advantage was its theoretically higher light efficiency, but recent improvements in coating of etalon plates have brought the two very close together in this regard.

The reflection echelon (§ 20.13) is expensive and difficult to produce and is as inflexible as the Lummer plate. It has the advantage of giving wavelengths by a simple linear reduction process, and theoretically it can be used throughout the spectrum, like the diffraction grating. Actually, its use in the vacuum region, where of high-resolution interferometers it alone appears usable, has been delayed in practical realization by the difficulty of producing plates thin enough to give sufficiently low orders at short wavelengths to avoid difficulties due to overlapping of orders. Its use is recommended only when a Fabry-Perot etalon will not serve or when it is needed to check wavelengths obtained with the etalon, in which somewhat tedious phase-shift corrections enter. The echelon produces disappointingly small-scale spectra unless lenses of very long focal lengths are used with it.

Extreme resolution can be obtained by using two Fabry-Perot etalons in series, as demonstrated by Houston,[10] or by using the Gehrcke-Lau[11] multiplex interference spectroscope, a pair of flat parallel-sided plates coated on both sides, so that each is an etalon in quartz or glass rather than in air. These complex interferometers have not attained wide use, probably because a simple Fabry-Perot etalon, when properly constructed and crossed with a simple spec-

---

[10] W. V. Houston, *Phys. Rev.*, **29**, 478 (1927).

[11] E. Gehrcke and E. Lau, *Zeitschr. f. tech. Phys.*, **8**, 157 (1927); *Phys. Zeitschr.*, **31**, 973 (1930); E. Lau and E. Ritter, *Zeitschr. f. Physik*, **76**, 190 (1932).

troscope, gives all the resolution and free spectral range needed for the narrowest spectrum lines yet produced. Meissner[12] has used etalons up to 20 cm separation, giving orders of interference up to 800,000 and theoretical resolving powers of more than 25,000,000.

20.4. Limitations of Diffraction Gratings at High Resolutions. The diffraction grating, though not an amplitude-splitting interferometer, with its rulings (up to 180,000 or more) produces from a single beam 180,000 or more diffracted beams that are caused to interfere. Except in the case of echelette gratings, only the orders from the first to the sixth are ordinarily used. Michelson ruled 9.3 in. of mirror surface with approximately 10,000 lines per inch, and obtained in the sixth order of this grating resolving powers of about 600,000, the highest yet claimed for a diffraction grating. Such resolution is ordinarily obtained only when a grating is used to produce

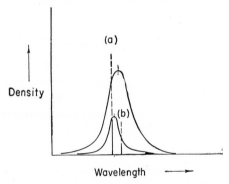

Fig. 20.7.   Shift in center of gravity of a spectrum line as its density increases, due to two components (a) and (b) or a principal line and a satellite.

faint pictures of strong lines, false lines from errors of ruling in the grating then being relatively weakened by the shape of the characteristic curve of the photographic emulsion.

The satellite lines discussed in § 5.3 cause changes in the center of gravity of a spectrum line produced by a grating as the density of the line increases, as shown in Fig. 20.7, and this shift appears to set the limit to precision found in measuring wavelengths with gratings, as discussed in § 9.12. Gratings that may be useful for resolution of hyperfine structure often prove valueless for determining wavelengths to a precision greater than 0.005 A when lines of different intensities

---

[12] K. W. Meissner, *Jour. Opt. Soc. Am.*, **31**, 405 (1941); *ibid.*, **32**, 185 (1942).

must be simultaneously photographed. Under these circumstances it is found convenient to use an etalon or other interferometer, despite the necessity of separating overlapping orders by the use of crossed dispersions.

An ideal interferometric spectroscope would be one having characteristics intermediate between the diffraction grating and the other three interferometric devices discussed in this chapter. Instead of using a large number of beams and a low order of interference, as in the grating, or a small number of beams and a high order number, as in the other interferometers, it would achieve a resolving power of, say, one million, by producing a thousand beams that interfered in approximately the one-thousandth order. Such a device would have intermediate characteristics of spectral range and dispersion that would make it extremely valuable. It should preferably be produced,

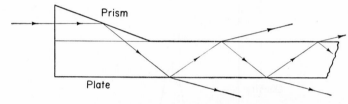

Fig. 20.8.   Ray paths in the Lummer-Gehrcke plate interferometer.   The prism is in optical contact with the plate.

not by poorly controllable methods like the engraving of rulings on a grating but by controlled optical methods of the sort used in producing plate interferometers.

The operation of the interferometers discussed in the following sections will be more clear if the reader is familiar with discussions of the production of interference patterns of various types, as given in General References 20.3 and 20.4.

20.5.   The Lummer-Gehrcke Plate.   For many years the single-plate interferometer introduced by Lummer[13] in 1901 and put into more practical form by Lummer and Gehrcke[14] in 1903 was the most commonly used type of interferometric spectroscope when high resolution was required.   Though still favored by a small number of workers with long experience in its use, it has yielded almost completely to the more flexible Fabry-Perot etalon for all but a few types of in-

---

[13] O. Lummer, *Verh. Deutsch. Phys. Ges.*, **3**, 85 (1901).

[14] O. Lummer and E. Gehrcke, *Ann. d. Physik*, **10**, 457 (1903).

vestigation.   It offers somewhat higher resolution for a given separation of orders than the etalon, but it must be readjusted in angle of
illumination for each new spectral region covered, so that its use is
restricted to hyperfine structure or other studies requiring high resolution over a restricted spectral range.

The operation of the plate interferometer is shown in Fig. 20.8.
Light entering the prism P is alternately reflected at an angle near
the critical angle of internal total reflection from the two parallel
surfaces of the plate, which is of glass or quartz.   Twenty to thirty
parallel beams are thus produced on each side of the plate, and if this
light is focused with a lens, sets of fringes are formed on either side.
The thinner the plate, the greater the range covered between orders;
and the longer the plate, the greater the number of beams produced,
and hence the higher the resolving power.   In practice, plates up to

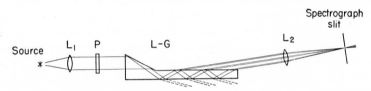

Fig. 20.9.   Optical arrangement in the external mounting of the Lummer-
Gehrcke plate $(L\text{-}G)$.   When the plate is of crystalline quartz, a polarizer P is
required to eliminate the effect of double refraction unless the plate itself is made
to serve this purpose.

20 cm in length are made, but it has not been found practicable to
make them thinner than 3.4 mm.

The plate is illuminated with parallel light and may be placed in
the beam between the collimator and prism of a spectroscope, so that
the dispersions will be crossed, as described by Schrammen.[15]   Alternatively, the plate may be externally mounted as in Fig. 20.9.
The latter method is generally preferred, since light scattered by dust,
surface scratches, and internal imperfections does not affect the
result; support and temperature control of the plate can be more
readily carried out; and focal properties of the plate itself, because of
flexure or nonparallelism of the two sides of the plate, can readily be
compensated for by proper focusing of the lens.   This should be an
achromat or similar lens of good quality.

---

[15] A. Schrammen, *Ann. d. Physik*, **83**, 1161 (1927).

The Lummer-Gehrcke plate requires the highest optical workmanship of any interferometer, since its surfaces must be worked, according to Tolansky,[16] to $\frac{1}{80}$ of a wavelength. Since the light beams may pass through as much as 30 cm of glass or quartz, this material must be of the highest homogeneity and uniformity. Glass plates can be used in the visible only and may be considered as almost outdated. Crystalline quartz plates have the advantage of suitability for use over the entire quartz range from 3 μ to 2000 A; and by using the extraordinary ray, very high reflection coefficients are available with internal total reflection throughout the spectrum. The instrument is thus theoretically more efficient in the use of light than is the Fabry-Perot etalon, in which much light is lost by absorption in the metallic reflecting films. This advantage has been diminished in recent years by the improved films developed for coating etalon plates (§ 20.8) and seems likely to decrease even further in the future.

It has been emphasized by Tolansky[16] that the Lummer-Gehrcke plate is not a Fabry-Perot etalon used at grazing incidence, because the dispersion of the glass or quartz used plays an important part in the resolution obtained. The dispersion obtained depends on the angle of incidence and the optical constants of the plate material, and not on the dimensions of the plate. The thinner the plate, however, the greater the order separation.

The Lummer-Gehrcke plate is particularly sensitive to temperature fluctuations and to mechanical flexure. It must be held to a temperature variation of not more than 0.05°C if a displacement or broadening of more than $\frac{1}{100}$ order is to be avoided. Unless the plate is carefully made and controlled, ghost images will appear. Owing to the fixed form of the plate it is necessary to use two or more Lummer plates of different thicknesses to unravel overlapping orders where broad patterns are being studied. All in all, the Lummer-Gehrcke interferometer offers little that cannot be obtained more cheaply and easily with a Fabry-Perot etalon having reflection coatings of fairly high efficiency. The reduction of fringes is no less complicated than with the latter instrument. The reader is referred to General Reference 20.4 for the details of pattern reduction.

20.6. The Fabry-Perot Etalon. This most widely used type of interference spectroscope was developed by Fabry and Perot[17] in 1897. It consists of two parallel partially reflecting plane surfaces,

[16] S. Tolansky, General Reference 20.4.
[17] Ch. Fabry and A. Perot, *Ann. de Chim. et de Phys.*, **12**, 459 (1897).

arranged as in Fig. 20.10 to split a beam of light into a large number
of beams of diminishing intensity, which are then caused to interfere.

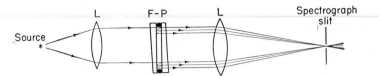

Fig. 20.10.   Schematic diagram of the Fabry-Perot etalon.

The interferometer may, but need not, be illuminated with parallel
light, and the fringes, being fringes of equal inclination of rays, are
produced at infinity.   By means of a lens, which should be of high
quality, they can be focused on the slit of a spectroscope with which
the dispersion of the etalon is to be crossed.   The fringes formed are
circular as in Fig. 20.11, and the slit is placed across a diameter.

The fundamental equation of the etalon[18] in air or vacuum can be
expressed in the form

$$m = m_0 + \epsilon = \frac{2t}{\lambda} + \frac{2tD^2}{8\lambda f^2} \qquad (20.2)$$

where m is the order of interference
at the center of the ring system, t is
the thickness of the etalon spacer,
D is the diameter of a ring or interference maximum corresponding to
wavelength λ, and f is the focal
length of the lens used to project the
fringes; m_0 is the integral order of
interference at the position of the
first maximum measured by D_0, the
diameter of the first ring, and ϵ is
the partial order of interference between this and the center.   The
highest order is at the center, and

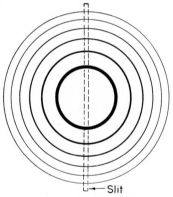

Fig. 20.11.   Image of the circular
fringes from a Fabry-Perot etalon.
This image is projected on the slit
of the spectrograph so that the slit
lies on a diameter of the circular
fringes.

succeeding rings are each of one order less than their preceding
neighbor.   The closer together the two etalon plates, the broader
and more widely separated will the fringes be.

[18] See K. W. Meissner, *Jour. Opt. Soc. Am.*, **31**, 405 (1941).

The resolving power of an etalon depends in a complex manner on reflecting powers and absorptions of the reflecting surfaces, which control the number of interfering beams, and on the thickness t, which controls the order of interference. Meissner[19] gives the approximate formula

$$P_r = \frac{2.98mr^{\frac{1}{2}}}{1 - r} \tag{20.3}$$

where $m = 2t/\lambda$ and r is the reflecting power of the film used. By properly coating the plates (§ 20.8), 30 or more interfering beams can be produced. To reach a resolving power of 1,000,000 it would then be necessary to work in the 33,000th order, and at wavelength 5000 A, $2t$ would be 16.5 mm, so that a spacer 8.25 mm thick would be required. In practice, the limit of resolution thus far obtained with the etalon is about 0.0025 cm^{-1}.

The dispersion in a fringe pattern varies from infinity at the center of the pattern to smaller values in accordance with the formula

$$\frac{dl}{d\lambda} = \frac{2f^2}{D\lambda} \tag{20.4}$$

The dispersion is thus seen to vary inversely with ring diameter and is otherwise independent of the etalon gap t. With a ring diameter of 2 cm and a lens of focal length 50 cm, the dispersion at 5000 A is seen to be 5 mm/A, and the plate factor 0.2 A/mm. At 2000 A, on the other hand, the dispersion is $\frac{5}{2}$ greater for a ring of the same diameter.

The free spectral range between orders is given by the formula

$$F_\lambda = \frac{\lambda}{m} = \frac{\lambda^2}{2t} \tag{20.5}$$

in angstroms, or

$$F_\sigma = \frac{1}{2t} \tag{20.6}$$

in wave numbers. Thus in the case given above, if $t = 1$ cm, F is 0.12 A, 0.50 cm^{-1}, or 0.625 mm. In terms of wave-number differences it is constant throughout the spectrum, depending on etalon thickness only.

20.7. **Operation and Design of the Etalon.** Although fixed etalons consisting of slabs of glass or quartz with plane-parallel sides both

19 K. W. Meissner, *ibid.*, page 415.

coated with thin metallic films have been used, these suffer from the disadvantages of the Lummer-Gehrcke plate plus other limitations. The flexibility given by variable plate separation is lost, the dispersion of the optical material in the interferometer enters in such a way as to make precise wavelength determinations more difficult, and the efficiency of the device as an interferometer is lowered. It is, however, convenient to have an interferometer that remains permanently in adjustment.

A more common form consists of two plates of glass or quartz separated by means of an etalon spacer that holds them a distance t apart, as shown in Fig. 20.12. The inner faces of the plates are made parallel to $\frac{1}{30}$ wavelength or better. The first face, marked F_1 in Fig. 20.12, need be plane to one or two wavelengths only and can be of condenser-lens quality, but it should be tilted at from 3 to 30' away from parallelism with F_2 and F_3 (5' is a good value) so that secondary images will be thrown on one side. The fourth face, F_4, should be inclined the same amount and should be plane to within one-fifth wave, that is, better than good lens quality.

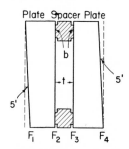

Fig. 20.12. A common form of the Fabry-Perot etalon using a fixed spacer.

If desired, the two plates can be held in mountings, one of which is arranged to be moved by a screw on parallel ways, so that the thickness t can be varied over wide limits. This arrangement gives great flexibility, but keeping the plates accurately parallel without frequent readjustment is difficult, and in general it is found more convenient to have available a series of fixed spacers of various thicknesses.

For general use at least three spacers should be provided. These should not be exact simple multiples of each other. Thicknesses of 3, 7.5, and 20 mm will be found convenient for most work, these being supplemented when possible by spacers of 5, 10, 25, 50, 100, and 200 mm for special work. When working in the range 10,000 to 2000 A, one should remember that at the long-wave end of the spectrum a 50-mm spacer is equivalent to a 10-mm spacer at the shorter end.

Plates of glass can be used only in the visible and very near infrared. Plates of quartz should be cut perpendicular to the crystalline axis, one of left-handed and one of right-handed quartz, to avoid double refraction. Such plates can be used between 3 μ and 2000 A. It seems probable that plates of calcium fluoride could be produced for use in the vacuum region down to 1200 A, but the optical difficulties of working this soft material to closer than $\frac{1}{100}$ of a fringe of yellow light would be great. Fused quartz plates would be ideal for the region of waves longer than 2400 A, but the second plate must be homogeneous to a degree not often found in this material.

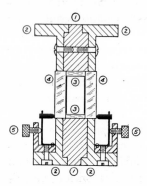

The plates, which are usually round, may be of any size between 25 and 100 mm in diameter, the larger plates being somewhat more useful since, if the full aperture is not needed, those areas of the plate can be selected which have surfaces most nearly plane-parallel. To give good mechanical rigidity, the plates should be not less than one-sixth as thick as their diameter, and preferably one-fourth.

Fig. 20.13. Cross section of mounting for the etalon. 1, Replaceable metal spacer to allow different etalon thicknesses; 2, metal end assembly of mounting; 3, fused quartz spacer; 4, Fabry-Perot plates; 5, screws for maintaining gentle spring pressure on the plates. There are three of these screws, spaced at 120 deg. on each metal end assembly.

The etalon spacers should consist of rings having three bosses on each side (b in Fig. 20.12), formed of a mechanically rigid material of low thermal expansion, such as fused quartz or invar. The bosses are sometimes rounded so as to make contact with the plate over a small area only, but Meissner[20] has shown that when optically flat surfaces of from 1 × 1 to 1.5 × 1.5 mm are formed accurately in the same plane and when optical contact is made between these bosses and the cleaned metal-free surface of the plate, the interferometer will stay in adjustment over long periods of time.

The two plates with their spacer are placed in a loose-fitting mounting arranged so that gentle spring pressure can be applied exactly opposite the positions of the bosses on the etalons. Such a mounting is shown in Fig. 20.13. The mounting should make possible the observation of contact fringes against each boss, to ensure firm optical contact. It should be held in good mechanical adjustment but should be arranged so that it can be rotated about a vertical axis,

---

[20] K. W. Meissner, *ibid.*, page 406.

tilted about a horizontal axis normal to the optical axis, raised or lowered, and moved sideways. It is convenient to have the etalon case rest on a point, line, and plane table so that it can be removed and quickly replaced in the same position.

When any but the shortest exposures are to be made, provision is needed for keeping the etalon at a constant temperature and the air within it at constant pressure. The mounting shown in Fig. 20.14 is convenient for this purpose. Two quartz windows are provided, which respectively should be of the quality of the lenses used next to them. The whole container can thus be sealed and kept at constant temperature with circulated thermostated water. The case is made of heavy metal to give good thermal lagging and to ensure rapid

Fig. 20.14.   Outer container and mounting for the etalon.

temperature equilibrium. For exposures of less than 10 min these precautions are not necessary, but the interferometer should always be allowed to come to equilibrium temperature before use after handling.

20.8. Plate Coatings for the Etalon. The etalon interferometer is somewhat slow and wasteful of light, owing to absorption at the coating as each beam is separated into a transmitted and a reflected beam. Transmission of a few per cent of the light at each reflection, and reflection of the remainder, is desired, with no absorption. In actual films, the thicker the film (up to a certain limit), the greater the reflection but also the greater the absorption. The efficiency of the etalon depends greatly, then, on the character of the metallic film selected and on its thickness.

The materials most frequently used in the past have been silver, gold, platinum, and aluminum. Of these, silver is the best between 10,000 and 5000 A, and aluminum between 5000 and 2000 A. The new techniques of multiple-layer evaporation, as developed for interference filters and other purposes, may lead to further improvements in efficiency of the etalon.

It is found [21] that silver coatings made by evaporation are superior to those laid down by sputtering, which in turn have higher efficiency than those put on by chemical deposition. Aluminum coatings are always put on by evaporation. Improvements have been reported as resulting from evaporating magnesium with the aluminum, and the Hochheim alloy,[22] a secret composition of aluminum and silver with perhaps magnesium and other materials, has given high efficiency. Occasional reports of abnormally high efficiencies, received with some skepticism, may be due to multiple-layer interference effects.

The optimum thickness of coating is extremely critical and must be carefully controlled. Tolansky[23] has pointed out that a change in reflecting power from 85 to 87 per cent cuts the intensity of the fringes in half while improving resolution only 16 per cent. Reflecting powers in the range 80 to 90 per cent are the most useful.

The proper thickness can be controlled to some extent during coating, by making provision for photoelectric measurement of the beam while the evaporation process takes place,[24] or by making resistance measurements on the film itself. A very sensitive means of measuring a pair of plates is to hold them nearly parallel close to the eye and observe the filament of a powerful incandescent lamp through them. When the plates are sufficiently parallel, multiple images of the filament will be seen; with a good pair of plates it should be possible to count 40 or more such images when a 60-watt bulb is used.

In preparing plates, one should not overlook the fact that it is of little advantage to be able to resolve lines narrower than any that are produced in the source being studied. Great gains can often be made by coating plates more lightly than for the highest resolution; reducing resolving power by a factor of 10 may result in no loss of

[21] See R. Ritschl, *Zeitschr. f. Physik*, **79**, 1 (1932).

[22] See also H. W. Edwards, *Phys. Rev.*, **43**, 205 (1933).

[23] S. Tolansky, General Reference 20.4, pages 98–113.

[24] See General Reference 20.5.

actual resolution and yet may be accompanied by a very large gain in light transmission and an equivalent reduction in exposure time.

20.9. Adjustment of the Etalon. Meissner[25] has described methods for rapid and correct adjustment of the etalon plates. A sheet of ground glass is placed in front of a cool mercury arc, and the etalon is set several meters in front of this. By relaxing the eye, which may be aided by using a low-power spectacle lens, and looking at the plates exactly perpendicularly, one can usually see the fringes. Adjustment of the various springs can then be made to center the fringes. When the plates are accurately parallel, movement of the eye from side to side across the field of view should result in no change in size or shape of the circular fringes.

Adjustment is somewhat more difficult for wide spacings; when the spacer is more than 50 mm thick, recourse should be had to the telescope method of Meissner.[26]

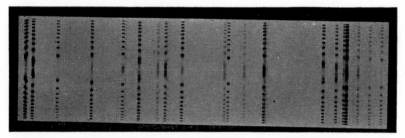

Fig. 20.15. A typical spectrogram obtained by crossing the Fabry-Perot etalon with the Wadsworth mounting of a concave grating.

20.10. Crossing of Etalon Dispersion with That of a Spectroscope. Because of overlapping of orders in an etalon, it is customary to cross its dispersion with that of a prism or grating spectrograph. Prism instruments have ordinarily been used, but the great improvements in speed of concave gratings have recently made grating instruments equally practical. A stigmatic spectroscope is required, however, since the interferometer fringe pattern is usually projected on the slit of the spectroscope by means of an achromatic lens or mirror. The rather wide slit of the spectroscope is adjusted to cut through the diameter of the fringe system, producing spectrograms like that shown in Fig. 20.15.

[25] See General Reference 20.3, page 415.
[26] K. W. Meissner, General Reference 20.3, page 415.

The interferometer can be illuminated by focusing an image of the source on the plates, as in Fig. 20.16, or by sending parallel light through it. The latter arrangement is preferred if the light intensity is great, since the interferometer is warmed more uniformly by the radiation; but where small sources are used, which must be greatly enlarged to fill the plate aperture, the difference is not great. The actual size of the fringe system depends on the focal length of the lens L or the equivalent mirror used, 500 mm being a useful focal length.

A typical arrangement is shown in Fig. 20.16. Light from a standard source T, such as a neon discharge tube, a standard cadmium lamp, or a hollow-cathode discharge, is focused with an aluminized concave mirror M of 10 cm diameter and 20 cm radius of curvature, on the center of the arc or other source of light being studied. This

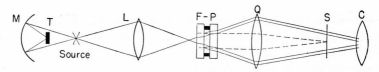

Fig. 20.16.   Optical system for the use of the etalon with a spectroscope
(nonparallel illumination).

focusing is done because of the necessity of illuminating the entire interferometer-spectroscope system similarly and simultaneously by light from the two sources being compared, to avoid differences in fringe shape. Light from both sources is then focused on the interferometer by means of the achromatic lens L, and again on the collimator of the spectrograph by means of the high quality achromat Q. This lens at the same time focuses the rings of the interferometer pattern on the slit S of the spectroscope.

A somewhat simpler and more compact arrangement is to put the interferometer between the collimator lens and dispersing system of the spectrograph. This can be done with prism spectrographs or with grating spectrographs of low aperture only, since very large interferometer plates must be used unless the aperture of the system is to be cut down. However, here the different zones of the slit receive light from different parts of the light source; and if the source emits slightly different wavelengths, variations that are averaged out in the first method will be produced. The plates in this method must be larger and more uniform than in the preceding one; for this reason the latter method is more often adopted.   Other methods of illumination are discussed by Meissner.[27]

20.11.   Reduction of Etalon Patterns.   The routine determination of wavelengths from etalon patterns is complex even though straightforward.   The plate is placed in a comparator, and settings are made on four or five fringes on either side of the center of a pattern.   The order of interference ϵ at the center of the pattern of the given line is thus determined by measuring the diameters D of successive rings, using Eq. (20.2).   A group of fringe diameters for a single line is usually reduced by root-mean-square methods.   The thickness of the etalon t having previously been measured as closely as possible with a micrometer, and the value of ϵ having been determined for a standard line, the nearest integral order of interference can be determined. Meissner[27] discusses various methods of reduction of the fringe patterns.

It is found that the wavelength determined for a line lying at some distance in the spectrum from a standard line used for determining t will vary with the thickness of t used.   This effect arises because of a wavelength dependency of the change in phase of light on reflection at a metallic surface.   By measuring a line with two or more etalon spacers, preferably one having a large and one a small value of t, the amount of this phase shift can be determined and a correction applied. For silver or aluminum plates, the correction needed may be as great as 0.01 A per 1000 A of separation.

Since standard wavelengths are measured in air under standard conditions of pressure and temperature, whereas wave numbers are always referred to vacuum, it is necessary to have the air within an etalon at the proper temperature and pressure, or to introduce corrections for deviations.   Since wave numbers are the fundamental quantities desired, it is probably most satisfactory to exhaust the etalon space and also the space surrounding the interferometer. Then wave numbers can be obtained directly from the reciprocals of wavelengths observed without the need for conversion tables involving the index of refraction of air.

The standard conversion tables for air to vacuum are those of Meggers and Peters,[28] which have been incorporated in Kayser's

---

[27] General Reference 20.3.
[28] W. F. Meggers and C. C. Peters, *Bull. Nat. Bur. Standards*, No. 14, 697 (1917).

Tabellen der Schwingungzahlen.[29]   These exact dispersion values have been called in question to some extent by later workers, especially at short wavelengths, but the matter is not yet resolved, and the tables are used as standard throughout the world.   When interferometry is carried out in vacuum, these tables are needed only for converting to standard wavelengths in air, which are less fundamental than wave numbers.

20.12.   Direct Determination of Wavelengths from Fabry-Perot Patterns.   Probably because of the complex and tiresome computations required for determinations of wavelengths by means of the etalon, fewer than 400 lines have been measured by this means in the history of spectroscopy, including all secondary wavelength standards. It has been desirable to give attention to simplified methods of wavelength determination from etalon patterns.   Burns[30] has described a special comparator that reads directly the squares of fringe diameters, thus eliminating the first stage of computation.   Harrison[31] has constructed a machine called the Winmac (wavelength interferometric measurement and computation) which carries out etalon computations automatically, permitting wavelengths to be read directly from dials as rapidly as the operator can set on the fringes.

Winmac forms an attachment to Harrison's automatic comparator (§ 9.11).   Light from a projection lamp is sent through the plate being measured, and an enlarged image of the line pattern is thrown on a screen in front of the operator, by means of an optical system that gives variable magnification without distortion greater than 1 part in 1000, between the limits $10\times$ and $20\times$.   On the screen is found a family of parabolic lines as shown in Fig. 20.17.   By means of a handle, the screen can be moved up and down until a position is found where each vertical fringe of the line pattern is intersected by a parabola, and all should be so intersected at the same time.   The partial order of interference ϵ can then be read directly from a dial connected to the screen.

The projection screen is prepared by first determining the constants in Eq. (20.2), arranged to include the magnification produced in the spectrograph.   The magnification is automatically adjusted to vary with $m_0^{\frac{1}{2}}$, and thus one set of parabolas serves for all patterns on a plate.

---

[29] H. Kayser, *Tabellen der Schwingungzahlen*, Revised by W. F. Meggers.   Edwards Brothers, Ann Arbor, Mich., 1944.

[30] K. Burns, *Jour. Opt. Soc. Am.*, **19**, 250 (1929).

[31] G. R. Harrison, *Jour. Opt. Soc. Am.*, **36**, 644 (1946).

To obtain eight-figure precision of wavelength measurement it is necessary only to control the projection magnification to 1 part in 1000, and this controlling is done mechanically by the machine. The automatic comparator gives wavelengths directly to five- or six-figure accuracy from the grating dispersion; these λ-values are converted mechanically to wave numbers, and by means of gears set to the proper value of t, the spacer thickness, they are converted again to orders of interference. The order m appears on an eight-figure dial, the last three figures of which may be compared directly with the dial

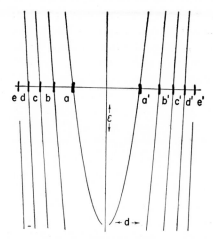

Fig. 20.17.   Family of parabolas for direct reading of ϵ, the order of interference, in the Winmac device.

giving ϵ. Thus to measure a line the operator first sets the line pattern on a horizontal cross hair, which gives λ, σ, and m to eight figures, of which only the first five are correct. The screen with its parabolic marks is then moved vertically until the fringes are intercepted, giving a value of ϵ correct to three figures. The last three figures on the m dial are then turned slightly until they read the same value of ϵ, whereupon the wave number and wavelength dials will also read correctly to seven or eight figures.

Harrison and Anderson[32] have developed a photoelectric scanning attachment for the machine described above. This attachment gives ϵ in a fraction of a second, and hence λ.

---

[32] Unpublished.

20.13. The Michelson-Williams Echelon. The echelon interferometer was first envisaged by Michelson[33] in the reflection form but proved too difficult of realization in this form, and the somewhat inferior transmission echelon was the only one realized for several

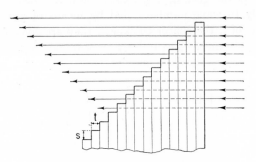

Fig. 20.18.   The transmission echelon.

decades. It consisted of from 20 to 40 glass plates of equal thickness, piled up as shown in Fig. 20.18. Ultimately W. E. Williams,[34] working with the firm of Adam Hilger, Ltd., succeeded in making a practicable reflecting instrument. By optically contacting fused quartz or silica plates and coating these with a reflecting layer of

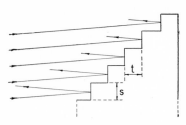

platinum, he was able to build up an interferometer in which the spacings between plates were held equal and the thicknesses of the plates were the same, to within $\frac{1}{10}$ fringe or better (Fig. 20.19). The optical requirements on the reflection echelon are approximately four times as great as on the transmission instrument, but it

Fig. 20.19.   The reflection echelon.

has the advantage of being usable at all wavelengths, and absolute wavelength values can be obtained with it. It is the most expensive and difficult to produce of all interferometers, requires lenses or mirrors of very long focal length to bring its patterns up to useful size, and gives patterns in which intensity values may be greatly distorted. It

[33] A. A. Michelson, *Astrophys. Jour.*, **8**, 37 (1898); *Proc. Am. Acad.*, **35**, 111 (1899).
[34] W. E. Williams, *Nature*, **127**, 816 (1931); *Proc. Phys. Soc.* (London), **45**, 699 (1933).

is inflexible, and if improperly constructed or supported may give rise to ghost images. It does not require a phase-change correction as does the Fabry-Perot, however, and is useful in supplementing that instrument for wavelength determinations. It has been recommended widely for use in the vacuum ultraviolet where no other interferometers are available, but has not as yet proved very practicable in that region because of the thin steps needed for short wavelengths. D. L. MacAdam has carried out experiments with the instrument in the far ultraviolet.

20.14. Optical Systems Using the Reflection Echelon. This interferometer, when used in conjunction with a spectroscope, must be

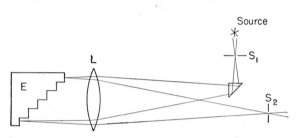

Fig. 20.20. The Williams mounting of the reflection echelon. Light from the source falls on a high-precision slit S, which is situated near the focus but slightly off the axis of the multiple lens L, a high-quality achromat. Parallel light falls on the echelon, E, which is mounted in a barostated, thermostated chamber capable of fine orientation. The return beam is brought to a focus at the spectrograph slit S_2.

mounted in parallel light. Various methods of mounting have been described by Williams,[34] Meissner,[35] and Tolansky.[36] The most flexible mounting, that of Williams, is shown in Fig. 20.20. Either crossed or parallel dispersions can be used, since that of the echelon is so small as not to interfere with a spectrum of moderate complexity.

Echelon spectra can be produced in either the single or two-order positions. To control this variability and to give a sensitive control over the exact order used, the instrument is commonly installed in an airtight case in which the pressure can be delicately controlled. Although the echelon is theoretically faster than the etalon when used in a practical optical system in a chamber enclosed with quartz

[35] General Reference 20.3, page 207.
[36] General Reference 20.4, page 231 *et seq.*

plates, Ritschl [37] has found that an etalon of corresponding dispersion is faster.

The dispersion of the reflection echelon is almost but not quite linear over a single order. According to a close approximation given by Meissner,[38]

$$\frac{dl}{d\lambda} = \frac{fm}{s} \tag{20.7}$$

in mm/A dispersion along the plate, or

$$\frac{dl}{d\lambda} = \frac{2tf}{\lambda s} \tag{20.8}$$

where t is the step thickness, f is the focal length of the projecting lens, and s is the width of a step. The dimensions s and t are usually about 1 and 7 mm, respectively, and 1700 mm is a reasonable value for f. From this value we obtain a dispersion of 4.76 mm/A at 5000 A, or a plate factor of 0.21 A/mm. The dispersion increases linearly with plate thickness and the focal length of the lens used, and as the wavelength and step width are reduced.

The resolving power of a reflection echelon is given by the usual formula Nm. In the case above, with 40 plates, N is 40. The order of interference $2t/\lambda$, or $14/5 \times 10^{-4}$, is 28,000, so that the resolving power is 1,150,000, whereas the limit of resolution is about 0.0125 cm^{-1}.

The free spectral range between successive orders is given by

$$F_\lambda = \frac{\lambda^2}{2t} \tag{20.9}$$

or in wave numbers $\frac{1}{2}t$, as for the etalon. Thus for the case given above, the range that can be covered at one setting (at 5000 A) without overlapping is 0.18 A, or 0.7 cm^{-1}. From the dispersion given above, it will be seen that this value represents only about 1 mm of plate length, which emphasizes the small scale of the patterns.

General References

20.1. Ch. Fabry, *Les Applications des interferences lumineuses.* Paris: Revue d'Optique, 1923.

---

[37] R. Ritschl, *Zeitschr. f. Physik*, **79**, 1 (1932).
[38] See General Reference 20.3, page 204.

20.2. W. E. Williams, *Applications of Interferometry.* New York: E. P. Dutton & Co., Inc., 1928.

20.3. K. W. Meissner, "Interference Spectroscopy," *Jour. Opt. Soc. Am.*, **31**, 405 (1941); **32**, 185 (1942).

20.4. S. Tolansky, *High Resolution Spectroscopy.* London: Methuen, 1947.

20.5. J. Strong, *Procedures in Experimental Physics.* New York: Prentice-Hall, Inc., 1945.

20.6. K. W. Meissner, *Rev. Mod. Phys.*, **14**, 68 (1942).

APPENDIX 1

Wavelength	Intensities		Sensitivity	Wavelength	Intensities		Sensitivity
	Arc	Spk.[Dis.]			Arc	Spk.[Dis.]	
A 18 Argon				**Au 79 Gold**			
8115.311	..	[5000]	U2				
7503.867	..	[700]	U4	2802.19	..	200	..
7067.217	..	[400]	U3	2675.95	250 R	100	U2
6965.430	..	[400]	U3	2427.95	400 R	100	U1
Ag 47 Silver				**B 5 Boron**			
5465.487	1000 R	500 R	U4				
5209.067	1500 R	1000 R	U3	3451.41	5	30	V2
3382.891	1000 R	700 R	U2	2497.733	500	400	U1
3280.683	2000 R	1000 R	U1	2496.778	300	300	U2
2437.791	60	500 wh	V2	**Ba 56 Barium**			
2246.412	25	300 hs	V3	5777.665	500 R	100 R	U2
Al 13 Aluminum				5535.551	1000 R	200 R	U1
6243.36	..	100	V3	5519.115	200 R	60 R	U3
6231.76	..	30	..	5424.616	100 R	30 R	U4
3961.527	3000	2000	U1	4934.086	400 h	400 h	V2
3944.032	2000	1000	U2	4554.042	1000 R	200	V1
3092.713	1000	1000	U3	4130.664	50 r	60 wh	V3
3082.155	800	800	U4	3891.785	18	25	V4
2816.179	10	100	V2	3071.591	100 R	50 R	U5
2669.166	3	100	V1	2335.269	60 R	100 R	..
2631.553	..	40	..	2304.235	60 R	80 R	..
As 33 Arsenic				**Be 4 Beryllium**			
2898.71	25 r	40	..				
2860.452	50 r	50	..	3321.343	1000 r	30	U2
2780.197	75 R	75	U5	3321.086	100	..	U3
2456.53	100 r	8	U4	3321.013	50	..	U4
2370.77	50 r	3	..	3131.072	200	150	V2
2369.67	40 r	..	..	3130.416	200	200	V1
2349.84	250 R	18	U3	2650.781	25	..	U5
2288.12	250 R	5	U3	2348.610	2000 R	50	U1

* Compiled from a combination of empirical and theoretical data selected from the literature, and reprinted by permission from the *M.I.T. Wavelength Tables*, G. R. Harrison, ed., published by John Wiley & Sons, Inc., and the Technology Press.

For the neutral atom, the most sensitive line (*raie ultime*) is indicated by U1, and other lines by U2, U3, and so on, in order of decreasing sensitivity. For the singly ionized atom, the corresponding designations are V1, V2, and soon. In cases where U1 or V1 is not given, the most sensitive lines lie outside the spectral range 10,000–2000 A.

Wave-length	Intensities		Sensi-tivity	Wave-length	Intensities		Sensi-tivity
	Arc	Spk. [Dis.]			Arc	Spk. [Dis.]	
Bi 83 Bismuth				**Cd 48 Cadmium**			
4722.552	1000	100	..	6438.4696	2000	1000	..
3067.716	3000 hR	2000 wh	U1	3610.510	1000	500	..
2989.029	250 wh	100 wh	..	3466.201	1000	500	..
2938.298	300 w	300 w	..	3403.653	800	500 h	..
2897.975	500 WR	500 WR	U2	3261.057	300	300	..
2809.625	200 w	100	..	2748.58	5	200	..
2780.521	200 w	100	..	2573.09	3	150	..
2276.578	100 R	40	..	2312.84	1	200	..
2061.70	300 R	100	..	2288.018	1500 R	300 R	U1
Br 35 Bromine				2265.017	25 d	300	V2
4816.71	..	[300]	V3	2144.382	50	200 R	V1
4785.50	..	[400]	V2	**Ce 58 Cerium**			
4704.86	..	[250]	V1	4186.599	80	25	..
C 6 Carbon				4165.606	40	6	..
4267.27	..	500	V2	4040.762	70	5	..
4267.02	..	350	V3	4012.388	60	20	..
2837.602	..	40	V5	**Cl 17 Chlorine**			
2836.710	..	200	V4	4819.46	..	[200]	V4
2478.573	400	[400]	U2	4810.06	..	[200]	V3
2296.89	..	200	..	4794.54	..	[250]	V2
Ca 20 Calcium				**Co 27 Cobalt**			
4454.781	200	..	U2	3529.813	1000 R	30	U3
4434.960	150	..	U3	3465.800	2000 R	25	U2
4425.441	100	..	U4	3453.505	3000 R	200	U1
4226.728	500 R	50 W	U1	3405.120	2000 R	150	..
3968.468	500 R	500 R	V2	2519.822	40	200	..
3933.666	600 R	600 R	V1	2388.918	10	35	..
3179.332	100	400 w	V3	2378.622	25	50 w	..
3158.869	100	300 w	V4	2363.787	25	50	..
Cb 41 Columbium				2307.857	25	50 w	..
4137.095	100	60	U5	2286.156	40	300 l	V1
4123.810	200	125	U4	**Cr 24 Chromium**			
4100.923	300 w	200 w	U3	5208.436	500 R	100	U4
4079.729	500 w	200 w	U2	5206.039	500 R	200	U5
4058.938	1000 w	400 w	U1	5204.518	400 R	100	U6
3225.479	150 w	800 wr	..	4289.721	3000 R	800 r	U3
3194.977	30	300	..	4274.803	4000 R	800 r	U2
3163.402	15	8	..	4254.346	5000 R	1000	U1
3130.786	100	100	..	2860.934	60	100	V5
3094.183	100	1000	V1				

Wave-length	Intensities		Sensitivity
	Arc	Spk.[Dis.]	
Cr 24 Chromium (cont.)			
2855.676	60	200 wh	V4
2849.838	80	150 r	V3
2843.252	125	400 r	V2
2835.633	100	400 r	V1
Cs 55 Caesium			
8943.50	2000 R	..	U2
8521.10	5000 R	..	U1
4593.177	1000 R	50	U4
4555.355	2000 R	100	U3
Cu 29 Copper			
5218.202	700	..	U3
5153.235	600	..	U4
5105.541	500	..	U5
3273.962	3000 R	1500 R	U2
3247.540	5000 R	2000 R	U1
2246.995	30	500	V3
2192.260	25	500 h	V2
2135.976	25	500 w	V1
Dy 66 Dysprosium			
4211.719	200	15	..
4167.966	50	12	..
4077.974	150 r	100	..
4045.983	150	12	..
4000.454	400	300	..
Er 68 Erbium			
3906.316	25	12	..
3692.652	20	12	..
3499.104	18	15	..
Eu 63 Europium			
4205.046	200 R	50	..
4129.737	150 R	50 R	..
F 9 Fluorine			
6902.46	..	[500]	U3
6856.02	..	[1000]	U2
5291.0	200	..	..

Wave-length	Intensities		Sensitivity
	Arc	Spk.[Dis.]	
Fe 26 Iron			
3748.264	500	200	U4
3745.903	150	100	U5
3745.564	500	500	U3
3737.133	1000 r	600	U2
3719.935	1000 R	700	U1
2413.309	60	100 h	V5
2410.517	50	70 h	V4
2404.882	50	100 wh	V3
2395.625	50	100 wh	V2
2382.039	40 r	100 R	V1
Ga 31 Gallium			
4172.056	2000 R	1000 R	U1
4032.982	1000 R	500 R	U2
2943.637	10	20 r	U3
2874.244	10	15 r	U4
Gd 64 Gadolinium			
3768.405	20	20	..
3646.196	200 w	150	..
Ge 32 Germanium			
4226.570	200	50	..
3269.494	300	300	U3
3039.064	1000	1000	U2
2709.626	30	20	..
2651.575	30	20	..
2651.178	40	20	..
H 1 Hydrogen			
6562.79	..	[3000]	U2
4861.327	..	[500]	U3
He 2 Helium			
5875.618	..	[1000]	U3
4685.75	..	[300]	..
3888.646	..	[1000]	U2
Hf 72 Hafnium			
4093.161	25	20	..
3134.718	80	125	..
3072.877	80	18	..
2940.772	60	12	..
2916.481	50	15	..
2904.408	30	6	..

Wave-length	Intensities		Sensi-tivity	Wave-length	Intensities		Sensi-tivity
	Arc	Spk. [Dis.]			Arc	Spk. [Dis.]	
Hf 72 Hafnium (cont.)				**Kr 36 Krypton**			
2898.259	50	12	..	5870.9158	..	[3000]	U2
2820.224	40	100	..	5570.2895	..	[2000]	U3
2773.357	25	60	..	**La 57 Lanthanum**			
2641.406	40	125	..				
2516.881	35	100	..	6249.929	300	..	U1
2513.028	25	70	..	5930.648	250	..	U2
Hg 80 Mercury				5455.146	200	1	U3
				4123.228	500	500	V4
5460.740	..	[2000]	..	4077.340	600	400	V3
4358.35	3000 w	500	..	3949.106	1000	800	V2
4046.561	200	300	..	**Li 3 Lithium**			
3663.276	500	400	U5				
3654.833	..	[200]	U4	6707.844	3000 R	200	U1
3650.146	200	500	U3	6103.642	2000 R	300	U3
2536.519	2000 R	1000 R	U2	4603.00	800	..	U4
Ho 67 Holmium				3232.61	1000 R	500	U2
				Lu 71 Lutecium			
3891.02	200	40	..				
3748.17	60	40	..	4518.57	300	40	..
2936.77	..	1000 R	..	3554.43	50	150	..
I 53 Iodine				3472.48	50	150	..
				3397.07	50	20 r	..
5464.61	..	[900]	..	2911.39	100	300	..
5161.188	..	[300]	..	2894.84	60	200	..
2062.38	..	[900]	..	**Mg 12 Magnesium**			
In 49 Indium							
				5183.618	500 wh	300	..
4511.323	5000 R	4000 R	U1	5172.699	200 wh	100 wh	..
4101.773	2000 R	1000 R	U2	5167.343	100 wh	50	..
3258.564	500 R	300 R	U5	3838.258	300	200	U2
3256.090	1500 R	600 R	U3	3832.306	250	200	U3
3039.356	1000 R	500 R	U4	3829.350	100 w	150	U4
Ir 77 Iridium				2852.129	300 R	100 R	U1
				2802.695	150	300	V2
3513.645	100 h	100	U2	2795.53	150	300	V1
3437.015	20	15	..	**Mn 25 Manganese**			
3220.780	100	30	U1				
2924.792	25 wh	15	..	4034.490	250 r	20	U3
2849.725	40 h	20 h	..	4033.073	400 r	20	U2
K 19 Potassium				4030.755	500 r	20	U1
				2605.688	100 R	500 R	V3
7698.979	5000 R	..	U2	2593.729	200 R	1000 R	V2
7664.907	9000 R	..	U1	2576.104	300 R	2000 R	V1
4047.201	400	200	U4				
4044.140	800	400	U3				

Wave-length	Intensities		Sensitivity
	Arc	Spk. [Dis.]	
Mo 42 Molybdenum			
3902.963	1000 R	500 R	U3
3864.110	1000 R	500 R	U2
3798.252	1000 R	1000 R	U1
2909.116	25	40 h	V5
2890.994	30	50 h	V4
2871.508	100	100 h	V3
2848.232	125	200 h	V2
2816.154	200	300 h	V1
N 7 Nitrogen			
5679.56	..	[500]	V2
5676.02	..	[100]	V4
5666.64	..	[300]	V3
4109.98	..	[1000]	U2
4103.37	..	[80]	..
4099.94	..	[150]	U3
4097.31	..	[100]	..
Na 11 Sodium			
5895.923	5000 R	500 R	U2
5889.953	9000 R	1000 R	U1
5688.224	300	..	..
5682.657	80	..	..
3302.988	300 R	150 R	U4
3302.323	600 R	300 R	U3
Nd 60 Neodymium			
4303.573	100	40	..
4177.321	15	25	..
3951.154	40	30	..
Ne 10 Neon			
6402.246	..	[2000]	..
5852.488	..	[2000]	..
5400.562	..	[2000]	..
Ni 28 Nickel			
3524.541	1000 R	100 wh	..
3515.054	1000 R	50 h	..
3492.956	1000 R	100 h	U2
3414.765	1000 R	50 wh	U1
2287.084	100	500	V1
2270.213	100	400	V2
2264.457	150	400	V3
2253.86	100	300	V4

Wave-length	Intensities		Sensitivity
	Arc	Spk. [Dis.]	
O 8 Oxygen			
7775.433	..	[100]	U4
7774.138	..	[300]	U3
7771.928	..	[1000]	U2
Os 76 Osmium			
4420.468	400 R	100	..
3267.945	400 R	30	..
3262.290	500 R	50	..
3058.66	500 R	500	..
2909.061	500 R	400	U1
P 15 Phosphorus			
2554.93	60	[20]	..
2553.28	80	[20]	U3
2535.65	100	[30]	U2
2534.01	50	[20]	..
Pb 82 Lead			
5608.8	..	[40]	V2
4057.820	2000 R	300 R	U1
3683.471	300	50	U2
3639.580	300	50 h	..
2833.069	500 R	80 R	..
2614.178	200 r	80	..
2203.505	50 W	5000 R	V1
2169.994	1000 R	1000 R	..
Pd 46 Palladium			
3634.695	2000 R	1000 R	U3
3609.548	1000 R	700 R	..
3516.943	1000 R	500 R	..
3421.24	2000 R	1000 R	U2
3404.580	2000 R	1000 R	U1
2854.581	4	500 h	..
2658.722	20	300	..
2505.739	3	30	..
2498.784	4	150 h	..
2488.921	10	30	..
Pr 59 Praseodymium			
4225.327	50	40	..
4189.518	100	50	..
4179.422	200	40	..
4062.817	150	50	..

Wave-length	Intensities		Sensi-tivity
	Arc	Spk. [Dis.]	

Pt 78 Platinum

Wave-length	Arc	Spk. [Dis.]	Sensi-tivity
3064.712	2000 R	300 R	U1
2997.967	1000 R	200 r	..
2929.794	800 R	200 w	..
2830.295	1000 R	600 r	..
2659.454	2000 R	500 R	U2

Ra 88 Radium

4825.91	..	[800]	U1
4682.28	..	[800]	V2
3814.42	..	[2000]	V1

Rb 37 Rubidium

7947.60	5000 R	..	U2
7800.227	9000 R	..	U1
4215.556	1000 R	300	U4
4201.851	2000 R	500	U3

Re 75 Rhenium

4889.17	2000 w	..	U2
3460.47	1000 W	..	U1

Rh 45 Rhodium

3692.357	500 hd	150 wd	..
3657.987	500 W	200 W	..
3434.893	1000 r	200 r	U1
3396.85	1000 w	500	..
3323.092	1000	200	..

Rn 86 Radon

7450.00	..	[600]	U2
7055.42	..	[400]	U3

Ru 44 Ruthenium

3596.179	30	100	U3
3498.942	500 R	200	U1
3436.737	300 R	150	U2
2976.586	60	200	..
2965.546	60	200	..
2945.668	60	300	..
2712.410	80	300	..
2692.065	8	200	..
2678.758	100	300	..

S 16 Sulphur

9237.49	..	[200]	U6
9228.11	..	[200]	U5
9212.91	..	[200]	U4
4696.25	..	[15]	U9
4695.45	..	[30]	U8
4694.13	..	[500]	U7

Sb 51 Antimony

3267.502	150	150 Wh	..
3232.499	150	250 wh	..
2877.915	250 W	150	..
2598.062	200	100	..
2528.535	300 R	200	..
2311.469	150 R	50	..
2175.890	300	40	U2
2068.38	300 R	3	U1

Sc 21 Scandium

4023.688	100	25	U3
4020.399	50	20	U4
3911.810	150	30	U1
3907.476	125	25	U2
3642.785	60	50	V3
3630.740	50	70	V2
3613.836	40	70	V1

Se 34 Selenium

4742.25	..	[500]	U6
4739.03	..	[800]	U5
4730.78	..	[1000]	U4
2062.788	..	[800]	U3
2039.851	..	[1000]	U2

Si 14 Silicon

3905.528	20	15 W	..
2881.578	500	400	U1
2528.516	400	500	U2
2516.123	500	500	U3
2506.899	300	200	U4

Sm 62 Samarium

4434.321	200	200	V2
4424.342	300	300	V1
4390.865	150	150	..

Wave-length	Intensities		Sensi-tivity
	Arc	Spk. [Dis.]	
	Sn 50 Tin		
4524.741	500 wh	50	..
3262.328	400 h	300 h	U3
3175.019	500 h	400 hr	..
3034.121	200 wh	150 wh	..
3009.147	300 h	200 h	..
2863.327	300 R	300 R	U2
2839.989	300 R	300 R	U1
	Sr 38 Strontium		
4962.263	40	..	U4
4872.493	25	..	U3
4832.075	200	8	U2
4607.331	1000 R	50 R	U1
4305.447	40	..	..
4215.524	300 r	400 W	V2
4077.714	400 r	500 W	V1
3474.887	80	50	..
3464.57	200	200	..
3380.711	150	200	..
	Ta 73 Tantalum		
3406.664	70 w	18 s	..
3318.840	125	35	..
3311.162	300 w	70 w	U1
	Tb 65 Terbium		
3874.18	200	200	..
3848.75	100	200	..
3561.74	200	200	..
3509.17	200	200	..
	Te 52 Tellurium		
2769.67	..	[30]	..
2530.70	..	[30]	..
2385.76	600	[300]	U2
2383.25	500	[300]	U3
2142.75	60 R	..	..
	Th 90 Thorium		
4019.137	8	8	..
3601.040	8	10	..
3538.75	..	50	..
3290.59	..	40 h	..

Wave-length	Intensities		Sensi-tivity
	Arc	Spk. [Dis.]	
	Ti 22 Titanium		
5007.213	200	40	..
4999.510	200	80	..
4991.066	200	100	..
4981.733	300	125	U1
3653.496	500	200	U2
3642.675	300	125	..
3635.463	200	100	..
3383.761	70	300 R	..
3372.800	80	400 R	V3
3361.213	100	600 R	V2
3349.035	125	800 R	V1
	Tl 81 Thallium		
5350.46	5000 R	2000 R	U1
3775.72	3000 R	1000 R	U2
3519.24	2000 R	1000 R	U3
3229.75	2000	800	..
2918.32	400 R	200 R	..
2767.87	400 R	300 R	..
	Tm 69 Thulium		
3761.917	200	120	..
3761.333	250	150	..
3462.21	200	100	..
	U 92 Uranium		
4241.669	40	50	..
3672.579	8	15	..
3552.172	8	12	..
	V 23 Vanadium		
4389.974	80 R	60 R	..
4384.722	125 R	125 R	..
4379.238	200 R	200 R	U1
3185.396	500 R	400 R	U2
3183.982	500 R	400 R	..
3183.406	200 R	100 R	..
3125.284	80	200 R	..
3118.383	70	200 R	V4
3110.706	70	300 R	V3
3102.299	70	300 R	V2
3093.108	100 R	400 R	V1

Wave-length	Intensities		Sensi-tivity
	Arc	Spk. [Dis.]	
W 74 Tungsten			
4302.108	60	60	U1
4294.614	50	50	U2
4008.753	45	45	U3
3613.790	10	30	..
3215.560	10	9	..
2589.167	15 d	25	..
2397.091	18	30	..
Xe 54 Xenon			
4671.226	..	[2000]	U2
4624.276	..	[1000]	U3
4500.977	..	[500]	U4
Yb 70 Ytterbium			
3987.994	1000 R	500 R	..
3694.203	500 R	1000 R	..
3289.37	500 R	1000 R	..
Yt 39 Yttrium			
4674.848	80	100	U1
4643.695	50	100	U2
3788.697	30	30	..
3774.332	12	100	..
3710.290	80	150	V1
3633.123	50	100	..
3600.734	100	300	..
3242.280	60	100	..

Wave-length	Intensities		Sensi-tivity
	Arc	Spk. [Dis.]	
Zn 30 Zinc			
6362.347	1000 Wh	500	..
4810.534	400 w	300 h	..
4722.159	400 w	300 h	..
4680.138	300 w	200 h	..
3345.020	800	300	U2
3302.588	800	300	U3
3282.333	500 R	300	U4
2557.958	10	300	V3
2502.001	20	400 w	V4
2138.56	800 R	500	U1
2061.91	100	100	V2
2025.51	200	200	V1
Zr 40 Zirconium			
4772.312	100	..	..
4739.478	100	..	..
4710.075	60	..	..
4687.803	125	..	U4
3601.193	400	15	U1
3572.473	60	80	V4
3547.682	200	12	U2
3519.605	100	10	U3
3496.210	100	100	V3
3438.230	250	200	V2
3391.975	300	400	V1

APPENDIX 2

Sensitive Lines of Elements Arranged in order of Wavelength*

Wavelength	Element	Arc	Spk.[Dis.]	Sensitivity	Wavelength	Element	Arc	Spk.[Dis.]	Sensitivity
9237.49	S I	..	[200]	U6	5519.115	Ba I	200 R	60 R	U3
9228.11	S I	..	[200]	U5	5465.487	Ag I	1000 R	500 R	U4
9212.91	S I	..	[200]	U4	5464.61	I II	..	[900]	..
8943.50	Cs I	2000 R	..	U2	5460.740	Hg I	..	[2000]	..
8521.10	Cs I	5000 R	..	U1	5455.146	La I	200	1	U3
8115.311	A I	..	[5000]	U2	5424.616	Ba I	100 R	30 R	U4
7947.60	Rb I	5000 R	..	U2	5400.562	Ne I	..	[2000]	..
7800.227	Rb I	9000 R	..	U1	5350.46	Tl I	5000 R	2000 R	U1
7775.433	O I	..	[100]	U4	5291.0	bh CaF	200	..	..
7774.138	O I	..	[300]	U3	5218.202	Cu I	700	..	U3
7771.928	O I	..	[1000]	U2	5209.067	Ag I	1500 R	1000 R	U3
7698.979	K I	5000 R	..	U2	5208.436	Cr I	500 R	100	U4
7664.907	K I	9000 R	..	U1	5206.039	Cr I	500 R	200	U5
7503.867	A I	..	[700]	U4	5204.518	Cr I	400 R	100	U6
7450.00	Rn I	..	[600]	U2	5183.618	Mg I	500 wh	300	..
7067.217	A I	..	[400]	U3	5172.699	Mg I	200 wh	100 wh	..
7055.42	Rn I	..	[400]	U3	5167.343	Mg I	100 wh	50	..
6965.430	A I	..	[400]	U3	5161.188	I II	..	[300]	..
6902.46	F I	..	[500]	U3	5153.235	Cu I	600	..	U4
6856.02	F I	..	[1000]	U2	5105.541	Cu I	500	..	U5
6707.844	Li I	3000 R	200	U1	5007.213	Ti I	200	40	..
6562.79	H I	..	[3000]	U2	4999.510	Ti I	200	80	..
6438.4696	Cd I	2000	1000	..	4991.066	Ti I	200	100	..
6402.246	Ne I	..	[2000]	..	4981.733	Ti I	300	125	U1
6362.347	Zn I	1000 Wh	500	..	4962.263	Sr I	40	..	U4
6249.929	La I	300	..	U1	4934.086	Ba II	400 h	400 h	V2
6243.36	Al II	..	100	V3	4889.17	Re I	2000 w	..	U2
6231.76	Al II	..	30	..	4872.493	Sr I	25	..	U3
6103.642	Li I	2000 R	300	U3	4861.327	H I	..	[500]	U3
5930.648	La I	250	..	U2	4832.075	Sr I	200	8	U2
5895.923	Na I	5000 R	500 R	U2	4825.91	Ra I	..	[800]	U1
5889.953	Na I	9000 R	1000 R	U1	4819.46	Cl II	..	[200]	V4
5875.618	He I	..	[1000]	U3	4816.71	Br II	..	[300]	V3
5870.9158	Kr I	..	[3000]	U2	4810.534	Zn I	400 w	300 h	..
5852.488	Ne I	..	[2000]	..	4810.06	Cl II	..	[200]	V3
5777.665	Ba I	500 R	100 R	U2	4794.54	Cl II	..	[250]	V2
5688.224	Na I	300	..	..	4785.50	Br II	..	[400]	V2
5682.657	Na I	80	..	..	4772.312	Zr I	100	..	..
5679.56	N II	..	[500]	V2	4742.25	Se I	..	[500]	U6
5676.02	N II	..	[100]	V4	4739.478	Zr I	100	..	..
5666.64	N II	..	[300]	V3	4739.03	Se I	..	[800]	U5
5608.8	Pb II	..	[40]	V2	4730.78	Se I	..	[1000]	U4
5570.2895	Kr I	..	[2000]	U3	4722.552	Bi I	1000	100	..
5535.551	Ba I	1000 R	200 R	U1	4722.159	Zn I	400 w	300 h	..

* Compiled from a combination of empirical and theoretical data selected from the literature, and reprinted by permission from the *M.I.T. Wavelength Tables*, G. R. Harrison, ed., published by John Wiley & Sons, Inc., and the Technology Press.

For the neutral atom, the most sensitive line (*raie ultime*) is indicated by U1, and other lines by U2, U3, and so on, in order of decreasing sensitivity. For the singly ionized atom, the corresponding designations are V1, V2, and so on. In cases where U1 or V1 is not given, the most sensitive lines lie outside the spectral range 10,000–2000 A.

Wave-length	Element	Intensities Arc	Intensities Spk.[Dis.]	Sensitivity	Wave-length	Element	Intensities Arc	Intensities Spk.[Dis.]	Sensitivity
4710.075	Zr I	60	..	..	4129.737	Eu II	150 R	50 R	..
4704.86	Br II	..	[250]	V1	4123.810	Cb I	200	125	U4
4696.25	S I	..	[15]	U9	4123.228	La II	500	500	V4
4695.45	S I	..	[30]	U8	4109.98	N I	..	[1000]	U2
4694.13	S I	..	[500]	U7	4103.37	N III	..	[80]	..
4687.803	Zr I	125	..	U4	4101.773	In I	2000 R	1000 R	U2
4685.75	He II	..	[300]	..	4100.923	Cb I	300 w	200 w	U3
4682.28	Ra II	..	[800]	V2	4099.94	N I	..	[150]	U3
4680.138	Zn I	300 w	200 h	..	4097.31	N III	..	[100]	..
4674.848	Yt I	80	100	U1	4093.161	Hf II	25	20	..
4671.226	Xe I	..	[2000]	U2	4079.729	Cb I	500 w	200 w	U2
4643.695	Yt I	50	100	U2	4077.974	Dy	150 r	100	..
4624.276	Xe I	..	[1000]	U3	4077.714	Sr II	400 r	500 W	V1
4607.331	Sr I	1000 R	50 R	U1	4077.340	La II	600	400	V3
4603.00	Li I	800	..	U4	4062.817	Pr	150	50	..
4593.177	Cs I	1000 R	50	U4	4058.938	Cb I	1000 w	400 w	U1
4555.355	Cs I	2000 R	100	U3	4057.820	Pb I	2000 R	300 R	U1
4554.042	Ba II	1000 R	200	V1	4047.201	K I	400	200	U4
4524.741	Sn	500 wh	50	..	4046.561	Hg I	200	300	..
4518.57	Lu	300	40	..	4045.983	Dy	150	12	..
4511.323	In I	5000 R	4000 R	U1	4044.140	K I	800	400	U3
4500.977	Xe I	..	[500]	U4	4040.762	Ce II	70	5	..
4454.781	Ca I	200	..	U2	4034.490	Mn I	250 r	20	U3
4434.960	Ca I	150	..	U3	4033.073	Mn I	400 r	20	U2
4434.321	Sm II	200	200	V2	4032.982	Ga I	1000 R	500 R	U2
4425.441	Ca I	100	..	U4	4030.755	Mn I	500 r	20	U1
4424.342	Sm II	300	300	V1	4023.688	Sc I	100	25	U3
4420.468	Os I	400 R	100	..	4020.399	Sc I	50	20	U4
4390.865	Sm II	150	150	..	4019.137	Th	8	8	..
4389.974	V I	80 R	60 R	..	4012.388	Ce I, II	60	20	..
4384.722	V I	125 R	125 R	..	4008.753	W I	45	45	U3
4379.238	V I	200 R	200 R	U1	4000.454	Dy	400	300	..
4358.35	Hg I	3000 w	500	..	3987.994	Yb	1000 R	500 R	..
4305.447	Sr II	40	..	..	3968.468	Ca II	500 R	500 R	V2
4303.573	Nd	100	40	..	3961.527	Al I	3000	2000	U1
4302.108	W I	60	60	U1	3951.154	Nd	40	30	..
4294.614	W I	50	50	U2	3949.106	La II	1000	800	V2
4289.721	Cr I	3000 R	800 r	U3	3944.032	Al I	2000	1000	U2
4274.803	Cr I	4000 R	800 r	U2	3933.666	Ca II	600 R	600 R	V1
4267.27	C II	..	500	V2	3911.810	Sc I	150	30	U1
4267.02	C II	..	350	V3	3907.476	Sc I	125	25	U2
4254.346	Cr I	5000 R	1000	U1	3906.316	Er	25	12	..
4241.669	U	40	50	..	3905.528	Si I	20	15 W	..
4226.728	Ca I	500 R	50 W	U1	3902.963	Mo I	1000 R	500 R	U3
4226.570	Ge I	200	50	..	3891.785	Ba II	18	25	V4
4225.327	Pr	50	40	..	3891.02	Ho	200	40	..
4215.556	Rb I	1000 R	300	U4	3888.646	He I	..	[1000]	U2
4215.524	Sr II	300 r	400 W	V2	3874.18	Tb	200	200	..
4211.719	Dy	200	15	..	3864.110	Mo I	1000 R	500 R	U2
4205.046	Eu II	200 R	50	..	3848.75	Tb	100	200	..
4201.851	Rb I	2000 R	500	U3	3838.258	Mg I	300	200	U2
4189.518	Pr	100	50	..	3832.306	Mg I	250	200	U3
4186.599	Ce II	80	25	..	3829.350	Mg I	100 w	150	U4
4179.422	Pr	200	40	..	3814.42	Ra II	..	[2000]	V1
4177.321	Nd	15	25	..	3798.252	Mo I	1000 R	1000 R	U1
4172.056	Ga I	2000 R	1000 R	U1	3788.697	Yt II	30	30	..
4167.966	Dy	50	12	..	3775.72	Tl I	3000 R	1000 R	U2
4165.606	Ce II	40	6	..	3774.332	Yt II	12	100	..
4137.095	Cb I	100	60	U5	3768.405	Gd	20	20	..
4130.664	Ba II	50 r	60 Wh	V3	3761.917	Tm	200	120	..

584   APPENDIX 2

Wavelength	Element	Arc	Spk. [Dis.]	Sensitivity	Wavelength	Element	Arc	Spk. [Dis.]	Sensitivity
3761.333	Tm	250	150	..	3451.41	B II	5	30	V2
3748.264	Fe I	500	200	U4	3438.230	Zr II	250	200	V2
3748.17	Ho	60	40	..	3437.015	Ir I	20	15	..
3745.903	Fe I	150	100	U5	3436.737	Ru I	300 R	150	U2
3745.564	Fe I	500	500	U3	3434.893	Rh	1000 R	200 r	U1
3737.133	Fe I	1000 r	600	U2	3421.24	Pd I	2000 R	1000 R	U2
3719.935	Fe I	1000 R	700	U1	3414.765	Ni I	1000 R	50 wh	U1
3710.290	Yt II	80	150	V1	3406.664	Ta	70 w	18 s	..
3694.203	Yb	500 R	1000 R	..	3405.120	Co I	2000 R	150	..
3692.652	Er	20	12	..	3404.580	Pd I	2000 R	1000 R	U1
3692.357	Rh I	500 hd	150 wd	..	3403.653	Cd I	800	500 h	..
3683.471	Pb I	300	50	U2	3397.07	Lu	50	20 r	..
3672.579	U	8	15	..	3396.85	Rh I	1000 w	500	..
3663.276	Hg I	500	400	U5	3391.975	Zr II	300	400	V1
3657.987	Rh I	500 W	200 W	..	3383.761	Ti II	70	300 R	..
3654.833	Hg I	..	[200]	U4	3382.891	Ag I	1000 R	700 R	U2
3653.496	Ti II	500	200	U2	3380.711	Sr II	150	200	..
3650.146	Hg I	200	500	U3	3372.800	Ti II	80	400 R	V3
3646.196	Gd	200 w	150	..	3361.213	Ti II	100	600 R	V2
3642.785	Sc II	60	50	V3	3349.035	Ti II	125	800 R	V1
3642.675	Ti I	300	125	..	3345.020	Zn I	800	300	U2
3639.580	Pb I	300	50 h	..	3323.092	Rh I	1000	200	..
3635.463	Ti I	200	100	..	3321.343	Be I	1000 r	30	U2
3634.695	Pd	2000 R	1000 R	U3	3321.086	Be I	100	..	U3
3633.123	Yt II	50	100	..	3321.013	Be I	50	..	U4
3630.740	Sc II	50	70	V2	3318.840	Ta	125	35	..
3613.836	Sc II	40	70	V1	3311.162	Ta	300 w	70 w	U1
3613.790	W II	10	30	..	3302.988	Na I	300 R	150 R	U4
3610.510	Cd I	1000	500	..	3302.588	Zn I	800	300	U3
3609.548	Pd I	1000 R	700 R	..	3302.323	Na I	600 R	300 R	U3
3601.193	Zr I	400	15	U1	3290.59	Th	..	40 h	..
3601.040	Th	8	10	..	3289.37	Yb	500 R	1000 R	..
3600.734	Yt II	100	300	..	3282.333	Zn I	500 R	300	U4
3596.179	Ru I	30	100	U3	3280.683	Ag I	2000 R	1000 R	U1
3572.473	Zr II	60	80	V4	3273.962	Cu I	3000 R	1500 R	U2
3561.74	Tb	200	200	..	3269.494	Ge I	300	300	U3
3554.43	Lu	50	150	..	3267.945	Os I	400 R	30	..
3552.172	U	8	12	..	3267.502	Sb I	150	150 Wh	..
3547.682	Zr I	200	12	U2	3262.328	Sn I	400 h	300 h	U3
3538.75	Th	..	50	..	3262.290	Os I	500 R	50	..
3529.813	Co I	1000 R	30	U3	3261.057	Cd I	300	300	..
3524.541	Ni I	1000 R	100 wh	..	3258.564	In I	500 R	300 R	U5
3519.605	Zr I	100	10	U3	3256.090	In I	1500 R	600 R	U3
3519.24	Tl I	2000 R	1000 R	U3	3247.540	Cu I	5000 R	2000 R	U1
3516.943	Pd I	1000 R	500 R	..	3242.280	Yt II	60	100	..
3515.054	Ni I	1000 R	50 h	..	3232.61	Li I	1000 R	500	U2
3513.645	Ir I	100 h	100	U2	3232.499	Sb I	150	250 wh	..
3509.17	Tb	200	200	..	3229.75	Tl I	2000	800	..
3499.104	Er	18	15	..	3225.479	Cb II	150 w	800 wr	..
3498.942	Ru I	500 R	200	U1	3220.780	Ir I	100	30	U1
3496.210	Zr II	100	100	V3	3215.560	W I	10	9	..
3492.956	Ni I	1000 R	100 h	U2	3194.977	Cb II	30	300	..
3474.887	Sr II	80	50	..	3185.396	V I	500 R	400 R	U2
3472.48	Lu	50	150	..	3183.982	V I	500 R	400 R	..
3466.201	Cd I	1000	500	..	3183.406	V I	200 R	100 R	..
3465.800	Co I	2000 R	25	U2	3179.332	Ca II	100	400 w	V3
3464.57	Sr II	200	200	..	3175.019	Sn I	500 h	400 hr	..
3462.21	Tm	200	100	..	3163.402	Cb II	15	8	..
3460.47	Re I	1000 W	..	U1	3158.869	Ca II	100	300 w	V4
3453.505	Co I	3000 R	200	U1	3134.718	Hf II	80	125	..

Wave-length	Element	Intensities Arc	Intensities Spk.[Dis.]	Sensitivity	Wave-length	Element	Intensities Arc	Intensities Spk.[Dis.]	Sensitivity
3131.072	Be II	200	150	V2	2833.069	Pb I	500 R	80 R	..
3130.786	Cb II	100	100	..	2830.295	Pt I	1000 R	600 r	..
3130.416	Be II	200	200	V1	2820.224	Hf II	40	100	..
3125.284	V II	80	200 R	..	2816.179	Al II	10	100	V2
3118.383	V II	70	200 R	V4	2816.154	Mo II	200	300 h	V1
3110.706	V II	70	300 R	V3	2809.625	Bi I	200 w	100	..
3102.299	V II	70	300 R	V2	2802.695	Mg II	150	300	V2
3094.183	Cb II	100	1000	V1	2802.19	Au	..	200	..
3093.108	V II	100 R	400 R	V1	2795.53	Mg II	150	300	V1
3092.713	Al I	1000	1000	U3	2780.521	Bi I	200 w	100	..
3082.155	Al I	800	800	U4	2780.197	As I	75 R	75	U5
3072.877	Hf I	80	18	..	2773.357	Hf II	25	60	..
3071.591	Ba I	100 R	50 R	U5	2769.67	Te I	..	[30]	..
3067.716	Bi I	3000 hR	2000 wh	U1	2767.87	Tl I	400 R	300 R	..
3064.712	Pt I	2000 R	300 R	U1	2748.58	Cd II	5	200	..
3058.66	Os I	500 R	500	..	2712.410	Ru	80	300	..
3039.356	In I	1000 R	500 R	U4	2709.626	Ge I	30	20	..
3039.064	Ge I	1000	1000	U2	2692.065	Ru	8	200	..
3034.121	Sn I	200 wh	150 wh	..	2678.758	Ru	100	300	..
3009.147	Sn I	300 h	200 h	..	2675.95	Au I	250 R	100	U2
2997.967	Pt I	1000 R	200 r	..	2669.166	Al II	3	100	V1
2989.029	Bi I	250 wh	100 wh	..	2659.454	Pt I	2000 R	500 R	U2
2976.586	Ru	60	200	..	2658.722	Pd II	20	300	..
2965.546	Ru	60	200	..	2651.575	Ge I	30	20	..
2945.668	Ru	60	300	..	2651.178	Ge I	40	20	..
2945.637	Ga I	10	20 r	U3	2650.781	Be I	25	..	U5
2940.772	Hf I	60	12	..	2641.406	Hf II	40	125	..
2938.298	Bi I	300 w	300 w	..	2631.553	Al II	..	40	..
2936.77	Ho	..	1000 R	..	2614.178	Pb	200 r	80	..
2929.794	Pt I	800 R	200 w	..	2605.688	Mn II	100 R	500 R	V3
2924.792	Ir I	25 wh	15	..	2598.062	Sb I	200	100	..
2918.32	Tl I	400 R	200 R	..	2593.729	Mn II	200 R	1000 R	V2
2916.481	Hf I	50	15	..	2589.167	W II	15 d	25	..
2911.39	Lu	100	300	..	2576.104	Mn II	300 R	2000 R	V1
2909.116	Mo II	25	40 h	V5	2573.09	Cd II	3	150	..
2909.061	Os I	500 R	400	U1	2557.958	Zn II	10	300	V3
2904.408	Hf I	30	6	..	2554.93	P I	60	[20]	..
2898.71	As I	25 r	40	..	2553.28	P I	80	[20]	U3
2898.259	Hf I	50	12	..	2536.519	Hg I	2000 R	1000 R	U2
2897.975	Bi I	500 WR	500 WR	U2	2535.65	P I	100	[30]	U2
2894.84	Lu	60	200	..	2534.01	P I	50	[20]	..
2890.994	Mo II	30	50 h	V4	2530.70	Te I	..	[30]	..
2881.578	Si I	500	400	U1	2528.535	Sb I	300 R	200	..
2877.915	Sb I	250 W	150	..	2528.516	Si I	400	500	U2
2874.244	Ga I	10	15 r	U4	2519.822	Co II	40	200	..
2871.508	Mo II	100	100 h	V3	2516.881	Hf II	35	100	..
2863.327	Sn I	300 R	300 R	U2	2516.123	Si I	500	500	U3
2860.934	Cr II	60	100	V5	2513.028	Hf II	25	70	..
2860.452	As I	50 r	50	..	2506.899	Si I	300	200	U4
2855.676	Cr II	60	200 Wh	V4	2505.739	Pd II	3	30	..
2854.581	Pd II	4	500 h	..	2502.001	Zn II	20	400 w	V4
2852.129	Mg I	300 R	100 R	U1	2498.784	Pd II	4	150 h	..
2849.838	Cr II	80	150 r	V3	2497.733	B I	500	400	U1
2849.725	Ir I	40 h	20 h	..	2496.778	B I	300	300	U2
2848.232	Mo II	125	200 h	V2	2488.921	Pd II	10	30	..
2843.252	Cr II	125	400 r	V2	2478.573	C I	400	[400]	U2
2839.989	Sn I	300 R	300 R	U1	2456.53	As I	100 r	8	U4
2837.602	C II	..	40	V5	2437.791	Ag II	60	500 wh	V2
2836.710	C II	..	200	V4	2427.95	Au I	400 R	100	U1
2835.633	Cr II	100	400 r	V1	2413.309	Fe II	60	100 h	V5

Wave-length	Element	Intensities		Sensitivity	Wave-length	Element	Intensities		Sensitivity
		Arc	Spk. [Dis.]				Arc	Spk. [Dis.]	
2410.517	Fe II	50	70 h	V4	2286.156	Co II	40	300 l	V1
2404.882	Fe II	50	100 wh	V3	2276.578	Bi I	100 R	40	..
2397.091	W II	18	30	..	2270.213	Ni II	100	400	V2
2395.625	Fe II	50	100 wh	V2	2265.017	Cd II	25 d	300	V2
2388.918	Co II	10	35	..	2264.457	Ni II	150	400	V3
2385.76	Te I	600	[300]	U2	2253.86	Ni II	100	300	V4
2383.25	Te I	500	[300]	U3	2246.995	Cu II	30	500	V3
2382.039	Fe II	40 r	100 R	V1	2246.412	Ag II	25	300 hs	V3
2378.622	Co II	25	50 w	..	2203.505	Pb II	50 W	5000 R	V1
2370.77	As I	50 r	3	..	2192.260	Cu II	25	500 h	V2
2369.67	As I	40 r	..	..	2175.890	Sb I	300	40	U2
2363.787	Co II	25	50	..	2169.994	Pb I	1000 R	1000 R	..
2349.84	As I	250 R	18	U3	2144.382	Cd II	50	200 R	V1
2348.610	Be I	2000 R	50	U1	2142.75	Te I	60 R	..	..
2335.269	Ba II	60 R	100 R	..	2138.56	Zn I	800 R	500	U1
2312.84	Cd II	1	200	..	2135.976	Cu II	25	500 w	V1
2311.469	Sb I	150 R	50	..	2068.38	Sb I	300 R	3	U1
2307.857	Co II	25	50 w	..	2062.788	Se I	..	[800]	U3
2304.235	Ba II	60 R	80 R	..	2062.38	I	..	[900]	..
2296.89	C III	..	200	..	2061.91	Zn II	100	100	V2
2288.12	As I	250 R	5	U3	2061.70	Bi I	300 R	100	..
2288.018	Cd I	1500 R	300 R	U1	2039.851	Se I	..	[1000]	U2
2287.084	Ni II	100	500	V1	2025.51	Zn II	200	200	V1

Name Index

Subject Index